Health, Illness, and Medicine in Canada

SEVENTH EDITION

Health, Illness, and Medicine in Canada

Juanne Nancarrow Clarke

OXFORD
UNIVERSITY PRESS

OXFORD

UNIVERSITY PRESS

Oxford University Press is a department of the University of Oxford.
It furthers the University's objective of excellence in research, scholarship,
and education by publishing worldwide. Oxford is a registered trade mark of
Oxford University Press in the UK and in certain other countries.

Published in Canada by
Oxford University Press
8 Sampson Mews, Suite 204,
Don Mills, Ontario M3C 0H5 Canada

www.oupcanada.com

Copyright © Oxford University Press Canada 2016

The moral rights of the author have been asserted

Database right Oxford University Press (maker)

Second Edition published in 1996
Third edition published in 2000
Fourth edition published in 2004
Fifth edition published in 2008
Sixth edition published in 2012

Original edition published by McClelland & Stewart Ltd.
75 Sherbourne Street, 5th floor, Toronto, Ontario
Copyright © 1990 by Juanne Nancarrow Clarke

Library and Archives Canada Cataloguing in Publication

Clarke, Juanne N. (Juanne Nancarrow), 1944-, author
Health, illness, and medicine in Canada / Juanne
Nancarrow Clarke. – Seventh edition.

Includes bibliographical references and index.
ISBN 978-0-19-901852-9 (paperback)

1. Social medicine–Canada. I. Title.

RA418.3.C3C53 2016   306.4'610971   C2016-900286-1

Cover image: © iStock/-Oxford-
Part opener image: © iStock/Xebeche

Oxford University Press is committed to our environment.
Wherever possible, our books are printed on paper which comes from
responsible sources.

Printed and bound in the United States of America

1 2 3 4 — 19 18 17 16

Contents

Part I   Sociological Perspectives   1

Part II   Sociology of Health and Illness   27

Part III   Sociology of Medicine   **201**

Additional Online Chapters

Online Chapter 1   Ways of Studying Health, Illness, and Medicine Sociologically

Online Chapter 2   The Medical Care System: Critical Issues

Figures

Tables

Boxes

Canada in a Global Context

Critical Thinking

Highlighted Issues

Remembering Our History

Spotlight on Ethics

Preface

Significant changes in the medical care system and in the degree of inequality in the Canadian population continue. Perhaps the most basic change confronting Canadians in terms of medical care today is the withering away of a universal medical care system. As federal transfer payments continue to decrease and the responsibility for medical care shifts to the provinces, the likelihood grows of inequality in the availability of services across the nation. Universal medical care has never been as threatened as it is now, as Canada shifts to the political right in the context of economic globalization. Unless there is a dramatic alteration in direction, inequality in medical services among provinces, between the rich and the poor, among racialized and ethnic groups, and between women and men will continue to grow. In the context of the globalization of neo-liberal ideology and policy, health differences resulting from inequalities in the social determinants of health are increasing in Canada and around the world.

Some argue that this crisis in the provision of allopathic medical care will have positive effects on the health of the population. The argument is that as the near-monopoly in allopathic medical care is weakened, complementary and alternative care strategies will grow in their availability for the population. In fact, already about 40 per cent of the US and Canadian populations use alternative or complementary health care. To the extent that the current medical care crisis destabilizes the hegemonic status of allopathic medicine and, in turn, other types of health care take up positions as possible health-care strategies for Canadians, this crisis in medical care must be seen as an opportunity.

Health promotion and disease prevention now predominate in the medical ideology of the federal government. These strategies have resulted in some benefits but are also problematic because they individualize health problems that result from social-structural inequalities and "blame the victim." Focusing on individual choice with respect to prevention issues such as seat-belt use, quitting smoking, moderation in alcohol consumption, low-fat diets, and exercise obscures the social, cultural, and structural constraints within which choice operates. The social determinants perspective on health refocuses attention on systemic and structural issues such as social class, education, occupation, employment, literacy, and racialization as precursors to illness or well-being.

With respect to the environment, the deleterious effects of numerous social and economic arrangements appear to be continuing unabated in spite of the apparently widespread concern about environmental issues such as climate change. Actions taken by citizens on an individual basis, such as recycling paper, metal, glass, and cardboard, and reducing and reusing whenever possible, have only a minor effect in an industrial and corporate context where environmental controls compete with profitability. Major environmental challenges, such as global warming, chlorinated water and the pervasive use of bleach in manufacturing, the widespread use of pesticides, herbicides, and fertilizers in agriculture, and the use of fossil fuels and nuclear energy, continue to affect the health of the population and threaten to do so in the future.

Wars and political violence, along with massive shifts in populations of people who are political and environmental refugees, are growing around the world. With these processes come new and increased levels of mental and physical illness as well as death.

Many have noted that sociology is approached from five different perspectives: structural-functional, conflict, symbolic interactionist, feminist/anti-racist/intersectional, and post-structural. Each of these is based on different assumptions, asks different questions, and uses different methods and rules of evidence. This book is organized into three major sections. The first part, Chapter 1, addresses some theoretical and methodological issues, and discusses some of the theories behind each of the five sociological perspectives. Included in this chapter are illustrations of each perspective as applied to concrete studies. What had been the second chapter in earlier editions is now found on the Oxford University Press website. It examines some of the methodologies employed by each perspective in studying health-related problems, as well as criticisms that have been levelled at each methodology.

The second part of the book, Chapters 2 to 7, explores the meaning and measurement of health and illness from these five different sociological perspectives. Chapter 2 examines Canadian mortality in historical and cross-cultural contexts. It examines questions such as: What are the chief causes of death and disease in the developing world and in Canada today? What were the chief causes of death 150 years ago? Why has the difference between male and female mortality rates increased over time?

Chapter 3 examines the impact on health of environmental, occupational, and other health and safety issues, as well as violence in society. It asks questions such as: What are the major threats to the environment? What do we know about their impact on the health of the population? Are the health effects of environmental degradation spread equally across Canada and throughout the global community? What occupations are safe? Is shift work bad for our health? Does violence affect the health of Canadians?

Chapter 4 focuses on the social determinants of health, that is, the impact of unequal social statuses on the health of the population. In particular, it looks at the effects of processes such as inclusion and exclusion. This chapter sets out the theoretical approaches that are discussed empirically in the next chapter. Questions such as the following are asked: Are poorer people more likely to be sick? Is education an important prerequisite to health? How does politics relate to health outcomes?

Chapter 5 examines specific aspects of inequity in the social system—age, gender, racialization, and ethnicity. Pertinent questions include: Is there evidence of ethnic differences in morbidity and mortality? Do people of different genders, ages, and "race"/ethnic backgrounds experience different health and life changes?

Chapter 6 looks at the social and psychological antecedents to illness and disease and considers such questions as: What is the relationship between stress and illness? Can the loss of a loved one lead to serious illness? Is the inability to express anger sometimes implicated in the onset of cancer? Can social support minimize the effects and shorten the duration of an illness?

Chapter 7 concerns the phenomenological experience of illness and answers questions such as: How does epilepsy, cancer, or multiple sclerosis affect the everyday life of patients and family members? Do diseases have social meanings?

The third part of the book deals with the social construction of medical research and practice and the organization of the Canadian medical care system. It addresses questions such as: Does a universal medical care insurance scheme guarantee universal accessibility? Why has the number of malpractice suits increased? What is the impact of the increasing number of female doctors? What is the fate of idealism in medical school?

Chapter 8 discusses the social basis of medical science and medical research. It also examines some strategies of lay resistance to conventional medicine. Questions asked include: Is allopathic medical practice entirely based on the findings of traditional medical science research? Is medical science objective? Are new medical technologies necessarily better? When and why do people sometimes resist medical prescriptions and diagnoses?

Chapter 9 examines the relationship between medicine and religion in cross-cultural and historical contexts. It considers questions such as the following: Is medicalization increasing? ("Medicalization" may be defined as a tendency for more and more of human social life to be considered relevant to medicine.) Is medical practice an art or a science? Do physicians act as moral entrepreneurs? What sort of ethical dilemmas do doctors face as they do their work?

Chapter 10 examines the history of universal medical care insurance in Canada. What is the impact of universal medical insurance on class-based differences in health status? What is the future of extra-billing? What role did Tommy Douglas play in the foundation of Canada's universal medical care system?

Chapter 11 examines medical practice as an occupation, and seeks to answer such questions as: Is medicine a profession? What is a profession? How do doctors handle mistakes? What is medical culture?

Chapter 12 describes other health-care providers—nurses and midwives. Typical questions are: What is the importance of Florence Nightingale for nursing work today? What are the consequences of the bureaucratic work organization of the hospital on the work of nurses? What is the status of the midwife in Canada?

Chapter 13 examines the place of complementary and alternative health care in Canadian and other Western industrialized societies. In-depth examinations of two alternative forms of health care, chiropractic and naturopathy, are included.

Chapter 14 examines the pharmaceutical industry as one component of the medical-industrial complex. It considers questions such as: How does the pharmaceutical industry maintain its position as one of the lowest-risk and highest-profit industries in Canada today? What is the role of doctors and pharmacists in prescribing drugs? Which Canadians are most likely to use mood-altering drugs?

Discussion of the Canadian medical care system is followed by a new concluding chapter. Chapter 15 looks at health care in international perspective and in the context of globalization, with particular focus on the health-care systems of Brazil, the United States, and the United Kingdom.

Many readers have mentioned that they missed the chapter on critical issues in the Canadian health-care system that appeared in the fourth and earlier editions. Rather than make the book bigger by restoring and updating this material for inclusion here, I have updated the discussion on topics such as models of health care, sexism, chronic illness and care, home care, maldistribution of medical care resources, and wait times, and this revised material can be found at the Oxford University Press website: www.oupcanada.com/Clarke7e.

Acknowledgements

Many people have contributed to this seventh edition, first of all my students, who have asked questions, shown enthusiasm, and made suggestions for the inclusion of new material. In addition, I am grateful to Michelle Skop-Dror, who recently completed her Ph.D. at Laurier and whose work on fibromyalgia as a new and contested illness, found especially among women, is shown in Box 8.3. Colleagues here at Laurier and at universities across the country have supported the previous editions and suggested and encouraged new directions. In particular, I would like to thank the following reviewers, whose thoughtful comments have helped shape this edition:

Kayla Baumgartner, University of Western Ontario
Robert Biezenski, University of Regina
Jennifer Boyko, Brock University
Linda Cohen, Memorial University of Newfoundland
James Falconer, McGill University
Ariel Fuenzalida, Carleton University/University of Ottawa
Alissa Overend, Grant MacEwan University
Steven M. Prus, Carleton University
Alexander Shvarts, Humber College

As always, I am grateful to Wilfrid Laurier University for the opportunities to do such writing as a part of teaching in a very busy sociology department. I am especially grateful to Amy Gordon at Oxford University Press for her keen interest in the topics covered in this book and for her brilliant ideas and creative thinking particularly as we reconfigured some aspects of the text, such as the Box program. Finally, Richard Tallman and Laurna Tallman, the fine editors for Oxford, have helped enormously, especially at the final stages, by noticing a myriad of small details and larger questions of substance and meaning that needed to be attended to before publication. I am also very grateful to have had their continued work on this book from the first edition because their interest in and engagement with many of the ideas improves my thinking and clarity and makes my reading of their responses both fun and challenging.

Sociological Perspectives

This book is divided into three sections. In Chapter 1 we discuss some of the most important theoretical and methodological underpinnings of the sociological study of health, illness, and medicine. They include (1) structural functionalism, (2) conflict theory, (3) symbolic interactionism/interpretive or social constructionist theory, (4) feminism, anti-racism, and intersectionality, and (5) post-structuralism. All of these theoretical approaches are included throughout the text in the different studies brought to bear on the specific arguments made. In Part II we discuss issues of relevance to the branch of the field called the sociology of health and illness. In Part III we focus on both the historical and contemporary features of the Canadian medical care system in the critical contexts of medicalization and biomedicalization. This first section, then, covers some of the basic concerns of the whole field of the sociology of health, illness, and medicine as it explains and illustrates the five principal sociological perspectives.

1

Ways of Thinking Sociologically about Health, Illness, and Medicine

wavebreakmedia/Shutterstock.com

CHAPTER OVERVIEW

▶ There are many different approaches to research and analysis in the field of sociology.

▶ In this book we have divided these into five different theories: structural-functional, conflict, symbolic interactionist/interpretive, feminist/critical race and intersectionality theories, and post-structuralism.

▶ Each perspective involves a fundamentally different paradigm or way of seeing the important issues in health and medical sociology as well as some distinct methodological strategies.

▶ Structural functionalism, based on the work of Émile Durkheim, sees society as a system of interlocking and functional parts.

▶ Conflict theory, from the work of Karl Marx, is concerned about the documentation and elimination of injustices, particularly those based on economic inequities.

▶ Symbolic interactionism, interpretive or social constructivist sociology, based initially on the writing of Max Weber, sees sociology as the study of social action insofar as it is socially meaningful.

▶ Feminist, critical race, and intersectionality theories are more recent, dating from the latter part of the last century. Gender and race were the original core concepts of analysis. The work of Canadian sociologist Dorothy Smith can be used to exemplify feminism and the work of George Sefa Dei, also Canadian, can be used to illustrate anti-racist theory. Intersectionality involves an expansion of these perspectives and the inclusion of other inequities in any and all analyses.

▶ The work of Michel Foucault exemplifies the post-structuralist focus on how power produces effects through reflexive and circulating discourses.

Introduction

Almost all of us have been sick at some time in our lives. When do we acknowledge that we are sick? Is it when we stay in bed for a day or two? Perhaps it is when we feel a pain but take a pill and go on with the day as planned? Or perhaps we may not truly claim sickness unless we go to the doctor to find a name for the unusual way we feel? Whatever our view, all of us experience illness in a social context: we recognize it because we have developed a vocabulary that allows us to think and talk about it with others in our immediate circle or in the larger social world; we learn what to do about it as we interact with others, with friends and families, at times with the formal medical system, and with our society through such media as television, magazines, or the Internet.

Are you aware of the relationship between ethnicity and sickle-cell anemia? It is much more common among people of African or Mediterranean background. Did you know that unemployment is often followed by ill health? What might the sociological explanations of such a finding be? Most types of morbidity and mortality are inversely related to income. That is, it is statistically correct to say that the lower the income, the higher the rates of sickness, disability, and death. What are the health consequences of the global spread of neo-liberalism? In many ways and in many places the gap has widened between the richer and the poorer countries and the rich and poor within individual countries. Increased inequality has limited progress towards better health and health care. The early and dramatic spread of HIV/AIDS among some of the poorest workers and their families in Africa is a case in point. The experiences or meanings of illness are constructed differently in various societies: socio-psychological conditions are linked to various diagnoses. These are the sorts of issues discussed in the sociology of health and illness. To provide a working definition, the sociology of health and illness seeks to describe and explain some of the social causes and consequences of illness, disease, disability, and death; to show the ways lay people and professionals construct their own distinct categories of disease and illness, and to describe the identities and experiences associated with illness and wellness. Table 1.1 lists examples of relevant topics.

When we think that we are sick, what do we do? Some of us treat ourselves with our favourite home

TABLE 1.1   Examples of Topics within the Sociology of Medicine and of Health and Illness

Sociology of Medicine	Sociology of Health and Illness
Medicalization and biomedicalization	The construction and distribution of disease and death in the context of medicalization and biomedicalization
The organization of the medical care system in the context of medicalization and biomedicalization	
The profession of medicine (and auxiliary and competing health-care professionals)	Disease and death in socio-historical context
Alternative health-care providers	Socio-demographic explanations for disease and death
The financing of medical care	Class, patriarchy, and sexism as explanations for disease and death
The medico-industrial complex	
Class, patriarchy, and sexism and the organization of medical care	Socio-psychological explanations for disease and death
The health-promotion industry	Experiencing and talking about disease and death
Medical care around the globe	Ways people construct or label certain signs as symptoms of disease
The development and perpetuation of medical discourse and ideology	Environmental conditions and health, occupational health, safety issues, and health consequences
	Health and illness around the globe

remedies such as bed rest, lemon tea, or chicken soup. Some of us seek advice from friends or family members. Some of us visit our general practitioner, a medical specialist, or a pharmacist. A few head off to the emergency room of the nearest hospital. A few others seek alternative health care such as homeopathy or acupuncture. When you seek the advice of a doctor, do you think you would receive better medical care from a physician who works in a fee-for-service setting or from one on a salary paid by the state, a corporation, or a clinic? Do practitioners in group practice provide better care than those in practice on their own? Does the Canadian government have adequate drug safety procedures to protect Canadians against another drug disaster such as thalidomide? Why does the universal medical insurance scheme provide guaranteed funds for medical practitioners but only limited funds, if any, for complementary and alternative health-care providers? How does medical care vary around the world? Do you think that medicine sometimes is used to fulfill dreams and aspirations, as in cosmetic surgery? Or is self-medication—such as drug use—sometimes used as a substitute for fulfilling dreams and aspirations? These are some of the questions we ponder in this text.

The sociology of medicine is the study of the ways the institutionalized medical systems construct what they deem to be illness out of what they recognize as signs and symptoms, and what they constitute as their responses to such "illness" through the treatments they prescribe (see Table 1.1). The medical care system also responds to the everyday demands of patients, the bidding of the disease-related support and advocacy groups, pharmaceutical regulations and advertising, the demands of governments and health insurance companies, and the innovations of medical device corporations, among other external forces. This field of sociology examines and offers explanations for such issues as **medicalization, biomedicalization**, the varying types of medical practice and medical **discourses**, the ideology and organization of medicine, different ways of financing medical care, the structure and operation of the hospital, and the occupational worlds of nurses, doctors, and the myriad of other health-care workers. It also attempts to explain the relationships among the different types of health care and the role of the medical care system in the context of the culture, the political economy of states, and the globalizing world.

Sociologists study the social world from a variety of perspectives. Depending on their perspective, they focus on some aspects of social life and ignore others, and ask different questions and use different ways to answer them. As you might expect, these varied sociological perspectives are manifest in the sociology of health and illness and of medicine. Sociologists have approached these fields with different or even contradictory assumptions. At times different sociologists have described or analyzed an aspect of illness or medicine from such widely differing points of view that they appear to be discussing different phenomena. Among sociologists you will find some agreement, amid a lot of debate, that the various perspectives can be distilled into five distinct paradigms. The present convention is to call these perspectives structural-functional theory, conflict theory, symbolic interactionist/interpretive/social constructionist theory, feminist/anti-racist theory, and post-structuralism. Table 1.2 outlines the principal characteristics of each approach.

Structural Functionalism

Structural functionalism dominated North American sociology for many years. It had been the reigning paradigm, the "normal" science of the discipline (Kuhn, 1962). Many sociological studies published in North America have adopted this perspective. (See, for instance, the major journal in health sociology in the United States, the *Journal of Health and Social Behavior,* as well as publications and research in the fields of mainstream public health and **epidemiology**, for continuing examples of the dominance of this perspective.) Auguste Comte (1798–1857), who first gave the name of "sociology" to the science of society, thought that sociology's goal was to better society so that it might become orderly

TABLE 1.2 The Five Central Sociological Perspectives

	Structural Functionalism	Conflict Theory	Symbolic Interactionist/ Interpretive Theory	Feminist/ Anti-Racist/ Intersectionality Theory	Post-structuralism
Exemplar	Émile Durkheim	Karl Marx	Max Weber	Dorothy Smith/ George Sefa Dei	Michel Foucault
Model of subject matter	Society is a social system of interlocking and inter-related parts of institutions.	Society is a system of classes.	Society is composed of selves who make their social lives meaningful through interaction.	Understanding social organization, structure, power, and knowledge from women's and visible minority perspective	Interrogate key social concerns through fundamental concepts: biopower, medical gaze, power/knowledge, governmentality, and technologies of the self/subjectivities
Model of the subject matter in process	Institutions perform (dys)functions that are both manifest and latent in the interest of the (dis)continuation of the social system in equilibrium.	Power groups with contradictory purposes, based on their relationship to the basic economic structures.	Selves create reality anew from situation to situation in interaction with others.	Selves and identities are tied to the relations of ruling. Feminist and anti-racist research has change as one of its goals. They emphasize critical analysis and transformation of patriarchal and racist social system.	Circulating discourses infuse everyday practices through power/knowledge, governmentality, technologies of the self, and subjectivities.
Ways of doing sociological analysis	System explainable and predictable through a series of "if x... then y" causal statements; x and y are social facts.	Power groups are understandable from a committed stance examining the conflicts in historical context.	Selves' world views and symbols arise out of interaction and are made understandable through process of interpretive, empathetic understanding—verstehen.	All methods of data collection may be used but a collaborative approach (between researcher and subjects of research) is advocated. Triangulation is suggested. Language is anti-racist and gender appropriate.	Research is archaeological, genealogical, and historical discourse analysis as well as contemporary discourse analysis.

continued

TABLE 1.2   *Continued*

	Structural Functionalism	Conflict Theory	Symbolic Interactionist/ Interpretive Theory	Feminist/ Anti-Racist/ Intersectionality Theory	Post-structuralism
Exemplar	**Émile Durkheim**	**Karl Marx**	**Max Weber**	**Dorothy Smith/ George Sefa Dei**	**Michel Foucault**
Objectivity/ subjectivity	Necessary to be objective and to study the social world objectively.	Value-committed perspective necessary.	Acknowledgement of the inevitability of contextual reflexivity of knower and known.	Quite often focuses on/ begins with the experience of racialized people and of women. Impossible to be objective. Therefore important to clarify standpoint and acknowledge reflexivity.	Objectivity is not possible because of the irreducible connection between power/ knowledge.
Image of human nature	Human beings believe, think/ feel, and do as the result of external constraining forces.	Human beings are alienated from self, others, and meaningful work, and need the liberation that would come from revolutionary change.	Human beings continually construct reality as they interact with others in their social worlds.	Differences by racialization, class, gender/power, sexual orientation, dis/ability limit generalization.	Subjectivity is continually recreated and resisted through technologies of the self-infused with power/ knowledge.

and progressive. He might be called the godfather of sociology. Émile Durkheim (1858–1917) provided both the theoretical and methodological models for structural functionalism. Durkheim defined sociology as a science of social facts. Social facts, he said, were to be treated and studied as if they were real, external to individuals, and yet capable of constraining and directing human behaviour and thought. The subject matter of sociology was these social facts and their impact on human behaviour. Constrained by the external world, human beings, in Durkheim's view, were predictable and controllable through the power of norms that exist in their own right, aside from their manifestations in individuals.

Sociology in the Durkheimian tradition is often called structural functionalism. It assumes that the proper level of study for the sociologist is the society or the system. The social system is said to be composed of parts, institutions that function to maintain order. Just as the organs in the human body are inextricably tied to one another and function as interrelated components, so, too, are the parts or the institutions of society—the family, the economy, the polity, and the educational, welfare, military, and medical care systems. All these institutions operate interdependently to keep the society functioning. The goal of maintaining a good working order in society motivates theorizing and research in this sociological perspective.

Structural-functional theory is associated with positivist methodologies. Positivists view sociology as a science in the same way that physicists view physics as a science. Positivists assume that social scientists should and can remain objective and value-free while observing, recording, and measuring external social facts and their impacts on people. Just as the natural sciences seek universally true, causal explanations of relationships in the natural world, so do positivist sociologists in the social world. As well, since positivists believe that social facts are to be treated as real and external, they tend to rely on data that are assumed to be objective, collected from interviews and questionnaires administered to individuals in survey research, and analyzed and organized to reflect the probability of the occurrence of certain behaviours among a certain aggregate or group of individuals.

Five principles distinguish structural functionalism from the other perspectives. They are the assumptions that: (1) sociology aims to discover and to explain the impact of social facts on human behaviour, attitudes, and feelings; (2) social facts are to be treated as things that are real and external to human actions, and that determine human behaviour; (3) social facts can be seen in aspects of the social structure such as the norms that guide behaviour through roles enacted in social institutions such as the family or the economy, and in social behaviours such as those in relationships, in marriage, or at work; (4) sociology is a science that seeks to describe the world in a series of universal causal laws related to the operations of social facts; and (5) this science considers that human behaviour is objectively and quantitatively measurable through methods such as experiments and survey research.

One of the most influential contributions to medical sociology from a structural-functional point of view is Talcott Parsons's work on the **sick role** (Parsons, 1951: 428–79). To understand Parsons's sick role, it is necessary to consider that each individual plays a number of roles in society. Roles arise out of the institutions with which the individual is associated. An individual may play a variety of work roles, neighbourhood roles, friendship roles, and so on. All roles reflect something of the intermeshing of the individual in society. The idea of role is a pivotal one in conceptualizing the relationship between the individual and society in structural functionalism.

Parsons's main concern was to describe the processes that maintain societal institutions and thus the stable workings of society. His notion of the sick role should be looked at in this context. Sickness could lead to societal breakdown resulting from the inability of the sick to fulfill their necessary social roles. Therefore sickness must be managed, and must be accorded a special role. However, this sick role legitimation is only temporary and is contingent on the fulfillment of certain obligations by the individual who claims the sick role. There are four components to the sick role. The first two are rights, the second two are duties. Both the rights and duties of the sick role must be fulfilled if the equilibrium of society is to be maintained.

(1) The sick person is exempt from "normal" social roles.

The sick individual has a legitimate excuse for missing an exam or a major presentation at work, for staying in bed all day and neglecting household chores, or for staying home from work. In order to win exemption, the individual may need formal, medical acknowledgement. The sick person may have to obtain an official medical diagnosis and even a medical certificate as proof of illness. Exemptions from examinations, for instance, generally require a formal written note from a physician.

(2) The sick person is not responsible for his or her condition.

The sickness must be the result of an accident or other circumstances beyond the control of the individual if that person is to be accorded the sick role. Thus, the individual is not to be blamed or punished. Influenza, a cold, and a broken leg are usually considered the results of misfortune, not of personal will or desire. Therefore, sympathy rather than blame is considered the appropriate reaction of others.

(3) The sick person should try to get well.

The sick role exemption is only temporary. The person who is given the legitimacy of the sick role is duty bound to try to get well. If an individual does not want to get well or does not try to get well, then the sick role is no longer considered legitimate. Thus, if a person has received a diagnosis of pneumonia, he or she must do what the doctor orders. If not, the legitimacy of the sick role deteriorates into the shame of such a label as "foolish," "careless," "immoral," or a "malingerer."

(4) The sick person should seek technically competent help and co-operate with the physician.

The duties associated with the sick role also require that the ill person seek "appropriate" medical attention and comply with the treatment provided. For example, a person with HIV/AIDS or another sexually transmitted infection who refuses both to accept medical care and to change certain sexual interactions would not be accorded the rights of the sick role and could be subject to legal punishment.

From the viewpoint of Parsons, illness is a form of deviance. It is a potential threat to the social system unless it is managed for the benefit of the social system. Medicine is the institution responsible for providing legitimation and justification and for bringing the sick back to wellness or "normality." Medical institutions can be seen as agents of social control in much the same way as are religious institutions and the criminal justice system.

Parsons's formulation of the sick role was primarily theoretical: it was not based on extensive systematic empirical investigation. Empirical analysis subjects his definition of the sick role to a number of criticisms. A few of these criticisms will be examined in the following sections.

(1) The sick person is exempt from "normal" social roles.

The extent to which a person is allowed exemption depends on the nature, severity, and longevity of the sickness, and also on the characteristics and normal social roles of the person. A short and self-limiting burn on the fingers merits only temporary, minimal exemptions from life roles. On the other hand, multiple sclerosis, a chronic, degenerative, and usually progressive disease, allows extensive exemptions.

The university student's sick role is mostly informal. Usually sick role exemption is not required. Most professors do not take attendance; students can avoid the library for weeks on end without any official notice being taken; they can stay in bed half the day and stay out half the night. These things are the student's own responsibility. It is only at the time of regularly scheduled deadlines for papers, presentations, and examinations that universities typically take any official notice of the student's actions. At these times the student may need to adopt the sick role formally by obtaining official legitimation from a physician through a note.

(2) The sick person is not responsible for her or his condition.

This belief varies depending on the nature of the condition and the circumstances through which the person is believed to have acquired the condition. The sick person may be held responsible for having a cold, for instance, if he or she stayed out overnight and walked miles in the freezing rain without a jacket. The notion of stress that is prevalent today often has an aspect of blame attached to it—that is, people who succumb to disease because they have been overworked or worried may be chastised for having failed to take preventive action. One of the implications, in fact, of the recent emphasis on health promotion through lifestyle change (moderating the drinking of alcoholic beverages, and so on) is that people who do not change and moderate their alcohol consumption may be more likely to be held responsible and blamed for cirrhosis of the liver, for example, or the person with AIDS may be blamed for his or her sexual habits or intravenous drug addiction. A number of diseases are thought to reflect on the moral and social worth of the individual, and when an individual succumbs to these diseases he or she is blamed according to the degree of social **stigma** (Goffman, 1963) attached to the condition.

There is considerable evidence that even though the specific causes of particular cancers are not known, there is a way in which the person with the disease is sometimes blamed for succumbing. For instance, the person with lung cancer may be held responsible if he/she has smoked or still smokes. A person diagnosed with HIV/AIDS may be blamed because of a "chosen lifestyle" or "immoral" sexual choices. Crandall and Moriarty (1995) asked people to examine case histories representing 66 illnesses and to rate the illnesses according to a number of dimensions. They found that the diseases most likely to lead to social rejection, i.e., to be stigmatized, were those (1) that were believed to be under personal onset control and (2) that were most severe. They did not find that gender, age, or ethnicity had an impact. Epilepsy, leprosy, mental illness, and venereal disease are among other frequently stigmatizing diseases (Schneider and Conrad, 1983; Markowitz, 1998). Today, though, sometimes a cancer diagnosis may seem almost a badge of honour and an opportunity for "growth" (Seale, 2001). In fact, many think that breast cancer ought to be an occasion to learn and practice "optimism" (Ehrenreich, 2009). It is used as a marketing ploy (King, 2006). Prostate cancer has spawned its own celebratory marketing through the growth of moustaches among more than 3 million men for the "Movember" fundraising movement (http://ca.movember.com/about/history).

(3) The sick person should want to get well.

The sick person should want to get well unless diagnosed as terminal. There are illnesses from which people cannot or are not expected to recover. People are expected to adjust to such illnesses, not to seek healing. A "terminal" illness is a case in point. Patients are not granted legitimacy for wanting to get well once they have been diagnosed with a terminal illness. In fact, if people continue to want to get well when they have been diagnosed as terminal, they are often criticized and possibly even diagnosed with a mental illness because they may be said to be denying reality. Similarly, people with a whole range of chronic illnesses are not expected to want to get well, but rather to adapt to daily limitations and disabilities.

(4) The sick person should seek technically competent help and co-operate with the physician.

The dominant medical care system is that of allopathic medicine. Allopathic medicine treats disease by trying to create a condition in the body that is opposite to or incompatible with the disease state. While this conventional medical care system still claims a monopoly and governmental support for the right to provide treatment and thus to legitimate sickness, there are competing medical systems with varying and growing degrees of legitimacy. A significant proportion of Canadians use alternative health-care providers. This includes those who have used self-help and complementary and alternative medicines (CAMs), such as meditation, herbs, vitamins and minerals, music therapy, or yoga, for their health. Moreover, allopathic medical practice is the subject of growing rejection and critique by a variety of consumer interest groups (see Breggin, 2014, for ongoing opposition to the **pharmaceuticalization** of children's mental health issues). Critical evaluations of such things as unnecessary surgery, side effects from taking prescribed drugs, and unnecessary medical intervention in childbirth raise the real possibility that co-operation with physicians may not always be the most efficacious road to good health. The determination of which profession is technically competent becomes quite problematic.

In spite of the serious problems raised above, the sick role concept is important in medical sociology. Parsons was the first to note explicitly that there are ways in which medical practice, its ideology, and its associated medical institutions serve to fulfill social control functions for the society. The concept of medicalization has been used to describe this process.

While **positivism** is the research methodology most closely associated with the structural-functional perspective, not all positivists are structural functionalists. Contemporary positivists study human health behaviours as both **independent** and **dependent variables**. An examination of the impact of a diagnosis, e.g., of cystic fibrosis, on the family of the ill person treats health behaviour related to the diagnosis as the independent variable. On the other hand, when the impact of income level on the **incidence** of disease is studied, human health behaviour becomes the dependent variable.

Today, positivists, following Durkheim, assume that the social has a constraining impact on individuals. Social-structural positions (social facts) determine individual thoughts, behaviours, feelings, and, in this case, health and illness, medical utilization, and so on. Research along these lines examines the effects of such things as gender, class, educational level, family type, marital status, age, rural/urban background, religious affiliation, religiosity, and political ideology on such (dependent) health-related variables as disease and death rates and utilization of medical care. The **social determinants of health** perspective is a contemporary illustration of this methodology (see Chapters 4 and 5 for examples of this type of research).

Conflict Theory

Conflict theory has had a less dominant role in the development of sociology in North America. It has provided a radical critique of the more conservative aspects of structural-functional sociology and of the economic and social arrangements found in society. In **conflict theory**, all social arrangements, all sociological theories, and all sociological methods have political and economic bases and consequences. Conflict theory tends to focus on class- or economic-based power relations and dynamics. Research topics, methodological approaches, and commitment to the use of findings all reflect the political and economic interests of the researcher.

The model of this paradigm is the work of Karl Marx (1818–83). Marx was directly involved in the analysis of and the organization for changes in his society. The author of numerous books, he was the leader of the First Communist International

TABLE 1.3   Methodological Assumptions of Positivist Social Science

Objectivity	Social science can be as objective as physical science and should be modelled on the physical sciences.
Generalizability	One of the most important goals of social science is to generalize and thereby to describe the world in a series of "if x then y" causal laws.
Validity: Construct	It is possible to design measures that accurately and briefly describe sociological concepts.
Validity: Internal	It is possible in any social scientific research design to say with a degree of surety that "x" is the probable cause of "y."
Validity: External	It is possible to select a sample so that generalization from the sample to the total population is accurate with a known but limited amount of error.
Reliability	It is possible for the same research to be completed in different settings and by different researchers and with essentially the same findings.
Causality	It is possible to demonstrate probable causal relationships between social science variables.
Adequacy	The data collected adequately describe and explain the phenomenon under investigation.
Data Collection Strategies	The usual data collection strategy involves survey research with either a questionnaire or an interview, administered either in person or over the telephone. Experimental laboratory research is sometimes done.
Quantification	Sociological phenomena can be quantified in statistical data.
Probability	Analysis is based on assumptions of probability, not determinism, i.e., hypotheses are put forward as possibilities.

in Europe during the nineteenth century, and was also a busy and effective investigative journalist. He asserted that human thought and behaviour were the result of socio-economic relations, and that both were alterable for human and social betterment. Believing that human beings could change their social order, Marx worked towards human liberation through a social and economic revolution.

Society, according to Marx, has historically been composed of a constantly varying balance of opposite forces that generate change through their ongoing struggle. The motivating force behind this continuous struggle is the way in which people interact with one another as they attempt to obtain their livelihood. Marx described the various modes of production with their corresponding types of social relations that occurred in consecutive historical periods as a period of struggle between classes. The class struggle is related to the means of production, e.g., the land or the factory, because members of one class own the means of production and members of the other class sell their labour for goods and services and cash. For Marx, an end to conflict was both possible and desirable in a communist state in which all citizens owned the means of production.

In doing sociology, conflict theorists use information from a variety of sources, but it tends to be historical and critical in focus. As with structural functionalism, the level of analysis is the social system, because ultimately the system must be changed and a new one established. What is distinct about some conflict theorists is that they may also be activists. Some see injustice everywhere, and some try to alleviate it.

Conflict theory can be distinguished in the following ways: (1) the sociologist's work is to discover and document injustice (and sometimes to attempt to change it); (2) all knowledge is rooted in social, material, and historical contexts; and (3) sociological research methods must acknowledge social, economic, and historical contexts. When the conflict theorist is particularly influenced by Marx's analysis, the primary subject of study is social classes, because they are thought of as the means to effect change.

Sociology from the perspective of conflict theory involves the documentation of injustice for the purpose of understanding its origins and causes in a historical and socio-political context. Social class and social injustice are everywhere, and medical institutions and disease rates are no exception.

A long tradition of scholarship documents the ways in which health and illness are related to unequal social arrangements. Marx's collaborator, Friedrich Engels, in *The Condition of the Working Class in England* (1845), showed how the working and living conditions that resulted from early capitalist production had negative health effects. Engels described how capitalism introduced mechanization on farms, resulting in a mass of unemployed rural workers who were forced to migrate to the cities to make a living. Capitalists in the city, driven to make a profit, kept their labour costs low, and thus the working classes could afford only very cheap shelter and food. The great slums that resulted were the perfect breeding grounds for the diseases endemic to such living conditions: rickets, tuberculosis, typhoid, scrofula, and other infectious diseases. Thus, ill health was related to the living conditions of the working class and the material conditions of capitalism.

More than a century and a half later, advanced monopoly capitalism, globalization, and neoliberalism (O'Connor, 1973; Turner, 1987; De Vogli, 2011) have generated considerably different but equally inhumane working conditions for workers and their families around the globe. Walmart, for example, while one of the richest companies in the world, pays its workers rates that frequently result in living standards below the poverty line (see wakeupwalmart.com/facts/; money.cnn.com/2009/06/05/news/companies/walmart.shareholders.meeting.fortune/index.htm). Standards of living have improved in the developed world. However, tremendous inequity is evident in the disparities in mortality and morbidity statistics and corresponding standards of living around the globe. Contemporary capitalism is dominated by huge international corporations such as General Electric, Berkshire Hathaway, Exxon Mobil, Wells

Fargo, Apple, Toyota, BP, Royal Dutch Shell Group, DaimlerChrysler, Samsung, Mitsubishi, and ING and is further characterized by attempts to enlarge profits through increased worker productivity, new time-saving technologies, and moving from developed into less-developed countries both for production and for markets. Profits are increased by getting workers and new technologies to produce more in the same time period, and by decreasing wages. As a result, a perpetual contradiction pits the needs of the workers—for a good living wage, good working conditions, adequate time for rest and relaxation, and meaningful, satisfying work (all of which are prerequisites to ongoing good health)—against the needs or desires of the capitalists for expansion and profit.

Vincente Navarro (1976) is one of the foremost conflict theorists of medical sociology in the North American (particularly US) context. He explains that there is a contradictory relationship between capitalism, which is an economic system fuelled by the profit motive, and the health needs of the population. Often the perceived need to make a profit requires that workers labour, live, and eat in unhealthy and unsafe environments. The manufacture, sale, and tax level of cigarettes around the world (www.who.int/mediacentre/news/releases/2003/pr27/en) illustrate how the desire for corporate profits and state tax revenues may outweigh the desire for good health for a population. Today, we are more likely to be warned about the dangers of terrorism than of cigarette smoking. Think of what you hear on the news about the threat of international terrorism as compared to cigarette smoking. The average annual number of deaths from cigarette smoking around the world is in the millions and about 300 times larger than deaths due to terrorism (Thomson and Wilson, 2005). The Global Terrorism Database as maintained by the US Department of Homeland Security lists the number of deaths globally due to terrorism in 2012–13 at 20,432. Cigarette smoking kills about 6 million people annually according to the World Health Organization (http: www.who .int/mediacentre/factsheets/fs339/en/).

The tobacco industry has maintained a successful profit margin by opening up new markets in spite of anti-smoking sentiments and some no-smoking legislation. In Canada, for example, the market has expanded into the younger age groups and women (Weeks, 2014; Begley, 2014). Though laws prohibit the sale of cigarettes to minors, they are rarely enforced, and even when they are enforced the fines are so low that they are virtually useless. Mini-cigars, flavoured as candy and lacking any warning labels, are one of the latest attempts to make inroads into the youth market (Begley, 2014). Similarly, in the interests of profit, as the overall rates of cigarette smoking are declining in the developed world, they are rapidly increasing in developing countries around the globe. Now almost 80 per cent of the world's smokers live in middle- and lower-income countries, according to the World Health Organization (http://www.who .int/mediacentre/factsheets/fs339/en/). It should be said, too, that once the tobacco industries were forced to provide warning pictures on cigarettes and the information of the deleterious effects of cigarettes became clearly and widely available, the rates of smoking declined precipitously in the US and Canada. This was followed by steep declines in the mortality rates of diseases such as lung cancer and cardiac diseases.

There are two main goals of contemporary capitalism: the concentration and protection of capital through such interventions as taxes and trade and the growth of the state to ensure these protections are in place. The state intervenes in the health sector to promote capitalist goals (Navarro, 1976). Some of the ways in which this occurs are, first, that the class structures of society are reproduced within the medical sector, so that the distribution of functions and responsibilities of occupational groups within the medical care system mirrors the class, ethnic, and gender hierarchies within the other sectors of capitalist society. Second, the medical system has a bourgeois ideology of medicine that regards both the cause and the cure of illness as the responsibility of the individual. Health itself becomes a commodity with a certain value within the marketplace. The medical model is a politically conservative model; it directs attention away from the social-structural causes of ill health, such as gender, "race," class, occupation, and environmental degradation. Third, the state supports alienation when people are not free to choose alternatives to physicians, such as chiropractors, naturopaths, masseuses, or dieticians. The state provides full financial support for only one type of medical service—that provided by the allopathic practitioner. Today, with globalization, many would argue that states have actually given away much of their power of governance to international capital through multinational corporations such as the pharmaceutical and medical technologies industries. This has resulted in innumerable threats to health and well-being (De Vogli, 2011).

The state also uses strategies to exclude conflicting ideologies from debate and discussion. One example is the emphases on individual and family, primarily mothers, responsibility in the causation of disease, in promoting early detection practices (such as mammograms), and health-promoting behaviours. Such viewpoints exclude analysis of the processes through which class origins, environmental pollutants, occupational hazards, and working conditions are significant causes of ill health.

A classic sociological analysis by Hilary Graham in *Women, Health and the Family* (1984) illustrates research in the conflict perspective. Although Graham's research was carried out in Great Britain several decades ago, it continues to raise questions for all societies regarding the home health-care work roles of women and the consequences of economic impoverishment for the health of families. This invisible work and the fact that it *is* invisible continue today. Still, policy for home care has not been adequately developed. (This topic will be explored in more depth in the second half of this book.) Graham analyzes the impact of poverty and the manifold effects of the relative scarcity of resources such as transportation, housing, fuel, food, and health care in the home on the health status of family members.

Home health-care work is composed of four elements. First is the provision of healthy conditions in the home. This involves the maintenance of a warm and clean home with sufficient space for rest and relaxation for all family members, sufficient and adequately nutritious foods, and clean water. Home health care also involves managing social relations and meeting emotional needs for the optimal mental health of family members. The second element is nursing the sick: much of the work of caring for the sick child or adult, and for elderly or disabled people, falls on the shoulders of the women in the home. Furthermore, increasing deinstitutionalization of the mentally, chronically, and acutely ill increases the level of intra-family responsibility. Nursing the sick is often a very time-consuming and exhausting job. It involves sleepless nights, heavy lifting, preparation of complicated menus, administering medicines, coping with bandages, and the like. A third element is teaching about health, including such things as modelling good health habits and giving instruction on diet, hygiene, and exercise. The fourth and final aspect of home health-care work is mediating with outsiders such as doctors and hospitals, making visits to clinics, talking with a social or public health worker, or getting advice from an expert in a health-related area, such as nutrition. The hidden health care work of women continues today in Canada and elsewhere (http://www.womenandhealthcare-reform.ca/publications/hiddenHealthCareWork_en.pdf). It reinforces gender inequality.

Graham also documents the existence of class differences in home health-care work and in associated mortality and morbidity rates. She notes the consistently inverse relationship between class and some of the most sensitive indicators of a nation's health: stillbirths, prenatal mortality, neonatal mortality, postnatal mortality, and infant mortality rates. These class differences in outcomes among infants are mirrored in the morbidity statistics for children and adults. Accidents, the largest single cause of childhood death, are probably one of the best indicators of an unsafe, inadequately supervised environment: the accident rate increases sharply among the lower social classes. Kronenfeld et al. (1997), using a survey research methodology with a sample of 1,247 young mothers, found that such parental resources as income and education were associated with better safety practices in respect to their children. Higher income was positively associated with safety behaviours such as not leaving a child alone in the house, not hiring babysitters younger than 13 years of age, not leaving a child alone in the bathtub, using an approved car seat, and a child's wearing a safety helmet while bicycling. Poorer families were more likely to suffer from other environmentally related causes of the death of children, such as respiratory diseases. The incidence of infections and parasitic illnesses is also class-related. There is evidence that the mortality rate for some childhood cancer is inversely related to class (de Kok et al., 2008).

Samuel S. Epstein is an epidemiologist with an expertise and a lengthy list of publications on the occupational and environmental causes of cancer. In an analysis of the policies of the National Cancer Institute (NCI) he drew our attention many years ago to conflicts of interest in medical practice and the funding of health-care organizations. He was one of the first critical analysts to document the high incidence of preventable cancer deaths and the minimal research investment of the NCI in understanding these preventable deaths. As Epstein says, "for decades the war on cancer has been dominated by powerful groups of interlocking professionals and financial interests, with the highly profitable drug development system at its hub—and a background that helps explain why 'treatment,' not prevention, has been and still is the overwhelming priority" (ibid., 20). According to the Cancer Prevention Coalition a similar emphasis continues today (www.preventcancer.com/losing/nci/why_prevent.htm). Furthermore, today cancer prevention itself is also heavily medicalized and biomedicalized. Prevention is widely understood to be early detection via such measures as mammograms, hormone replacements (HRT), and mandated HPV vaccinations, for example. Early detection technologies are aspects of medicine and medicalization. They are not and should not be thought of as prevention. This link conflates two processes

that should be distinguished one from another. Moreover, the safety and effectiveness of such early detection interventions as mammograms and HRT are equivocal and may cause disease at times. The fact that doctors may be financially invested in these technologies is also problematic.

Devra Davis (2007) provides a critical historical overview of the so-called "war on cancer," which was started in the US by President Nixon in the 1970s. She documents how the "war" was plagued by ongoing conflict of interest among cancer policy-makers because of their roles as directors in other industries that are either known to or thought to cause cancer over decades of exposure to their products and by-products. For instance, she shows how the leaders of industry who were responsible for the manufacture, advertising, and sale of cancer-causing products such as cigarettes were also in positions of power in the supposed fight against cancer. These leaders clearly paid lip service to the eradication of cancer even while they fought to suppress the scientific evidence of many of its fundamental causes via popular consumer products and related industries. For example, she states "Some of the early leaders of the American Cancer Society and the National Cancer Institute left their posts to work directly for the tobacco industry . . . they were hired to generate uncertainty about the association between tobacco and lung cancer" (Davis, 2007: xv). Davis also documents how the media presentations of public research and information about trendy new products obfuscate the potential threats of some contemporary commodities such as cosmetics and other personal care merchandise, pharmaceuticals such as Ritalin, the sugar-free sweetener aspartame, and cell phones. Davis has been trying to warn people that while the data are not all in yet, the idea that cell phones are bad for the brain cannot be ignored (see, e.g., www.huffingtonpost.com/devra-davis-phd/cell-phones-cancer_b_874361.html). Meanwhile the National Cancer Institute continues to argue that the research on this link is inconclusive (http://www.cancer.gov/cancertopics/factsheet/Risk/cellphones). In a situation in which there are powerful interests in support of such new technologies, caution in their uptake is important. This stand on the adoption of new technologies is called the **precautionary principle**.

The lack of emphasis on prevention has been and continues to be true in Canada as well. For example, a vanishingly small amount of money dedicated to investigating cancer in either children and adolescents or adults is dedicated to prevention. Possible environmental causes of cancer, such as pesticides and herbicides, are seldom a research focus. Treatment and biology receive the greatest proportion of the financial investment in cancer research (see Figure 1.1).

Samantha King (2006) has documented how popular breast cancer activism has often led to an obfuscation of the links between the economy, the environment, and breast cancer through an emphasis on "cause or social marketing." Social marketing is a type of fundraising that essentially blurs the boundaries between the responsibility of governments for caring for their citizens and intervening for prevention, as opposed to prioritizing the profit needs of corporations. It encourages people to buy products through advertising the association between the philanthropic activities of the business and the disease. At the same time, such

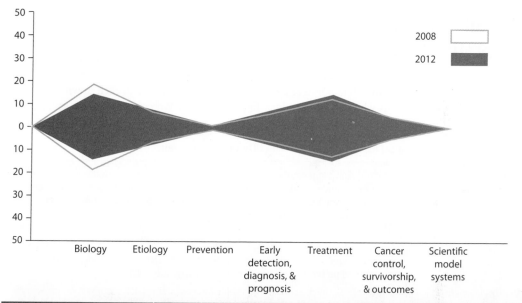

	Biology	Etiology	Prevention	Early detection, diagnosis, & prognosis	Treatment	Cancer control, survivorship, & outcomes	Scientific model systems
Proportion of investment in 2008 (%)	37.1	13.5	2.3	12.3	25.0	9.5	0.3
Proportion of investment in 2012 (%)	28.8	15.4	2.4	13.9	29.2	10.0	0.3
2008 investment ($M)	180.8	65.8	11.1	60.1	121.8	46.5	1.3
2012 investment ($M)	156.2	83.3	13.2	75.5	157.9	53.9	1.6
Percent change in investment from 2008 to 2012	−14	27	19	26	30	16	23

FIGURE 1.1   Distribution of Cancer Research Investment by CSO Category, 2008 and 2012

*CSO = Common Scientific Outline, a classification system used to differentiate among seven broad categories related to cancer research.

Source: Slide 17 in PowerPoint presentation entitled "Cancer Research Investment in Canada, 2012: Highlights from the Canadian Cancer Research Survey." Canadian Cancer Research Alliance. March 2015. Reprinted with permission.

an emphasis obscures the disease-causing effects of the cosmetic products made by those who support such social marketing as the Look Good . . . Feel Better campaign dedicated to "makeovers" for women with cancer (www.lookgoodfeelbetter.org). The dominance of such fundraising strategies supports the **neo-liberalism** and **privatization** that characterize the modern economy including its valorization of the market along with individual responsibility or "responsibilization."

The methodological assumptions of this theoretical perspective are illustrated in Table 1.4.

Symbolic Interactionist/ Interpretive Theory

What is the meaning of illness? Does cancer have the same meaningful impact when it happens to an 80-year-old man or woman as when a 10-year-old child is diagnosed with it? What are the processes through which the slow onset of Alzheimer's comes to be noted by family, friends, and the patient? How do families work through their changing understanding of the uncertainty and then the certainty of the death of one of their members? How does the self-identity of the person with AIDS alter once he or she has received the diagnosis? How do others alter the ways they relate to the person with AIDS? These are the sorts of questions asked by those who study health and illness issues from the perspective of **symbolic interactionist/interpretive/social constructionist theory**.

Max Weber provided a relevant definition of sociology: "a science which attempts the interpretive understanding of social action in order thereby to arrive at a causal explanation of its course and its effects" (Weber, 1947: 88). There are two crucial elements in this statement, each of which exemplifies an aspect of Weber's work. First, social action,

TABLE 1.4	Methodological Assumptions of Conflict Theory Social Science
Value Commitment	Rather than seeking objectivity, the conflict theorist believes that sociologists must discover, document, and record recurrent patterns and dynamics of power/class/gender relations both because they have no choice (members of a society are committed to the ongoing action of the society) and because they believe that this is the morally correct position.
Historical Specificity	Rather than looking for generalizations, conflict theorists assert the necessity of understanding the unique features of the particular situation in its socio-historical context as an example of these recurrent patterns of power/class/gender relations.
Validity: Construct	Formal tests of validity are considered irrelevant. Researchers, it is assumed, of necessity study what they claim they are studying.
Validity: Internal	Formal statistical tests of causal relationships are not always necessary. Rather, logical meaningfulness may be the relevant criterion of causality.
Validity: External	The conflict theorist assumes that inequities based on power/class/gender relations are ubiquitous, yet analyzes the components separately in each historical situation.
Ethical Concerns	The primary importance in the research of the conflict theorist is the commitment to such ethical and humanitarian principles as justice and equality.
Data Collection	The usual sources of data are historical documents. As well, the conflict theorist may use other data collection methods, including surveys, statistical data, and methods such as unstructured interviews and participant observation that provide subjective and descriptive data.
Objectivity	Objectivity is not possible. Knowledge cannot be separated from the power/class/gender relations of the researcher and the subjects.
Quantification	While numerical data may be used to document an argument, they are not always available.

as defined by Weber, meant action to which the individual attached subjective meaning. Second, the sociologist, while looking for what Weber calls causal explanation, was actually directed to interpret empathetically the meaning of a situation from the viewpoint of the subject.

Symbolic interactionist/interpretive sociologists study how the subjective definitions of social reality and discourses are constructed and how this reality is experienced and described by the social actors. Human beings create their social worlds. As W.I. Thomas said, if a situation is defined as real, it is real in its consequences (Martindale, 1960: 347–53).

The paradox here is that, just as the subjects who are being studied are busy defining reality for themselves, so, too, are the researchers. Thus, the symbolic interactionist is faced with the problem, when collecting data, of intersubjectivity or reflexivity, that is, that the data are given a subjective slant both by the people being studied and by the researcher. The symbolic interactionist researcher must face a second problem: that the research act itself creates and changes meanings and processes. From the perspective of symbolic interactionism it is impossible to gather objective data. All social reality is subjectively defined and experienced and can be studied only through the subjective processes of social researchers.

Empathetic understanding, or what has come to be called, following Weber, **verstehen**, is the desirable methodological stance of the researcher. Generally, sociologists adopting this stance collect data by observing social action in close participation with the subjects or by long, unstructured interviews. The level of analysis is not of the system but rather of individual interaction with others, the mind or the self, and meaning; this study is micro-analysis. The structural-functional and conflict theories, because they focus on systems, are macro analyses.

Three assumptions are characteristic of this perspective: (1) sociology is a science, the purpose of which is to understand the social meanings of human social action and interaction; (2) reflexivity or intersubjectivity, rather than objectivity

or critical analysis, characterizes the relationship between the subject and the researcher; and (3) rich, carefully detailed description and analysis of unique social situations from the perspective of the subjects under investigation is typical of symbolic interactionist research.

The sociological problem to be understood and explained in the symbolic interactionist tradition is the meanings that individuals see in the actions of themselves, of others, of institutions, and so on (Weber, 1968). Analysis of society demands different methods from those used to describe and explain the natural world. It requires methods that attempt to grasp the motives and meanings of social acts. Sociology is a science that must deal with the subjective meanings of events to social actors.

A classic example of work in this perspective is the study of the meaning of the diagnosis of epilepsy within the lives of a sample of people with this disease. *Having Epilepsy* (Schneider and Conrad, 1983) is based on long, semi-structured interviews with a number of people who have been diagnosed with epilepsy. The authors make the point that it is important that sociologists provide an antidote to medical research. It is crucial, they note, to distinguish between disease and illness. Disease is the pathology of the human body; illness is the meaning of the experience associated with a given pathology. In this research the subjects were selected for study because they have epilepsy. However, they live most of the time without the symptoms of the disorder being present. They go about their daily activities, eating, dressing, working, cooking, cleaning, visiting, enjoying leisure and social activities, unrestrained and unconstrained by an awareness of their disease.

Medicine attempts to understand the nature and cause of disease and to formulate methods for its treatment. One of the tasks of the sociologist is to describe the impact of disease and diagnosis on the individual's self and on his or her relationships with others. As Schneider and Conrad say: "We cannot understand illness experiences by studying disease alone, for disease refers merely to the undesirable changes in the body. Illness, however, is primarily about social meanings, experiences, relationships, and conduct that exist around putative disease" (ibid., 205).

Schneider and Conrad suggest that one of the most pervasive aspects of epilepsy is a continuing sense of uncertainty. From the earliest stages of pre-diagnosis and throughout the illness, a sense of uncertainty is a defining quality of this and other chronic conditions. People with epilepsy, as do those with cancer, Alzheimer's disease, diabetes, or multiple sclerosis (just a few of the chronic conditions to which this analysis is relevant), at first wonder what is happening to their bodies or their minds. They wonder whether or not to take this or that small sign of change as a symptom of a disease. They wonder whether it is a symptom of a serious or a minor disease.

Once diagnosed, they wonder how severe their illness will become and whether they will live for long or only for a short time. They ask whether they will be seriously debilitated or only mildly affected. Relationships are altered. Others respond to this sense of uncertainty with their own confusion about the disorder and its likely course. Not only does relating to the self become tinged with ambiguity arising from dealing with change, but relating to others also becomes unclear. The lack of easy, honest, open, and straightforward communication is frequently seen as one of the most painful aspects of the disorder. Cancer patients, for instance, have said that the difficulties of communication (born of **uncertainty**) are frequently even more painful than the disease or its treatment (Dunkel-Schetter and Wortman, 1982). Arthur Frank (1991) has noted how we now live in a **remission society** because of the ongoing sense held by so many people who have lived through serious diagnoses that anything can happen and the disease or another just like it may occur. It takes a long while for people who have survived some serious disease to feel "normal" again—if they ever do. Conceptualizing life after diagnosis and treatment in terms of the five-year survival rate, and so on, adds to this continuous uncertainly for people in the remission society.

Another source of uncertainty surrounding some chronic illnesses is the fact that many are poorly understood by the medical profession and by the lay public including those diagnosed. There is a general lack of knowledge about the probable prognosis of some chronic illnesses. Some chronic diseases receive a considerable amount of press; others receive very little. Some are well recognized by the lay public; most are not. Some have been diagnosable for many, many years. Others, such as Alzheimer's, are relatively recent diagnoses. For some, the norms of possible remissions, plateaus, and disease exacerbations have long been charted. The short history of others means that there are few standards for what to expect.

Epilepsy is a disease with a long history. It has often been thought to reflect not just the state of the physical body, but also the moral character of the person. At times the person with epilepsy has been considered to be divine, at other times satanic. At various times and places seizures have been understood as signs both of prophetic ability and of madness.

Chronic illness requires symptom control. This is particularly necessary when the symptoms can be highly disruptive, as in diabetes, which can exhibit diabetic reaction or coma; or in colitis, which may involve unexpected evacuation; or in epilepsy, if there is a grand mal seizure. Symptom control can involve following the doctor's orders. It can also involve non-medical procedures such as biofeedback, hypnosis, diet change, meditation, exercise, relaxation, vitamin therapy, and others. Managing medical regimens does not necessarily mean following the medical rules. Instead, people often manage their medicines according to their own values, habits, activities, relationships, and side effects.

People with epilepsy control their drug use in such a way as to moderate the number and severity of seizures to a level with which they feel comfortable. Doctors' orders are only one of several sources of information upon which people with epilepsy choose to base their use of medication. Drug-use patterns develop as an outcome of a complex of self-perceived considerations such as (1) the meaning of the seizure

---

TABLE 1.5   Methodological Assumptions of Symbolic Interactionist/Interpretive/Social Constructivist Social Science

Reflexivity	Social researchers interpret the sayings and behaviour of their subjects from the subject's perspectives and within the context of the researcher's perspective. The researchers are affected by the needs and expectations of their subjects and the subjects' knowledge of the data collection process, and at the same time, they change the subjects' understanding. Thus, it is impossible to measure human social behaviour objectively.
Ethical Concerns	Just as it is impossible to study human social action as if it were the action of so many atoms, molecules, neutrons, and protons, so it is impossible not to change the social situation that is the subject of the analysis.
Generalizability	While the method of analytic induction, one of the operating logics of this perspective, claims universality, most research in this paradigm is based on the specificity of human social action.
Causality	Causality is recognized in this perspective as a subject of study, e.g., "I believe I have cancer because I sinned against God," rather than the "if x . . . then y" causality of positivism.
Proof	The most stringent criterion of proof is sometimes required within this perspective—negative case analysis.
Validity	Validity is always hampered by intersubjectivity, but the depth and detail of the description of the data and their "meanings" are considered important criteria.
Reliability	This is considered less important than validity because it is assumed that different researchers would be researching different situations and would therefore have (at least somewhat) different findings.
Scope of Analysis	The symbolic interactionist sociologist is generally content to describe the social world of a small population of people in rich complexity and detail.
Advocacy	Some symbolic interactionists view their work as advocacy (e.g., Millman, 1977). Others fervently argue for the value of knowledge for its own sake.

to the subject, (2) the personal view of the effectiveness of the drug, (3) the personal estimation of the costs of side effects, (4) the desire to test whether the epilepsy is still present, (5) the wish to avoid having others recognize that one has epilepsy, and (6) the need to protect oneself from seizures in particular situations (Schneider and Conrad, 1983). Medication use is a social process and as such is vulnerable to the social needs and experiences of users.

The research of Schneider and Conrad exemplifies the symbolic interactionist approach to understanding behaviour in health and illness. Through the presentation of quotations from the subjects interspersed with sociological analysis, the authors have provided a work with relevance to others in similar health circumstances, to their families, to health-care workers who deal with people with such diagnoses, and to the academic sociological community.

Feminist, Critical Anti-racist, and Intersectionality Theories

Feminist theory and feminist methods have grown rapidly in the past four-plus decades. A number of journals in a wide variety of academic areas are now dedicated to feminist, women's, and men's studies and they abound in many fields of scholarship. The social sciences, in particular, have been challenged and critiqued as having been "male-stream" in subject matter, research strategies, and theoretical assumptions. Whole new fields of women's studies, men's studies, and gender studies are now institutionalized as mainstream in universities, with undergraduate majors and master's and doctoral degrees. Following in the wake of Betty Friedan's *The Feminine Mystique* (1963), the women's health movement can be seen as a major impetus to feminist scholarship and policy. The organization of women in the late sixties and seventies for abortion and other health-care reforms and the widespread prescription of the birth control pill were crucial steps in the second wave of the women's movement in the twentieth century. The women's health movement, as exemplified by such monumental publications as *Our Bodies, Our Selves* (Boston Women's Health Collective, 2011 [1971]), led to a radical critique of the patriarchal, allopathic medical care system and practice (http://www.ourbodiesourselves.org/publications/our-bodies-ourselves-2011/).

A major theme in a feminist analysis of health has been a criticism of the medicalization of women's lives. Much of this analysis has focused on the dominance of the medical care system, medical practitioners, and the medical constructions of knowledge and power over women especially in regard to reproductive issues such as birth control and childbirth (Oakley, 1984), PMS (Pirie, 1988), and menopause (McCrea, 1983; Kaufert and Gilbert, 1987; Walters, 1991). Other feminist researchers have examined gender differences in disease and death as well as reactions to disease and interactions with the health-care system. A variety of theorists and researchers have explained how women's (poor) health is a result of social-structural inequities, such as class, racialization, participation in the labour force, or of familial and domestic roles (Hankivsky et al., 2011).

Today, sexuality, pregnancy, birth, and child-rearing are understood within the prisms of gender, knowledge, and power in Western democracies including Canada. All of these aspects of women's lives are subject to the risk-based, uncertainty characteristic of the political turn to the right in the West and neo-liberalism and gendered public health policies. Godderis (2010) shows how women's bodies and minds are increasingly likely to be subject to medicalization in areas related to reproduction such as the period of time immediately after childbirth. In the 1960s some few women were thought to become depressed after childbirth. By the 1980s this experience acquired a name and a specific, serious, and much more common

diagnosis of PPD or postpartum depression. This condition was situated as a disease that constituted one more instance of a greater proclivity for women's passage through formerly "normal" life stages to be accompanied by mental illness. Premenstrual syndrome was previously considered a variable experience that included a variety of personal challenges including acne, tiredness, and tender breasts (http://www.womenshealth.gov/publications/our-publications/fact-sheet/premenstrual-syndrome.html). Through expanding medicalization it became a specific diagnosis (and with it came specific treatments) of premenstrual dysphoric disorder (PMDD). Further, according to Goddeiris (2010) this new diagnosis of PPD was linked to a continuum of suffering said to beset up to 92 per cent of women after they had given birth including baby blues, postpartum depression and, in the worst-case scenario, postpartum psychosis. The spread of the discourses surrounding these issues opens up new requirements for the surveillance or monitoring of women' bodies and minds during these life transitions. Having a baby has become a risky endeavour as have many other public health concerns involving potential illness in the "risk society" (Beck, 1992). Ironically, too, much of the concern regarding the possibility of PPD focuses on the duty of mothers to "watch themselves and get help if they need it" in order that their children do not suffer.

Anti-racist theory expands feminism by including a focus on the fundamental significance of racialization (the term "racialization" cues us to the idea that "race" is a socially constructed concept with real consequences through racism) and racism, along with gender, class, and sexual identities, in understanding and theorizing the social world (Sefa Dei, 1999). "Race" and other differences implicate the social theorist within the subjects of study. This theoretical position asserts that all knowledge is racialized and associated with power and wealth. Individual identities around the globe are patterned by racism (along with other differences such as those noted above). There is no objective truth outside of that which is constructed in the context of inequality. In this context, power and dominance are gained by those who possess (or claim) knowledge; and this knowledge effectively determines what people think, feel, believe, and so on. Colonialism has led to the hegemonic dominance of European/Western knowledge and thought processes. As Sefa Dei says, "there exists a racialised, gendered, sexualized, and classed discursive practice." In practice this means that, for example, black immigrants are 76 per cent more likely than other immigrant groups to consider themselves to be unhealthy (Nestel, 2012). This perspective has generated significant study of the links between racialization and health in Canada, as this 2013 document demonstrates with respect to various health inequities by racial groups in Toronto (http://www.toronto.ca/legdocs/mmis/2013/hl/bgrd/backgroundfile-62904.pdf). This issue will be discussed further in Chapter 5.

Not only can we see that health and differences in health care mirror racial and other inequitable distinctions, but how questions are asked, topics are chosen for consideration, and definitions of health and illness are created take place in the context of racism and therefore are not objective in the way they are assumed to be. Knowledges are now being questioned for potentially racist assumptions. This work is largely in its infancy and sometimes is as likely to generate additional racism as it is to lead to anti-racism (Bonnett, 2006; Carrim, 2000; Pederson et al., 2005; Butler et al., 2003; Gourvish, 1995). According to **intersectionality** theory it is crucial to move beyond attention to one variable (such as race) at a time to a consideration of their dynamic interplay in the context of shifting powers (Hankivsky et al., 2011). In reality, none of us is merely "gendered" or "raced"; we also can—and must, for a good understanding of our health determinants and related health policy—be described in terms of our education, age, sexual identities, gender identities, "abilities," citizenship, and so on.

Table 1.6 presents some of the methodological considerations for research from the theoretical perspectives of feminism, anti-racism, and intersectionality.

Post-structuralism

A number of theorists are associated with the field now called **post-structuralism,** but the most influential for health and medical sociology is Michel

---

TABLE 1.6 Methodological Assumptions of Feminist, Anti-racist, and Intersectionality Theory in Social Science

Objectivity	It is impossible to be objective in social research. Therefore, it is important to be as clear as possible about the biases that are brought to any research study. The necessity for continuous reflexivity in research is acknowledged.
Generalizability	Class, gender, race, and power differences between researcher and subjects limit generalizability.
Subjectivity	Often focuses on women's experiences and those of racialized people and/or their viewpoints.
Subject Matter	Gender and race are always an important component of the investigations.
Language	Uses gender-neutral language where appropriate and specifies actual gender when relevant. Using non-racialized terminology.
Data Collection Methods	All methods are used but a collaborative approach between research and subjects of research is advocated. Triangulation is suggested.
Purpose	Feminist and anti-oppression research has change as one of its goals. It emphasizes the empowerment of women and of the racialized along with the transformation of patriarchal and white-dominated social structures.

Foucault. The work of Foucault both builds on and provides a radical reconsideration of the work exemplified by the perspectives described previously in this chapter. Rather than see power or inequalities as structural forces that exist outside of some individuals who might have been called powerless, Foucault directs our attention to the ways that power is imbricated in mutual relations and infused by socially constructed knowledges and everyday micro practices supported by state policies and circulating discourses. One of the most important of these for our purposes is biopower. Biopower is Foucault's answer to how social control and power occur in modern democratic and capitalist states. The population is controlled, in his view, by learning to govern itself as the government categorizes, counts, and develops policies relating to managing "bodies" through "public health," science, and medicine. The medical or clinical gaze is a part of these new technologies of power. Thus, our very notion of what constitutes a human body—anatomy, physiology, relation to the mind, and so on—is determined by circulating disciplinary knowledge such as medical science through popular discourses. What we consider to be disease, illness, wellness, and good functioning are continually recreated as we are subjected to, create, and resist prevailing discourses via everyday conversation and the mass media and by interaction with the medical care system.

Foucault's influence in the English-speaking world was originally due to his work on mental illness, *Madness and Civilization* (1964), and then *The Birth of the Clinic* (1973) and the three-volume *The History of Sexuality* (1978, 1984) in which he developed the notion of biopower. His early work was consistent with the writings of the powerful anti-psychiatric movement ideas articulated by scholars such as Thomas Szasz in *The Myth of Mental Illness* (1974 [1961]) and *The Manufacture of Madness* (1997 [1970]) and R.D. Laing and A. Esterson in *Sanity, Madness and the Family* (1970 [1964]). It was consistent, too, with Howard Becker's labelling theory as found, for instance, in *Outsiders* (1963). Today, through his enormous

influence on the field of mental illness, medicine, and sexuality, Foucault's ideas have moved well beyond reinterpreting and contributing to our understandings of mental illness to problematize all notions of the normal and abnormal body and their links to notions of governmentality, identity, and the medical or clinical gaze. In a sense, our ideas about and practices surrounding health constitute a sort of policing to ensure the "normal" functioning of the body/mind by individuals and by many others, such as professional groups including psychiatrists and other medical doctors.

One recent Canadian example of powerful governmentality is the rapid, widespread uptake of the HPV vaccine applied to young girls, ostensibly to prevent cervical cancer and genital warts (Connell and Hunt, 2010). The authors of this study analyze the ways in which the speedy adoption of the vaccine across countries was publicly justified through new and particular types of power/knowledge that were linked among governments, pharmaceutical interests, biological and medical scientists, and medical organizations. In 2006 a new vaccine, Gardasil, was approved by Health Canada. By the beginning of 2007 the National Advisory Committee on Immunization recommended that all Canadian girls between the ages of nine and 13 be immunized. The federal government assigned $300 million to this end. A number of medical groups such as the Canadian Pediatric Society, the Canadian Cancer Society, and the Federation of Medical Women of Canada supported this decision. Stories addressed both to mothers and to their daughters advocating the vaccine and emphasizing the risk to young women of not partaking of it spread through a sudden deluge of mass media. School boards took up the call and were offered as locations for the vaccination process. Notably, too, these dominating discourses raising concerns about the risks of cervical cancer and warts in young women prevailed, despite the fact that cervical cancer has the lowest incidence of all female cancers, has had a very stable rate of incidence for many years, and was already well controlled in the presence of the

CRITICAL THINKING

BOX 1.1   Should We Interrogate the Critical Thinker?

In some fields, such as literature, a tradition of debate has continued for many years about whether or not the personal facts—the biographies—of authors and their works are important to understanding the works themselves. Some would argue that in sociology generally and especially in social theory this has been less of an issue—the social facts speak for themselves and who originated them or why is not to the point. Thus, for example, Jean-Jacques Rousseau, the eighteenth-century French theorist, wrote extensively—and with considerable influence—about children and childhood, yet he and his mistress abandoned all five of their children to an orphanage. Should this matter to our understanding of his theories? Friedrich Nietzsche, the nineteenth-century German nihilist who wrote of "the death of God" and claimed that "man" must pursue a "will to power," has been a major influence on others, including ideologists of the political right and

such thinkers as Michel Foucault (who claimed that "madness" as an illness was invented by those with power to control those without power). Yet Nietzsche was a megalomaniac who struggled with depression throughout his career, and he was psychotic for the last 10 years of his relatively short life, which were spent in institutions and in the care of his sister. Does this call into question his influence and its basis? And then there is Foucault, whose interest in and influential theorizing about mental illness, about prisons, and about sexuality stemmed from his own experiences as a suicidal mental patient, his own early fascination with torture and the macabre, and his openly sado-masochistic homosexuality that led to his early death from AIDS. Are such biographical details irrelevant to our understanding or appreciation of the ideas of the theorist, or should we interrogate the critical thinker? What do you think?

early detection mechanism of the Pap test. A less expensive and less aggressive intervention might have been to ensure that marginalized populations who had not taken the Pap test would do so. As HPV expert Dr Diane Harper reports on the dangers of Gardasil:

> Pap smears have never killed anyone. Pap smears are an effective screening tool to prevent cervical cancer. Pap smears alone prevent more cervical cancers than can the vaccines alone.
>
> Gardasil is associated with serious adverse events, including death. If Gardasil is given to 11 year olds, and the vaccine does not last at least fifteen years, then there is no benefit—and only risk—for the young girl. Vaccinating will not reduce the population

incidence of cervical cancer if the woman continues to get Pap screening throughout her life. (Yerman, 2011)

In addition, the long-term consequences of the vaccine, including side effects, were not known, nor was it clear how frequently the three "shot" administration would have to be repeated and over how many years. Further, it was targeted at girls/women even though boys/men were clearly implicated in its transmission and were themselves vulnerable through the same viruses to penile, anal, and back-of-the-throat cancers (http://www.cdc.gov/std/hpv/stdfact-hpv-and-men.htm) as well as genital warts (see also Lippman et al., 2007). A few years later it was also approved for young men (http://www.cdc.gov/std/hpv/stdfact-hpv-and-men.htm) as well as genital warts (see also Lippman et al., 2007).

TABLE 1.7   Methodological Assumptions of Post-structuralism in Social Science

Objectivity	It is impossible to be objective as a researcher in the social world because the linkage between power and knowledge imbricates the entire social world through circulating discourses.
Generalizability	Generalization is irrelevant because of the focus on micro practices in historical social contexts.
Subjectivity	Researchers and their subjectivities are irreducibly tied to the social and the historical.
Subject Matter	Disease and wellness are understood through concepts such as biopower, the medical gaze, and governmentality.
Language	Uses gender-neutral language where appropriate and specifies actual gender when relevant. Uses non-racialized terminology.
Data Collection Methods	Historically situated practices are studied as discourses and through Foucault's genealogy and archaeology.
Purpose	To understand and critically expose circulating power/knowledge discourses.

SUMMARY

1. Illness is experienced in a social context: we learn to think and talk about it with a vocabulary that others share and we learn what to do about it through interactions with family and friends, the formal medical system, and the media.

2. The sociology of health and illness describes and explains the social causes and consequences of illness, disease, disability, and death. The sociology of medicine is the study of the institutionalized medical recognition of and response to illness.

3. Sociologists use a number of perspectives to study the social world: structural-functional theory, conflict theory, symbolic interactionist/interpretive/social constructivist theory, feminist and anti-racist and post-structuralist theories. Each of these perspectives makes different assumptions about the social world and, therefore, has different ways of understanding it.

4. Structural-functional theory was first discussed by Émile Durkheim. Its goal is to understand the social causes of social facts; it does this by studying the causal relationships among institutions. The parts of society are inextricably bound together to form a harmonious system. Human beings are constrained by the external world and

they are, therefore, predictable and controllable through the knowledge of social facts.

5. The origin of the conflict perspective is attributed to Karl Marx. Conflict theorists study competing groups within societies through history. The basic competing forces are the different classes. Conflict theorists are committed to the description and documentation of injustice through the understanding of economic arrangements and their impact on other conditions of social life. In the conflict perspective, it is argued that health and illness are related to the unequal social arrangements found in capitalist, patriarchal societies.

6. Symbolic interactionist/interpretive/social constructionist theory is based on the definition of sociology given by Max Weber. Symbolic interactionists attempt to understand the subjective meanings and causes that social actors attribute to events. The meaning social actors give to their diseases affects their self-concepts and their relationships with others.

7. The feminist, anti-racist, and intersectionality perspectives provide a critique of sociology and a corrective to its narrow, neglectful, or biased representations. It attempts to remedy inequities in

gender, class, "race," disability, sexual orientation, and so on.

8. Post-structuralism highlights the ways that power produces its effects through the bodies and minds of individuals and populations. It describes how changes in public health and medicine provide new ways of governing populations.

KEY TERMS

anti-racist theory
biomedicalization
conflict theory
dependent variables
discourses
epidemiology
feminist theory
home health-care work
incidence
independent variables

intersectionality
medicalization
neo-liberalism
pharmaceuticalization
positivism
post-structuralism
precautionary principle
privatization
remission society
sick role

social determinants of health
stigma
structural functionalism
symbolic interactionist/
    interpretive/social
    constructionist theory
uncertainty
verstehen

QUESTIONS FOR STUDY AND DISCUSSION

1. Many university students, particularly during the first year, are likely to drink alcohol and become drunk more often than they had done in the past. Explain using one of the theories articulated in the chapter.

2. Several of your roommates have been taking anti-depressant drugs given to them by the health services doctors at the university health clinic. They do not appear to be taking them appropriately but rather in handfuls when they say they feel depressed or stressed. How would the theories discussed in this chapter help to explain this situation?

3. Male and female students tend to enrol in different disciplines, and they also tend to use health services at different rates and for different issues. How might the five theories presented in this chapter be used to explain this phenomenon?

4. The uptake of the HPV vaccine was rapid, particularly in Canada and the US. How could you use each theoretical perspective to understand this?

5. Power is an endemic feature of human social interaction. It is implicated in decisions as to the "normal" and "abnormal," the "ill" and the "well." How do the various theories help us to understand this?

SUGGESTED READINGS

Aneshel, C.S., J.C. Phelen, and A. Bierman, eds. 2013. *Handbook for the Sociology of Mental Health*. New York: Springer. Edited collection surveying some of the most important and most recent research in the sociology of mental health and illness.

Ayo, N. 2012. "Understanding Health Promotion in a Neoliberal Climate and the Making of Health Conscious Citizens." *Critical Public Health* 22, 1: 99–105. This short, scholarly article provides an excellent and brief overview of the highlights of neo-liberalism.

Foucault, M. 1994. *The Birth of the Clinic: An Archeology of Medical Perception*. New York, Vintage Books. A complex and intriguing history of medicine.

———. 2006. *History of Madness*. Ed. and trans. J. Khalfa; trans. J. Murphy. Abingdon, Oxford: Routledge. Another of the classic works by Foucault, this time focusing on "madness."

Horwitz, A.V. 2013. *Anxiety: A Short History of Anxiety*. Baltimore: Johns Hopkins University Press. An excellent critical analysis of one of the many increasingly "popular" and inclusive mental health diagnoses.

Levy, Jennifer, Donna Ansara, and Andi Stover. 2013. *Racialization and Health Inequities in Toronto*. Toronto Public Health. http://www.toronto. ca/legdocs/mmis/2013/hl/bgrd/background-file-62904.pdf. Overview of the impacts of racialization on health.

Navarro, V., and V. Shi. 2003. "The Political Context of Social Inequalities and Health." In Richard Hofrichter, ed., *Health and Social Justice: Politics, Ideology and Inequality in the Distribution of Disease*. San Francisco: Jossey-Bass. An overview and analysis of health inequalities using a political economy perspective.

Pescosolido, B.A., J.K. Martin, J.D McLeod, and A. Rogers, eds. 2011. *Handbook for the Sociology of Health, Illness and Healing*. New York: Springer. An edited collection on key contemporary issues in the field.

Sociology of Health and Illness

PART
II

The next six chapters of the book illustrate the theoretical perspectives we have discussed already through empirical research findings in the sociology of health and illness. Chapter 2 describes some of the changes in mortality and morbidity around the world and in Canada today and over the past century and a half and some reasons for these changes. Chapter 3 describes environmental and occupational health and disease in the context of Canadian society as a whole. Chapter 4 examines the relevance of the social determinants of health—such as inequality, poverty, and racialization—to sickness and disease in Canada. Chapter 5 examines the inequities based on social-structural positions such as gender, age, social class, immigrant and refugee status, and racism and considers, in particular, the situation of First Nations people of Canada. Chapter 6 focuses on the social-psychological behaviour of the individual in relation to illness and death. Chapter 7 is interpretive, social constructivist, and phenomenological in its focus on the description of the meaning of the illness experience from the perspective of those who are ill or aspire to "improve themselves" through medical interventions.

Table II.1 provides an overview of many of the factors to be considered in explaining the health of a population. Notice that the context for this table is medicalization and bio-medicalization. This table points to the importance of biopower or medical power in determining (1) what constitutes disease and death and (2) what is relevant to medical social constructions or discourses. Disease and death are seldom the result of isolated conditions or incidents. Death rates, and most deaths, are the result of complex social, biological, and other causes, including the direct, medically determined cause of death. In the case of cancer, for instance, starvation might be the direct cause; the underlying cause might be the growth of malignancies; the bridging cause might be the malfunctioning of the stomach resulting from malignant growth so that food cannot be absorbed; contributing causes might include smoking and excess alcohol ingestion; predisposing conditions might be air pollution resulting from a certain industrial process; and generating conditions might be the economic position of the worker who had no choice but to work in an asbestos mine. However, this empirical complexity is obfuscated by the "simplification" required by death

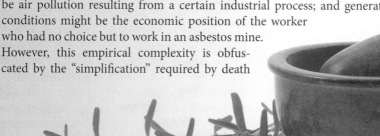

certification. Thus, the meaning and interpretation of the recorded causes of death are variable and subject to sociological, not merely medical, analyses. This table lists a number of different groups of causes of death. Keep in mind, though, that each declared cause is the result of a series of decisions and not an "absolute truth."

The chapters in Part II examine some of these causes of morbidity and mortality in detail. Others are not dealt with because of space limitations and/or because of a lack of informative research. Generally speaking, Chapters 2 and 3 focus on predisposing conditions ("A" in Table II.1) and, to a limited extent, social-structural position within society ("B" in Table II.1); Chapters 4 and 5 focus on social-structural inequities (B) and, to a limited extent, predisposing conditions such as historical and environmental factors (A); Chapter 6 focuses on social-psychological (C) and

TABLE II.1   Conditions Affecting Life Expectancy

Predisposing Conditions	Generating Conditions
History (A) **Medicalization and** **Biomedicalization Global** **Environmental/Ecological/** **Geographical Conditions** natural disasters (e.g., earthquake, 　tornado, tsunami, heat wave, war, 　famine, drought, epidemic) **Environmental** quality and quantity of water quality of air quality and quantity of foodstuffs 　(nutrition) safety: roads, airways, waterways, 　transportation vehicles, workplace, 　home, tools, equipment birth control **Medical** immunization antibiotics other chemotherapy surgery radiation **Societal Structure** political-economic system cultural values	**Social-Structural Position within a** **Society (B)** age sex sexual orientation marital and family status class education level occupation rural/urban location religion religiosity region ethnicity racialization **Socio-Psychological Conditions (C)** stress experience and stress 　management type A or B behaviour sense of coherence gender role expectations **Social support** resilience **Lifestyle Conditions (D)** smoking habits seat-belt use alcohol consumption rate sexual behaviour drug use and abuse **Existential Factors (E)** the meaning of the illness experience of illness hope for self-improvement cogni- 　tively, emotionally, or aesthetically

lifestyle (D) conditions; and Chapter 7 focuses on existential factors (E). They all are understood as dependent on the forces of medicalization and biomedicalization within a society.

Definitions and measurements of disease, illness, and health are complex and debatable and vary substantially from cultural group to cultural group within a diverse society and world. In the Western medical tradition disease is measured and determined in a number of ways, including *self-reporting,* which involves asking respondents to describe their own state of health; *clinical records,* which include the records of physicians as well as hospital statistics; and *physical measurements,* which include such things as blood pressure readings and tests of tissue pathology. Each of these methods may record a disease state at a different level of development or potential acknowledgement; for example, a Papanicolaou (Pap) test may indicate evidence of precancerous or cancerous tissue before either the physician or the woman would be able to notice it. None of these methods alone can be considered a "true" or "objective" way to determine illness. In combination, however, they may point to "true disease" (or some other condition). On the other hand, methods and tests may also contradict each other. For instance, people with chronic fatigue syndrome, fibromyalgia, and multiple sclerosis often have to go through many different tests, or even to consult a variety of doctors, before they are able to get a diagnosis and even then it is more likely to be a "negative diagnosis" (a diagnosis in which certain other possibilities are ruled out). Most progress in allopathic medical knowledge entails *revising a misapprehension* of what had been considered to be "good practice" in which doctors and patients had placed their confidence. Thus, medical "failure" and medical "success" are intermingled and changeable over time.

In addition to understanding multiple factors in disease causation, students of the sociology of medicine are interested in questions regarding the socially and culturally specific constructions and discourses about disease—the differentiation of variable meanings among "disease," "sickness," and "illness" (Chapter 7) and the socio-psychological precursors to disease. Finally, sociologists take a critical approach to "official" statistics regarding both disease and death, looking at social factors that may impugn the validity of those data.

2

Disease and Death: Canada in International and Historical Context

© Sf2301420max | Dreamstime.com

CHAPTER OVERVIEW

▶ Life expectancy has ranged widely over the years in Canada and continues to vary around the globe.

▶ Several explanations have been offered for these variations, including the demographic transition, social determinants, post-structuralist, and political economy perspectives.

▶ In a global context death, disease, and disability are related to poverty, inequality, food security, physical and social environments, safety, security and stability, the social position of women, birth control, pregnancy and childbirth, comprehensive health care, and immunization, among others.

▶ In Canada, the chief causes of death are the "diseases of civilization": circulatory diseases, cancer, and accidents.

▶ PYLL or potential years of life lost is a particularly useful way of conceptualizing the cases of death because of its policy implications.

▶ The behavioural "risk factors" or prerequisites to disease, in health promotion discourse, are thought to include alcohol consumption, cigarette smoking, the amount of physical activity, weight, and sexual activity, among others. The individualistic and medicalized aspects of these perspectives are critiqued.

▶ New infectious diseases of concern have surfaced in Canada and around the world.

Introduction

What are the major causes of death in the world today? What were the major causes of death in Canada a century ago? What is the average life expectancy in Canada today? How long, on average, did Canadians live when your grandparents were children, or 150 years ago? How important have modern medical discoveries been to the increase in life expectancy over the last century or so? You have probably heard that antibiotics are "wonder drugs." Were antibiotics or immunizations important in the overall improvement of the health of the nation? This chapter will consider these and similar questions as it places Canadian rates of disease and death—historically and today—in an international context.

Life Expectancy

The average life expectancy for men and women has varied considerably over thousands of years and through many different types of social and economic arrangements. For example, the average life expectancy of late Ice Age hunter-gatherers of about 11,000 years ago has been estimated to have been approximately 38 years (Eyer, 1984). According to available records and estimates, the average life expectancy in Europe varied between 20 and 40 years from the thirteenth to the seventeenth centuries (Goldscheider, 1971). In Canada, too, there have been wide variations in life expectancy. In 1831 the average for Canadians is estimated to have been 39 years. According to the latest available statistics females can expect to live for about 83 years, while males can expect to live for about 79 years (http://www.statcan.gc.ca/tables-tableaux/sum-som/l01/cst01/health72a-eng.htm). A significant, four-year gap in life expectancy exists between males and females, although the gap has declined over the latter part of the last century. Life expectancy has also increased for people over 65. According to data from Statistics Canada in 2012, males who were 65 years of age could expect to live another 18.5 years. Females at 65 could expect to live another 21.6 years (http://www.statcan.gc.ca/tables-tableaux/sum-som/l01/cst01/health72a-eng.htm).

The dramatic changes in life expectancy that have occurred in the past 100–150 years in Canada (and elsewhere in the developed world) can be explained by a host of factors. One is the epidemiological transition (Omran, 1979), which is based on the theory of demographic transition. Simply put, this idea suggests that as the economy changes from low to high per capita income, a corresponding transition occurs from high mortality and high fertility to low mortality and low fertility. Changes in the patterns of disease occur in three distinct stages: the Age of Pestilence and Famine, the Age of Receding Pandemics, and the Age of Degenerative and Man-Made Diseases (ibid.).

The Age of Pestilence and Famine is characterized by socio-economic conditions in which communities are traditional, economically underdeveloped with a low per capita income, and generally agrarian. Women usually have low status, the family is extended, and illiteracy is high. The high mortality rate is largely attributable to famine and infectious diseases. The Age of Receding Pandemics is characterized by a decrease in epidemics and famine and a consequent decline in the mortality rate. At this point the fertility rate continues to be high, resulting in a "population explosion." The fertility rate then begins to decline as people begin to live longer and to die of emerging industrial and degenerative diseases such as cancer, stroke, and heart disease, which characterize the Age of Degenerative and Man-Made Disease.

There are several other explanations for the overall decline in the **mortality rate** and the increase in life expectancy in the developed world. McKeown (1976) has offered one explanation based on studies of the decline in mortality in Britain (and supported by findings for Sweden, France, Ireland, and Hungary) over the last few hundred years. First, the decline in the mortality rate was almost entirely due to a decline in infectious disease. Second, the decline in infectious disease was largely the result of three

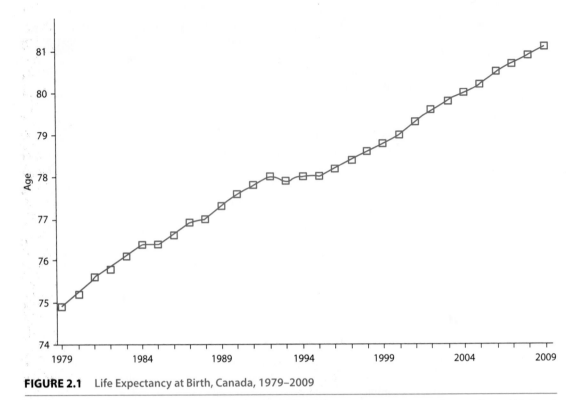

FIGURE 2.1   Life Expectancy at Birth, Canada, 1979–2009

Source: For 1979 to 1990, Statistics Canada, "Life expectancy, abridged life table, at birth and at age 65, by sex, Canada, provinces and territories (Comparable Indicators), annual (years)" (CANSIM Table 102-0025) (Ottawa: Statistics Canada, 2008); for 1991 to 1993, Statistics Canada, "Life expectancy, abridged life table, at birth and at age 65, by sex, Canada, provinces and territories, annual (years)" (CANSIM Table 102-0511) (Ottawa: Statistics Canada, 2008); for 1994 to 2009, Statistics Canada, "Life expectancy, at birth and at age 65, by sex, Canada, provinces and territories, annual (years)" (CANSIM Table 102-0512) (Ottawa: Statistics Canada, 2012), http://www4.hrsdc.gc.ca/.3ndic.1t.4r@-eng.jsp?iid=3. Employment and Social Development Canada. "Indicators of Well-Being in Canada: Health—Life Expectancy at Birth." Statistics Canada.

basic changes: (1) improvements in nutrition, (2) improvements in hygiene, and (3) increasing control of disease-causing micro-organisms. Improvements in birth control were another factor.

A second study by McKeown and Record (1975) spanning the period 1901–71 showed that this increase in overall life expectancy was the result of conditions in the twentieth century very similar to those described above for previous centuries. Improved nutrition accounted for about half the increase, and better hygiene—resulting in fewer water- and food-borne diseases—accounted for about one-sixth of the improvement. Immunization and medical therapy were together responsible for about one-tenth of the increased life expectancy. Recent study has confirmed McKeown's fundamental claim about the role of changing environments in the decline of adult

mortality but suggested that the decline in mortality rates that included children were also linked to changes in fertility patterns and the improvement of labour laws that protected child workers (Ostry and Frank, 2010).

A book called *The Spirit Level* (Wilkinson and Pickett, 2010) documents the continuing effects of social life on death and disease as well as a variety of other social issues such as imprisonment, homicide rates, and so forth. See the following document for a number of relevant tables and links to rich discussion (https://www.dur.ac.uk/resources/wolfson.institute/events/Wilkinson372010.pdf) and the following link to view several engaging lectures on the topic (http://www.closingthegap.org.nz/site-map/the-spirit-level/).

SES both within a nation and in comparing nation to nation, is a pre-eminent factor in health and social problems. Why do inequalities continue throughout the world? The **political economy perspective** takes the position that the place of workers in the global economy, in terms of occupational conditions such as employment, income, security, and safety, is the prime determinant of equality, living conditions, and, ultimately both directly and indirectly, of health and well-being. Dependency

TABLE 2.1   Global and Regional Life Expectancies and Healthy Life Expectancies, 2000 and 2012

Region	Healthy Life Expectancy at Birth (years)		Life expectancy at Birth (years)	
	2000	2012	2000	2012
Both Sexes Combined				
World	58.0	61.7	66.2	70.3
High-income countries	67.3	69.8	76.0	78.9
Low- and middle-income countries				
African Region	43.1	49.6	50.2	57.7
Region of the Americas	64.9	67.1	73.9	76.4
Eastern Mediterranean Region	55.4	58.3	64.9	67.8
European Region	63.9	66.9	72.4	76.1
South East Asian Region	54.2	58.5	62.9	67.5
Western Pacific Region	64.8	68.1	72.3	75.9
Males				
World	56.4	60.1	63.9	68.1
High-income countries	64.7	67.5	72.4	75.8
Low- and middle-income countries				
African Region	42.4	48.8	49.0	56.3
Region of the Americas	62.7	64.9	70.8	73.5
Eastern Mediterranean Region	54.8	57.4	63.6	66.1
European Region	60.7	64.2	68.2	72.4
South East Asian Region	53.5	57.4	61.6	65.7
Western Pacific Region	63.0	66.6	70.0	73.9
Females				
World	59.7	63.4	68.5	72.7
High-income countries	70.0	72.0	79.6	82.0
Low- and middle-income countries				
African Region	43.8	50.4	51.4	59.0
Region of the Americas	67.2	69.1	77.0	79.3
Eastern Mediterranean Region	56.1	59.2	66.4	69.7
European Region	67.1	69.6	76.7	79.6
South East Asian Region	55.0	59.7	64.3	69.4
Western Pacific Region	66.7	69.8	74.8	78.1

Source: World Health Organization. "WHO methods for life expectancy and healthy life expectancy", Department of Health Statistics and Information Systems, p. 13. www.who.int/healthinfo/statistics/LT_method.pdf.

theory explains how the global economic order and globalization are prime determinants of global inequality. It also explains how multinational expansion by the wealthy and powerful nations maintains under-development in the rest of the world. Trade relations and political interventions also buttress the continuation of dependency.

World systems theory names three types of national economic actors (Wermuth, 2003): **core, periphery, and semi-periphery countries**. Core countries include countries such as Canada, the US, the UK, Japan, Germany, France, Spain, and Sweden. These countries have diversified economies, strong and stable governance structures, and large middle classes. In brief, these are the industrial/post-industrial democracies. Civil liberties tend to be relatively strongly supported and there is little overt class conflict. Core countries exploit countries in the periphery and semi-periphery by extracting raw materials (e.g., oil, lumber, and metals), employing them as inexpensive labour, and using these poorer countries as consumers at the end of the process of manufacture and distribution. Periphery countries such as Cambodia, Haiti, Peru, and Ethiopia have considerably less-developed or diversified economies and limited infrastructure and technology (such as transportation and communication networks). Their economies are based on subsistence agriculture and a few simple products such as tea, fruits, coffee, metals, or lumber. They tend to have weak state organization and to be exploited for raw materials, cheap labour, and markets by core countries. At the same time, these countries have a greater proportion of people unable to meet their basic needs. Countries on the periphery of the global economy may need foreign capital and may make agreements with international corporations to give these firms special access to raw materials, a compliant labour force, and product marketing. In the long run, neither corporate investment nor intensive "aid" have helped these countries substantially and people live, on average, on a few dollars per day (ibid.). The semi-periphery countries fall between core and periphery countries and include, for instance, Mexico, Chile, Korea,

and Saudi Arabia. Over time, the periphery and semi-periphery countries may become less likely to develop because the corporations have substantial levels of power and control in the context of global capitalism and neo-liberalism. Thus, from this perspective, the ultimate explanation for different health outcomes around the world is location in the world economy (ibid.). Table 2.1 offers a comparison of life expectancies and healthy life expectancies in high-income as compared to middle- and low-income countries around the world. Figure 2.2 portrays global and regional life expectancies where you can again see the effects of inequality on health outcomes.

Death, Disease, and Disability in Global Context

About 6.6 million children under five years of age died in 2012, according to the World Health Organization (http://www.who.int/mediacentre/factsheets/fs178/en/). Most of these children and infants died of easily prevented or treated disease such as pneumonia, diarrhea, birth asphyxia, malaria, and preterm birth complications. Although this figure has been decreasing over the past 20 or so years, progress has begun to slow in parts of the world. Children in sub-Saharan Africa are substantially more likely to die than children in the developed world. Childhood poverty, malnutrition, and lack of clean water and adequate sanitation are significant factors in the vast majority of these deaths. Figure 2.4 indicates the mortality rates of children under five around the world.

In a worldwide context, the prime determinant of health is the (absolute) ability of individuals and families to meet their basic human needs. In addition to absolute levels of material well-being, most research has found that the greater the relative inequality in societies, the higher the rates of disease and death (Wermuth, 2003; Wilkinson and Pickett, 2010). Inequality has both direct and indirect effects on health. Greater inequality is coincident both with greater proportions of a

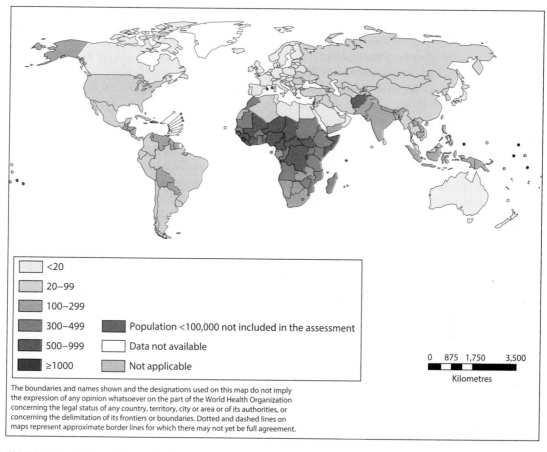

FIGURE 2.2   Maternal Mortality Ratio per 100,000 Live Births, 2013

Source: Trends in Maternal Mortality, 1990–2013: Estimates by WHO, UNICEF, UNFPA, World Bank, and the United Nations Population Division, http://apps.who.int/iris/bitstream/10665/112697/1/WHO_RHR_14.13_eng.pdf.

population living in poverty and also with governments that are less likely to invest in infrastructure such as education, transportation, adequate and affordable housing, food production and distribution, and other goods and services that provide the fundamentals to health. Inequality also has indirect effects on health through the psychosocial issues and feelings such as shame and anger experienced particularly by the relatively poor (Wermuth, 2003; Wilkinson and Pickett, 2010).

To the end of equalizing development internationally the United Nations members signed The Millennium Declaration in 2000. The eight interrelated goals include: (1) the eradication of poverty and hunger; (2) the achievement of universal primary education; (3) the promotion of gender equality; (4) the reduction in child mortality; (5) the improvement of maternal health; (6) reducing HIV/AIDS, malaria, and other diseases; (7) ensuring environmental sustainability; and (8) developing global partnerships to achieve the aforementioned goals (United Nations, 2000). While the targets have not all been reached, the very fact that there are targets and explicit goals is reason to be optimistic. According to the recent report card progress continues to be made along with some setbacks (see this detailed assessment by the World Health Organization: http://www.odi.org.uk/sites/odi.org.uk/files/odi-assets/publications-opinion-files/6172.pdf).

Poverty and Inequality

Both the overall level of income and the relative income of a people have obvious impacts on health. Income level is the context for all of the other elements of daily life such as work, education, food, shelter, transportation, green space, water, hygiene, and sanitation. Poverty often is associated with political powerlessness and marginalization. While the economic growth of a whole country is not necessarily associated with better health for all, economic decline usually affects the standard of living and, consequently, the health of many. The health costs of an economic recession tend to fall most heavily on those who were least well-off. Public policies regarding income security also are associated with **infant mortality rates**. Figure 2.3 (http://www.oecd-ilibrary.org/social-issues-migration-health/infant-mortality_20758480-table9) indicate infant mortality rates for Canada and select OECD countries. The lowest infant mortality rate is in Iceland at 0.9 and the highest is in Mexico at 13.6 (per 1,000 live births). While figures for Canada are not available on this particular representation they stand at approximately 5.1 for boys and 4.7 for girls per 1,000 live births (as of 2009). Notice the relatively low rates of infant mortality in the more equal democratic socialist countries such as Sweden, Norway, and Finland as compared to the more inequitable countries of Turkey, Mexico, and the United States.

Food Security

The term **food security** refers to a situation, either chronic or acute, in which people do not have access to enough safe, nutritious, and culturally acceptable food (www.unmilleniumproject.org/reports/reports2.htm). The availability of an

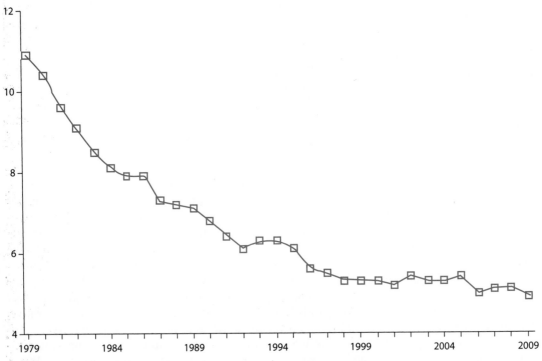

FIGURE 2.3   Infant Mortality, Canada, 1979–2009 (per 1,000 live births)

Source: Statistics Canada, "Infant mortality, by sex and birth weight, Canada, provinces and territories, annual" (CANSIM Table 102-0504) (Ottawa: Statistics Canada, 2012), http://www4.hrsdc.gc.ca/.3ndic.1t.4r@-eng.jsp?iid=2. Employment and Social Development Canada. "Indicators of Well-Being in Canada: Family Life—Infant Mortality." Statistcs Canada.

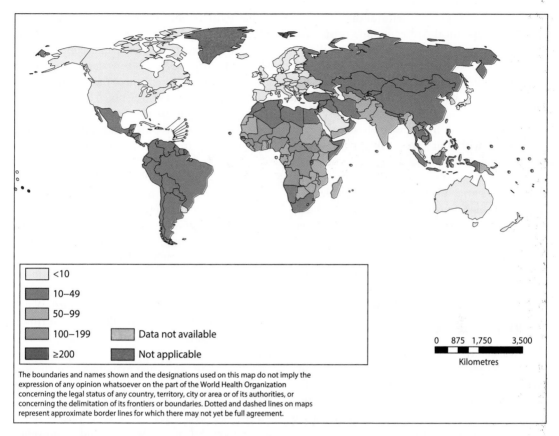

The boundaries and names shown and the designations used on this map do not imply the expression of any opinion whatsoever on the part of the World Health Organization concerning the legal status of any country, territory, city or area or of its authorities, or concerning the delimitation of its frontiers or boundaries. Dotted and dashed lines on maps represent approximate border lines for which there may not yet be full agreement.

FIGURE 2.4   Under-Five Mortality Rate (probability of dying by age 5 per 100 live births), 2012

Source: WHO, Levels and trends in child mortality: Report 2012: Estimates developed by the UN Inter-agency Group for Child Mortality Estimation, United Nations Children's Fund (2012), p. 11. http://www.who.int/maternal_child_adolescent/documents/levels_trends_child_mortality_2012.pdf?ua=1.

adequate amount of nutritious food is fundamental to the health of a population and, especially the protein component, has a larger impact on **morbidity** and mortality than any other public health or medical measure. Millions of people around the globe presently lack adequate nutrients for daily life and even more people lack essential micronutrients such as iodine, vitamin A, and iron (WHO, 1997). More than half of the deaths occurring each year in the developing world are associated with malnutrition. Inadequate nutrients limit neurological development and productivity, overall health and well-being, and make people even more vulnerable to a cascading effect of disease and subsequent death (see this UNICEF

report for an in-depth discussion of this topic (http://www.unicef.org/nutritioncluster/files/ IPC_NutMortalityIndicatorsReviewFinal.pdf).

Nutrient deficiency in women is an even more prevalent and significant problem than in men. Because women bear and breast-feed their children, they have a greater need for calories at times. A low standard of nutrition among women is pivotal, too, for the health of their offspring. In brief, underweight babies are born to women who suffer nutritional inadequacies. Underweight babies are more likely to die as infants and to suffer from any one of a number of diseases, as well as to have intellectual and physical disabilities. In addition, food insecurity results from war, poverty, natural disasters, epidemics, and political and economic crises. One of the most important correlates of nutrition is a mother's education. For instance, Smith and Haddad (2002) found that women's education was associated with almost 43 per cent of the reduction in child malnutrition in developing countries. Education for women usually provides them with more power in the household, access to income-generating work, and health and nutrition information, among other relevant benefits. Malaria, a significant cause of death in areas with high transmission rates such as sub-Saharan Africa can also be exacerbated by malnutrition, HIV/AIDS, and anaemia (www.cdc.gov/malaria/impact/index.htm).

The Physical and Social Environment

The availability of a sufficient amount of clean drinking water is another crucial factor in health. Available statistics indicate that more than 1 billion people, or one-sixth of the world's population, lack access to safe drinking water. According to the *Human Development Report* of the United Nations the world is not running out of water, yet 700 million people in 43 countries live below the water stress level of 1,700 cubic metres of water per person per year (hdr.undp.org/hdr2006/chapter4.htm). Thus, the shortages of clean, potable water are not absolute but rather due to political and economic conditions. Numerous fatal and debilitating chronic illnesses are spread by unsanitary water. Two of the most prevalent are cholera and dysentery. **Diarrheal disease** is a leading cause of the death of children in the developing world (www.cdc.gov/malaria/impact/index.htm). Its prevention depends on changes in water supply, hygiene, and sanitation. Yet the infrastructure developments necessary for adequate improvements are extensive. They include drainage systems for the disposal of human and animal wastes, access to potable water, and water for irrigation. According to the most recent WHO report card, access to water has been one of the most successful of the changes occurring with the establishment of the Millennium Goals. Access to water has improved in approximately 82 per cent of the countries studied. However, it must also be noted that such access declined in about 10 per cent of the countries targeted (http://www.odi.org.uk/sites/odi.org.uk/files/odi-assets/publications-opinion-files/6172.pdf, p. 71).

The lack of available and affordable drinking water was one of the factors in the crisis that occurred in the developing world over the seemingly innocuous question of how best to feed infants. Starting in 1969, a new market for infant feeding formula was developed in Third World countries. It was regarded as a wise and humane intervention that would extend the lives of many of the millions of children in the Third World who died annually as a result of malnutrition. Advertising and promotion for infant feeding formula quickly became successful. Free samples donated by the companies manufacturing the formula were given to women who had just given birth. In the Third World, feeding babies formula rather than breast milk was very quickly taken to be a symbol of mother love and responsibility, in part because formula was associated in the minds of Third World peoples with the successful middle and upper classes in the Western world. A number of unexpected negative consequences resulted.

1. When women used the free samples given to them at the birth of their babies, their milk supply would dry up and breast-feeding would become impossible.
2. When women went home with their babies, they were often ill-prepared to continue with the infant feeding formula for a variety of reasons.
    (a) Formula was frequently unavailable in the small villages and communities, and as women's breast milk had dried up, the babies starved to death.

(b) When the formula was available, there were often no instructions on how to use it, the mothers were illiterate, or the instructions were in a language the mothers could not read. Thus, many women mixed the formula with too much water, so that the nutrients in the mixture were inadequate for the baby's growth.

(c) Generally, the formula was sold in powdered form, to be mixed with water. Frequently, the water source was polluted, resulting in unnecessary illnesses and death.

(d) The bottles and nipples used for feeding the babies should have been sterilized. Many Third World mothers were unable to sterilize the bottles because they lacked clean water, a heat source, or a chemical sterilizing agent.

(e) Aside from the problems enumerated above, one other fact stands out: breast milk is actually better for babies because it passes important immunities from mother to offspring. In the developing world, babies breast-fed for less than six months are five to 10 times more likely to die than those breast-fed for a longer period.

When the dangers of infant formula became clear to the Western world, the companies manufacturing infant formula were boycotted, especially Nestlé's, which held more than 50 per cent of the world market. A World Health Organization conference called in 1979 initiated the adoption of a code to govern infant formula sales. The infant formula companies agreed to support the code. While the extent of the problem declined, there were, and continue to be, numerous violations of the code. This problem is ongoing. According to the *New York Times*, public health officials have decided that failing to breast-feed may be hazardous to the health of a new baby. Recent evidence links breast-feeding for a period of at least six months to protection from colds, influenzas, ear infections, diarrhoea, and obesity. Scientists who study the value of breast milk describe it as the "gold standard" against which other options are decidedly inferior (*Business Week*, 1979; Zabolai-Csekme, 1983; WHO, 1981; Rabin, 2006).

Safety, Security, and Stability

Personal safety is of great concern, particularly in times of heightened national tensions. Civil war, international warfare, and violence in communities, workplaces, and the home all are threats to fundamental safety. As local and international inequities grow, so, too, do violence and war. The consequences of violence have expanded dramatically globally along with population growth. Almost a half a million people (437,000) were murdered in 2012 around the world (http://www.unodc.org/unodc/en/press/releases/2014/April/some-437000-people-murdered-worldwide-in-2012-according-to-new-unodc-study.html). Eight of 10 of the murdered and 95 per cent of the perpetrators were men. Over half of the victims of homicide are under 30 years old and about 8 per cent are children under 15. Others at high risk of violence are more likely to be children, adolescents, old people, the homeless, the unemployed, migrants, refugees, members of visible ethnic minorities, the chronically ill and mentally disabled, and victims of war. In both the developing and developed world, 20 to 40 per cent of the deaths of young men aged 15–34 result from suicide or homicide. In the US alone, 14,827 people were murdered, 84,376 were raped, and 760,739 were victims of aggravated assault, according to the Federal Bureau of Investigation statistics (http://www.fbi.gov/news/stories/2013/september/latest-crime-stats-released/latest-crime-stats-released). However, in some locations, violent deaths and other crimes have decreased over time. This is the case in Canada according to Statistics Canada (http://www.statcan.gc.ca/pub/85-002-x/2013001/article/11854-eng.htm?fpv=269303). Still, however, the deployment of young Canadian men and women to Afghanistan has resulted in death to some and long-term devastation to the lives of other soldiers and their families.

The Position of Women

For a number of reasons the position of women in a society has a significant impact on the health of the people. In a worldwide context women's health is considerably poorer than that of men. In no region of the world are men and women equal in legal, economic, or social rights. This is particularly true in the developing world although there were significant improvements in the last half of the twentieth century. In many areas of the world women are unable to own land, do business, or even to travel without the approval of their husbands. Despite improvements in education of women around the globe, women continue to have fewer occupational opportunities and to earn less than men. The share of women holding national political office (i.e., parliamentarians) worldwide had climbed to 22 per cent by 2015 almost double the figure for 1995 (11.3 per cent) according to figures from the United Nations (www.unwomen.org/en/what-we-do/leadership-and-political-participation/facts-and-figures), but one out of every five office-holders is a far stretch from gender equality. In Canada in 2014, 64 out of 308 seats were held by women federally, i.e., 20.8 per cent were women. Canada ranked forty-fourth in a worldwide context with respect to women holding political power (http://www.cbc.ca/news2/inter-actives/map-cda-womenpolitics/). These gender disparities are exacerbated by poverty. Thus, women in the poorest of circumstances are even less likely to have economic or political power. According to the World Bank Gender and Development Group the relationships between gender inequality and poverty are mutually reinforcing, and causal links move in both directions. Reducing poverty will lead to an increase in the status of women, and such an increase will enhance economic development. As the *Human Development Report* (2010: 73) notes, "Joint deprivations come about where inequalities in health and education coincide with income inequality—which in turn may overlap with ethnicity and gender."

It is important that women have power in households because they are more likely than men to use available resources for food, education, and health-related expenditures for their children. Countries with the largest gaps in educational and income status between men and women are also countries with the highest rates of and the fastest growth in HIV infections. Productivity, economic growth, health, health care, and effective governance all are increased by gender equity. However, a great deal of gender inequity remains. Table 2.2 shows the gender inequality rankings of the 10 top and the 10 bottom nations in the world in 2012 (https://data.undp.org/dataset/Table-4-Gender-Inequality-Index/pq34-nwq7).

Birth Control, Pregnancy, and Childbirth

Effective birth control is another important cause of the decline in the mortality rate around the globe. Too many pregnancies, or pregnancies spaced too closely together, are a threat to the health of the mother and the child for a number of reasons. First, when the pregnancy is unwanted, women may seek illegal abortions, which are extremely dangerous. Second, as a result of malnutrition, women's bodies may be undernourished and small, their pelvises misshapen, and they may experience fatigue during pregnancy and a difficult delivery. Third, pregnancy itself takes a toll on a woman's body because nutrients are needed for the baby as well as the mother. During pregnancy large increases in calories, vitamins, and minerals are required, including more iron, vitamin B12, and folic acid, especially during the last trimester of pregnancy. Fourth, because energy is used up during pregnancy, rest, especially in the last trimester, is important. Most women in developing nations, however, do not have the leisure to take the necessary rest. Fifth, childbirth itself, because of the lack of sanitation, prenatal care, or emergency medical services, is responsible for a much higher rate of maternal mortality in the developing nations than in the developed nations. Some of the most prevalent causes of childbirth-related deaths are postpartum haemorrhage, which occurs when a woman has anaemia, and sepsis (infection), which occurs because of inadequate sanitation or because of hypertensive disorders of pregnancy.

TABLE 2.2 Gender Inequality: Top Ten and Bottom Ten Countries, 2014

HDI Rank	Country	Gender Inequality Index Value 2013	Gender Inequality Index Rank 2013	2010 Maternal Mortality Ratio (deaths per 100,000 live births)	2010–15 Adolescent Birth Rate (births per 1,000 women aged 15–19)	2013 Share of Seats in Parliament (% held by women)	Population with at Least Some Secondary Education (% aged 25 and above) Female 2005–12	Note 2	Population with at Least Some Secondary Education (% aged 25 and above) Male 2005–12	Note 3	Labour Force Participation Rate (% aged 15 and above) Female 2012	Labour Force Participation Rate (% aged 15 and above) Male 2012
1	Norway	0.068	9	7	7.8	39.6	97.4		96.7		61.5	69.5
2	Australia	0.113	19	7	12.1	29.2	94.3	c	94.6	c	58.8	71.9
3	Switzerland	0.030	2	8	1.9	27.2	95		96.6		61.2	75.3
4	Netherlands	0.057	7	6	6.2	37.8	87.7		90.5		79.9	87.3
5	United States	0.262	47	21	31	18.2	95.1		94.8		56.8	69.3
6	Germany	0.046	3	7	3.8	32.4	96.3		97		53.5	66.4
7	New Zealand	0.185	34	15	25.3	32.2	95		95.3		62.1	73.9
8	Canada	0.136	23	12	14.5	28	100		100		61.6	71.2
9	Singapore	0.090	15	3	6	24.2	74.1		81		59	77.5
10	Denmark	0.056	5	12	5.1	39.1	95.5	d	96.6	d	59.1	67.5
...												
178	Mozambique	0.657	146	490	137.8	39.2	1.5	e	6	e	26.3	75.8
179	Guinea	...	...	610	131						65.5	78.3
180	Burundi	0.501	104	800	30.3	34.9	5.2	e	9.3	e	83.2	81.8
181	Burkina Faso	0.607	133	300	115.4	15.7	0.9	e	3.2		77.1	90.1
182	Eritrea	...	...	240	65.3	22					79.9	89.8
183	Sierra Leone	0.643	141	890	100.7	12.4	9.5	e	20.4	e	65.7	68.9
184	Chad	0.707	150	1100	152	14.9	1.7		9.9		64	79.2
185	Central African Republic	0.654	144	890	98.3	12.5	10.3	e	26.2	e	72.5	85.1
186	Congo (Democratic Republic of the)	0.669	147	540	135.3	8.3	10.7	e	36.2	e	70.7	73.2
187	Niger	0.709	151	590	204.8	13.3	2.5	e	7.6	e	39.9	89.8

Source: Adapted from United Nations Development Programme, "Statistical Table for the 2014 Human Development Report: Table 4: Gender Inequality Index." UNDP (2014): https://data.undp.org/dataset/Table-4-Gender-Inequality-Index/ku9i-8fxp.

The levels of maternal mortality remain high. Every day about 800 women die from preventable causes in childbirth according to the World Health Organization (http://www.who.int/mediacentre/factsheets/fs348/en/). Fertility is another important component of the health of women. The global fertility rate has decreased from 5.0 births per woman in 1960 to 2.45 in 2013 (www.indexmundi.com/world/total_fertility_rate.html). However, many women are unable to control their pregnancies. There are still about 70–80 million unintended pregnancies each year in developing countries (UNFPA, 2011). The power to space births is also a significant component in childhood deaths and women's health (ibid.). On the other hand, abortion for gender selection and for trivial purposes such as the zodiac sign under which the birth would occur has shifted the male-to-female proportions of the population in certain countries. This has become a significant problem in various parts of the world. For example, the number of bachelors in China who cannot be matched with a female is equivalent to the entire male population of England (www.guardian.co.uk/world/2011/sep/02/china-village-of-bachelors). Furthermore, abortions can be very dangerous. Nearly half of abortions performed worldwide are unsafe and 98 per cent of unsafe abortions occur in developing countries. Nevertheless, the overall estimates of induced abortion worldwide are about 43.8 million in one year or about 28 per 1,000 women between ages 15 and 44, according to the Guttmacher Institute (http://www.guttmacher.org/sections/abortion.php?gclid=CILD2cfWiL8CFVQiMgodn20AZw).

Another threat to women's health worldwide is what is sometimes called female genital mutilation or female circumcision. The two terms reflect something of the contrasting ideas about this procedure. Some argue that female genital surgery is mutilation, others that so-called female circumcision is beautification. Some say it is a form of violence against women done to maintain their subordinate status, to control their reproduction, and for the purposes of beautification. There are (at least) three different types of procedures: circumcision, where the hood of the clitoris is cut; excision, where the clitoris and all or part of the labia minora are cut out; and infibulation, which includes cutting the clitoris, labia minora, and at least part of the labia majora. The two sides of the vulva are then sutured to obliterate the vaginal area except for a small opening for passage of urine and menstrual blood. The size of the opening is that of a corn kernel.

Infibulation prevents female sexual pleasure and is believed to assure the faithfulness of women to their husbands. It reinforces the male's right to control and dominance, and the female's dependence. Women's imputed attractiveness to men may depend on infibulation. In some places, virtually 100 per cent of young girls of ages 4–10 years undergo infibulation. Little girls know that it's essential to their marriageability and thus want to have it done. It is also associated with gift-giving for the girls. Never having seen it occur, they may be unaware of the pain involved. The procedure is not only painful, however, but may also be dangerous because the tools used and the hands that use the tools are often unhygienic and the stitching may be done with silk, catgut, or even thorns. Girls may have their legs bound together for a period of weeks to ensure the buildup of scar tissue. Sexual intercourse is forever likely to be painful and even dangerous for infibulated women.

The issue of circumcision is not exclusive to other countries. Canada has long supported infant male circumcision although the rates are decreasing dramatically to about 32 per cent today. This seems to reflect growing knowledge regarding the some of the negative side effects of the practice. Some hospitals provide new mothers with medical information about circumcision. This intervention may elicit a thoughtful response rather than an automatic cultural affirmative when staff asks whether or not the newborn baby is to be circumcised. The Canadian Paediatric Society indicates that because the medical costs and benefits are mixed the decision should be up to the parents (http://o.canada.com/news/canadas-pediatricians-set-to-reveal-new-policy-on-circumcision). The side effects include both a diminution in sexual pleasure and an increase in certain health problems as well as the risks associated with any surgical procedure. Some people argue that circumcision is a violation of a child's rights and that, therefore, all children should be protected under the Criminal Code against this "aggravated assault."

Approximately one in five women around the world will be a victim of rape or attempted rape at some time in her life according to studies undertaken by the United Nations (http://www.un.org/en/globalissues/briefingpapers/endviol/). Forced marriage between a child and an older male is another problem with long-term health and gynecological consequences. One way of conceptualizing the health effects is in terms of disability-adjusted life years (DALY). Rape and domestic violence are major causes of disability and death around the globe, especially among women in their reproductive years. Sexual violence is also an important component of women's high rates of HIV/AIDS, especially in Africa. The rape of women in war or in terrorism is another serious concern. For instance, approximately 1,100 women are raped every month in the ongoing wars and unrest in the Democratic Republic of Congo (DRC). In 2014 hundreds of girls were kidnapped (some to be married, some to be raped, some sold in sexual or other slavery, and others kept for the purposes of the abductors) from their school by the Islamist militants Boko Haram in Nigeria. Boko Haram has threatened to continue this practice across West Africa unless their demands, including that girls not be educated, are met (http://www.bbc.com/news/world-africa-13809501). Dowry murder, honour killings, and sexual trafficking in female children are well institutionalized around the world in developing nations and also occur in North America, especially trafficking. Malala Yousafzai, who was viciously attacked and seriously wounded by extremist militant Taliban on a school bus in Pakistan, has become renowned (and shared the Nobel Peace Prize in 2014 with Kallash Satyarthi of India, a long-time proponent of children's rights and education) throughout the world for standing up for the right of girls to be educated. Virtually daily the news reports one or another of myriad gender-based sexual and/or violent crimes against girls and women.

Statistics Canada estimates that one out of every 10 sexual assaults against women is reported and it is thus difficult to be sure of the actual figures for Canada (http://www.statcan.gc.ca/pub/85f0033m/2008019/hl-fs-eng.htm). This lack of valid statistical counts is undoubtedly similar throughout the world. An organization designed to offer support to victims of rape says that one in 17 women is raped during her lifetime and a woman is sexually assaulted every 17 minutes (http://www.assaultcare.ca/index.php?option=com_content&view=article&id=49&Itemid=58). Sexual predation by physicians on their female patients has been reported in Canada and elsewhere (www.thestar.com/news/insight/article/972102--less-than-zero-tolerance-on-patient-abuse) and a database accessible to the public of "bad doctors" has been suggested (www.thestar.com/news/article/1068227). Further rape, sexual assault, and gender-based harassment of women in the military and in policing are critical issues that have come to light in the news recently (http://www.thestar.com/news/canada/2015/04/30/5-proposals-from-the-canadian-forces-sexual-harassment-report.html). Rape on college campuses has become a particular problem in recent years. Some even argue that there is a "culture of rape" on college campuses in Canada (http://news.nationalpost.com/2014/03/07/is-there-an-epidemic-of-rape-culture-at-canadian-universities/). Women have responded by organizing and protesting in some creative and novel ways, including the Take Back the Night and Slut Walks.

The health consequences of and the continuous fear of rape and sexual assault include psychological distress, socio-cultural impacts, and somatic consequences. Psychological distress may last throughout the lifetime of the woman who has been raped. The symptoms can be diverse and extensive. In North America they have been diagnosed by the psychiatric profession as a type of post-traumatic stress disorder (PTSD). Survivors of rape and violence are also more likely to experience depression, to self-harm, to have flashbacks, to abuse alcohol and drugs, and to have sexually transmitted infections, among other potentially long-term and powerful types of suffering (https://rainn.org/get-information/effects-of-sexual-assault). All of these problems are also likely to be exacerbated by the silence and shame that accompany rape in our culture.

Socio-cultural effects are those that spread beyond the suffering of the individual woman and lead non-victimized women to change their behaviour and restrict their movements out of fear. Surveys done in countries around the world indicate that many women consider the fear of rape a major stress in their lives. In some countries women who have been raped may be doubly abused. For instance, in parts of Asia and the Middle East, consequences of rape may include being divorced by one's husband, ostracized by one's family, or even murdered by family members to "cleanse the family honour." Rape can lead the victim to commit suicide. Physical illnesses that are disproportionately diagnosed among women who have been raped include chronic pelvic pain, arthritis, gastrointestinal disorders, headaches, chronic pain, psychogenic seizures, premenstrual symptoms, and substance abuse. Women who have been victims of rape and other assaults report more symptoms of illness across virtually all bodily systems and perceive their health less favourably than non-victimized women. Numerous reproduction-related issues that may result from rape and sexual abuse including premature menarche, pregnancy, sexually transmitted diseases, high-risk sexual behaviours afterwards, and loss of self-esteem (Koss et al.,1994).

Comprehensive Health Care

Comprehensive health care, although relatively ineffective without such fundamentals as adequate food and clean water, is also an important factor in good health. Health care can be divided into three types, sometimes called three levels of prevention. **Primary health care** emphasizes equitably distributed prevention through community development and education. Environmental issues may also be addressed. **Secondary health care** is directed towards disease treatment in hospital and community via various (usually Western-style) medical practitioners. **Tertiary care** especially occurs in a teaching hospital attached to a university and has a

side emphasis on health promotion. Primary health care such as oral rehydration therapy, vaccinations and antibiotics, and disease-specific initiatives (such as malaria reduction programs), along with smaller family sizes and improved socio-economic status, have made a difference—the mortality rates and the numbers of children dying around the world have decreased over the past few decades in some places. The topic of global health care is explored in depth in Chapter 15.

Immunization

Immunization makes an important contribution to the health of a population, although its historical importance appears to have been overemphasized. McKinlay and McKinlay (1977), following our earlier discussions of McKeown's work on this topic, used American data since about 1900 to show that most of the decline in mortality from the infectious diseases prevalent in 1900 (about 40 per cent of the deaths in 1900 were attributable to infectious diseases) was the result of public health measures such as water purification and improvements in nutrition and birth control. Data for tuberculosis, typhoid, measles, scarlet fever, polio, whooping cough, influenza, diphtheria, and pneumonia demonstrate that the significant decline in mortality for each disease came before the introduction of the vaccine or drug to treat it. This is not to argue that vaccinations are ineffective, just that they are ultimately effective only in the context of good public health and environmental infrastructure.

In the developing world, only a fraction of children receive protection from measles, tuberculosis, whooping cough, polio, tetanus, and diphtheria, and, perhaps more significantly, basic public health measures, as noted above, are lacking in many communities and regions. Millions of children still die from these diseases or are disabled, annually. The WHO has stated that it intends to ensure universal immunization by 2020 (http://www.who.int/immunization/monitoring_surveillance/en/).

In the midst of confusing information about their safety and efficacy, as well as some skepticism about the "motives" of pharmaceutical companies, even in Canada parents of infants and children do not universally take up immunization. Significant numbers of children in Canada are not receiving adequate immunization for potentially fatal and disabling diseases such as polio, diphtheria, and measles even though vaccinations are widely available and free (www.phac-aspc.gc.ca/publicat/ccdr-rmtc/04pdf/cdr3005.pdf). This is partly the result of opposition to some vaccinations and the lobbying efforts of anti-vaccine movements. Some of the proponents of this view believe that autism and other diseases can result from vaccines. Organizing through the Internet has been a powerful method for some of these groups to plan their opposition. Some vaccines contain mercury (Thimerosal), an additional concern (www.cdc.gov/vaccines/pubs/pink-book/downloads/appendices/B/excipient-table-2. pdf). The efficacy of flu vaccinations has been called into question (http://www.thelancet.com/journals/laninf/artic99(11)70295-X/abstract) especially by alternative and complementary health-care providers. Nevertheless, vaccines have been advocated prior to having sufficient evidence of effectiveness and safety, especially for the elderly (ibid.).

Serious infectious and bacterial diseases have all but disappeared in the developed world (with the notable exception of HIV/AIDS). However, as the "anti-vaccine" and "slow-vaccine" (one vaccine at a time and spread out over time) movements grow, with international travel and migration we are seeing the re-emergence of such diseases as measles (http://www.ncbi.nlm.nih.gov/pmc/articles/PMC3905323/). Moreover, the developed world awaits a seemingly inevitable global pandemic of new strains of infectious and contagious disease such as the avian or the H1N1 influenza. Except for international co-operation, excellent surveillance, and interventions, SARS might have been a global pandemic. The World Health Organization in co-operation with countries around the globe has ongoing monitoring and response systems in place to observe the development of a new disease. Of course, too, the continuing threat that new diseases may be ignored too long to enable the development of prevention and treatment protocols is worrisome. In an era characterized by constant international travel for pleasure and commerce, the rapid spread of a new disease appears to be likely.

Figure 2.5 presents a picture of the decline in mortality rates over the twentieth century. Notice

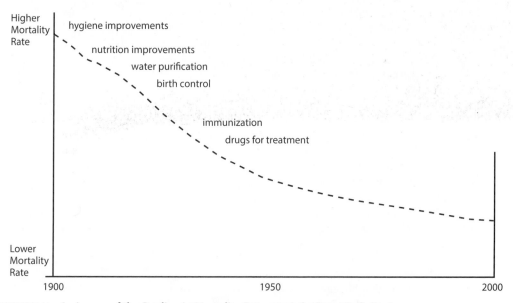

FIGURE 2.5   An Image of the Decline in Mortality Rates over the Twentieth Century

Source: Adapted from information in McKinlay and McKinlay, "Medical Measures and the Decline of Mortality," in Howard D. Schwartz, ed., Dominant Issues in Medical Sociology, 2e. New York: Random House (1987).

CANADA IN A GLOBAL CONTEXT

BOX 2.1   The Growth in Global Inequality

Global inequality has been growing over the past half-century or so (De Vogli, 2011) under neo-liberal globalization. Paralleled by an increase in inequity in Canada, as well as in other developed nations such as the United Kingdom, the United States, Australia, New Zealand, and Sweden, these inequities are concomitant to the changing economic policies favouring the dominance of market principles in governing over principles of justice and equity. Rather than enacting policies that focus on a balance between the protection of the weak, poor, and vulnerable in society and on economic prosperity and growth, current policies increasingly support free markets first and foremost. There has been growing evidence of declines in government involvement in the provision of adequate and universal health and social services, coupled with decreasing taxes for corporations and the richest members of society. Societies with greater inequality tend to have higher morbidity and mortality rates. Countries with more internal equity, such as Japan, tend to have higher levels of life expectancy. As well as the overall degree of relative societal equality and inequality, the socio-economic status of individuals within societies is negatively correlated with both morbidity and mortality. Those lower in the socio-economic hierarchy tend to have higher levels of sickness and death. Those higher in a societal socio-economic hierarchy tend to have lower levels of morbidity and mortality. If the availability of material goods and services accounted for all health disparities between people located at different places in the social structure, then overall inequity in a society would not affect life expectancy or other health outcomes. However, it does. Do people feel unhappy and stressed when they live in a society where there is a great deal of disparity? Are people happier and less stressed when they feel that life circumstances and life chances are generally similar among most other people in their country? If so, how does this work to affect their health and well-being? A number of explanations have been discussed in this chapter for the fact that poorer people and more inequitable societies tend to have higher rates of disease and death.

For some evidence and interesting illustrations, see Table 2.3 and the Global Wealth Pyramid, Figure 2.6. At the top of the pyramid 98,663 individuals are worth more than US$50 million. At the next level 1,087,641 individuals are worth between $10 million and $50 million. As you go down the pyramid the number of people who are worth less and less grows. The very wealthy in the US have increased most

TABLE 2.3   Forbes World Billionaires, 2000–1 to 2010

Country	Number of Billionaires		
	2000–1	2005	2010
Canada	18	17	24
France	19	14	12
Germany	47	57	51
Italy	17	10	13
Japan	43	24	22
United Kingdom	18	24	29
United States	269	342	405
G7 Total	**431**	**488**	**556**
Brazil	10	9	18
China	1	2	64
India	9	13	50
Russia	8	26	63
BRIC Total	**28**	**50**	**195**
World	**613**	**693**	**1,011**

Source: Adapted from Table 1 in Credit Suisse Research Institute, "Global Wealth Report 2013", p. 28. https://publications.credit-suisse.com/tasks/render/file/?fileID=BCDB1364-A105-0560-1332EC9100FF5C83.

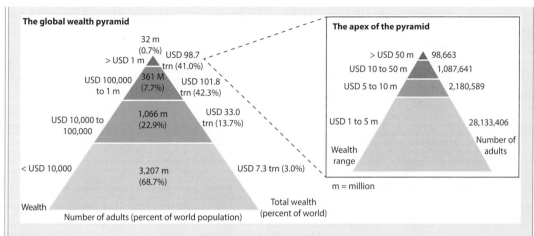

The global wealth pyramid

32 m (0.7%) > USD 1 m   USD 98.7 trn (41.0%)

USD 100,000 to 1 m   361 M (7.7%)   USD 101.8 trn (42.3%)

USD 10,000 to 100,000   1,066 m (22.9%)   USD 33.0 trn (13.7%)

< USD 10,000   3,207 m (68.7%)   USD 7.3 trn (3.0%)

Wealth
Number of adults (percent of world population)   Total wealth (percent of world)

The apex of the pyramid

> USD 50 m   98,663
USD 10 to 50 m   1,087,641
USD 5 to 10 m   2,180,589
USD 1 to 5 m   28,133,406

Wealth range   Number of adults

m = million

FIGURE 2.6   The Global Wealth Pyramid, and the Apex of the Pyramid

Source: Adapted from *Global Wealth Report*, https://publications.credit-suisse.com/tasks/render/file/?fileID=BCDB1364-A105-0560-1332EC9100FF5C83.

rapidly in recent years, and as Table 2.3 shows the US houses substantially more billionaires (405) than anywhere else. Countries such as Canada, the United Kingdom, the United States, and the BRIC economies—Brazil, China, India, and Russia—have grown in internal inequity, as is reflected in the increasing numbers of billionaires (Table 2.3). It is now widely accepted that global structural adjustment designed to enable the poor nations to pay their debts to the rich nations has led to greater inequality than existed prior to structural adjustment policies. In stark contrast, even as the richest countries of the world have gotten richer, they have become less politically and economically stable.

The burden of global inequality falls most heavily on women around the world. Yet, the legal position of women has in many ways improved. Almost all of the countries of the world have signed the Convention for the Elimination of All Forms of Discrimination Against Women (CEDAW) (http://www.un.org/womenwatch/daw/cedaw/). Gender equity is now a cornerstone of economic and other development projects around the globe. In fact, the Canadian International Development Agency is widely thought to have one of the best—if not the best—gender equity screening processes for development. It has become a model for the rest of the world. Gender equity has repeatedly been shown to be associated with lower fertility and better health for women and children as well as overall economic development. Gender equity seems to be important for health both at the level of the public economy and within individual households. Within the household, decision-making power, equity and allocation of resources, as well as education for girls and women, are now seen as fundamental forms of human capital investment.

the historical place of immunization and drug development in the overall trajectory of decline along with the impacts of social changes. This historical decline in mortality could end abruptly in the face of a global pandemic.

The Impact of Specific Diseases Worldwide

Three of the most significant health problems around the globe are HIV/AIDS, mental disorders, and wars and natural disasters. HIV/AIDS, as most informed people today know, is one of the most devastating diseases worldwide. Globalization has had a significant impact on the spread of the disease around the world. It was first described and isolated in the US in the early 1980s. Then, it was discovered to exist elsewhere. Since that time it has spread virtually all around the globe. By the end of 2012 an estimated 35.3 (32.2–35.8) million people were living with HIV/AIDS (https://www.google.ca/search?q=global+statistics+of+hiv&oq=global+incidence+of+HIV&aqs=chrome.2.69i57j0l5.8005j0j7&sourceid=chrome&es_sm=119&ie=UTF-8). The majority of these people are in sub-Saharan Africa. The increasingly mobile human population increases the risk of the spread of HIV/AIDS. This includes not only those who travel voluntarily but also the millions of people who are displaced by wars and famine and environmental disasters.

HIV/AIDS strikes the poor and socially marginalized hardest and it leaves many children as orphans. Millions of children live with an HIV/AIDS diagnosis themselves or with the effects of HIV/AIDS through the death and illness of parents. Today, women have a greater risk of contracting HIV than have men, and, because of their domestic roles are much more likely to be affected by HIV/AIDS as caregivers of sick family members and or children orphaned by the disease. Women constituted just over 50 per cent of the adults with HIV/AIDS worldwide in 2014. Economics and family structures mean that many men from this region travel and live away from home in order to make a living for themselves and their families. In the process of travelling to and from work, these men often avail themselves of the services of paid sex workers infected with HIV/AIDS. Thus, when men return to their families and communities with the virus they are liable to spread it. Women's low social status, which results in a greater likelihood of (1) lack of access to sufficient nutrients and clean water, (2) poverty, and (3) susceptibility to being raped in countries torn apart by conflict, also contributes to the problem of HIV/AIDS in women and children in Africa. Young people between the ages of about 20 and 35 or so are those most likely to be newly diagnosed as having HIV/AIDS. There are

devastating impacts on all areas of life because of HIV/AIDS diagnoses.

Various attempts are being made to combat HIV/AIDS by countries and foundations globally, including the United Nations and the World Health Organization. They focus on both treatment and prevention. However, in many areas the disease continues to spread and also in areas where drug treatments are not accessible. Thus, the long-term effects of the epidemic have not been adequately dealt with. Nor, for that matter, have treatment interventions been nearly sufficient—the majority of infected people around the world are not likely receiving sufficient medical care or treatment.

Mental illnesses are another of the most significant contributions to the disease burden of people around the globe and cause years of disability in the lives of millions. Mental illness is related to poverty, economic insecurity, and low levels of education (Patel and Kleinman, 2003). Hopelessness, poor physical health, and rapid change in social status, as well as constrained opportunities resulting from educational impoverishment, are related to mental illness rates. Throughout the world, individuals suffering from mental illnesses often experience stigmatization, isolation, and increased mortality (www.who.int.mental_health/en/). It is estimated that each year about 800,000 people die by suicide. This is about one person every 40 seconds. Suicide is the leading cause of death for young adults between 15 and 44 in many countries (http://www.who.int/mental_health/prevention/suicide/suicideprevent/en/). The World Health Organization estimates that 154 million people suffer from depression, 25 million people from schizophrenia, 91 million from alcohol-related disorders, 15 million from drug-related disorders, about 50 million from epilepsy, and 24 million from Alzheimer's and other forms of dementia (www.who.int/mental_health/en). Moreover, the capacity to deal with people who suffer from mental illnesses varies across the world, and the influence of modern medical care is unevenly distributed so that poorer nations are less likely to have mental health policies and plans to care for those who suffer (http://whqlibdoc.

TABLE 2.4   Presence of Mental Health Plan by World Bank Income Group

Income Group	Countries with Mental Health Plan	% with Mental Health Plan	Population Coverage (%)
Low	24/39	61.5	72.1
Lower-middle	37/51	72.5	98.1
Upper-middle	28/43	65.1	96.3
High	42/48	87.5	99.5
World	131/181	72.4	94.8

Source: Table 1.2.2, "Presence of mental health plan by World Bank income group," in "Mental Health Atlas 2011", World Health Organization (2011), p. 21. http://whqlibdoc.who.int/publications/2011/9799241564359_eng.pdf.

who.int/publications/2011/9799241564359_eng. pdf). However, the impact of (American and pharmaceutical) treatments for the mentally ill is not always positive. There is some evidence that some of the indigenous treatments in the developing world may be more beneficial in some cases, for instance, in the care for people with schizophrenia (Whitaker, 2010).

Living in a war-torn country is not conducive to mental or physical health. Wars obviously cause death, disability, and ongoing diseases for combatants, but there are enormous associated health costs for civilians. Millions of people are regularly displaced as a result of wars and natural disasters (www.unmillenniumproject.org/reports/reports2.htm). Millions seek help in refugee camps. Others are wandering and fleeing to seek safety and assistance. Clearly, such events contribute to food insecurity, lack of access to clean water, poverty, and innumerable other social, economic, and human health problems. Deforestation, flooding, and numerous other threats to the environment that take a long recovery time mean that affected people may not be able to care for themselves, their families, or their communities for generations.

CANADA IN A GLOBAL CONTEXT

BOX 2.2   The Horrors of War

Not only are millions of people wounded, killed, maimed, and raped as a result of wars, but the consequences of being in a war can be extremely problematic for survivors. Western governments are now realizing the potential for returning soldiers to suffer from a variety of types of psychological problems including **post-traumatic stress disorder (PTSD)**. It is so widely accepted as a real possibility for returning veterans today that the government has published a book of information online for Canadian veterans about the signs and symptoms of PTSD (http://www.veterans.gc.ca/pdf/mental-health/ptsd_warstress_e.pdf). Among the symptoms of PTSD are the following: avoidance of any reminders of the trauma; gaps in memory; loss of interest in normal activities; feeling detached from loved ones; feeling flat or numb; and difficulty imagining a future. Under "intrusive symptoms" the handbook for veterans mentions the following: distressing memories or images; nightmares; flashbacks; upset; and physical symptoms such as sweating, increased heart rate, and muscle tension.

continued

All of these symptoms are heightened when the soldier remembers a particularly difficult or traumatic situation (http://www.veterans.gc.ca/pdf/mental-health/ptsd_warstress_e.pdf).

At times PTSD has led to suicide. About 50 Canadian soldiers are known to have killed themselves between 2005 and 2009, another 50 between 2000 and 2004, and another 53 between 1995 and 1999 (http://www.forces.gc.ca/en/news/article.page?doc=suicide-and-suicide-prevention-in-the-canadian-armed-forces/hgq87xvu). Between 2002 and 2011, when the combat mission ended, 158 soldiers had been killed in combat in Afghanistan. Evidently, being killed in action is hardly more prevalent than taking one's life after returning home (http://www.forces.gc.ca/en/news/article.page?doc=suicide-and-suicide-prevention-in-the-canadian-armed-forces/hgq87xvu). In a recent study published in the *Canadian Medical Association Journal*, 13.5 per cent of the 40,000 soldiers deployed from Canada to Afghanistan returned with a mental disorder that was said to be the result of their time in Afghanistan. Of these 5,400 military personnel, only 26 were reported to have sought help (Boulos and Zamorski, 2013), possibly because of the stigma attached to mental illness (especially in a largely male, conflict-oriented environment) and possibly because they believed or recognized that psychiatric services, as presently constituted, could provide little help. Canadian psychiatrist Norman Doidge's recent book, *The Brain's Way of Healing* (2015; see also Tallman, 2011), is one of few works by a medically trained doctor who begins to appreciate how ear damage can affect an individual's behaviour and health across many measures. (Note that post-traumatic stress disorder or PTSD used to be called "shell shock.") A Kingston psychiatrist, Janet McCulloch, has used an elaborate sound-stimulation program for soldiers from the Trenton, Ontario, base who are suffering from PTSD (http://www.osmt.org/uploads/Neurofeedback%20Training%20in%20Clinical%20Practice.pdf).

Other returning soldiers have committed murder, possibly as a result of PTSD. It may be that these murders are one of the consequences of the experiences that soldiers undergo as they do their work. Another one of the tragic long-term effects of engaging in conflict is the heightened risk among former military personnel of homelessness upon return (Metraux et al., 2013). Canadian Forces officials have become especially sensitized to the issues facing returning soldiers because of the outspoken work of General Roméo Dallaire, who had headed a United Nations peacekeeping mission in Rwanda and was unable to halt or alert the world about the atrocities and genocide. He has continued to speak openly about the effects of his experiences on his life and his family. Clearly, the effects of war are far reaching and profound, even in countries far removed from the ongoing conflict, as soldiers return home.

Death, Disease, and Disability in Canadian Society

In Canada the infant mortality rate, one of the most sensitive indicators of the health of a nation, has dropped significantly as a result of better nutrition and living standards for the mother and baby, coupled with improved prenatal and postnatal medical care (see Figure 2.3). With the exception of Japan, Canada had the most significant drop in infant mortality rates over the period 1960–95. In 1995, the infant mortality rate for Canada was 6.1 per 1,000 as compared to 27.3 per 1,000 in 1960 (Statistics Canada, 1995b). By 2012 the rate was about 4.8 per 1,000. Just over 100 years earlier, in 1901, 134 of every 1,000 infants (about one in seven) died in the first year of life (*Canada Year Book*, 2001). Canadian infant mortality compares positively to the rate in the US, where the corresponding figure is 6.22 per 1,000 (www.cia.gov/

library/publications/the-world-factbook/geos/us.html). However, some large discrepancies arise across Canadian provinces and territories. The infant mortality rate in Yukon is 8.5, in Manitoba 7.3, in Newfoundland and Labrador 7.5, in Alberta 6.0, and in Nunavut 16.1 (www40.statcan.gc.ca/l01/cst01/health21a-eng.htm). A significant aspect of the higher rates of infant mortality in the select provinces is the proportion of Aboriginal Canadians. The death rate for infants and young children in the Aboriginal community is approximately 1.5 to 4 times the general Canadian rate (Mikkonen and Raphael, 2010), primarily as a result of sudden infant death syndrome, respiratory diseases, and pneumonia.

The chief causes of death in Canada today are cancer, heart disease, cerebrovascular diseases, and accidents (*Canada Year Book*, 2009: 206; http://www.statcan.gc.ca/pub/84-215-x/2012001/table-tableau/tbl001-eng.htm). Cancer is the largest cause of death in Canada. The proportion of deaths from heart disease has decreased by about 30 per cent over the past quarter-century or so and has continued to do so (*Canada Year Book*, 1994). This trend reverses the historical situation when heart disease was the first and growing cause of death. However, "since 1952, the cardiovascular death rate in Canada has declined by more than 75 per cent—and nearly 40 per cent in the last decade" (http://www.heartandstroke.com/site/lookup.asp?c=ikIQLcMWJtE&b=3483991#decline). Table 2.5 compares the causes of death in Canada for 1921–5, 1996–7, and 2011. See Table 2.6 for the leading causes of death in Canada today.

TABLE 2.5   Leading Causes of Death Changed Dramatically during the Twentieth Century

	Rate per 100,000
1921–5	
All causes	1,030.0
Cardiovascular and renal diseases	221.9
Influenza, bronchitis, and pneumonia	141.1
Diseases of early infancy	111.0
Tuberculosis	85.1
Cancer	75.9
Gastritis, duodenitis, enteritis, and colitis	72.2
Accidents	51.5
Communicable diseases	47.1
1996–7	
All causes	654.4
Cardiovascular diseases (heart disease and stroke)	240.2
Cancer	184.8
Chronic obstructive pulmonary diseases	28.4
Unintentional injuries	27.7
Pneumonia and influenza	22.1
Diabetes mellitus	16.7
Hereditary and degenerative diseases of the central nervous system	14.7
Diseases of arteries, arterioles, and capillaries	14.3

continued

TABLE 2.5   *Continued*

	Rate per 100,000
2011	
All causes	489.0
Malignant neoplasms (cancer)	154.1
Diseases of the heart (heart disease)	91.0
Cerebrovascular diseases (stroke)	24.8
Chronic lower respiratory diseases	22.1
Accidents (unintentional injuries)	24.2
Diabetes mellitus (diabetes)	14.5
Alzheimer's disease	10.8
Influenza and pneumonia	10.4

Note: Disease categories not identical over time. Rates in 1996–7 and 2011 are age-standardized.

Source: Adapted from Statistics Canada, *Canadian Social Trends*, Catalogue no. 11–008 (Winter 2000): 13, http://publications.gc.ca/Collection-R/Statcan/11-008-XIE/0030011-008-XIE.pdf; Statistics Canada, CANSIM table 102–0563, http://www.statcan.gc.ca/pub/82-625-x/2014001/article/11897-eng.htm.

About 15 per cent of Canadians (2009–10) 12 years or older suffered an injury that required them to take time away from their regular activities (http://www.statcan.gc.ca/pub/82-624-x/2011001/article/11506-eng.htm). The leading cause of injury among all major injury cases in Canada (the injured individuals had to have been seen in or admitted to hospital for the injury to be reported) was falls. Falls accounted for 63 per cent of all injuries among seniors, more than half among

TABLE 2.6   Ranking and Number of Deaths for the 10 Leading Causes, Canada, 2011

Leading Causes of Death	Rank	Number of Deaths
Malignant neoplasms (cancer)	1	72,476
Diseases of the heart (heart disease)	2	47,627
Cerebrovascular diseases (stroke)	3	13,238
Chronic lower respiratory diseases	4	11,184
Accidents (unintentional injuries)	5	10,716
Diabetes mellitus (diabetes)	6	7,194
Alzheimer's disease	7	6,356
Influenza and pneumonia	8	5,757
Intentional self-harm (suicide)	9	3,728
Nephritis, nephrotic syndrome, and nephrosis (kidney diseases)	10	3,294

Source: Statistics Canada, Table 102–0561, "Leading causes of death, total population, by age group and sex, Canada, annual," CANSIM (database), http://www5.statcan.gc.ca/cansim/a26?lang=eng&retrLang=eng&id=1020561&paSer=&pattern=&stByVal=1&p1=1&p2=37&tabMode=dataTable&csid=.

adolescents, and 35 per cent among adults. Sixty-six per cent of adolescent injuries were related to sports and about one-half of adult injuries were associated with work or sports. Injuries among seniors occurred while walking or doing household chores.

Heart disease, cancer, and accidents are called the **diseases of civilization** or diseases of affluence, or what Omran (1979) has called "man-made" diseases. Their causes are different from those of the diseases of development. Food security and lack of clean water and birth control are no longer problems for most people in most of the developed world. Rather, socio-economic inequity within developed societies, lifestyle, and environmental, work-related, and other factors are important in explaining Canada's present mortality rates. Aboriginal Canadians are an exception in that they experience both diseases of development and diseases of civilization, and their health status will be discussed more thoroughly in Chapter 5.

Precursors to the Major Causes of Disease and Death in Canada

Marc Lalonde, who in 1974 was the Minister of Health under Pierre Trudeau, published what was to become a significant and foundational health policy document in Canada and elsewhere. In it he argued for a broadened model of the explicit causes of disease beyond those confined to a biomedical model and treated in the office of the doctor or in the hospital. He distinguished three causes of mortality: self-imposed, environmental, and biological host factors. At the time this was a revolutionary perspective because it moved beyond the malfunctioning of the body to that of public health policy. Now it is widely assumed as relevant to national health policy. By self-imposed factors, Lalonde meant such things as (1) excessive alcohol consumption, (2) smoking, (3) drug abuse, (4) nutritional inadequacies such as overconsumption of sugar or fat, (5) lack of exercise or

recreation, and overwork, (6) careless driving and failure to wear seat belts, and (7) promiscuity and sexual carelessness. Environmental factors include physical factors, such as contaminated water, acid rain, and air pollution, as well as socio-economic factors such as urbanization and working conditions, including inadequate health and safety measures on the job. Finally, host factors are the result of individual biological heritage or genetics. The following sections will examine "self-imposed" factors. It is important to re-emphasize that sociologists see health behaviours as related both to individual agency or choice and also to social and structural determinants. Thus, cigarette smoking is both a behaviour that an individual chooses from within a narrow range of behavioural options and also a behaviour patterned by social structure, so that those in the lower socio-economic levels (and those, increasingly, in the poorer countries) are more likely to smoke. Individual behaviour always occurs in social contexts and amid circulating and powerful discourses. The approach that focuses on social factors such as gender, age, and racialization is the social determinants perspective (see Chapters 4 and 5 for detailed explanations and examples). Moreover, some persons are affected by their mental condition such that they do not have the capacity for "choice" in the ordinary sense of that word, a concept already recognized in law (dsp-psd.pwgsc.gc.ca/Collection-R/LoPBdP/BP/prb9922-e.htm) but not always taken into account with citizens or patients.

The Impact of Alcohol and Street Drugs

Alcohol ingestion appears to affect health in paradoxical ways. On the one hand, excess consumption is known to be associated with morbidity and mortality through alcoholism, cirrhosis, malnutrition, accidents, obesity, suicide, homicide, and other violent behaviour, as well as foetal alcohol syndrome when an excess of alcohol is ingested by a pregnant woman. On the other hand, moderate drinking, particularly of red wine, appears to have a beneficial impact on health. While most Canadians drink alcohol, the proportion of the population who drink is declining (www.hc-sc.

gc.ca/hc-ps/drugs-drogues/stat/index-eng.php). Seventy-eight per cent of Canadians reported drinking at least one alcoholic drink in the previous year in 2011. Heavy drinking has become less common and has reportedly declined. Men are more likely to consume alcohol than women (www.hc-sc.gc.ca/hc-ps/drugs-drogues/stat/index-eng.php). They drink both more frequently and more heavily. However, alcohol advertising is increasingly targeting young women (Flegel, 2013) and this may foretell changes among women.

Street drugs can cause a multitude of health effects ranging from immediate death as a result of an overdose or poisoned drug intake, to diseases and disabilities resulting from the results of long-term addiction. These include malnutrition, emotional instability, neurological impairments including psychosis, inadequate or no housing,

and lacks in all of the other social determinants of health discussed in Chapter 4. Injection drug use in particular is associated with various disease outcomes. For instance, a sizable minority of Canadians, particularly those who live on the streets, are at risk of contracting and spreading sexually transmitted infections (STIs) including HIV/AIDS, as well as blood-borne infections, as a result of their drug use and sexual behaviours (www.phac-aspc.gc.ca/sti-its-surv-epi/qf-fr/differ_e.html). About 9 per cent of people 15 and over used cannabis in 2011 (http://www.hc-sc.gc.ca/hc-ps/drugs-drogues/stat/_2011/summary-sommaire-eng.php#a3). Young people were about three times as likely to use cannabis as adults. Males were about twice as likely as females to use cannabis. The previous figures represent cannabis use for recreational purposes. About 1 per cent of Canadians used cannabis for medical purposes

CRITICAL THINKING

BOX 2.3   Is There Too Much Pressure to Drink Alcohol on Campus?

How often do you go to the pub? How do you feel about it? Is it fun for you or is it just something to do with your friends who seem to want "to go pubbing"? Since the late 1970s, most universities have permitted at least one pub on campus. In addition, bars and pubs have grown up around college campuses around the country. Drinking alcohol is a major social activity for many young people in university and college today.

Many people are concerned about the excessive amount and the frequency of alcohol consumption on campuses. It appears to be normative to go to the pub regularly, as well as on "special" occasions as a part of celebrations such as "frosh week." Students say they drink to enhance their social activities and to "break the ice" in a new social situation (Syre, 1997). Stress reduction and celebrating milestones in the school year (e.g., finishing a test or a paper and exams) are among the other reasons students say they consume alcohol. As well as such

personal and peer-based reasons, many universities institutionalize alcohol consumption as a regular part of campus life by including it in college-sponsored activities such as orientation week and residence socials. The presence of bars on campus and their centrality as meeting places for students living off campus, as well as in residences, implicitly support some degree of alcohol consumption. Cheaper beer prices, careless checking of age and identity cards, and the linking of alcohol with other forms of entertainment such as music are ways to increase consumption of alcoholic beverages on campus and in nearby venues.

This sometimes becomes a problem. For example, students have died from excess consumption. Police have had to be called as the result of a riot from too much St Patrick Day's celebrating. Other students have become addicted and left school (Tamburri, 2012). Should anything be done?

in 2011 and that number may increase now that policies regarding medical marijuana use have been liberalized. The top five illicit drugs used in 2011, besides cannabis, included salvia, ecstasy, cocaine or crack, and speed. In addition, some Canadians become addicted to psychoactive pharmaceuticals such as opioids, stimulants, and tranquilizers, often originally as prescribed by a doctor and then obtained illicitly. While it is difficult to obtain valid percentages of illegal drug use, Health Canada estimates that possibly slightly less than 1 per cent of the total population may do so (ibid.). Various jurisdictions are working on developing programs to prevent and limit the effects of opioid overdoses (Leece et al., 2013). Insite was Canada's first government-sanctioned and supervised facility to aid people who are addicted to injection drugs to use them "safely." It is located in Vancouver, and its former director, Dr Gabor Maté, is a popular writer and lecturer on the program. There was a great deal of opposition to this and the principle of "harm reduction" upon which it was based. This principle was founded on the idea that some people would not or could not stay off drugs and thus should be supported in their use by the provision of clean needles and other social and health services. The previous theory of addictions treatment was "zero tolerance." This did not seem to work with everyone. Nevertheless, many thought that zero tolerance was the only legal and moral route for drug policy and treatment. After a Supreme Court decision in 2011, Insite was allowed to continue to operate after first being threatened by the federal government with closure. This issue continues to be very controversial. Some argue that in keeping the facility operating the government is condoning illegal drug use. Others argue that in the face of addiction the principle of least harm should operate (Zlotozynska et al., 2013). What do you think?

Impact of Cigarette Smoking

Cigarette smoking is considered to be the leading cause of preventable death in Canada. According to the most recent results of the Canadian Tobacco Use Monitoring Survey (CTUMS) in 2012 about 16 percent of the population now smokes as compared to 25 per cent in 1999 and 35 per cent in 1985. (http://www.hc-sc.gc.ca/hc-ps/tobac-tabac/research-recherche/stat/ctums-esutc_2012-eng.php). People affected by smoking go well beyond those who actually smoke and include those vulnerable to the numerous health effects of secondhand smoke (*Canada Year Book*, 2009). Smoking in the car with passengers under 16 is now illegal in most provinces in Canada (http://www.cbc.ca/news/health/bans-on-smoking-in-cars-with-kids-deemed-a-success-1.1330628). More males smoke than females by about 5 per cent (http://www.tobaccoreport.ca/2013/TobaccoUseinCanada_2013.pdf). Women smoke for the same reasons that men do, and for some additional reasons as well. Among the reasons are (1) because of addiction, (2) to enhance social acceptability, (3) to improve self-esteem and to relieve stress, and (4) to control weight (Cunningham, 1996: 165–73). **Prevalence** of smoking declines as people age, because of both quitting and the relatively earlier deaths of those who do smoke. The decline in smoking has been associated with public health campaigns, warnings on cigarette packages, banning of cigarette advertising, and increased tax levels. Smoking is also negatively associated with education levels. Those with less formal education are more likely to smoke.

Very few adults begin smoking. New smokers usually begin in their youth. However, in the homes of adult smokers, children typically "try smoking" as early as five years old and most have tried by seven or eight years old. The tobacco industry's advertising is directed towards a young market. Tobacco manufacturers regularly do surveys and hold focus groups for the youth market. Candy cigarettes are one way of enticing children to adopt smoking (Weeks, 2014). The Statistics Canada publication *The Daily* reported in June 2004 that "between 1994 and 2002, the rate of smoking among Canadian youths in Grades 5 to 9 declined by more than half (from 13.6 per cent to 6.2 per cent), according to new data from the Youth Smoking Survey" (Statistics Canada, 2004). In 2011, 5.5 per cent of youth in Grades 6–9 have tried smoking and 24.3 per cent of youth aged 15–19 in 2011 had ever smoked a whole cigarette.

After years of obfuscating debate sponsored by tobacco companies it is now clear that smoking has harmful effects on health (Novotny, 2013). Today, although the smoking rates for youth have declined, at least in part due to the high cost, recent research, which involved analysis of cigarette butts in public places where school students regularly smoke during school recesses and breaks, found that 30 per cent of these discarded butts in Ontario and 45 per cent in Quebec were from contraband cigarettes. Thus, a surprising portion of teen smokers are circumventing the high price of cigarettes by purchasing illegal, untaxed tobacco products. Interestingly, this "on-the-ground" study was conducted for the Canadian Convenience Stores Association, whose members are facing declining revenues (Canadian Press, 2009). An additional issue is the poorly enforced regulations regarding contraband (untaxed) cigarettes. People who use such products are heavier smokers, are more likely to perceive themselves as heavy smokers, and experience more barriers to quitting (Mecredy et al., 2013). Furthermore the Canadian government, which had been a world leader in smoking cessation efforts and had advocated for visual and textual

warnings on cigarette packages, has now fallen behind. In 2000 Canada became the first country in the world to require full-colour representations of the dangers of smoking on at least 50 per cent of the package for cigarettes. In 2012, in the face of lobbying by the tobacco industry, the government resisted the call for 75 per cent warning coverage. In addition, there are no warnings at all on products such as chewing tobacco, cigars, cigarillos, and so on. The World Health Organization has advocated regulating e-cigarettes, which use battery-charged cartridges to produce nicotine to be inhaled in vapour. The industry says that they are safe because they lack the tars and other toxins of nicotine cigarettes. On the other hand, health advocates insist that they still contain carcinogens and other particulates that are bad for the lungs (Begley, 2014).

The Link between Social Class and Cigarette Smoking

Cigarette smoking is a major public health concern and a cause of premature mortality in the developed world today, although its effects and use are declining and have been for the last quarter of a century (http://www.med.uottawa.ca/sim/data/Smoking_Rates_e.htm). However, cigarette

---

SPOTLIGHT ON ETHICS

BOX 2.4   Aesthetics for Whom?

There are some dangerous health consequences faced by those who work in the aesthetics services. Hairdressers have to work around toxic fumes, in water, with aerosols, dyes, bleach, and permanent solutions. Links have been made to a variety of minor skin conditions as well as serious long-term respiratory conditions and cancer because of the ingredients in these products. Manicurists and pedicurists are vulnerable to a number of skin conditions: solvents, resins, fragrances, and gums may cause numerous different skins disorders leading to rashes, itchiness, and ongoing

pain; to bacterial, viral and fungal infections; and to skin cancer and other cancers. The ergonomics of standing for most of the day when doing hair and sitting uncomfortably when doing nails are unhealthy and can lead to problems in the back, neck, legs, and feet. Such workers are often poorly paid, are possibly only able to get part-time work, and may be particularly vulnerable because of immigrant status and racialization.

Canadian health and safety standards do not adequately protect these workers. What should be done?

smoking is spreading rapidly in the developing world where tobacco is quickly becoming a major cause of death (http://siteresources.worldbank.org/INTETC/Resources/375990-1089904539172/474683-1089904575523/Overview.pdf). By 2030, at the current rates, smoking can be expected to kill 10 million people across the world. Seventy per cent of these deaths are predicted to occur in the low- and middle-income countries and among the poor in the high-income countries. Its addictive nature means that once a person begins to smoke quitting is very difficult.

Deaths from diseases such as bronchitis and emphysema, lung cancer, cardiovascular disease, and all cancers combined increase in the presence of cigarette smoking. In addition, people who smoke have lower rates of self-rated health and higher rates of death from crime, violence, accidents, and alcohol abuse. There is a strong link between cigarette smoking and social class so that lower in the class hierarchy and in poorer countries the rates of cigarette smoking are higher. These socio-economic status and smoking links are associated with high levels of premature morbidity and of mortality, by social class, both within Canada and cross-nationally. Thus, it is important to understand how and why poorer people are drawn to smoking. Today about half of cigarette smokers die from smoking, and this usually occurs in middle age. In some of the poorest households in the globe, 10 per cent of the total household expenditure is on tobacco (www.who.int/tobacco/health_priority/en/index.hym). About 80 per cent of smokers now live in low- and middle-income countries (ibid.).

Do you smoke cigarettes? If so, do you remember how and why you started? Have you ever tried to quit smoking? Smoking among young people is affected by a number of different factors. We will note just a few here. Consider some of the reasons not included in those listed here.

1. Smoking among young people is affected by school policy and by teaching in the schools.
2. Students who attend schools that ban cigarette smoking entirely on school property are less likely to smoke than students attending schools that offer restricted areas for smoking; 13 per cent of the student population smoke in schools that have banned smoking as compared to 20 per cent of students in schools that have simply restricted smoking areas.
3. Smoking rates are also related to the levels of academic achievement in young people. Eight per cent of those who report that their academic achievement is above average smoke as compared with 15 per cent of those who say their achievement is average and with 25 per cent of those who say their achievement is below average. More than half of those who have quit school—53 per cent—smoke.
4. Having a smoker in the home is also associated with smoking in young people: 50 per cent of those in homes where both parents smoked, 33 per cent of those in homes where one parent smoked, and only 10 per cent of those in homes where no one smoked. Prices of cigarettes and taxes also affect levels of smoking.
5. When the government decreased the tax on cigarettes in 1994 in response to the high rates of smuggling of cigarettes across the US border there was an immediate increase in smoking among 5 per cent of smokers 15–19 years old. Moreover, 19 per cent of those in this age group began smoking.
6. Smoking cigarettes also is related to drinking alcohol and using soft drugs (Clark, 1996).

Why is there a link between smoking and social class? The materialist explanation is not appropriate here. Cigarettes are expensive and their cost is a more significant component of the overall budget of the relatively lower-income groups. From the point of view of cost alone we would expect that cigarette smoking would increase with socio-economic status. Instead, there is an inverse relationship. A number of explanations have been proposed.

Socio-psychological explanations would suggest that the reason might be the sense of relative deprivation felt by the poorer people in a society. This experience, the argument goes, causes emotional, social, and psychological stress and smoking is taken up and continued as a "cheap" form of therapy and stress reduction. Poorer people usually cannot afford warm vacations in the cold winter months, cottages in the north, ski trips, psychotherapy, massage therapy, or other individual therapeutic interventions chosen by those with higher incomes.

Alternatively, people of lower status may tend to have generally higher levels of fatalism and anomie because they realize the almost impermeable borders between their own life chances and circumstances and those of people further up the socio-economic hierarchy. They may not know how or to believe that it is possible to change their own socio-economic position. Feeling blocked and expecting to live shorter and sicker lives, they may think that smoking cessation does not really matter in their situation. After years of negative experiences, they may not feel that they have the self-efficacy to change their lives or those of their families.

Social capital is another possible explanation for the negative relationship between smoking and social status. Evidence suggests that those lower in status have less social capital—friendship, neighbourhood support, and acquaintance networks—to develop and maintain experiences of social cohesion via networks of trust, shared values, and common goals and obligations. Lacking strong relational networks, poorer people are less likely to have alternative coping strategies; they have fewer social control mechanisms offered to them; and they may have less efficacious social support.

Another explanation comes from diffusion theory. In this regard, innovations are generally picked up first by the wealthier and more highly placed individuals in a society. Only later are innovations picked up by those lower on the social hierarchy. Thus, the correlation between high rates of cigarette smoking and lower social class is related to the fact that cigarettes have more recently been adopted by the lower-status groups even as those higher on the social ladder have already rejected them. Pampel's extensive research, which included data from 15 European nations, demonstrated that diffusion theory rather than social inequality is the better explanation of status-based smoking patterns (2002).

It is worth asking yourself the question asked above about the link between socio-economic status and smoking rates.

Physical Activity

A little more than half of all Canadians over 12 years of age engage in physical activity in their leisure time (53.9 per cent). This percentage is slightly higher among males (56.2 per cent) than among females (51.6 per cent) (http://www.statcan.gc.ca/tables-tableaux/sum-som/l01/cst01/health77b-eng.htm). It also declines regularly as people age: 51.4 per cent of males over 65 engage in physical activity for recreation and approximately 41.7 per cent of females do so. Physical activity is negatively related to socio-economic status for a number of reasons. For example, some recreational activities such as golf or skiing can be very expensive. Fitness clubs may be costly and unaffordable yet necessary in some seasons of the year in Canada. Leisure time itself may be scarcer for those who work shifts or more than one job. Clothing and equipment may be other constraints. Do you have other insights into the socio-economic correlations with physical activity?

The Impact of Weight, Body Image, and Eating Disorders

The number of overweight Canadians has increased. Between 1985 and 2011 the prevalence of obesity in adults nearly tripled and grew from 6.1 per cent to 18.3 per cent (Twells et al., 2014). Thirty-five per cent of Canadians are now overweight and 24 per cent are obese (www4.hrsdc.gc.ca/.3ndic.1t.4r@-eng.jsp?iid=6). Overweight is more common among older Canadians. Forty-four per cent of those over 55 are overweight. The obesity rate was highest for those between 65 and 74, at 34 per cent. Men are more likely to be overweight and obese than women, but women are more likely to be underweight. Despite women's tendency to underweight (especially when young), a sizable proportion of Canadian women with normal weights believe that they weigh too much. Now considered an epidemic, obesity is a significant risk factor for a variety of diseases, including cardiovascular disease, non-insulin-dependent diabetes mellitus (NIDDM), cancer of the breast, colon, and prostate, musculoskeletal problems, and gall bladder disease (Katzmarzyk, 2002). Obesity also leads to declines in the quality of life. There is a direct relationship between excess body weight and higher mortality.

The incidence of both overweight and obesity is growing in spite of the proliferation of a wide range of products and services designed to help people lose weight. Fat-free, low-fat, and sugar-free products now control major market shares of every conceivable foodstuff and beverage category. The ownership of personal exercise machines continues to accelerate and health and fitness clubs have become routine locations for social interaction. Obesity in children is a particular problem as they may be more likely to face a number of health problems, including hypertension, glucose intolerance, and orthopaedic problems as well as interpersonal and socio-psychological issues related to self-acceptance and body image.

Think for a minute about the causes of eating and of food choice. When do you eat? Are you always hungry before you eat? Are you hungry after you eat? When you are hungry, how often do you stop to make a fresh salad or to eat a piece of fruit? How often do you stop at a fast-food outlet? What do you know about nutrients in various foods? What social changes do you think have led to the "obesity epidemic"?

Of course, as sociologists we are concerned, too, about the ways in which the social construction of obesity as an epidemic serves the interests of those who profit from it, such as pharmaceutical firms, food and drink companies, "health" clubs, the diet industry, the manufacturers of exercise equipment, and even, as this book's editor suggests, medical sociologists (!). One study found a link between the body mass indexes (BMI) of a population and the density and proximity of fast-food restaurants (Reitzel et al., 2014). Another experimental study found that children preferred food wrapped in decorative and colourful wrapping to other food, despite the actual equivalence of the food being tasted (Elliott et al., 2013). There is no doubt that advertising can be highly effective.

TABLE 2.7 Estimated Prevalence of Obesity in the Canadian Population, 2003–11, Adjusted Self-Reported Data

Year	% Self-Reported Obesity Rate, Canadian Community Health Survey
2003	22.3
2005	22.8
2007	23.8
2008	24.2
2009	24.9
2010	25.1
2011	25.3

Source: Gotay, et al., "Updating the Canadian Obesity Maps: An Epidemic in Progress." Canadian Public Health Association, 2013. Volume 104, No.1, p. e64. Reprinted with permission of the Canadian Public Health Association.

Sexuality and AIDS

Sexuality is considered to be another aspect of the public health of Canadians that is monitored regularly as an indication of the effectiveness of public health policy. About 30 per cent of teenagers between 15 and 17 have had sex at least once. Sixty-eight per cent of those 18–19 years old have had sexual intercourse at least once (Rotermann, 2012). Clearly, premarital sex is now normative. Beginning sexual activity early is more likely to result in engaging in sex with several or numerous partners over time. Only about 68 per cent of teenagers indicated using a condom during their last sexual encounter. In the absence of consistent condom use it is no wonder that there is an increase in sexually transmitted infections (STIs) in Canada (http://www.phac-aspc.gc.ca/sti-its-surv-epi/sum-som-eng.php). These figures reflect a need for continuing concern about unwanted pregnancies and the spread of AIDS and other sexually transmitted diseases among Canadian young people. We will focus on HIV/AIDS in the subsequent discussion.

AIDS is a highly infectious and contagious disease. One important means of transmission is unprotected sex with someone carrying the virus. Discovered in the late 1970s in the US, its presence was not officially noted until 1981. The first case recorded in Canada was in 1982 (Frank, 1996). By 1991 an estimated 50,000 Canadians were infected with the HIV virus, the precursor of AIDS and, by 1995, 9,133 Canadians had died due to AIDS-related conditions (ibid.). As of 2001, 55,000 Canadians were living with an HIV diagnosis and there had been 62,247 reported cases of HIV/AIDS sin Canada (Ghosh, 2002). As of 2011 approximately 71,300 Canadians were living with HIV (or an increase of 11 per cent since 2008), according to CATIE, the organization supported by Health Canada that monitors HIV/AIDS in Canada and is a source for information about the infection (http://www.catie.ca/en/fact-sheets/epidemiology/epidemiology-hiv-canada?utm_source=google&utm_medium=cpc&utm_content=en&utm_campaign=wad+hiv+stats#hivstatistics). A further about 17,980 people living with HIV were not diagnosed. Any lack of diagnosis in an infected person is a problem for others because infection is spread from person to person via bodily fluids.

Transmission rates by various social groupings or categories follow: about 50 per cent of those living with HIV are men who have sex with men (MSM). About 20 per cent are injection drug users. About 30 per cent of the transmission appears to be through heterosexual sex. A small minority of 600 people have HIV due to other means of transmission, most likely blood transfusions, needle-stick injuries at work, and mother-to-child transmission (http://www.catie.ca/en/fact-sheets/epidemiology/epidemiology-hiv-canada?utm_source=google&utm). The incidence of HIV/AIDS among women is increasing in Canada. In 1986, 2 per cent of the HIV-positive population

was female; by 1993, 15 per cent of the cases were female; and by 2001, 25 per cent of newly reported cases were female (Ghosh, 2002). In 2009 women accounted for approximately 25.7 per cent of all positive test results. Visible minorities, including Aboriginal Canadians and blacks, are over-represented among AIDS cases according to the Public Health Agency of Canada (http://www.phac-aspc.gc.ca/aids-sida/publication/survreport/estimat2011-eng.php). In the 2001 census Aboriginal people and blacks accounted for approximately 3.3 per cent and 2.2 per cent of Canada's population, respectively; but they had 15.2 per cent and 6.4 per cent of AIDS cases of known ethnicity. By 2007, these proportions were 15.0 per cent for Aboriginal people and 5.4 per cent for black people. Aboriginal people made up about 8.0 per cent of those living with HIV in Canada in 2008. These figures may under-represent the ethnic proportions because ethnicity is not necessarily reported with HIV/AIDS incidence reports (www.avert.org/canada-aids.htm). Worldwide, in 2010 the number of adults and children living with AIDS was 34 million, of whom those newly infected comprised 2.7 million (http://www.who.int/hiv/pub/progress_report2011/en/).

The presence of HIV/AIDS raises a very important legal/public health issue. Should people be required to divulge their HIV/AIDS status prior to engaging in sexual activity? The Supreme Court of Canada has said yes, if there is a "significant risk" or "realistic risk" of HIV transmission. However, significant/realistic risk is difficult to determine. Further, there are those who argue that this requirement may inhibit the willingness of people to be tested. Others think of this as a matter of individual rights versus public health. What do you think?

SUMMARY

1. Over the past 150 years there have been dramatic changes in life expectancy in Canada and other developed nations. Many explanations have been suggested for this change, such as improvements in public health, immunization,

improved nutrition, improvements in hygiene, and improvements in birth control.

2. Among the major issues affecting health are poverty and inequality, safety, security and stability, the social position of women,

birth control, pregnancy and childbirth supports, comprehensive health care, and immunization.

3. Three problems with health consequences are of particular concern in a worldwide context—HIV/AIDS, mental disorders, and conflicts and natural disasters.

4. The chief causes of disease and death in Canada today are cancer, heart disease, cerebrovascular disease, and accidents. These can be referred to as "diseases of civilization and affluence" and are typical of developed nations. Causes of death are related to lifestyle, environmental,

and work-related factors. "Self-imposed" contributions to mortality include smoking, drug abuse, excessive alcohol consumption, nutritional inadequacies, lack of exercise or recreation, overwork, reckless driving, and sexual carelessness, all of which are also tightly tied to social status and social class.

5. Physical activity and obesity levels are related to health.

6. AIDS is a devastating new disease that is still spreading in populations around the world. At present, the greatest incidence of AIDS is in sub-Saharan Africa.

KEY TERMS

core, periphery, and semi-periphery countries
diarrheal disease
diseases of civilization
food security
infant mortality rates

life expectancy
morbidity
mortality rate
political economy perspective
post-traumatic stress disorder (PTSD)

prevalence
primary health care
secondary health care
tertiary care

QUESTIONS FOR STUDY AND DISCUSSION

1. What is the relevance of medical treatment to the overall extension of life expectancy in Canada today?

2. Why do women tend to live longer than men?

3. What are the major causes of global disparities in health and death rates?

4. Why is the position of women central to social and economic development in a worldwide context?

5. Explain the changing gender ratio with respect to HIV/AIDS.

SUGGESTED READINGS

Boulos, D., and M.A. Zamorski. 2013. "Deployment-related Mental Disorders among Canadian Forces Personnel Deployed in Support of the Mission in Afghanistan 2001–2008." *Canadian Medical Association Journal* 185, 11: 545–52. One study of the after-effects of the global and national issue of war.

Flegel, K. 2013. "Big Alcohol Catches Up with Adolescent Girls." *Canadian Medical Association Journal* 185, 10: 859. A critical analysis of gendered advertising to increase alcohol consumption among young women.

Leece, P.N., S. Hopkins, C. Marshall, A. Orkin, M.A. Gassanov, and R.M. Shabin. 2013. "Development and Implementation of an Opioid Overdose Prevention and Response Program in Toronto, Ontario." *Canadian Review of Public Health* 104, 3: 200–4. Description of POINT (Prevent Overdose in Toronto), Canada's first public health opioid overdose program.

Lewis, Stephen. 2005. *Race against Time.* Toronto: House of Anansi Press. An impassioned plea for the world to care about the AIDS crisis in Africa by the former United Nations AIDS ambassador to Africa and former Ontario NDP leader.

Moore, S., A. Teixeira, and A. Shiell. 2006. "The Health of Nations in a Global Context: Trade, Global Stratification, and Infant Mortality Rates." *Social Science and Medicine* 63: 165–78. An article linking the big economic picture to health.

3

Environmental and Occupational Health and Illness

© Fotokostic | Dreamstime.com

CHAPTER OVERVIEW

- ▶ Water, air, and land are three fundamental parts of the environment upon which we depend for health.

- ▶ Environmental threats to all three are ubiquitous and increasing in their potential for destructiveness.

- ▶ Among the important environmental threats are climate change, chemicals, air pollution, second-hand smoke, medical pollution, land pollution, e-waste, loss of biodiversity, and lack of food safety and security.

- ▶ Occupational health and safety are significant causes of morbidity and mortality in Canada and around the world. Major issues are shift work, time-loss injuries, stress, the health-care industry, and agricultural work.

- ▶ Work can be dangerous in Canada. Significant differences according to occupational group, age, and gender occur in accidents related to the workplace.

- ▶ Traffic, sports, and other accidents and violence pose important challenges to health and life in Canada and especially among younger Canadians.

Introduction

Have you heard of the **twentieth-century disease**? Do you know anyone diagnosed with allergies or asthma? Are occupational hazards greater for people working in the labour force or for those working at home? Is environmental degradation a threat to health? What are the specific relationships between environments, occupations, and health? What is the significance, for health, of the following disasters: Chernobyl, Bhopal, Love Canal, PCBs in the Great Lakes, the tsunami in Japan, the depletion of the Newfoundland fisheries, Walkerton, or the Westray mine disaster? The purpose of this chapter is to provide an overview of some of the major environmental and occupational health hazards, their effects on health, and possible sociological explanations.

The Major Environmental Issues

There are three fundamental components of the environment: air, water, and land. They affect our health both directly (e.g., through the air we breathe and water we drink) and indirectly (e.g., through the food we eat). Environmental hazards in air, water, and land have increased tremendously over the last century. It has been estimated, although widely disputed and difficult to prove or disprove, that from 60 to 90 per cent of all cancers are in some way environmentally or occupationally caused. The link between particular environmental issues and health is difficult to substantiate. This is partly because environmental hazards may affect our health in ways that are unseen in the short term and only evident in the long term in the health of the people as they age or in future generations. Separating specific effects from an infinitely complex environmental "soup" is very complicated. Only by accumulating different types of studies—epidemiological, animal, genetic, and others—all of which address the same environmental issue, will it be possible to demonstrate adequately the effects of specific aspects of the environment on health. Many diseases of major organ systems—lungs, heart, liver, and kidneys—as well as reproductive problems, birth defects, and behavioural disorders, may be associated with environmental factors. There are estimated to be 50,000 to 70,000 chemical substances in commercial use in the farming, manufacturing, and forestry industries. Every year new chemicals are introduced in North America and worldwide, many of which have not been tested for potential ill effects. Many are used in the home in cleaning products or in makeup, toothpaste, and other personal care items. Radioactive waste, with a half-life of 250 centuries, uranium mine tailings, and low-level radiation leakage from routinely functioning nuclear power plants and weapons facilities are taken for granted as an inevitable part of the environment by most Canadians. Other countries, however, are extremely concerned about nuclear accidents, the German moratorium on further nuclear development as a reaction to the Japanese disaster in 2011 being a case in point. Nuclear accidents are taken for granted by some as the cost of "doing business" and providing energy for modern societies. Yet, they and other developments have the ongoing potential for massive death and destruction as the earthquake and tsunami in Japan demonstrated. This prevailing sense of uncertainty, coupled with the certainty that things will go wrong sometime, lies at the heart of the so-called **risk society**.

Environmental risks are now ubiquitous—and growing in potential destructiveness. The whole world is a **global ecosystem**. Changes in one nation-state's environmental policies and procedures, in the amounts of allowable air, water, and land pollution, for example, have the capacity to affect aspects of the ecology of the rest of the world. Even the snows of the remote, virtually uninhabited Antarctic contain residues of PCBs, DDT, and lead, which have emanated directly from industries and combustion in developed and developing nations. Water, air, soil, ice, and snow have been infiltrated with various types and degrees of toxic chemicals.

Like other health threats, environmental hazards are unequally distributed. Poorer people in both the developed and developing worlds are less likely to be able to move away from a toxic waste dump, to drink bottled water (which, ironically, may itself be a significant health hazard because of the leaching of chemicals from the plastic to the water and the quality of the water in the bottle), to buy organically grown foodstuffs (which have their own particular dangers such as the greater possibility of e-coli contamination), and so on. Poorer people are more threatened by various environmental hazards and are more likely to live near contaminated land, water, and air. In addition, decisions about locating noxious facilities are less likely to affect the well-off than the poorer in the population. Table 3.1 shows how greenhouse gas emissions in Canada have increased since 1990, the benchmark year for what clearly became the unmet and unattainable **Kyoto Protocol** targets that Canada committed to in 2002 but that the Conservative government opted out of in December 2011 regardless of the international clamour against such a decision. Figure 3.1 models the impacts of a degraded environment on human health.

The poorer, less-developed countries, are unequally subject to the destructive effects of environmental degradation when they, for instance, allow the destruction of precious rainforests for agribusiness, especially cattle ranching, and to provide timber for furniture, housing, or other purposes for the developed world. Moreover, cash-strapped economies of the developing world, lacking alternatives, are more likely to allow the dumping of wastes within their borders in return for cash payments. Thus, the environment of the underdeveloped South, in spite of a relative lack of industrialization, is more vulnerable in some ways than that of the developed North.

Climate Change

A number of environmental issues threaten the everyday health and safety of all people on the planet. Among the most critical environmental issues is **climate change**, sometimes referred to

TABLE 3.1   National Greenhouse Gas Emissions, Canada, 1990–2013

Year	Total greenhouse gas emissions (megatonnes of carbon dioxide equivalent)
1990	613
1991	605
1992	623
1993	625
1994	646
1995	664
1996	685
1997	701
1998	709
1999	722
2000	745
2001	735
2002	738
2003	756
2004	758
2005	749
2006	740
2007	761
2008	741
2009	699
2010	707
2011	709
2012	715
2013	726

Note: Emission levels for some previous years have been revised in light of improvements to estimation methods and availability of new data

Source: Adapted from Environment Canada, 2015, https://www.ec.gc.ca/indicateurs-indicators/default.asp?lang=en&n=FBF8455E-1.

as global warming. This is chiefly the result of the production of carbon dioxide by the burning of fossil fuels used to provide heat for residential

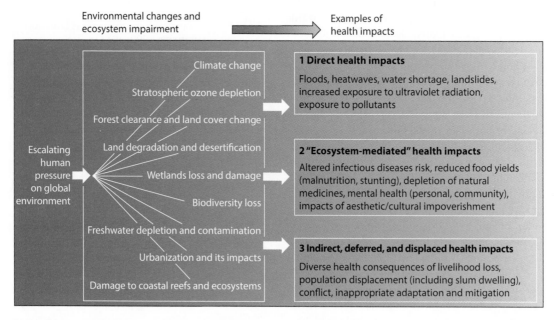

Environmental changes and ecosystem impairment → Examples of health impacts

Escalating human pressure on global environment

Climate change

Stratospheric ozone depletion

Forest clearance and land cover change

Land degradation and desertification

Wetlands loss and damage

Biodiversity loss

Freshwater depletion and contamination

Urbanization and its impacts

Damage to coastal reefs and ecosystems

1 Direct health impacts

Floods, heatwaves, water shortage, landslides, increased exposure to ultraviolet radiation, exposure to pollutants

2 "Ecosystem-mediated" health impacts

Altered infectious diseases risk, reduced food yields (malnutrition, stunting), depletion of natural medicines, mental health (personal, community), impacts of aesthetic/cultural impoverishment

3 Indirect, deferred, and displaced health impacts

Diverse health consequences of livelihood loss, population displacement (including slum dwelling), conflict, inappropriate adaptation and mitigation

FIGURE 3.1   A Model for the Impact of the Environment on Human Health

Source: World Health Organization, "Climate Change and Human Health: Global Environmental Change." WHO (2015). http://www.who.int/globalchange/environment/en/.

purposes and power for industry and automobiles, and of methane produced through livestock production. Some argue that the methane from this animal waste is responsible for as much global warming as all of the other gases added together (www.earthsave.org/globalwarming.htm). Carbon dioxide and other air pollutants, including methane and nitrous oxide, reflect the sun's radiant energy back to earth, causing a warming trend that affects, among other things, the growing of crops and the probability of flooding from the melting of glaciers. As glaciers retreat and shrink and snow cover decreases, the earth absorbs more heat from the sun rather than reflecting this radiant heat back into space (the albedo effect). According to recent estimates the average surface temperature of the globe has grown between 0.2 and 0.6 per cent since the end of the nineteenth century. The earth's mean temperature has increased about 1.53 degrees Fahrenheit from 1880 to 2012 according to the Intergovernmental Panel on Climate Change

(https://www2.ucar.edu/climate/faq/how-much-has-global-temperature-risen-last-100-years), and in northern Canada the temperature increase has been and may continue to be greater than average. Estimates are that the average temperature of the surface of the globe will continue to increase over the next century if changes are not made quickly. This could result in a continuation of severe weather patterns, a rise in sea levels that could displace coastal and island people, droughts and flooding, and other problematic changes.

Global warming has both direct and indirect effects on human health. The indirect effects operate through the many changes in the physical environment in Canada, such as drought on the Prairies, decline of water supplies in southern Canada, soil degradation, erosion, and flooding of coastal regions and extreme weather events. In Canada's North, sea ice is already declining dramatically and is expected to decline further. Wildlife has been affected and wildlife hunting patterns have altered. These changes will continue to result in fundamental changes in quality and availability of primary requisites for human life—food and water for people in the North. Temperature increases may also directly cause certain health problems, especially affecting the cardiovascular, cerebrovascular, and respiratory systems. As well, the northward migration of tropical and subtropical health risks such as malaria and Lyme disease will likely increase. As the concentration of carbon dioxide increases, the number of deaths can be expected to increase. For example, during summer heat waves in Los Angeles, when temperatures averaged about 41°C, the peak mortality was between 172 per cent and 445 per cent higher than would have been expected (at all ages) at lower temperatures. Among people over 85 the peak mortality was considerably higher. It ranged from 257 per cent to 810 per cent more than the expected mortality levels. The 2003 heat wave in Paris is said to have resulted in 14,802 deaths (www.usatoday.com/weather/news/2003-09-25-france-heat_x.htm). More than 700 people were said to have died in the Chicago heat wave in 1995 (Semenza et al., 1996). The European heat wave of 2003 is said to have claimed more than 35,000 lives (www.newscientist.com/article/dn4259-european-heatwave-caused-35000-deaths.html). The 2013 heat wave in the UK is said to have caused between 540 and 760 deaths along with a dramatic increase in the use of hospital emergency rooms (http://www.telegraph.co.uk/topics/weather/10187140/Heatwave-deaths-760-lives-claimed-by-hot-weather-as-high-temperatures-continue.html). In Canada work-related illnesses linked to excessive heat exposure are already and may continue to be a growing problem (Fortune et al., 2013).

Canada's global role in climate change is significant. In 2003 we Canadians emitted an estimated 740 million tonnes of **greenhouse gases (GHGs)** into the atmosphere (*Canada Year Book*, 2006: 117). From 2007 to 2012 Canada's GHG emissions dropped from 761 to 715 megatonnes (Table 3.1). However, in fact, our rate of production of GHGs has surpassed even the rate of population growth. When Canada ratified the Kyoto Accord in December 2002, it made a commitment to reduce emissions to 6 per cent below the levels in 1990 by 2008–12. Canada, however, never had a clear plan for implementation and failed to meet its commitment. By 2008 its greenhouse gas emissions, driven primarily by energy-intensive projects in Alberta's tar sands, were 24 per cent above 1990 emissions and 31 per cent higher than the Kyoto target (Commissioner of the Environment and Sustainable Development, 2011: 47). Canada formally reneged on its commitment at the United Nations Climate Change Conference in Durban, South Africa, in December 2011, where countries of the world, after much dispute, agreed to try to reach a new agreement by 2015! Regardless of any significant international agreements in the foreseeable future, the likelihood is negligible of Canada meeting any firm targets, especially since the hugely polluting tar sands projects and related pipeline developments in Alberta, British Columbia, and elsewhere across the country are supported by the federal government. However, the stalwart resistance of some First Nations communities and their supporters, as well as environmentalists and some provincial governments, may mean long delays for further development if not cancellation.

Chemicals and Health

The World Health Organization has summarized research on the major threats to health caused by a few select and well-researched chemicals that are part of the everyday life of people around the globe (www.euro.who.int). These substances—lead, methylmercury, dioxins, dibenzofurans, polychlorinated biphenyls (PCBs), nitrates, nitrites, and benzene—are especially problematic for the most biologically vulnerable around the world, including children, infants, and fetuses. Lead is the most problematic of these chemicals as it is associated with neurotoxic effects such as neuro-developmental impairment, learning disabilities, attention deficit, poor motor co-ordination, poor language development, and anemia. Children are especially susceptible because of their frequent hand/mouth activity and their tendency to eat chalk (some but not all of which has been found to contain lead), sand, and dirt, and lead and other harmful toxins are found in some antique toys and in toys imported from countries with different standards of production (http://www.cdc.gov/nceh/lead/tips/toys.htm). Pencils, however, are made of non-toxic graphite, not lead; the term "lead pencil" is a misnomer (http://pencils.com/the-unleaded-pencil/). People, including children, are exposed to lead through emissions from automobiles, water from lead-lined pipes, old paint, and so on.

Methylmercury, derived mainly from combustion in incinerators and coal plants, as well as from the decomposition of vegetation when land is flooded by dams built for hydroelectric projects, is deposited into water systems where fish take it up. Eating such fish (particularly freshwater fish such as trout, pike, and bass; and saltwater shark and swordfish) inserts mercury into the human system. Mercury is a neurotoxin associated with seizures, blindness, deafness, cerebral palsy, and developmental delays. It can be passed through breast milk. Dioxins, dibenzofurans, and PCBs result from industrial processes and incineration. Human exposure is mostly from food, including breast milk. Among the health consequences are neuron-developmental and reproductive problems.

Pesticides (including fungicides, herbicides, and insecticides) are used extensively in agriculture and for other, sometimes cosmetic, purposes (e.g., lawn care). Exposure is through food, water, inhalation, and skin absorption. Some pesticides can cause cancer and damage to the nervous, reproductive, and immune systems. Poisoning due to pesticides is a leading cause of poisoning in Canada (www.cape.ca/toxics/pesticides.html). According to the World Wildlife Fund Canada there are approximately 6,000 different pesticides in Canada. Nitrates can be reduced to nitrites in the body, which are associated with changes in the blood and stomach and esophageal cancers, although there do seem to be cardiovascular benefits (http://www.ncbi.nlm.nih.gov/pubmed/21102328; http://www.livestrong.com/article/509298-how-nitrates-nitrites-affect-our-bodies/; http://des.nh.gov/organization/commissioner/pip/factsheets/ard/documents/ard-ehp-16.pdf). Pesticides have also been linked to attention deficit hyperactivity disorder (ADHD) through an epidemiological study of 1,139 children. Pesticides were found in 94 per cent of all of the children in this study, but those with higher levels of pesticides in their blood were more likely to have been diagnosed with ADHD. Children living on and near farms are especially vulnerable to pesticide ingestion but all children (and adults) who eat non-organic food regularly absorb pesticides (Johnson, 2010).

It has been estimated that there are 21,000 premature deaths attributable to air pollution in Canada every year. This figure is nine times that of the number of people who die in traffic accidents each year (Brauer et al., 2013). Benzene is one of the products of gas combustion. Several studies have found a link between living near a busy road and a 50 per cent increase in leukemia in children. One study (Rundell et al., 2006) has raised concern about the vehicular air pollution that occurs when children's playgrounds, school playgrounds, and athletic fields are located near busy traffic roadways. The study found a strong relationship between distance from high-traffic roads and levels of particulate matter in the air. Numerous potential policy options have been put forward. Our continued dependence on the car for transportation ensures that this is an ongoing source of major pollutants. It is essential to the healthy future of the country and Canadians that we support the use of alternative means of transportation such as electric cars, GPS-activated regularized road tolls, bicycle lanes, and forms of public mass transportation that do not rely on gas and oil and are less polluting or not at all polluting.

BOX 3.1   Bhopal and Fukushima

One historical example of the effects of the political economy on the environment and the health of peoples in the developing world brings to light a number of issues. In 1984, in one of the worst industrial disasters ever, an explosion in a Union Carbide plant in Bhopal, India, spewed more than 40 tons of lethal methyl isocyanate gas into the slums immediately surrounding the plant. More than 6,000 people were killed. Many thousands of others were blinded, disabled, and diseased as a result of the "accident."

This tragedy was absolutely avoidable; that it happened is the result of a number of important factors common in industries imported from the developed to the developing world. First, the Union Carbide plant in Bhopal was relatively unprofitable as compared to other divisions of Union Carbide elsewhere in the world. At the time of the accident, the Bhopal plant was for sale. It lacked top-level interest or support within the corporation. A number of divisions within the plant had been closed down. Personnel had been let go and not replaced. Thus, it was operating with only a partial complement of workers and with equipment in poor repair. It was also, however, involved in the manufacture of dangerous chemicals such as methyl isocyanate. In spite of the objections of the municipal authorities, the central and state governments allowed it to continue operating without adequate safety precautions and regulations. There were no adequate plans for dealing with a major accident, and the company personnel did not really understand the potentially lethal effects of the chemical they were producing (methyl isocyanate gas). The external regulation was extremely weak. In the interest of fostering the importation and investment of capital to their countries, governments in developing countries frequently ignore or are unaware of even minimal health and safety standards. The "accident" at Bhopal is just one example of the potential for widespread industrial-based devastation in the developing world.

More recently, Canadians witnessed the effects of the March 2011 earthquake followed by the tsunami in Japan, one of the most successfully developed and populated countries in the world. These ecological catastrophes led to the nuclear meltdowns at Fukushima nuclear plant and the nearly immediate deaths from drowning and other environmental destruction of about 20,000 people. The most serious nuclear crisis since Chernobyl in Russia, the consequences of the Fukushima disaster threatened the ocean waters near Japan and the land upon which millions depend for food and a place to live. Debris continues to wash ashore on the west coast of Canada. The long-term effects of the radiation exposure resulting from the meltdown are still unknown. Although a nuclear plume reached Canada's Pacific coast in 2014, it had become so diffused by the current that it did not pose any threat to the environment or to human health; rather, it helped oceanographers learn more about Pacific Ocean currents (http://www.theweathernetwork.com/news/articles/scientists-use-fukushima-radiation-plume-to-track-ocean-currents/43196/).

Air Pollution and Human Health

Both indoor and outdoor air contribute at least low levels of pollutants, including ozone, sulphur oxides, nitrogen oxides, carbon monoxide, and other particulates that may irritate eyes and inflame the respiratory tract. Long-term exposure may have a negative effect on the immune system and be implicated in chronic respiratory problems such as emphysema and chronic bronchitis, cancer,

CRITICAL THINKING

BOX 3.2   Environmental Illness

An increasing number of North Americans are suffering from what they claim to be the results of low-level exposures to synthetic chemicals and what has been called by a variety of names, including "multiple chemical sensitivity," "chemically induced hyper-susceptibility," "immune system dysregulation," **"environmental illness"** or EI, and "twentieth-century disease" (see, e.g., www.multiplechemicalsensitivity.org). Multiple sensitivity disorder is, according to the highly respected Cleveland Clinic, the only disease in which both the symptoms and the causes are subjectively defined by the putative patient. The sufferer is subject to a range of signs and symptoms, of varying severity, some of which change considerably from day to day. Among the various symptoms often reported are headaches, rashes, depression, shortness of breath, muscle pains, and irritability (http://my.clevelandclinic.org/disorders/multiple_chemical_sensitivity/hic_multiple_chemical_sensitivity_fact_or_fiction.aspx.). Equally troubling is the fact that symptoms often cannot be detected by standard methods. Nor can their intermediary effects on such things as the immune system be measured. They are not caused by known pathogens. Thus, sufferers are sometimes thought to be malingering or mentally ill.

In 1965 a small group of physicians, scientists, and health professionals founded the Society for Clinical Ecology to address the issues being brought forward by sufferers. Today, this organization is combined with occupational medicine and renamed the Occupational and Environmental Medical Association of Canada. It has become a well-established medical association with physicians from across the country (http://oemac.org/?page_id=66#cid=781&did=4) and annual research meetings. The Environmental Research Foundation and the National Academy of Scientists in the United States suggested that between 15 and 20 per cent of the US population may have allergic sensitivity to chemicals in the environment. The Environmental Protection Agency has also stated that health problems result, for some people, at levels of exposure considered below regulatory concern. People with environmental sensitivities have to be careful about where they live, where they go to school and play, what they eat, drink, and smell. Their whole lives may be affected by their sensitivities.

Because of the many biological systems involved in EI or MCS, the multitude of ever-changing symptoms and the time lag there may be between exposure and the development of health problems, this, like fibromyalgia and chronic fatigue syndrome, may take searching from doctor to doctor for someone who believes in the problem and is willing to offer a diagnosis. As a recent headline in 2013 in *Discover* magazine proclaimed, environmental sensitivity, now called toxicant-induced loss of tolerance or TILT, is essentially an allergy to life (http://discovermagazine.com/2013/nov/13-allergic-life). TILT is an example of those illnesses for which one has to "fight to get a diagnosis" (Dumit, 2006).

Varieties of perfumes and fragrant anti-shave products that used to be pervasive in the air are virtually absent and often banned because so many people have developed responses ranging from severe health reactions to nausea and discomfort. Peanut allergies have become so common that many parents assume they cannot send peanut butter to school on their children's sandwiches. Discuss the many sociological causes of such changes.

asthma, cardiovascular disease, chronic obstruct- ive pulmonary disease, and various respiratory infections (Raven et al., 1993: 435). Ground-level ozone has been linked to health impacts ran- ging from minor respiratory problems to cardio- vascular disease, hospitalizations, and premature death. It also has associated economic effects, including lower labour force participation and increased health-care costs (www.environment- andresources.gc.ca.remote.libproxy.wlu.ca/default. asp?lang=En&n=6F66F932-1).

Air pollution is already known to kill men and women in Canadian cities. It also affects gen- eral human health, principally through the res- piratory and the cardiovascular systems (www. hc.gc.ca/ewh-semt/air/out-ext/effe/health_effects- effets_santee.html). Among the illnesses most likely linked to or exacerbated by air pollution are minor lung illnesses, such as the common cold, as well as lung infections such as pneumonia, asthma, chronic obstructive pulmonary disease (COPD), lung cancer, and coronary artery disease (ibid.); and restricted activity, emergency room visits, hospital admissions, and deaths. Burnett, Cakmak, and Brook (1998) examined daily deaths in 11 Canadian cities from 1980 to 1991 and evaluated the association of these deaths to concentrations of ambient gaseous air pollutants. They found that nitrogen dioxide had the largest effect on mortality, a 14.1 per cent increased risk, followed by ozone (1.8 per cent), sulphur dioxide (1.4 per cent), and carbon monoxide (0.9 per cent). The five cit- ies (Montreal, Toronto, Winnipeg, Edmonton, and Vancouver) that were able to reduce sulphur content in gas to 30 ppm were able to show a risk reduction. The Canadian government's response has "privatized" the problem. Environment Canada offers a website where people can calculate their own level of risk (depending on such things as age and gender) as well as specific location in the country on any given day (http://weather.gc.ca/ airquality/pages/onaq-009_e.html). This example is another demonstration of the privatization of risk under neo-liberalism. An extreme case of indoor pollution is the "sick-building syndrome"

in which the presence of air pollution inside tightly sealed buildings can lead to a variety of illnesses. Total environmental sensitivity, in which a person is allergic to myriad components in the modern environment, has forced some people to live in totally sterile environments.

The chief source of air pollutants is industrial manufacturing and the second is transportation. Since the proportion of the Canadian economy dependent on manufacturing is decreasing that portion of the cause of the problems should also decrease. The reduction in transportation depend- ent on fossil fuels should also make a significant difference in air pollution in the long run. The countryside contributes a share of greenhouse gases largely via methane gas. About 9 per cent is from natural processes such as wetlands, animal manure, and the like. The really serious problem with methane is that it traps CO_2 and thus magnifies about 20 times the effect of global warming over 100 years (http://epa.gov/climatechange/ghgemis- sions/gases/ch4.html).

The most seriously harmful indoor pollut- ant may be radon, a tasteless, odourless gas that forms naturally during the radioactive decay of uranium in the earth's crust. Radon seeps through the earth and into basements. It greatly increases the deleterious effects of smoking on the lungs of smokers. Recently published research has linked high radon levels in the home to lung cancer. One geographic study positively documented the asso- ciation between levels of radon across the coun- try of Canada and levels of lung cancer (Hystad et al., 2014). Another indoor pollutant with serious health costs is asbestos. Often used as insulation because it does not conduct heat or electricity, asbestos can break down into almost invisible fibres that can be inhaled. When inhaled, asbestos irritates the lungs and is known to be related to lung cancer and mesothelioma, a rare and almost always fatal cancer. Many millions of workers in Canada and around the world have been exposed to asbestos in mining, textile industries, and con- struction industries (Firth et al., 1997). Canada has a very poor record in this regard (http://www.cbc.

ca/news/business/asbestos-mining-stops-for-first-time-in-130-years-1.1103672) and continued to mine asbestos until 2011, long after information about its destructive effects was known (http://www.canadianasbestosexports.ca/).

In the last several decades various levels of government have acknowledged the dangers of asbestos that have been known since the 1920s and have introduced laws to remove asbestos insulation from public buildings such as schools and offices and eliminate its use in new buildings.

Unfortunately, some research has shown that removing asbestos can release fibres that would otherwise remain stable; thus, it is sometimes safer to seal asbestos in place. The Canadian government, however, continues to reject the idea of a ban on asbestos such as has been supported by developed countries around the world, including Japan, Sweden, Britain, and Australia (Galloway, 2014). This is surprising because more than 1,200 successful claims for fatality benefits were made in Canada by workers between 2007 and 2012.

CRITICAL THINKING

BOX 3.3   Last Gasp

Asthma is often considered an elusive disease. Although it tends to run in families, it also develops in those who have no history of asthma among their kin. This disease may strike at any age, but children, with their small breathing tubes, are particularly vulnerable. Asthma is also more likely to occur among people in certain occupational groups such as hairdressers (Albin et al., 2002). More than 2 million or approximately 8 per cent of Canadians have been diagnosed with asthma according to Statistics Canada in 2012 (www.asthma.ca/corp/newsroom/pdf/asthmastats.pdf).

Millions of Canadians continue suffer from asthma, the sometimes lethal inflammation of the airways to the lungs. In asthma sufferers, the bronchial tubes or airways are extremely sensitive to a variety of triggers unique to each patient. These triggers include those in modern office buildings, such as the more than 900 chemical and biological agents in the air, including chromium dust, acrylates, and epoxy resins. In factories and shops, there are more unseen dangers like fluorocarbon propellants breathed in by beauticians, sulphur dioxide fumes inhaled by brewery workers, and chlorine gas encountered by petrochemical workers.

There are other triggers in homes. Central heating, mattresses and upholstering, and wall-to-wall carpeting are breeding grounds for dust mites, microscopic animals that produce a potent allergen in their dung. Common household products such as vapours from cleaning solvents and paint thinners and the fumes from such personal products as spray deodorants and scented cosmetics can also set off an asthmatic attack. Some individuals display fewer and milder symptoms while others face life-threatening attacks. While the most popular instant treatment, the puffer, may at times save lives, it also is associated with iatrogenic diseases. Frequent, long-time use may even prove dangerous to the health of the user. However, they are sometimes lifesavers. One Ontario mother is campaigning to allow children to carry puffers to school after her own son died because he needed it when it was locked in the principal's office (http://www.cbc.ca/news/canada/ottawa/ontario-mom-urges-schools-to-let-asthmatic-kids-carry-puffers-1.2455861). What are the issues on both sides of the debate and what position do you take on the use of puffers in schools?

Second-hand smoke is both an environmental and an occupational health issue. It is an environmental issue because smoking may affect others in homes, on the streets, in public buildings, on public transportation, and in restaurants and stores. It is a workplace issue because workers may be involuntarily exposed to the second-hand smoke of their colleagues. As discussed in the previous chapter, however, most provinces in Canada have banned indoor smoking in all public buildings (www.hc-sc.gc.ca/hl-vs/tobac-tabac/res/news-nouvelles/fs-if/ban-interdiction-public_e.html). Further, most Canadian provinces have banned smoking in cars when children are present and 91 per cent of households have decided to voluntarily ban smoking within their homes (http://www.cbc.ca/news/health/bans-on-smoking-in-cars-with-kids-deemed-a-success-1.1330628). Second-hand smoke contains over 100 chemical agents, including carcinogens and toxins (www.ocat.org/health-effects/index.html#4). Substantial documentation now shows that second-hand smoke is associated with higher risks of various other diseases. There are two sources of second-hand smoke: sidestream smoke (given off by the burning tip of a cigarette, pipe, or cigar) and exhaled smoke (puffed out by the smoker). Among the toxic chemicals released into the air in these ways are nicotine, tar, carbon monoxide, formaldehyde, hydrogen cyanide, ammonia, and nitrogen oxide. The health effects include lung cancer, nasal sinus cancer, bronchitis, emphysema, asthma, hay fever, cystic fibrosis, headaches, coughs, throat irritation, heart and circulatory diseases, pregnancy complications, sudden infant death syndrome (SIDS), and low-birth-weight babies.

Automobiles and other motor vehicles continue to be a major source of air pollution (Goodall, 1992), although emissions per vehicle have been reduced since the Clean Air Act of 1971. However, the number of vehicles has grown as the population has increased (www.statcan.gc.ca/pub/16-002-x/2007001/article/10177-eng.htm) and the total number of kilometres driven per car has increased. There were 607 cars per 1,000 people in Canada in 2009, according to World Bank estimates (http://data.worldbank.org/indicator/IS.VEH.NVEH.P3) as compared to 797 per 1,000 people in the US. Canada ranks fifteenth in a worldwide context with respect to the number of cars per capita (http://www.theglobeandmail.com/globe-drive/news/industry-news/canadians-vs-americans-top-10-differences-in-auto-ownership/article18800449/). About 78 per cent of people of driving age own vehicles in Canada. Pickup trucks and sports utility vehicles (SUVs) are relatively popular and make up 30.6 per cent and 25.7 per cent of the market, respectively. In overall terms there has been a shift in the types of vehicles used for personal transportation from automobiles to mini-vans, SUVs, and light-duty gasoline-powered trucks. Not only do these vehicles consume more petroleum products but they also release more emissions. Four common air contaminants from automobiles are carbon monoxide, nitrogen oxides, hydrocarbon, and ground-level ozone. In high concentrations, these substances can affect pulmonary function, suppress immune responses, and result in toxic and carcinogenic effects and even, in high enough concentrations, death. They also contribute to acid rain, depletion of the ozone layer, and global warming or climate change.

Another significant source of pollution comes from household cleaners and **pharmaceuticals and personal care products** (PPCPs) such as cosmetics, shampoos, and prescribed and over-the-counter medicines. Any of these may contain chemicals that are bad for your health. Although the amounts may be very small or "trace," the fact that we may rub them into our skin and use them daily has potential ill health effects to the user. Many people are intolerant of or allergic to some scents and chemicals, even when used by others, because they circulate in the air, much like second-hand smoke (Weeks, 2010). Researchers have been finding chemicals in the water supply from cosmetics, toiletries, food additives, veterinary drugs, and pharmaceuticals for humans (Batt, 2004, 2010). PPCPs are growing in use and building up in the water when we flush them down the toilet or drains. Eventually, those chemicals reappear in the consumable water supply. Farm animals are another significant source of pharmaceuticals, particularly of hormones and antibiotics, which are excreted onto the land and then absorbed by humans who eat animal products and then, in turn, excrete a portion of the chemicals. Even cemeteries are a major source of PPCPs as they are emitted after death from individuals who ingested highly toxic chemicals as part of their health care. Routinely, as we use PPCPs our bodies absorb only a portion and the rest is expelled. PPCPs are building up in the air, water, and earth and have the potential to increase pollution.

Water Pollution and Human Health

The World Health Organization reports that water and sanitation are the major focuses of public health worldwide. Unclean water is linked to many different diseases, including but not limited to diarrhea, malaria, schistosomiasis, Japanese encephalitis, and hepatitis A (www.who. int/mediacentre/factsheets/fs256/en/print.html), and cholera and typhoid (http://www.who.int/ water_sanitation_health/dwq/S01.pdf). One international investigation estimated that problems with water, sanitation, and hygiene were responsible for 4 per cent of all deaths globally and 5.7 per cent of the total disease burden (Pruss et al., 2002). The Great Lakes comprise one-fifth of the world's fresh surface water. Canada also has 7 per cent of the world's renewable water flow (*Canada Year Book*, 2006). *Most* of this water—about 94 per cent—is used by industry and agriculture. Six per cent is used by households, schools, and hospitals (*Canada Year Book*, 2006). The destruction of the Great Lakes would be a disaster because the Great Lakes are a source of drinking water for more than 40 million people on both sides of the Canada–US border. Still, however, the cleanliness of the Great Lakes is threatened by farming and industries on both sides of the borders. The Canadian and US governments have dedicated substantial monies to rehabilitate fish stocks and wildlife, improve the sediment and the overall quality of the water in the

lakes, and to improve wastewater treatment plants (http://www.ec.gc.ca/doc/eau-water/grandslacs-greatlakes_e.htm).

The overuse of water is another environmental threat, and Canada is among the top water consumers in a global comparison. Free trade agreements and pressure from the US to divert some of Canada's water to the south potentially comprise a great hazard to the Canadian water supply and health. Domestically and industrially, Canada is a major consumer of water. Of 16 Western European and North American countries, plus Japan and Australia, only the US consumes more water per capita than Canada, and "Canada's water withdrawals are nearly double that of the 16-country average" (www.conferenceboard.ca/hcp/details/environment/water-consumption.aspx).

While oil spills, pollutants released into water from pulp mills, chemical companies, and other industries, and hydroelectric dams have caused serious water pollution, killed fish, and irrevocably damaged health in particular areas, human exploitation of freshwater and ocean resources has been even more devastating. Overfishing and bottom dredging by foreign and Canadian trawlers exhausted the cod stocks off Newfoundland. In response, the Canadian government declared a moratorium on the cod fishery in 1992. This chain of events has been a disaster for Newfoundland and Labrador, as cod had been the basis for the economy for hundreds of years. The World Wildlife Foundation has posted a notice that the cod fishery will soon be restored with new guidelines to govern fishing policies. As these guidelines will in all likelihood involve conditions for international fishers to meet, overseeing the policies may very well be "tricky" (http://www.wwf.ca/newsroom/?14901/Newfoundland-cod-fishery-announces-milestone-sustainability-assessment). According to the CBC and the Department of Fisheries and Oceans Canada, cod fishing was restored to the south coast in March 2014 (http://www.wwf.ca/newsroom/?14901/Newfoundland-cod-fishery-announces-milestone-sustainability-assessment). On the west coast of Canada, beginning early in the twentieth century, hydroelectric dams cut off salmon from their spawning grounds in some rivers. Overfishing, Canada–US disputes regarding quotas, and the continued pollution of salmon rivers have significantly reduced the wild salmon fishery. At the same time, salmon farms pollute coastal estuaries and foster viral diseases (alexandramorton.typepad.com/alexandra_morton/2011/10/lethal-atlantic-salmon-virus-now-in-bc-sockeye.html). The demand for fish pellets as feed in aqua farming places food chains and fisheries in other parts of the world under severe stress. Thus, on both sides of Canada the health of the oceans is threatened.

Land Pollution and Human Health

One of the most contested of contemporary issues is what to do with solid waste—domestic, manufacturing, hospital, radioactive, e-waste, or waste from any other source. Literature on hazardous waste disposal in Canada and the United States points to a problem with fewer and fewer solutions as land masses on both sides of the border and, indeed, around the world become populated. Debates about such waste disposal have spawned a popular acronym, NIMBY (not in my backyard). Without doubt, this environmental problem concerns the effect on humankind of the thousands of by-products and wastes of our industrial society, ranging from slightly annoying products to deadly toxins and chemicals. Canada is both an importer and exporter of hazardous wastes for disposal. Some of the hazardous materials Canada accepts are ammonia, asbestos, chlorine, fuel oils, hydrogen peroxide, lead, mercury, nickel, PCBs, uranium, and zinc. According to the Canadian Institute for Environmental Law and Policy, 6 million tonnes of hazardous waste and hazardous recyclable materials are produced in Canada annually (http://www.cielap.org/pdf/hwfactsheet.pdf). About 500,000 tonnes of hazardous waste were imported into Canada in 2005 (www.ec.gc.ca/wmd-dgd/defaut.asp?lang-En&n-f345CA54-1).

Some progress has been made in reducing the import, export, and manufacturing of hazardous wastes in Canada (http://ec.gc.ca/gdd-mw/default.asp?lang=En&n=1BA99A34-1#Figure1). As the deleterious effects of hazardous waste disposal become more widely known, dumping wastes becomes a complicated legal and political issue. Chapter 14 discusses drug dumping in the less-developed world. Hazardous waste dumping in countries of the global South is a similar problem. When some industries in the richer developed world have needed to get rid of hazardous wastes they have shipped them to countries in the developing world. Some nations around the world have tentatively committed to some controls on international shipments of wastes, such as those from hospitals and pharmaceutical companies, PCBs, mercury, lead, and other chemicals that are known to be harmful. Such commitments are almost impossible to monitor effectively.

E-Waste

E-waste refers to all waste that comes from or is caused by electronics. It contains materials such as lead, mercury, arsenic, and chromium—all known or suspected agents of harm to wildlife and human health. E-waste is a major concern because of our heavy reliance on electronics of various types. This includes electronic technologies such as cell phones and computers and the many new "devices" that regularly enter the market place because such items are readily discarded as they quickly become obsolete. E-waste is growing at three times the rate of other hazardous waste in Canada (http://www.therecord.com/news-story/4591752-local-e-waste-buyers-capitalizing-on-disposable-society/). It now comprises 70 per cent of the hazardous waste in the US (https://www.dosomething.org/facts/11-facts-about-e-waste). According to Environment Canada, 140,000 tonnes of e-waste are dumped annually in landfills—an amount that continues to increase. In 2000, Ontario was home to four companies in the business of e-waste recycling; by 2004, there were 14 companies (*Canada Year Book*, 2006). This number continues to grow as entrepreneurs develop markets for the various valuable components of computers, televisions, and other electronic devices. Still the problem continues to grow even as small companies are trying to manage it. Several provinces have introduced e-waste diversion programs for some products that transfer the cost of removal from the municipalities to the companies that produce the products (www.blakes.com/english/view.asp?ID=2997). This has usually involved charging the consumer the fee for disposal of the device upfront. In this way Ontario alone received $83.6 million in 2012 (http://www.therecord.com/news-story/4591752-local-e-waste-buyers-capitalizing-on-disposable-society/). Ninety per cent of computer parts can be recycled but only about 40 per cent of the population recycles. About half of those who do not recycle say it is because they do not know where to do so (http://

www.therecord.com/news-story/4591752-local-e-waste-buyers-capitalizing-on-disposable-society/). Fifty-two per cent of Canadians with unwanted computers sent them to a drop-off centre for recycling. About one-quarter disposed of their cell phones safely and about 44 per cent just kept them in their houses, according to Statistics Canada (http://www.statcan.gc.ca/pub/11-526-x/2013001/aftertoc-aprestdm1-eng.htm). Clearly, we have far to go in ensuring that all e-waste makes it to recycling centres.

Biodiversity

All of these threats to the air, water, and land have another profound implication for the future of life on the planet—the decline in biodiversity. For

CANADA IN A GLOBAL CONTEXT

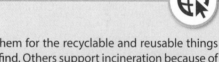

BOX 3.4   Dumps around the World

All around the world there are places where people live on the proceeds of the materials left by those richer than they are. They live on and off dumps. See the following website for garbage dumps/sources of livelihood around the world (https://andymulligantrash.wordpress.com/around-the-world-in-80-dumps/). Delhi's dumps are just one example and have been called "public health time bombs" (Glauser, 2013a). The Okhla landfill is one of three major dumps in New Delhi. It receives about 8,000 tons of waste on a daily basis. New Delhi's solution is to incinerate the waste to produce energy, but dumpsite workers ("rag pickers") are unhappy about this possibility. The introduction of the first incinerator for garbage in New Delhi has resulted in the elimination of hundreds of jobs. As sickening as the dumpsite work is (with bacteria and infections, biological hazards, and other unwanted and unsafe and polluting materials), it has provided a squalid but basic income for thousands of children and families. Some people argue that the government, instead of throwing these people out of work, should equip them with safety gear and

pay them for the recyclable and reusable things they find. Others support incineration because of the multitude of dangerous contaminants faced by the "rag pickers." What side would you take on this issue in a debate? Why?

The working conditions for waste pickers, such as these men, women, and children from India, are known to cause serious health issues. Despite this, and despite the positive effect that their work has for society, these workers are not provided anything to improve their working conditions by their governments or the international community.

Source: Daniel Berehulak/ Thinkstock.com.

instance, although the rain forests comprise only 7 per cent of the Earth's surface, they are home to almost half of the living species on the planet. While it is impossible to know exactly how many species exist at present, some scientific estimates suggest that the total number of species is in the range of 30 million. For example, researchers have identified more than 1,000 species of ant (Wilson, 1991). The impact of the decline in biodiversity on the health of human populations is not entirely known. However, the enormous interdependence in this complex ecosystem implies that the extinction of some species may indirectly lead to the extinction of others and ultimately may lead to the destruction of species that serve to protect human life. Many of you are

aware of the serious concerns raised by collapse of some honey bee colonies (colony collapse disorder). This is not just a problem of the decline of available honey but has the possibility of widespread, catastrophic ramifications on other natural phenomena, such as the pollination of a wide variety of plants—including many nut trees, berries, vegetables, and fruits—according to the US Department of Agriculture (http://www.ars. usda.gov/News/docs.htm?docid=15572).

Food Safety

In August of 2014 a California slaughterhouse was indicted for selling beef that was infected with cancer. The owners face up to 20 years in

---

HIGHLIGHTED ISSUES

BOX 3.5   Why Is It Difficult to Demonstrate Effects of the Environment on Health?

For a number of reasons it is difficult to assess the effects of elements of the environment on health. Among these are the following:

- The environment is complex: differentiating among different parts of the environment and their independent effects is practically impossible.
- Since new chemicals are released into the environment almost daily, noting and then measuring the particular amount of the chemical in the changing environment is exceedingly difficult.
- The ratio of the potential contaminant to the environment is usually so extremely small that instruments capable of measuring such minuscule amounts are not readily available.
- Double-blind studies of the effects of potentially noxious substances using human subjects are unethical, although they do occur in some populations such as prisons and mental hospitals. The exception is patients deemed terminal who may wish to participate in limited trials in an experiment.

- The amount of a contaminant necessary to account for time lag (experiments with non-human animals cannot be longitudinal to match the human life span) and for the low weight of the typical laboratory mammal (rat) is relatively enormous. Drawing conclusions applicable to humans from such discrepancies is hazardous.
- Synergistic relationships are inevitable in the environment, yet because all of the elements in the synergistic relationship are not known, the effects of the environment cannot be duplicated in the laboratory.
- There is a variable latency period between exposure and the onset of disease. This variability in latency and its length make identifying causal connections between toxic substance and illness difficult.
- Few physicians are trained in environmental and occupational health.
- A cause-effect demonstration is required as proof of the deleterious effect of a substance on humans.

continued

Consequently, the causes of only a small number of environmentally based illnesses have yet been proven and only a fraction of occupationally caused illnesses has arguably been compensated. The ideological/financial issues include the following:

- Frequently, sponsors of research of the potentially environmentally caused illnesses are pharmaceutical and medical device companies with a vested interest in research that involves their products and proves them and their manufacture safe.
- When research is funded by interest groups, objective research is difficult, at best.

- Medical journals, the major legitimate purveyors of new scientific findings, often are funded by major pharmaceutical and other "interested" companies, compromising their objectivity.
- Certain types of basic research have dominated medical research and, because of the peer-review system (an "old boys' network," some say), basic research using small samples and experimental designs (the so-called gold standard of medical research) has a greater likelihood of garnering support than other types of research.

---

jail and hundreds of thousands of dollars in fines from trying to avoid detection, misbranding the meat, and placing it in the market (http://www.medicaldaily.com/california-slaughterhouse-indicted-over-known-sale-cancerous-beef-avoid-high-costs-298894). Alberta, in 2012, witnessed the largest meat recall in Canadian history (http://www.huffingtonpost.ca/2013/09/08/xl-foods-beef-recall_n_3889947.html). In September 2006, Canadians were warned not to eat spinach packaged in the US after an outbreak of E. coli was linked to raw spinach by the US Food and Drug Administration. In October 2006 two Toronto residents became paralyzed after drinking organic carrot juice infected with botulism. Three brands of organic carrot juice produced in the US were taken from the market (CBC News, 2006). Food safety has emerged as an important environmental and public health issue in the last three decades or so. Frequent outbreaks of food-borne diseases (FBD) have caught the attention of the media and, thus, the public, including but not limited to bovine spongiform encephalitis (BSE). BSE, commonly called "mad cow disease," generated significant focus on food safety in Canada in 2003. Since then, according to the Canadian Food Inspection Agency, at least 11 cases have been reported in

Canada (www.inspection.gc.ca). This disease was first isolated in 1986 in the UK, where it was found to be linked to a disease of the brain called variant Creutzfeldt-Jakob disease for those who ingested contaminated meat. The use of antibiotics in animal husbandry has also been associated with the growing problem of antibiotic resistance in humans, although estimates are difficult to make because of a lack of consistent reporting of intestinal and other likely symptoms. According to the Public Health Agency of Canada, about one in eight Canadians suffers from a food-borne illness every year (http://www.phac-aspc.gc.ca/efwd-emoha/efbi-emoa-eng.php). This estimate means that about 4 million people suffer each year from bacteria, viruses, and parasites or other pathogens in their food eaten and prepared at home or in restaurants. Additionally, contamination of food occurs through air, water, and soil pollution by such toxins as toxic metals, PCBs, and dioxins. In addition, some intermittent poisoning occurs via pesticides (ibid.). Poorly prepared, cleaned, and cooked food is also a health hazard. Clearly, work needs to be done in cleaning the food supply and developing higher levels of kitchen hygiene and cooking and storing food so that it is safe to consume. About one in six people in the United States is said to suffer (about 48 million people annually as of 2011) and 3,000 are estimated to die every year from food-based diseases (http://www.cdc.gov/foodborneburden/2011-foodborne-estimates.html). Extrapolating from these figures, between 200 and 300 Canadians may die annually from food-borne illnesses, although this estimate may very well be low as there is no requirement for reporting to Health Canada or any other regulatory body.

One of the most tragic of recent food-related outbreaks in Canada was related to the bacteria listeria. In 2008 at least 57 people became sick and 23 died as a result of listeriosis in some packaged meats (www.phac-aspc.gc.ca/alert-alerte/listeria/listeria_20100413-eng.php). A follow-up investigation suggested several areas for improvement that would help to mitigate or prevent another generalized outbreak. The suggestions (which can be found at www.inspection.gc.ca/english/agen/eval/listeria1/listeria1de.shtml#a8-3) include hiring and training more inspectors and immediate communication to various levels of government and the public at the first sign of an outbreak. Such proactive policies are, of course, limited by the prevailing ideologies supporting neo-liberalism, with its greater reliance on arm's length monitoring of regulation compliance, that is, of industry monitoring itself.

Many people have turned to organic foods in the past few decades as a way to avoid the pesticides and fertilizer and other contaminants that may be found in food grown in the standard way. This trend continues to grow (http://www.ota.com/otacanada/stats.html0). In 2001 the retail sales of organic foods in the US, Canada, Japan, Europe, and Oceania were said to be about $19 billion. Fruits and vegetables comprise the majority of this market, beverages are second, and breads and grains third. The majority of Canadians today have tried organic foods. Forty per cent of Canadians (12 million people) report that they purchase organic foods fairly often (ibid., 4). In 2012 the market share of organics in Canada alone comprised $3.5 billion, reflecting a growth rate in the organic sector that has outstripped that of the market for regular foods (http://www.ota.com/otacanada/stats.html). The demand is apparently greater than the production capacities and this keeps the costs relatively high and, thus, the market, relatively speaking, limited to those who can afford to purchase organic. The reasons people buy organic food include a belief that it is healthier, that it lacks pesticides, that it is not genetically modified, and to prevent allergic reactions. However, and perhaps ironically, organic foods are not necessarily safer than non-organic foods (www.theglobeandmail.com/life/article664467.ece). The Canadian government certainly claims that pesticide residues on food are not at harmful levels (http://www.hc-sc.gc.ca/cps-spc/pubs/pest/_fact-fiche/pesticide-food-alim/index-eng.php). Another important issue affecting the quality of food both in the short term and in the long run is genetic modification. There are those who argue that it enables, for instance, the reduction in pesticide use and is therefore of great promise and future value. However, others are seriously opposed to genetically modified foods. The Canadian government (as well as governments around the world) do make some attempts to regulate GMOs (genetically modified organisms). Genetically modified crops have already been widely introduced in Canada and the US (but not in Europe) despite these attempts—as well as the lack of evidence as to their safety. The European Union may have the strictest limits to GMOs in the world (http://www.gmo-free-regions.org/gmo-free-regions.html). We still do not know whether GMOs constitute a serious problem for the quality of foodstuffs in the long run and the precautionary principle may, again, be advisable.

Occupational Health and Safety

Some Canadians face a relatively high degree of danger when they go to work. Statistics on workplace accidents and work-related injuries likely underestimate the number of injuries that occur because many injured people do not receive or request compensation. Some people may be unaware of their labour rights or be unwilling to pursue claims for any of a variety of reasons such as the necessity of making a living even while working through severe pain and disability. Some workers may fear job loss if they report injury or disability or may lack belief in the fairness of the Workplace Safety and Insurance Board (WSIB). Others may be transferred to lighter jobs during the time of recuperation so that reporting compensation is unnecessary. In 2009 there were 198,132 claims allowed with the WSIB in Ontario alone (www.wsib.on.ca/wsib/wsibobj.nsf/LookupFiles/ DownloadableFile2005StatisticalSupplement/$F ile/2278A_StatSup.pdf) (see Table 3.2). The three largest industrial sectors from which these claims emanate are the service industry, manufacturing, and chemical processing. In 2012 there were 977 reported workplace-related fatalities in Canada, which was just above the average of 972 fatalities for the years 2000–12 (Schwartz, 2014).

The highest incidence of death was found in manufacturing, construction, transportation, and mining. Between 2010 and 2012 there were more than 156,000 time-loss injuries among men and 91,000 among women, according to the Association of Workers Compensation Boards of Canada statistics (http://awcbc.org/?page_id=14#injuries). Some have argued that the very counting of lives lost and injuries suffered reflects a commodification of human beings, their health, and their labour (this topic is discussed at greater length in the next chapter). Debates continue about the extent to which the subjective experiences of suffering reported can be considered as legitimate for claiming compensation. This place is another where we observe the valorization of conventional or allopathic medicine because of its power and capacity to support or reject the claim made by an individual as legitimate or not. Clearly, too, the interests of those who must pay compensation are pitted against the needs of the workers.

In addition to workplace accidents, workers face a number of hazards on the job. These can be classified as physical (e.g., noise, heat or cold, postural, radiation), chemical (e.g., solvents, heavy metals, pesticides, pharmaceuticals), biological (e.g., HIV, hepatitis B and C), and psychological (e.g., stress and violence). Workplace hazards are (like accidents and death on the job) likely to continue to increase under globalization and free trade. To attract multinational companies, poor countries will compete with one another by lowering labour costs, banning workers' unionization, reducing environmental standards, and creating free-trade industrial zones such as the maquiladoras along the US border in Mexico. Lower labour costs and the lack of unionization result in, among other things, fewer health and safety precautions for workers as well as an absence of workers' compensation for job-related injuries. We probably all remember with horror learning about the fire in the clothing manufacturing factory in Bangladesh, particularly as a portion of the clothes were being constructed at very low cost to be sold through the popular Canadian label "Joe Fresh." Several hundred people were killed and others burned and maimed as a result. In a sense, we all support similarly unsafe working conditions around the world when we shop for certain cheaper brands.

Some have estimated that up to 90 per cent of cancers are related, in part, to the working environment (Epstein, 1998; Firth et al., 1997). However, documenting a link between work and a disease such as cancer that takes a long time to develop is very difficult and is challenging for the many other reasons discussed earlier in the chapter. According to the Workplace Safety and Insurance Board (WSIB), none of the diseases that have been determined to be occupationally linked are "neoplasms, tumours and cancer." This compares to 48.1 per cent of the workplace claims for injuries said to result in sprains and strains (www.wsib.on.ca/ wsib/wsibobj.nsf/LookupFiles/DownloadableFile 2005StatisticalSupplement/$File/2278A_StatSup. pdf). However, more specific research has found that exposure to the following substances increases the risk of cancer by the amount indicated in brackets: arsenic (2 to 8 times for lung cancer); benzene (2 to 3 times for leukemia); coal, tar, pitch, and coke-oven emissions (2 to 6 times for cancer

TABLE 3.2   Motor Vehicle Accidents Causing Death, by Sex and Age Group

	2007	2008	2009	2010	2011
Rate per 100,000 population (males)	12.7	11.3	10.3	10.1	9.1
Rate per 100,000 population (females)	4.9	4.6	4.1	4.3	3.5

	Number of Accidents									
	Males	Females	Males	Females	Males	Females	Males	Females	Males	Females
All ages	2075	807	1863	765	1717	689	1718	732	1553	605
Age at time of death										
< 1 year (8)	4	2	1	1	3	0	1	3	1	2
1–4 years (9)	13	10	8	10	9	9	15	11	9	6
5–9 years	17	22	17	14	13	6	11	10	10	8
10–14 years	25	26	21	10	18	9	18	16	21	9
15–19 years	222	86	190	92	179	79	183	85	151	61
20–4 years	305	90	254	83	220	69	211	78	208	60
25–9 years	184	47	174	51	148	50	158	36	136	45
30–4 years	147	60	133	44	132	41	115	31	109	32
35–9 years	149	32	132	37	101	32	112	43	92	32
40–4 years	161	47	115	42	115	44	122	43	96	27
45–9 years	171	56	163	54	152	47	119	53	121	25
50–4 years	152	53	134	58	134	51	132	67	110	45
55–9 years	114	61	127	46	115	45	115	27	98	38
60–4 years	90	34	92	44	88	30	94	43	79	29
65–9 years	74	40	70	36	46	28	69	33	68	38
70–4 years	65	39	62	41	58	35	78	35	66	39
75–9 years	63	32	57	36	76	36	56	46	62	34
80–4 years	75	37	59	25	68	36	57	33	57	38
85–9 years	35	24	39	32	30	32	37	25	40	28
90+ years	9	9	15	9	12	10	15	14	19	9

Source: Statistics Canada, CANSIM, table 102-0551.

of the lung, larynx, skin, and scrotum); vinyl chloride (200, 4, and 1.9, respectively for cancer of the lining of the heart, brain, and lung); chromium (3 to 40 for cancers of the sinus, lung, and larynx) (Tataryn, 1979: 157–8). High exposure to constant levels of toxic substances and consequent risks are more prevalent among the working classes and those with lower incomes (ibid., 158). One tragic instance involved the Sahtu Dene community of Deline, Northwest Territories, which became known as the "Village of Widows" because, in the 1950s, men of the community were hired to offload and onload heavy bags of uranium ore during its transport from a mine on Great Bear Lake to the Mackenzie River, and many of these men in the ensuing years died of radiation-induced cancers (Bone, 2016: ch. 6). Firth et al. (1997) document the extensive occupationally induced health problems from asbestos in Thetford Mines, Quebec, and at Bendix Automotive in Windsor, Ontario; radiation exposure in Elliot Lake, Ontario; and arsenic exposure in drinking water. About 125 million people around the globe are exposed to asbestos at work and approximately 107,000 people will die each year as a result of this exposure (http://www.asbestos.com/asbestos/regulatory-organizations.php). Until recently, Canada had continued to export asbestos to the less-developed world amid growing resistance around the world (http://www.thestar.com/opinion/commentary/2013/05/05/russia_zimbabwe_pick_up_the_asbestos_baton_from_canada.html).

Women, Work, and Stress

Occupational health and safety are major concerns for all working women, for those who work in the paid labour force and those who do not. Less publicized than the hazards associated with men's blue-collar work are the places where most Canadian women work, including service sector, clerical, and administrative jobs in places such as banks, retail stores, offices, child care institutions, schools and clinics or hospitals. Each of these occupations has its own peculiar health risks. Clerical workers may be subject to poor lighting and ventilation, excessive noise, and toxic substances such as emissions from computer terminals. They spend long hours sitting on uncomfortable furniture, which may lead to back and neck pain; working at keyboards that can cause repetitive strain injuries, such as carpal tunnel syndrome; and working at relatively tedious jobs, which may lead to stress, boredom, anxiety, and other related psychological harms. Retail and service workers may be vulnerable to health hazards from bending, lifting, and carrying; varicose veins and foot, neck, and back problems are often experienced. Dealing with varieties of customers offers its own special challenges. Hochschild (1983, 2012) calls such labour "emotion work" and suggests that health-threatening consequences attend selling or "commodification of feeling." Hairdressers, who usually stand all day, suffer neck, back, foot, and leg problems along with the dangers of exposure to toxic chemicals such as hair permanents, dyes, and aerosol sprays. Respiratory difficulties and skin reactions may occur. Teachers and child-care workers are continually exposed to a variety of contagious and infectious diseases. Health-care workers may be exposed to radiation, toxic chemicals, and contagious diseases, and may have to cope as well with excessive lifting, bending, and standing as well as the aggression of patients. Women who work at home may be subject to dangers from all sorts of household cleaning substances, including abrasives, astringents, soaps, and detergents (ibid., 85–8), as well as to the possibility of injury due to falls and the like. Loneliness and isolation can lead to mental health issues, including depression and anxiety.

Occupational stress has been recognized as a significant problem associated with a number of health problems, even by the World Health Organization (http://www.who.int/occupational_health/topics/stressatwp/en/). According to the World Health Organization workplace stress can arise from the content of work, workload and pace, working hours, and lack of control over the working environment. It also results from the work context including such things as the value placed on the work in the society at large, the position in the hierarchy of workplace, pay and other compensation such as holidays and benefits, work–life balance, organizational culture, and bullying by colleagues, among other things. Persistent stress can cause all manner of physical and mental health symptoms such as depression, increased blood pressure, increased blood serum cholesterol, increased risk of coronary disease, migraine headaches, and increased drug and alcohol consumption (Geran, 1992: 14) as well as sleep deprivation, depression, anxiety, and so on. The topic of stress is developed in Chapter 6.

Many women work in female-dominated job ghettos at jobs that are different from the work men do. Many jobs done by women provide lower pay, less power, and, often, little independence, autonomy, or control. Despite an acceptance of the principle of equality of opportunity as a basic tenet of human development and well-being, according to the Conference Board of Canada, the Canadian economy earns a "C" in terms of an international comparison of the gender gap in wages. Women between the ages of 25 and 34 earned 78.3 cents for every dollar earned by men in 2010 and women between 35 and 54 years of age earned 75.7 cents for every dollar earned by similarly aged men. While there are differences in the gap among different occupational sectors, the gender gap is largest in health care, where women earned less than half, 47 per cent, of what men earned in 2010 (http://www.conferenceboard.ca/hcp/details/society/gender-income-gap.aspx). Today, education makes a difference in this gap. Women with graduate or professional degrees who work full time earn 96 cents for every dollar earned by men. Women with bachelor's degrees earn 89 cents for every dollar men earn, and women with apprenticeship or trades certification earn 67 cents for every dollar earned by men.

Frequently, women are the last hired and the first fired. To the extent that women's jobs are considered less important than men's jobs, women have less power to demand safe, clean, and healthy working standards. Women's occupational health and safety issues are thus both different from and potentially more problematic than those of men. Even if the risks women face tend not to be as dramatic and acute—that is, they are not as likely to result in

immediate or almost-immediate death—the long-term chronic health problems that result are serious. Women workers are exposed to a broad range of occupationally related health hazards. In clerical work, which continues to be dominated by women, the types of problems are wide-ranging. In addition, the work life of women is problematic because of their multiple roles. Observations made about the relative poverty and lack of control in the female-dominated parts of the labour force are exacerbated among women of minority status who may be likely to work in even more marginalized settings such as domestic work, office cleaning, agriculture, cottage industries, and prostitution. Women with disabilities are also more likely to be underemployed and unemployed and invisible in our society.

Estimating the actual prevalence of occupationally related disease is complex. The issues are similar in many ways to those discussed above with regard to the assessment of environmental health issues. Most importantly, there may be a long period of latency between exposure to the damaging substance or activity and a resultant disease. Second, there may be a lack of information about work-related health and safety concerns. For example, there may be equivocation from owners about which chemicals are being used in ways that could harm workers, and about which chemicals or activities have damaging long-term effects. Even when information is available about the negative consequences of a substance, the information may be withheld. Workers may be reluctant to complain about work-related problems for fear of losing their jobs. One additional set of problems has to do with the fact that physicians usually are poorly trained in recognizing occupationally related diseases.

Shift Work

About one-quarter of employed Canadians work shifts (http://www.iwh.on.ca/at-work/60/shift-work-and-health-what-is-the-research-telling-us). Canada has long needed 24-hour service from the medical, elder care, police and fire protection, and transportation sectors, but "24/7" has become a catchword for commercial, financial, and industrial services in the neo-liberal economy. There are, however, documented health costs associated with shift work, including cardiovascular disease, hypertension, gastrointestinal disorders, reproductive problems, and breast cancer among women, and a greater likelihood among teens who work shifts to later develop multiple sclerosis, according to a recent Swedish report (www.news.com.au/breaking-news/teens-who-work-nights-have-double-risk-of-ms-swedish-study/story-e6frfku0-1226170146884). In addition, shift work may exacerbate such chronic conditions as asthma, diabetes, and epilepsy (Shields, 2003). Some research has found that people who work shifts also tend to have an increased propensity for heavy drinking, poor eating habits, and weight problems. Although the precise reasons for the links between shift work and health challenges are not known, evidence suggests that the association may be due to the disruption of the circadian rhythms, which can lead to stress and to the adoption of unhealthy habits among other problems. Various psychosocial problems are more likely to result from shift work, including those related to mental health issues such as depression and family problems (ibid.). Following is a list of some of the effects of shift work on health.

1. Persistent fatigue is common. Sleep problems are frequent.
2. Possibly because shift work disrupts the circadian rhythms when engaged in over the long term, it is associated with breast and colorectal cancers, mental health problems, gastrointestinal disorders, and preterm childbirth.
3. Shift workers are more vulnerable to heart disease and heart attacks. In general, shift workers have lifestyles associated with ill health, including smoking, obesity, little recreation or regular exercise, and poor diets.
4. Medication may affect the person on shift work in an unpredictable way.
5. Shift work has negative effects on family activities and relationships, which can lead to depression, isolation, broken relationships, and loneliness. The lack of daycare associated

with most shift work may mean that children sometimes are left unattended. Participation in "normal" parent–child, husband–wife, and family socializing is severely restricted because of the unpredictability of the schedule.
6. Some evidence indicates that more work-related accidents occur among shift workers.
7. Working conditions can be substandard (lighting, ventilation, cafeteria services) and opportunities for socializing may be restricted.
8. The rates of psychological stress are high.
9. There are increased odds of being diagnosed with a chronic condition (www.statcan.ca/Daily/English/020725/d020725b.htm; http://www.iwh.on.ca/at-work/60/shift-work-and-health-what-is-the-research-telling-us).

Agricultural Work

Agriculture has long been associated with a pastoral, idyllic, and healthy style of life. However, after mining and construction, agricultural work can be one of the most health-threatening of occupations. Not only do agricultural workers suffer a high rate of accidents and associated fatalities but the working conditions, including working with and repairing farm machinery, the intensification of the farm labour process, poor housing and sanitation, low wages and long hours of hard labour, in all kinds of variable weather, constitute a heavy burden. There are times, too, when it is impossible to take a break or a holiday because of the relentless demands of the farming. As the ozone layer thins, the rate of skin cancer is bound to increase among farm labourers.

Pesticides are major threats to human health, as a result of direct ingestion via pesticide-coated fruits and vegetables and of indirect ingestion via long-term accumulation in soil, water, and air. Pesticides are known to have a tendency to break down or to combine with other compounds over time, which may be even more dangerous to human health. Short-term effects of mild pesticide poisoning include nausea, vomiting, and headaches, as well as more serious permanent damage to the nervous system, miscarriage, birth defects, sterility, and reproductive disorders. Long-term pesticide exposure has been found to be associated with various cancers of the lungs, brain, and testicles (the herbicide 2,4-D, for example, has been found to be associated with a type of lymphoma, birth defects, hormone disruption, and soft-tissue sarcoma). It has been suggested that pesticide use—whether insecticide, herbicide, fungicide, or rodenticide—constitutes a potentially catastrophic experiment with human life (Raven et al., 1993).

Compounding the problems resulting from agricultural work itself is the fact that much of the hired labour force is composed of vulnerable and often temporary, immigrant, illegal, or undocumented workers (http://www.cbc.ca/news/canada/canada-s-migrant-farm-worker-system-what-works-and-what-s-lacking-1.1142489). The tenuous nature of a stay in Canada for such immigrants and refugees has meant that many have had to take whatever job was offered and to accept these working conditions without complaint. Racism, a lack of language facility, and, in some instances, a lack of skills or training render these people particularly vulnerable. Our immigration and temporary worker laws, the lack of employment options once in Canada, poverty and lack of jobs in the country from which workers emigrate, and the lack of unionization in the temporary work sector place many foreign workers in a weak position in relation to their employers. In 2011, as a terrible highlight of the vulnerable situation of temporary migrant farm workers in Ontario, 11 migrant farm workers were killed in a van accident as they returned from a long day at work. This accident raised awareness again about the tenuous health and safety conditions experienced by migrant farm (and other industry) workers (http://www.cbc.ca/news/canada/migrant-workers-killed-in-crash-were-breadwinners-1.1142487).

Other Accidents and Violence

Automobile accidents are another major cause of injury among all age groups. To some extent accidents result from human error—driving under the influence of alcohol and drugs or driving at excessive speed, for example, can be avoided. Many traffic fatalities and deaths from accidental falls and fires result from alcohol-related impairments. A new source of traffic accidents is associated with the use of cell phones (Min and Redelmeier, 1998). In consequence, growing numbers of jurisdictions have laws that prevent the use of a cell phone while driving (www.cellular-news.com/car_bans). A recent news report indicated that almost 50 per cent of teenagers had texted while driving. One investigation of 167 crashes and 518 near-crashes of inexperienced drivers noted the increased odds of about 8 to 1 if dialling a cell phone, 7 to 1 if reaching for a cell phone, 4 to 1 for texting, and about 3 to 1 for eating while driving. The odds ratios regarding dialling a cell phone were lower among experienced drivers (2.49 to 1) but still important (Klauer et al., 2014). Traffic accidents are predicted to be the fifth leading cause of death by 2030 around the globe. Current yearly losses in global context amount to about 1.2 million people. Twenty million people are said to survive with disabilities. Some argue that medical policy has ignored these huge causes of death and suffering (Redelmeier and McLellan, 2013).

In 2009–10, 4.27 million people over 12 years of age (or 15 per cent of the population) suffered an injury that was severe enough to limit their usual activities. The largest cause of injuries was falls. Sixty-three per cent of the injuries of seniors were due to falls. One-half of those occurring in adolescents were the result of falls and 35 per cent of working-age adults who suffered injuries did so as the result of falling. Overall, young people, at 27 per cent, are most likely to suffer injury (http://www.statcan.gc.ca/pub/82-624-x/2011001/article/11506-eng.htm).

Sports-related accidents comprise a significant proportion of all accidents—approximately two-thirds of accidents among adolescents and one-half among adults occur while engaging in sporting activities. Participation in sports has many psychological and physical health benefits. It can, however, be dangerous. The 15–24 group is considerably more likely to experience sports injuries than those in any other age group. In the

US, high school athletes alone account for approximately 2 million injuries, 500,000 doctor visits, and 30,000 hospitalizations each year. One study found that the rate of serious injury was 2.4 injuries per 1,000 games or practices engaged in by the athletes (www.cdc.gov/mmwr/preview/mmwrhtml/mm5538a1.htm). Another significant cause of sports-related impairment relates to the widespread abuse of performance-enhancing drugs in both amateur and professional sports. Recently, attention has turned to the devastating and long-term effects of concussions resulting from injuries to the brain, occurring most notably in football and in Canada's most popular sport, hockey.

Violence against women and children is an important factor in ill health and death, a factor that has long been under-reported. In 1993, Statistics Canada conducted the Violence Against Women survey (Strike, 1995). The World Health Organization has reported that about one-quarter of Canadian women have experienced domestic violence or sexual violence in their lifetimes (McInturff, 2013). About one-quarter of women have experienced violence in the last five years. Seventy per cent of the women who have experienced spousal violence were working women and one-third were from households with an income of $100,000 or greater (ibid.). Women who leave home because of violence are 20 times as likely to use food banks within the first three years. The health consequences are not entirely clear, but some evidence suggests that they are serious and last a long time. Aside from long-term health consequences, women who have been assaulted are more likely to be afraid in various situations, such as taking public transportation, entering or leaving a car alone, or staying alone in their home. Violence reflects prevalent socialization patterns and culturally based value systems. It is extolled as glamorous and exciting. It is featured in popular television shows, films, and video games, with the brutality of mixed martial arts becoming a staple of sports television in recent years, and young boys are given toy guns and military equipment to play with, while macho superheroes are provided as role models. The several cases of mass shootings at Canadian and US schools in recent years are not entirely shocking when we consider, among other things, the prevalence of the culture of "macho" violence and the availability of guns and of psychosis-producing SSRIs, neuroleptics, and other medications, such as prednisone (www.plosmedicine.org/article/info:doi/10.1371/journal.pmed.0030372). On the other hand, it should be noted that domestic violence against men also has serious consequences, including depression, anxiety, loss of self-esteem, drug and alcohol abuse, and fear of losing one's children (http://www.mayoclinic.org/healthy-lifestyle/adult-health/in-depth/domestic-violence-against-men/art-20045149), as well as inability to work, the injuries caused by the abuse, suppressed anger, isolating behaviour, and reduced libido.

SUMMARY

1. Water, air, and land are the three fundamental parts of the environment on which we depend for health.
2. The major environmental issues facing Canadians today include: climate change, chemicals, air pollution, second-hand smoke, medical pollution, land pollution, e-waste, biodiversity, and food safety.
3. Pollution of water in the Great Lakes continues to be a serious concern.
4. With respect to land, the issue of waste disposal is critical.
5. Occupational health and safety issues are a major concern, even in today's post-technological era. It has been estimated that a significant proportion of all cancers are related to working and the environment.
6. The health and safety issues of working women in female job ghettos, while less dramatic (and less studied) than those of predominantly

male occupations, are nevertheless myriad and consequential.

7. Particular health and safety issues are related to work in agriculture, the health-care industry, and shift work.

8. Traffic and sports accidents are a significant cause of morbidity and mortality, especially among young people.

9. Accidents and violence have a considerable impact on the morbidity and mortality rates of Canadians.

KEY TERMS

climate change
"environmental illness"
e-waste
global ecosystem

greenhouse gases
 (GHGs)
Kyoto Protocol
occupational stress

pharmaceuticals and personal
 care products (PPCPs)
risk society
twentieth-century disease

QUESTIONS FOR DISCUSSION

1. Why is it difficult to demonstrate the effects of the environment on human health? Scientifically? Politically?

2. Could the industrial accident in Fukushima have been prevented? How? Explain.

3. What are the most significant threats to the sustainability of the globe? Explain.

4. Why is cancer prevention under-emphasized by the Canadian cancer establishment?

5. What problems do pesticides cause? Should they be banned?

SUGGESTED READINGS

Beck, U. 1994. *Ecological Politics in an Age of Risk*. London: Polity Press. A classic text for the new modernity.

Boulos, D., and M.A. Zamorski. 2013. "Deployment-related Mental Disorders among Canadian Forces Personnel Deployed in Support of the Mission in Afghanistan 2001–2008." *Canadian Medical Association Journal* 185, 11: 545–52. One study of the after-effects of the global and national issue of war.

Brauer, M., C. Reynolds, and P. Hystad. 2013. "Traffic-related Air Pollution and Health in Canada." *Canadian Medical Association Journal* 185, 18: 1557–8. This article brings to light an under-recognized health concern with a growing level of impact.

Flegel, K. 2013. "Big Alcohol Catches up with Adolescent Girls." *Canadian Medical Association Journal* 185, 10: 859. A critical analysis of gendered advertising to increase alcohol consumption among young women.

Fortune, M.K., C. Mustard, and J.J.C. Etches. 2013. "Work-attributed Illness Arising from Excess Heat Exposure in Ontario, 2004–2010." *Canadian Review of Public Health* 104, 5: 420–6. A paper pointing to the problem of excessive heat in the workplace.

Galloway, G. 2014. "Government Mum on Asbestos Policy." *Globe and Mail*, 18 June. A critical note on the Canadian policy on asbestos.

Hystad, P., M. Brauer, P.A. Demers, K.C. Johnson, E. Setton, A. Cervantes-Larios, K. Poplawski, A. McFarlane, A. Whitehead, and A.M. Nichol. 2014. "Geographic Variation in Radon and Associated Lung Cancer risk in Canada." *Canadian Journal of Public Health* 105, 1: 4–10. A recently documented environmental issue that requires ongoing monitoring.

Kiec-Swierczynska, M., D. Chomiczewska-Skora, D. Swierczyriska-Machura, and B. Krecisz. 2013. "Manicurists and Pedicurists—Occupation Group at High Risk of Dermatoses." *Medycyna Prasy* [*Medical Practice* (Warsaw)] 64, 4: 579–91. This draws our attention to the costs of working in the "aesthetics industry."

Neo-liberalism, Social Inequity, Disease, and Death: The Social Determinants of Health

4

© Zurijeta | Dreamstime.com

CHAPTER OVERVIEW

- ▶ Health, illness, and death are not randomly distributed across society.

- ▶ Morbidity and mortality rates are linked to inequalities.

- ▶ The "social determinants of health" approach helps us understand the reasons for health inequalities in the population.

- ▶ Three explanations for the value of the social determinants approach to understanding disease and mortality outcomes are the materialist, the neo-materialist, and the life course approaches.

- ▶ Social inclusion/exclusion and social capital are important in health outcomes.

- ▶ Politics and economics are major determinants of health outcomes.

- ▶ Ideology affects health outcomes.

- ▶ Inequality, employment, unemployment, food security, housing, poverty, and education all are significant as social determinants of health.

- ▶ Social theory, including the commodification, of health helps to explain the findings presented in this chapter.

- ▶ Inequality is growing in Canada and around the world.

Introduction

The next two chapters will focus on one of the most important conceptual frameworks for understanding the health of people in Canada and in nations around the world: the causes and consequences of numerous inequities in social structure and how they are linked to the distribution of death, illness, disease, and disabilities. The notion of social structure is used here as a metaphor or a tool for thinking about the ways that people in society differ from one another, in the sense that some people have more than others of various benefits necessary to, or valued in, social and material life. The social structure can be thought of as hierarchical. Hierarchy, or placement up and down an invisible ladder, can be observed along a number of different dimensions. It can be seen in economic, educational, gender, and social status variations, among others. For example, it is possible to consider that society is structured so that those with more money are at the top and those with less money are at the bottom. It is also structured so that those with more education, or those who hold more prestige because of their families or jobs, for example, can be seen as being located at or near the top of an invisible hierarchy. Cross-cutting indicators of inequity both reinforce one another and/or contradict one another. The relationship between gender and income provides an example of how inequities can be reinforcing. The well-documented fact that women are more likely to be poor than men illustrates two "variables" (gender and socio-economic status) or conditions working together or reinforcing one another. If we add Aboriginal status to the equation we can think about how the gender differences in levels of income are exacerbated by Aboriginal status. Thus, Aboriginal women are likely to be poorer than Aboriginal men and non-Aboriginal women. This reflects a situation in which cross-cutting sources of inequity (in this case, gender and Aboriginal status) can exacerbate the health and income circumstances of certain doubly (or multiply) defined groups of people and of individuals within those groups. This dynamic interaction of many variables at a time is the issue intersectionality bears upon, as described in Chapter 1. Often, systems of inequality and inequity are linked together so that, for example, the elderly are more likely to be female, and the elderly also are more likely to be poor. From the perspective of conflict theory and of social justice, hierarchical structure is indicative of inequality. Inequality becomes inequity when we judge the inequality as morally wrong.

How Do Inequity and Health Relate?

How does inequity relate to health and illness? There is a consistent and positive relationship between good health and location further up the social-structural hierarchy. This means that in a society such as Canada, people who have more wealth tend also to be healthier and to live longer lives and people who have less wealth tend to have poorer health and to live shorter lives. Thus, the individual level of well-being tends to correspond to the location of the individual in the social structure. In addition, there is general agreement that the overall degree of equity or inequity within society affects the well-being of everyone within the society, including those at the top and those at the bottom of the income hierarchy. Societies in which the differences between levels of the hierarchy are smaller tend to have better overall health among all of the people in the population than those that are more differentiated. As the degree of overall inequality declines or increases, so, too, will the level of health be likely to vary (Figures 4.1 and 4.2).

How do these processes work? First, why would relative economic equality in a society be associated with health while a lower position in the economic structure is associated with illness? A number of different mechanisms and answers have been proposed. Dennis Raphael (e.g., 2002a, 2002b, 2004; Mikkonen and Raphael, 2010), especially, has helped to explain the consequences of inequality and health consequences for Canadians.

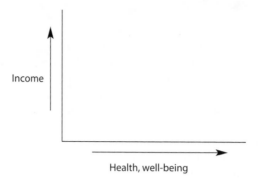

Hypothetical Explanations for Health Differences
Among People of Different SES Backgrounds

Material Resources

Housing

Food

Clean water

Clean air

Access to necessary
   immunization, drugs, and
   health care

Lifestyle

Smoking

Drinking

Exercise

Sexual safety

Risk-taking

Family/Community

Stability/integration into family
   and community

Supportive mutual aid
   relationships

Decision-making authority

Privacy

Social-Psychological Resources

Stable, secure employment

Supportive work relationships

Education

Coping abilities

Sense of coherence

Social readjustment

Emotional stability

Sense of efficacy

FIGURE 4.1   A Hypothetical Model of the Relationship between Socio-economic Status and Health for an
Individual

The most obvious one is that health is linked to the provision of basic material goods and services. This has been called the **materialist approach** to the social determinants of health. From this perspective human health depends fundamentally on available, accessible, and good-quality nutritious food; clean, accessible, and available water; good transportation systems and infrastructure, including public transit; stable, safe, adequately compensated, interesting, fulfilling employment; safe, available, appropriate, and affordable housing; and other essential components of life. Without these, health is compromised and challenged. Income is central to health in the materialist view. At least two aspects of income are relevant: income sufficiency or adequacy for such things as the purchase of food, shelter, transportation, and recreational or leisure activities; and income stability so

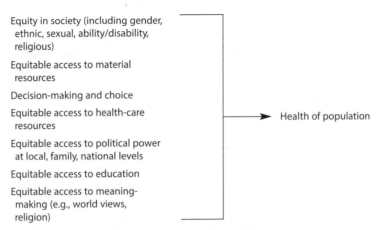

Equity in society (including gender, ethnic, sexual, ability/disability, religious)

Equitable access to material resources

Decision-making and choice

Equitable access to health-care resources

Equitable access to political power at local, family, national levels

Equitable access to education

Equitable access to meaning-making (e.g., world views, religion)

Health of population

FIGURE 4.2   A Hypothetical Model of the Contributions of Equity to the Health of a Population

that the money is available consistently and pre-dictably from month to month and from year to year. Access to material goods is absolutely neces-sary for the health of the individual and the family. Moreover, there are ways that income inequality perpetuates itself and leads to poorer health status for disadvantaged families through the genera-tions and tends to grow, the way a snowball does, through the life course of an impoverished individ-ual. Similarly, the children born of those further up the income hierarchy tend to experience health benefits throughout their lives.

Material circumstances can influence health directly through assaults to the physical body, for example, from the spread of infections among homeless or poorly housed people. Nutritional inadequacies due to insufficient funds for healthy foods are linked to a variety of illnesses such as the potentially serious and even fatal adult-onset dia-betes. Once a person is ill, relative poverty leads to a diminished capacity to cope and to earn income, particularly in the case of the growing numbers of chronic illnesses requiring complex manage-ment regimes, such as heart diseases or HIV/AIDS. Violence and accidents also occur more often in situations lacking material adequacy. Children may be more likely to be left alone or to become the victims of domestic violence and child abuse. In addition, material insufficiencies are associated with challenges to mental health and well-being.

Poorer people are more likely to suffer from such difficulties as depression, stress, and challenges to self-esteem. They may be less resilient. All of these are directly linked to human physical as well as mental health. For instance, the stress response may be a chronic reaction to continuous relative impoverishment or sudden loss of a job, among other things. The stress response, described in more detail in Chapter 6, weakens the immune system and may lead to the onset of specific stress-related diseases.

Poorer people are also more likely to cope by engaging in some behaviours that may have health-threatening results, such as eating diets high in carbohydrates, sugar, and trans fats and low in protein, along with a paucity of fresh fruits and vegetables and inadequate exercise. A correlation is known to exist between a person's position in the invisible social-structural hierarchy and specific behaviours known to be associated with particular disease processes. Cigarette smoking, for example, is irrefutably linked to lung cancer both for the smoker and for those who inhale the second-hand smoke. Cigarette smoking is also negatively asso-ciated with income and education. Thus, poorer and less-educated people are more likely to smoke cigarettes.

A second explanation for the link between inequality and health has been called the **neo-materialist approach**. This perspective acknowledges the importance of a basic level of material adequacy but then centres its attention on the significance of the relative distribution of material and social goods in societies. The argument here is that once a certain degree of absolute material adequacy has been reached, certainly enough for living above the poverty line (at least), then equity in the society and perceived equity become essential to the overall health of a population. This argument has substantial empirical support (see, for instance, Wilkinson and Pickett, 2010). Societies with progressive redistribution and equalization policies designed to ensure the basic material and social welfare of their whole populations, such as a basic guaranteed annual income, unemployment insurance, generous leave policies for sickness, compassionate care, disability insurance and income, early childhood education and care programs, universal education, and adequate pension policies, are more likely to have a population with lower infant mortality, longer life expectancy, and longer disability-free life expectancy.

A third explanation for the links between social determinants and health shows how the materialist and neo-materialist theories might work empirically at the level of individual social-psychological functioning. It focuses attention on the impacts of inequity and highlights the importance of social inclusion or exclusion to the ongoing daily social processes of life for individual people as social beings in a community. **Social capital** is said to enhance inclusion. Social capital can be defined and measured in a variety of ways. Access to, as well as the presence of, certain social benefits is one way of defining social capital. We are familiar with the idea that capital is an economic resource that provides access to material benefits. Aday (2005) builds on the work of Bourdieu (1986), who distinguishes among *social, cultural,* and *economic capital* and theorizes about how they work together in providing resources to people in societies, through social networks and community inclusion. Aday (2005) expands this notion in reference to the types of capital or resources that are necessary for health. She includes natural capital (parks and environmental conditions of various sorts, e.g., access to green spaces); human capital (education type, amount, and quality, e.g., universal early education or child-care programs); material capital (occupation, income, and employment); and social and cultural capital (including social support, absence of discrimination, and freedom from stereotyping). We could add the component of psychological capital (a sense of well-being, self-esteem) and bodily capital (a genetic background leading to strength and health, and aspects of body shape, size, and functioning). Those with adequate social capital are less likely to be marginalized and more likely to be included in social life (Spitzer, 2005).

Social inclusion is related to social capital and is evident in characteristics of communities, such as civic engagement, voter turnout, and the representation of people of diverse backgrounds in positions of power in local governments, community organization, and distant governments. The presence of a well-functioning infrastructure, including availability of and access to green spaces, public transportation, free or inexpensive libraries, sports arenas, community centres, and the like, is thought to contribute to a high level of social inclusion. On the other hand, private education, health clubs, and sports complexes and the lack of publicly accessible services for transportation, the arts, recreation, and so on marginalize some people, particularly those unable to pay for private goods and services. The lack of such universally available infrastructure, a lack that that excludes some members of the community, leads to negative social comparisons, lowered self-esteem, and, finally, poorer health. This explanation highlights the integral nature of the body–mind connection that is further explored in Chapter 6.

The **life course approach** to health outcomes overlaps with the previous three emphases but draws attention to the fact that the harms caused by impoverishment, inequity, a lack of redistributive policies, social exclusion, and negative social comparisons are compounded when they occur to and among children because, in a multitude of ways, they persist and accumulate throughout life. The health costs of early childhood poverty are heightened and their consequences increased

HIGHLIGHTED ISSUES

BOX 4.1   The Social and Personal Costs of Alzheimer's Disease

Have you ever forgotten the name of a person or the word for a thing? Among the most troubling and important of the disorders facing elderly Canadians are the various types of dementia, and memory loss is one of the most noticeable symptoms of dementia, a condition that increases sharply as people age.

Alzheimer's disease, the most common form of dementia, is characterized by a progressive deterioration and destruction of cells in the brain and leads to increasingly severe declines in memory, thinking, and reasoning. People suffering from Alzheimer's often begin with an inability to remember information, words, or names. Over unpredictable periods of time, these memory difficulties result in greater and greater problems with reasoning, judgement, and emotional and personality stability. Denial that anything is wrong by the Alzheimer's patient can be one of the most difficult stages of the disease, both for the patient and for the caregiver. Eventually, people with the disease become unable to care for their own basic needs or to engage in the activities of daily living on their own. Alzheimer's is a fatal disease, though many sufferers die from other causes linked to old age.

It is still impossible to diagnose Alzheimer's with certainty until biopsy, but, according to the Alzheimer Society (www.alz.org/AboutUs/faq.htm), widely accepted practice criteria, including such diagnostic tests as the "mini mental inventory," have led to a diagnosis accuracy rate of about 90 per cent. Numerous different hypotheses regarding disease causation have been examined, but there are still no definitive conclusions. While no medical treatments are available for the cure of the disease, several drugs now work to delay and moderate temporarily the worsening of symptoms. Numerous experimental treatments and preventative strategies are being developed and tested in various places around the world. In addition, Alzheimer's patients who have been encouraged to sing have reversed symptoms of moderate to severe levels of impairment (http://www.aplaceformom.com/senior-care-resources/articles/dementia-therapy-and-music), suggesting that the loss of ear function in aging is a contributing cause of symptoms.

In the context of an aging population and lack of clear or certain methods of prevention, the disease is likely to grow in the next 30 years or so as the approximately 10 million baby boomers turn 75, 85, and 95. In the absence of effective treatments, knowledge about prevention, or adequate financing and support for home or institutional care, the burden of this disease for the sufferers and their friends and families is bound to increase. Today, one in 13 people over 65 is estimated to have Alzheimer's or another related dementia. By 2031 approximately three-quarters of a million Canadians likely will be affected (Figure 4.3). About 110,000 new cases of dementia were diagnosed in 2010. Women, possibly because of their longer lives, account for approximately 72 per cent of those diagnosed with Alzheimer's and 62 per cent of those diagnosed with dementia (www.alzheimer.ca/english/media/adfacts2011.htm).

About one-half of those diagnosed with dementia live in institutions such as nursing homes, homes for the aged, and retirement homes. Others typically live at home, i.e., the residence of the caregivers, and are cared for by family members—spouses, daughters, daughters-in-law, sons, grandchildren—with only a small amount of voluntary or paid assistance. Apparently, a mere 3.4 per cent of family caregivers use respite care (designed to give caregivers a brief break). Partly because of inadequate levels of home care and support services for people with dementia and partly due to the financial cost of respite care, informal

continued

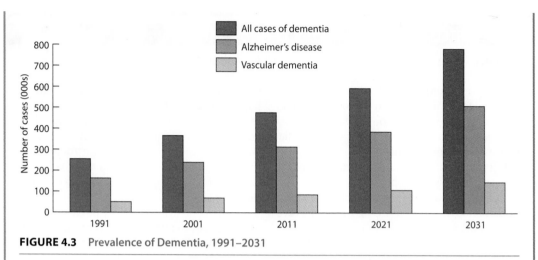

FIGURE 4.3   Prevalence of Dementia, 1991–2031

Source: Burke et al. (1997: 25), from *CMAJ* 150, 6 (1994: 906).

caregivers seem to have more chronic health problems than others in their age cohort. A significant number of those caring for a person with severe or moderate Alzheimer's report symptoms of depression. Depression is twice as prevalent among caregivers of Alzheimer's patients as it is among other caregivers (www.alzheimer.ca/english/disease/stats-caregiving.htm).

One of the challenges facing the health-care system of the future, in the absence of discoveries leading to prevention, is that of providing programs and supports for caregivers and sufferers of Alzheimer's to enable both to cope as well as possible in difficult circumstances.

A great deal of research has been carried out on the biomedical aspects of the disease. For example, it has been discovered that the plaque associated with the disease does not originate in the brain but in the liver (http://www.kpbs.org/news/2011/mar/08/liver-not-brain-likely-source-alzheimers-plaque/). Significant additional study of the related social, sociological, and personal issues is needed, along with a range of possible ways to ameliorate the effects of the condition. It is important for us to realize that the problematic effects of Alzheimer's on sufferers and their families and caregivers are exacerbated by income inadequacy, inequality, and ageism.

through pathway, latency, and cumulative effects. Some have called this the **fundamental cause** of health and illness (Chang and Lauderdale 2009) and the **cumulative advantage theory** (Willson et al., 2007). These theories seek to explain how advantage and disadvantage build up over time. Like a snowball that gets bigger as it rolls so, too, do social and health benefits grow over time. Another way of conceptualizing this tendency for the components of health and illness to accumulate is through the following three ideas: pathway effects, latency effects, and cumulative effects. **Pathway effects** set children on a direction, a road,

or a course resulting either from unhelpful or from helpful early experiences through compounding effects. For example, a child who begins school already counting and familiar with books, crayons, pencils, and paper is likely to fare much better in kindergarten. Doing well in kindergarten sets the child on the path to higher marks and a better educational and social life in elementary school and high school. This, in turn, preconditions the child, now an adolescent, for success in post-secondary training, apprenticeship, college, or university. And success in training, college, or university leads the young adult into a better-paying job and greater life chances. **Latency effects** occur in the early developmental stages and also influence later life. Premature birth, for instance, is a strong predictor of a variety of developmental delays in cognitive and physical functioning. It is associated with a number of different disease (and pre-disease) states later on. Underweight and overweight infants are more likely than those born at normal weight to suffer from overweight and obesity later on. Overweight and obesity are linked to diabetes and various cardiovascular diseases, among other things. **Cumulative effects** are the repeated additions of disadvantage or advantage over a lifetime and include combinations of both latency and pathway effects that lead to health and/or disease in the adult. This is not to say that people cannot take control over aspects of their difficult start in life, but they may have more difficulty doing so.

An example of the generational and life course approaches may be seen through an examination of class-associated premarital or teenage pregnancy. Working-class and lower-class teenage girls are more likely to become pregnant out of wedlock. Teenage and unmarried women tend not to have adequate economic, emotional, and social support to take good care of themselves; thus, if they become pregnant, this lack of support affects the growth of their fetuses and babies. Compared to those whose pregnancies are planned, they may have access only to insufficient or non-nutritious diets and may be less able to engage in prenatal care and healthy prenatal behaviours. Lacking social acceptance, they may try to hide their pregnancies and maintain their media-inspired "desired" body image. Stress may lead them to consume alcohol and other potentially harmful substances. Low-birth-weight babies are more likely to be born to women in these circumstances. Low birth weight is a significant problem that tends to result in all manner of difficulties for the child, including a greater likelihood of death, disability, and disease. Low-birth-weight babies, as they reach school age, tend to be poorer students and to have learning difficulties and various chronic illnesses. Thus, the results of this one behaviour associated with income may lead to complex and extensive health- and income-related threats to the newborn and to the growing child.

Political Explanations for Inequality and Poor Health

Health inequities result from forces and decisions at the global and national political and economic levels. Navarro and Shi have compared four different types of politically organized nation-states with respect to inequities and to health outcomes. They divided countries in the Organization for Economic Co-operation and Development (OECD) into the following political categories: social democratic, Christian democratic, "liberal" (i.e., "neo-liberal" in the taxonomy that we have described above), and ex-fascist. Then, they compared them over the period 1945–80, "the golden years of capitalism" (Navarro and Shi, 2003: 195). The comparison focused on the degree of inequality, public expenditures and health-care benefits, public support for families, and the overall health, disease, and death in a population. Note that all of these are developed Western nations and among the richest in the world. The social democratic countries, characterized by the most extensive taxation and redistribution policies, included Sweden, Denmark, Norway, Finland, and Austria. Those categorized as Christian democratic were Belgium, the Netherlands, Germany, France, Italy, and Switzerland. The liberal (neo-liberal) countries included Canada, the United Kingdom, the United States, and Ireland. The ex-fascist countries were Spain, Greece, and Portugal. The social democratic countries, which were more "committed to redistributive policies (both economic and social) and full-employment policies, . . . were generally more successful in improving the health of populations" (ibid.). The social democratic countries also had relatively high levels of union involvement, full-employment policies, high levels of expenditures on the social "safety net," high levels of taxation (as a percentage of the GDP), and a relatively high percentage of employment in health, education, and welfare. Social democratic countries were characterized by high rates of female engagement in the labour market. The infant mortality rates in the social democratic countries ranged from 4.0 to 5.1 in 1996 and from 3.0 to 5.0 in 2011 (www.who.int/whosis/whostat/EN_WHS2011_Full.pdf, p. 24). By comparison, the infant mortality rates in the liberal countries ranged from 5.5 (Ireland) to 7.8 (US) in 1996, and from 4.0 (Ireland) to 8.0 (US) in 2011 (ibid.). In 2011, the average infant mortality rate is highest in the (neo-) liberal countries and lowest in the social democratic countries (see Table 4.1). Canada's infant mortality rate was fairly high at 6.0 in 1996, remaining at 6.0 in 2011. Although the study by Navarro and Shi cannot be taken as conclusive, it supports the theories regarding the importance of social determinants to the health of populations. The infant mortality rate, while only one indicator of social health, is a highly sensitive measure of the overall health of a nation. Table 4.1 shows estimates of infant mortality rates for the countries in this study.

TABLE 4.1   Infant Mortality, Selected OECD Countries, 1970–2011

	Deaths per 1,000 Live Births				
	1970	**1980**	**1990**	**1996**	**2011**
Social Democratic Political Economies					
Austria	25.9	14.3	7.8	5.1	5.0
Sweden	11.0	6.9	6.0	4.0	3.0
Denmark	14.2	8.4	7.5	5.2	4.0
Norway	12.7	9.1	7.0	4.0	4.0
Finland	13.2	7.6	5.6	4.0	3.0
Mean	15.4	9.1	6.8	4.5	3.8
Christian Democratic Political Economies					
Belgium	21.1	12.1	8.0	6.0	5.0
Germany	23.6	12.6	7.0	5.0	4.0
Netherlands	12.7	8.6	7.1	5.2	5.0
France	18.2	10.1	7.3	4.9	4.0
Italy	29.6	14.6	8.2	5.8	4.0
Switzerland	15.1	9.1	6.8	4.7	4.0
Mean	20.1	11.2	7.4	5.3	4.3
Liberal Anglo-Saxon Political Economies					
United Kingdom	18.5	12.1	7.9	6.1	5.0
Ireland	19.5	11.1	8.2	5.5	4.0
United States	20.0	12.6	9.2	7.8	8.0
Canada	18.8	10.4	6.8	6.0	6.0
Mean	19.2	11.6	8.0	6.4	5.8
Former Fascist Dictatorships					
Spain	26.3	12.3	7.6	5.0	4.0
Portugal	55.1	24.3	11.0	6.9	4.0
Greece	29.6	17.9	9.7	7.3	4.0
Mean	37.0	18.2	9.4	6.4	4.0

Sources: Navarro and Shi (2003: 210). Source for updated 2011 data: WHO, '2. Under-five mortality rate (probability of dying by age 5 per 1000 live births)' World Health Statistics 2011, page 24.

Inequality and inequity have been growing since 1980, the justification for which is rooted in the ideology of neo-liberalism. This ideology is the one most students reading this book grew up with. According to the Canadian sociologist David Coburn, the chief assumptions of neo-liberalism are: (1) "that markets are the best and most efficient allocators of resources in production and distribution"; (2) "that societies are composed of autonomous individuals (producers and consumers) motivated chiefly or entirely by material or economic considerations"; and (3) "that competition is the major market vehicle for innovation" (Coburn, 2003: 340). He argues that this ideology undergirds development and has spread around the globe in the past 35 years at varying rates, from the time of deregulation of markets and the push for free (or freer) trade by the Thatcher Conservatives in the UK, the Reagan Republicans in the US, and, in Canada, the Progressive Conservatives under Brian Mulroney and continued by Stephen Harper. It is this fundamental and dominant ideological belief that drives the globalization of capital. Neo-liberalism is antithetical to redistribution of goods and services because any interference with the free-wheeling powers of the market is believed to fetter economic growth, and economic growth, above all else, is thought to be the "good" that societies produce. Thus, taxing corporations limits their freedom to take risks and respond creatively to the needs (or create needs through advertising and so on) of the populace for new consumer products such as pharmaceuticals or the next generation of electronic widgets. Rather than policies designed explicitly by the state to ensure, for instance, that unemployed people have access to training, unemployment insurance, and government-sponsored assistance in locating a new job, the ideology of neo-liberalism advances the proposition that everyone in society will do better if the market is allowed to generate jobs willy-nilly as it creates wealth. This is said to happen through what has been called the "trickle-down" effect. The market will generate wealth and consumer goods and will automatically, in this perspective, provide work and income for all (if not in the short

run, then certainly in the middle and long runs). Coburn also makes the point that the ideology of neo-liberalism, both theoretically and in practice, is able to tolerate a high degree of inequality within and between states because of its fundamental assertion that the markets will ultimately prevail and lead to wealth for all. The neo-liberal position is consistent with a low degree of social cohesion, based as it is on a philosophy that cherishes individual rights and freedoms over collective integration or societal well-being. In effect, then, the prevailing economic doctrine of the late twentieth century and the early years of the twenty-first century produces and justifies high levels of inequality within and between nations and high levels of social exclusion. As has been argued, both social exclusion and inequality are linked to poor health among the peoples of the world.

An Operating Model for the Social Determinants of Health

As we have argued, health, illness, and death are not randomly distributed in a society. Rather, their incidence and prevalence are inextricably linked to the social organization of the society. One aspect of this social organization, as noted above, is the extent of inequity or inequality in the social structure. Inequity causes different life chances and experiences, as well as unequal access to fundamental social resources such as food, recreation, satisfying work, and adequate shelter. Because of unequal access, people who differ in age, sex, income, occupation, race, ethnicity, marital status, rural or urban background, and religiosity differ in their rates of sickness and death. As a first step to this analysis, however, it is essential to put the relationship between illness and death and the social structure into a broad, comprehensive context. Table 4.2 is a model of the major social variables and their possible connection with rates of illness and death.

On the broadest level, (1) the globalization of capital—i.e., trade rules and regulations, as well as the ease and quickness with which investment capital and business decisions can move around the

TABLE 4.2   A Model for Analysis of Morbidity and Mortality Rates at the Societal Level

Culture	Political-Economic System	Ecological System	Social Structure	Social Psychology	Micro Meaning
the degree of medicalization/ biomedicalization	Capitalism/ neo-liberalism Socialism Communism	environmental and condition (water, air) quality of agricultural land and foods transportation and communication systems	gender age ethnicity education religious affiliation	stress type A behaviour* sense of coherence* perceived social support	the definition and meaning of health, disease, and death

*These will be defined fully in Chapter 6.

globe via electronic media—and (2) the neo-liberal ideologies at the level of states have encouraged the dominance of free markets and free-flowing capital. The spread of this political-economic regime has affected the disease burdens of peoples around the world. In addition, numerous cultural, ecological, and historical differences between societies manifest themselves through such things as varying definitions of health and illness and varying views regarding appropriate types of medical treatment. For example, some societies are more "medicalized" than others. Developing societies are increasingly influenced by the discourses and practices of allopathic medical explanations and treatments that often are pharmaceutical for what might be seen as social or educational problems. An example is hyperactivity, which used to be regarded as naughtiness but is now widely treated with a drug such as Ritalin, and another is depression for the "normal" sadness of bereavement, which is often treated with anti-depressants. In addition, as discussed in Chapter 2, there are many other components to global health disparities. (Medicalization will be discussed further, in more detail and more critically, in Chapters 8 and 9.) Differences in mortality and morbidity are related to political-economic systems at the level

of the nation-state, as well as to national cultural differences. The level and distribution of numerous resources, such as food, shelter, access to meaningful work, environment quality, and satisfying social relations, vary within societies. As long as the political-economic system causes differences in people's access to resources, there will be structured inequities in rates of death and illness.

Social policies have a significant impact on the health of populations. The presence of such policy measures as a guaranteed annual wage, early childhood education and care, laws against discrimination and promoting special status for those who are disadvantaged, pension availability, and the provision of unemployment, sickness, and compassionate-care insurance help to redistribute income within a society and to improve the health of everyone. Health depends, as well, on the availability of regulations and monitoring to ensure safe consumer products such as foods, drugs, sterile needles, and condoms; safe physical structures such as bridges, well-lit streets, and buildings constructed to satisfy adequate safety criteria; and public service advertisements and other cultural messages promoting health-related behaviours. Our health-care system and many social and medical policies still, however, support a **downstream**

model rather than an **upstream model** of health. The metaphor used in these concepts points to the fact that our health-care policies focus on providing diagnosis and treatment once a problem has been detected (upstream) rather than preventing the development of health problems in the first place (downstream). Note the following visual representation of upstream and downstream thinking. This policy preference for upstream medical intervention tends to allow stressors from the social determinants of health such as poverty, racism, unhealthy or insufficient food, violence, poor neighbourhood conditions, lack of easily accessible health care, and so on to accumulate over time so that disease finally occurs. The notion that all social policies potentially have health consequences is exemplified by the phrase **health in all policies (HiAP)**. Attention to the impact of social policy on health has been recently adopted in parts of the world where there is a concerted effort to minimize the stresses and strains of inadequate social determinants of health and to maximize healthy social and economic arrangements (Peña, 2013).

Cultures differ in the interpretation of symptoms and behaviours associated with health and illness. For example, for Aboriginal people, health always includes spirituality. This means that feeling or being disconnected from community, history, and Mother Earth may be seen as signs of a lack of wellness by Native peoples. Relatively stable and unchangeable social-structural positions such as gender, age, racialization, ethnicity, sexual orientation, dis/abilities, and so on are related to health outcomes. People who are in different positions in an invisible but effective hierarchical social structure are more or less likely to suffer from mental and physical illness. For example, women are more likely to be diagnosed with depression and men, possibly in the face of the same feelings and circumstances, are more likely to engage in excessive alcohol consumption.

The social determinants of health operate through such things as the availability, accessibility, and quality of food, water, housing, income, education and literacy, and early childhood education and care. In addition, education and ongoing

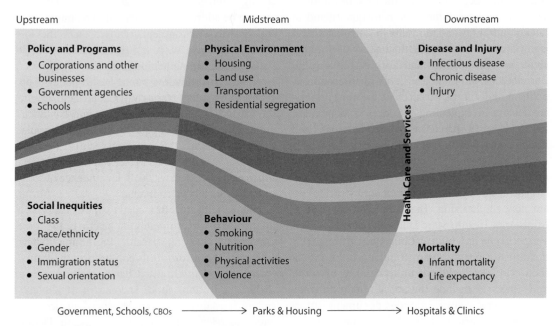

FIGURE 4.4   The Health in All Policies Approach

Source: Health in All Policies: Richmond Adopts a Health in All Policies (HiAP) Strategy and Ordinance ! City of Richmond (2014).

choices in education through the life course are significant determinants of the health of a society.

Individual behaviours and coping responses, including smoking, alcohol consumption, seat-belt use, stress, self-esteem, sense of coherence, social and instrumental support, resilience and religiosity, are implicated in health outcomes. The socio-psychological and phenomenological strategies people use contribute to illness rates and ultimately even to death rates.

Health outcomes from all of these factors are seen in mortality and morbidity rates, disability rates, subjective assessments of health and well-being, and clinical health measures.

The Social Determinants of Health: Evidence from Canada

Inequality and relative poverty become translated into ill health through specific mechanisms. These determinants have been conceptualized in a variety of ways historically and geographically. Before we consider the social and economic reasons for intra- and inter-societal differences in inequality and in rates of morbidity and mortality in Canada today, it is important to understand the history of thinking about the causes of illness and death. As Navarro and Borrell (2004: 221) say, "a society's socio-economic, political, and cultural variables are the most important factors in explaining the level of population health." Until 1974, in terms of Canadian social and health policy, health was considered to be mostly limited to that which the medical care system managed. It was understood as a biological process and largely outside of the concerns of equity such as we are now emphasizing. Then, in 1974, the federal Minister of Health, Marc Lalonde, released *A New Perspective on the Health of Canadians*. Through this document, Canada began to influence the rest of the world, broadening the understanding of health and illness to include the social, environmental, and economic causes. Lalonde's document distinguished four factors in health and illness: human biology, environment, lifestyle, and health-care organization. "Human biology" covered all aspects

of mental and physical health integral to the body, including genetic inheritance, the processes of maturation and aging, and the many complex internal systems in the body. "Environment" included all factors external to the body that affect health, such as clean drinking water, clean air, adequate foodstuffs, garbage and sewage disposal, and the social environment—gender, social class, ethnic, and cultural differences. "Lifestyle" referred to different individual health habits, such as exercise, diet, smoking, alcohol use, seat-belt use, and promiscuity and sexual carelessness. "Health-care organization" covered the technologies, facilities, personnel, and organizations devoted to medical care.

In the intervening years, understanding about the social, cultural, and economic causes of health and illness has changed significantly. In 1986 another Canadian Health Minister, Jake Epp, was responsible for a document that proposed a framework for promoting the health of Canadians through various social and policy interventions. Included in Epp's framework were the health challenges of reducing inequities, increasing prevention, and enhancing coping abilities in the population. These strategies were to be addressed through self-care, mutual aid, and healthy environments, and through the following implementation strategies: fostering public participation, strengthening community health services, and co-ordinating public health policy (Epp, 1986). More recent research in Canada and around the world has built on this history and has documented the primacy of equality for healthy populations. To reiterate, this new approach is called the *social determinants of health* (see Raphael, 2009, and Mikkonen and Raphael, 2010, for evidence of some Canadian social determinants).

One useful and often-cited method of approach to the social determinants of health is the 1986 Ottawa Charter for Health Promotion (www.who.int/healthpromotion/conferences/previous/ottawa/en/). The Ottawa Charter includes peace, shelter, education, food, income, a stable ecosystem, sustainable resources, social justice, and equity as relevant prerequisites for health. Dennis Raphael, in *Social Determinants of Health: Canadian Perspectives* (2009), lists the following as basic determinants of health and illness: Aboriginal status (to be Aboriginal is to experience threats to health); early life experiences; education, employment, and working conditions; food security; health-care services; housing; income and its distribution; a social safety net; social exclusion and unemployment; and employment security (Raphael, 2009: 7).

In the next section we will examine some of the social determinants of health or differences in social capital among people in Canada. First, it is important to note regional and other geographic differences in the distribution of social determinants and the health of Canadians across the country. One recent

study demonstrating associations between communities, socio-economic and demographic indices, and health outcomes divided the country into 10 "peer groups." These peer group clusters were based on population size, average years of schooling, percentage visible minority or Aboriginal status, population density, unemployment rate, income inequality, average income, percentage of single parents, elderly, low income, and the extent of migration since the previous census. These 10 groups were then compared with respect to their performance on key indicators of health: life expectancy; risk factors such as smoking, heavy drinking, obesity, stress

---

CRITICAL THINKING

BOX 4.2   Are the Elderly Responsible for Increases in Health Costs?

You have probably heard the concern voiced that as the population ages in the next several decades in Canada as a result of the increase in age among the baby-boom generation that the costs to health care will skyrocket. In fact, people over 65 are more likely to be ill than adults at other ages. Moreover, they are also more likely to use the health-care system when they are ill. Recent research from the Canadian Health Services Research Foundation demonstrates that the increasing use of medical care by seniors is not only the result of their increasing numbers in the population but also their relatively higher rates of use. Interestingly, however, evidence suggests that it is healthy seniors, not sick seniors, who are responsible for a significant part of the increase in utilization and, therefore, costs. Thus, "well-person checkups" and early detection measures drive up the costs to everyone of the aging population. Further, although the costs of health care are expected to rise as the whole population ages, the impact of aging itself is only a small part of the overall increase. Other, more significant cost-drivers include inflation and technological innovations. Aging, of itself, is expected to contribute about 1 per cent per year of the increase in health-care costs between 2010 and 2036.

The picture is complex, because aging, inflation, and innovation are difficult to separate as the standards change for what can and should be done as people age and approach death. For instance, older people are now much more likely to have knee replacements and coronary bypass surgery than they were in 1990. Is this a function of aging or of new technologies? The short answer is "both." Which is more important? It is hard to say (CHSRF, 2001; CFHI, 2011). Furthermore, we do not have enough palliative or long-term care beds for the level of need that exists. Living in hospital with chronic illness and during an acute terminal process is expensive unless community-supported long-term/palliative care beds are available. Expanding hospice services and similar caring locations for the dying and for those with long-term care needs would alleviate the very high costs of hospitalization. Thus, many elderly people languish in hospitals at great expense because we have failed to provide enough spaces for their long-term needs. Health policies and investments lag behind needs. Discuss the ethical and policy issues raised above.

Source: CFHI (2011).

levels, and depression; and self-perceived health. This research found that the socio-demographic factors (social determinants of health) explained a significant amount of the differences among communities in health outcomes—from 25 per cent to over 55 per cent. Among the interesting findings was that people living in Canada's largest cities were among the healthiest (these peer groups were notably characterized by high average levels of education and high proportions of visible minorities). They had the longest life expectancies and disability-free life expectancies across Canada. They also tended to engage in healthier behaviours. Remote northern communities had the poorest health outcomes. Rates for unhealthy behaviours such as smoking, heavy drinking, and obesity were higher than the Canadian averages, and life expectancy and disability-free life expectancy were the lowest. On the other hand, northerners reported lower levels of stress and depression (www.statcan.ca/daily/English/020704/d020704b.htm).

Inequality

We have reiterated that inequality in a society is a significant predictor of the health of its population. To understand this further, let us compare the degree of inequality and the health outcomes of three different developed societies—Japan, the US, and Canada. Japan had the highest life expectancy for both males and females at 80.0 years for males and 86.0 years for females in 2011, as compared to 79.0 for males and 83.0 for females in Canada and 76.0 for males and 81.0 for females in the US (WHO, 2011: 48). This relative longevity in Japan has been a long-standing phenomenon, and despite the fact that the smoking rate in that country is twice as high as in Canada, the smoking-related mortality rate is just half that of Canada. Japan's success in health terms arguably is related to the relative equity within the country. After World War II, Japan articulated an emphasis on pursuing income equality and began to redistribute income throughout the whole society. The redistribution of income likely resulted in a greater degree of equality among Japanese people regarding their "uptake" of the social determinants of health that are within their control, such as quality housing, increased education,

and a greater possibility of locating fulfilling, stable, safe, and interesting work. These advantages in the various social determinants of health undoubtedly result in greater well-being. The significance of and the value placed on income equity to the communal identity of the Japanese are somewhat akin to the identification of Canadians with our national health-care system. For instance, in an economic crisis, some top Japanese executives and managers took pay cuts rather than lay off workers (artcles.latimes.com/1992-05-17/business/fi-131_1_top-executives-mr-iacocca-pay). This action was considered the honourable thing to do. Japan is a cohesive society in which income equity is a chief value. By contrast, Mikkonen and Raphael (2010: 4) have estimated that Canadians lose a significant portion—approximately one-quarter—of their lives prematurely because of income differences (http://www.thecanadianfacts.org/The_Canadian_Facts.pdf).

In the US, the differences between the richest and the poorest citizens have been growing, and the US is characterized by relatively high rates of mortality and by a high degree of income inequality. According to a recent study by Piketty (2014), the top 10 per cent of the US population controls 71 per cent of the country's wealth and takes home 48 per cent of the income. Further, under the current political economy wealth and inequality will continue to grow. In tandem the poorest Americans are getting poorer and this trend will continue if the current neo-liberal processes continue. As is the case in the US, racialization and racism are important contributors to the income gaps in Canada. The average income for all Canadian earners in 2001 was $29,769. For those from the African community the average income was $23,787 and the Haitian Canadian average was $19,782 (Mikkonen and Raphael, 2010: 49). Moreover, relatively little evidence points to government efforts to minimize these economic disparities. The US and Canada ranked in the bottom half of the OECD countries with respect to income equality in the mid-2000s (ibid., 14). The growing disparity between rich and poor around the world, including in the developed countries, is linked in part to globalization. That health is affected is evident in many indicators.

Three of the most important are life expectancy at birth, child injury, and infant mortality. The US ranked 20 out of 30 OECD countries in life expectancy at birth, and US child injury and infant mortality rates also are relatively poor. In respect to child injury rates, the US ranked 23 out of 26 OECD countries with equivalent data and Canada ranked eighteenth; Sweden ranked first. Despite spending more on health care than any other OECD nation, the US compares poorly on outcomes. Canada, too, has a relatively poor showing (2003; www.who.int/research/en/). The political explanation offered by Navarro and Shi (2003) in regard to income equality, as described above, is significant, as is the prevalence of neo-liberalism.

Another very sensitive indicator of the effects of inequality on health can be found in the rates of self-harm and suicide. Both of these behaviours are correlated with socio-economic status (Eggertson, 2013). The highest rates of hospitalization for self-harm in Canada in 2011–12 were in the neighbourhoods with the lowest income. Moreover, people who live in the North had exceptionally high rates of hospitalization due to self-harm (almost six times the national rate) for causes such as hanging, drug overdoses, and cutting. The rate of self-harm resulting in suicide was 10 times as high as the national average among Inuit people. The Canadian Institutes of Health notes that the numbers of people hospitalized for self-harm would be 27 per cent lower if those in the poorer neighbourhoods were hospitalized at the same rates as those in the most well-off neighbourhoods. About 70 per cent of those hospitalized for these reasons would not have been.

Food Security

Hunger is a problem in Canada. Children go to school hungry and stay home sick because of hunger and diseases exacerbated or caused by malnutrition. All sorts of people depend on food banks to feed themselves and their families. Many universities now have food banks. Is there one at your university? The first food bank was established in Canada about 25 years ago, in Edmonton. Since then the number of people using food banks has continued to grow and

is now higher than it was during the recent recession (http://www.foodbankscanada.ca/FoodBanks/MediaLibrary/HungerCount/HungerCount2013.pdf). Today there are more than 700 food banks across the country. A disproportionate 11 per cent of food bank users are Aboriginal and another 11 per cent are immigrants to Canada. These figures reflect racism in employment, housing, and government and industry policies regarding training equivalencies between place of origin and Canada. Twelve per cent of food bank users are currently employed. About 36 per cent are children. Approximately 833,098 people used a food bank in March of 2013 (ibid.). Figure 4.5 presents estimates of the use of provincial food banks for the years 2001–11. The use of food banks represents an ongoing inequity in Canada. Food bank use also perpetuates inequity through indirectly contributing to both mental and physical illness because of the food banks' lack of healthy foods such as fresh fruits and vegetables. Children's feelings of worry, sadness, and unhappiness are associated with the quality of their diet (Martin et al., 2013). Relying on a food bank because of the relatively poor nutritional value of the canned and dried foods available and the lack of fresh fruits and vegetables contributes not only to poorer physical health among the children who depend on food banks but also to their poorer mental health. This outcome is in addition to the complex and difficult feelings of embarrassment, anger, and shame that having to depend on a food bank elicits in users.

Among those who are most vulnerable to food insecurity in Canada are the elderly (Payette and Shatenstein, 2005). Approximately 34 per cent (4.1 million people) 65 and over are on the brink of malnutrition in Canada according to the Community Health Survey–Healthy Aging (Chenier, 2013). This malnourishment is partly due to diminishing appetites and decline in sensitivity to smell and taste as people age. However, it is due, also, to the inability of the elderly to get to the store to purchase healthy food and to their mobility limitations in daily life. Depression, loneliness, and the grief of loss may also affect the nutritional level of the elderly through a lack of energy to maintain mealtime routines, shop for food, cook, bake, and so on.

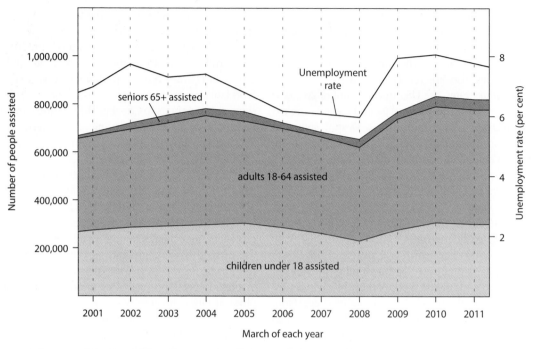

FIGURE 4.5   Number of People Assisted by Food Banks in Canada, 2001–11

Source: Food Banks Canada, HungerCount, 2011 (Toronto: Food Banks Canada, 2011).

Food insecurity is a serious problem in Canada. Are we committing a type of economic abuse when, as a society, we fail to provide sufficient money for adequate nutrition? Clearly, an economic gradient is evident in the levels of consumption of nutritious food (Power, 2005). One study examined the cost of food in 43 randomly selected grocery stores and estimated the cost of a nutritious diet for people living on a minimum-wage job (Williams et al., 2006). According to the authors of this study, people living on a minimum wage could not afford to purchase an adequately nutritious diet. Moreover, cost estimates suggested that Canadians living at this level of poverty could not afford other routinely required products such as those needed for cleaning, personal hygiene, or unusual and unexpected needs such as medication.

Ironically, food insecurity and, most likely, food bank use are associated with both obesity and hunger. This is because foods that are higher in caloric content and often full of sugar and carbohydrates tend to be cheaper than the much more nutritious foods, such as fresh fruits and vegetables and proteins such as meat, cheese, and nuts. Obesity, or excess body fat, is a growing problem associated with inequality, poverty, and low levels of education (Institute for Clinical Evaluative Sciences, 2006: 1), and is an increasing problem among Canadian young people as discussed in Chapter 2. Those factors are linked to hypertension, type 2 diabetes, heart disease, osteoporosis, and mental health problems (ibid., 3). It must be noted that parallel to the increasing concerns about obesity is an equally vocal oppositional position that thinks the problem of the obesity epidemic in overdrawn and even manufactured. The idea of "fat fabrications" is a concept that points to this debate (Monaghan et al., 2013)

Poverty

The definition of poverty is a political matter. What counts as "poverty" for the purposes of state interventions is different from what counts as poverty in the perspective of poverty activists or those living in impoverished situations. However defined, "poverty" refers to the economic position and stability of people who have a difficult time or who fail to meet their own and their family's basic needs for food, shelter, water, clothing, transportation, and access to education, community facilities and services, and health care. In Canada "poverty" is defined as the low-income cut-off point. Currently (although the definition changes from one year to the next), those people who spend at least 20 per cent more of their income on food, shelter, and clothing than the average Canadian spends on those essentials are considered to be below this "poverty line." This definition is hotly debated. Perhaps the most useful approach is to compare, using consistent definitions, Canada's poverty line with that of other similar countries. In this regard Canada's poverty level is now above the average of our comparator countries in the OECD. In the mid-1990s we were substantially below the mean of the OECD countries. Figure 4.6 provides a visual portrayal of the impacts of Canadian neo-liberalism on the poverty rate.

In 1989, the federal Canadian Parliament unanimously proclaimed its intent to eradicate child poverty by the year 2000. Whether this was merely a gesture on the part of Canada's

parliamentarians or they failed to realize how intractable poverty is and what would be required to meet such a goal is not known. More than 25 years later child poverty in Canada certainly has not been eradicated. Indeed, it has increased consistently each year since the mid-1990s. Children living in poverty are more likely to experience developmental delays, and such delays often lead to a lifetime of underachievement and, consequently, the continuance of poverty from one generation to the next. They are also more likely to experience various childhood illnesses, some of which are directly related to their probable lower birth weights. In Canada, according to Statistics Canada, the child poverty rate for Canada was 14.3 per cent in 2011. As shown in Figure 4.7, there has been some improvement in the percentage of children living in poverty, but we still compare poorly to our peer countries, as is demonstrated in Figure 4.8.

As noted, definitions of poverty are political and contested. Progressive political parties and societies governed by them are more likely to be generous in their definitions of poverty—that is, they are likely to think that more people are poor and in need—and conservative political parties are more likely to think that a greater proportion of people are above the poverty line. For the purposes of this book, although there are differences

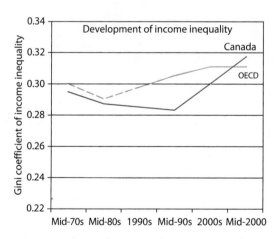
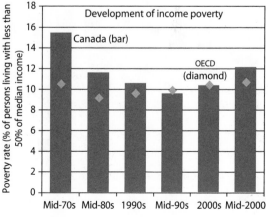

FIGURE 4.6   Development of Income Inequality and Income Poverty, mid-1970s to mid-2000s

Source: Country Note: Canada: Growing Unequal?: Income Distribution and Poverty in OECD Countries. OECD (2008), p. 1., http://www.oecd.org/social/soc/41525292.pdf.

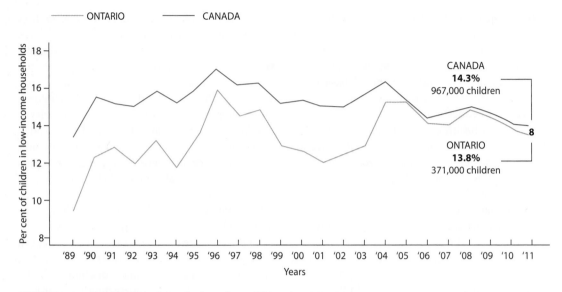

FIGURE 4.7   Child Poverty Rates in Canada and Ontario, 1989–2011

Source: Statistics Canada, 2013, based on Monsebraaten, "Child poverty rates in Canada, Ontario remain high." Toronto Star, November 25, 2013 http://www.thestar.com/news/gta/2013/11/25/child_poverty_rates_in_canada_ontario_remain_high.html.

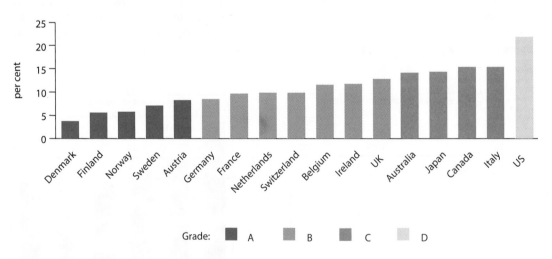

FIGURE 4.8   Child Poverty Rate, Late 2000s

Source: How Canada Performs: Child Poverty, by Conference Board of Canada, 2013, http://www.conferenceboard.ca/hcp/details/society/child-poverty.aspx.

in the presumed poverty rates, they all indicate that a substantial number of children today live in families where their basic needs are not being met. Furthermore, and to the point of this book, those living in poverty, even in advanced industrial and post-industrial societies, are more likely to experience diseases than those in other social classes in the same country. Among these diseases are influenza and tuberculosis, both of which spread rapidly in dense living quarters and among those who lack private living spaces and/or the ability to practise such safety precautions as frequent hand-cleaning (see, e.g., www.hc.-sc.gc.ca/dc-ma/influenza/index_e.html). Children living in poverty are also more frequently dealing with learning disabilities, language delay, and anti-social behaviour (Spitzer, 2005: S85). In addition, impoverishment is associated with various mental health problems, chronic diseases, distress, and low self-esteem (ibid.). An impoverished child with a disease such as childhood cancer is disadvantaged because the treatment carries on for a long time and because one parent (usually) has to provide continual home (and in-hospital) health-care work taking the child back and forth to medical care and testing. Further, because the treatments often involve assaults to the immune system through chemotherapy drugs, children may become very vulnerable to infectious diseases and frequently have to stay home from school or any other public gathering. Parents have lost homes and jobs as a result of having to stay home to care for their children when they are ill with a chronic or terminal illness such as cancer. While we do not have good research on the social class correlates of childhood cancer it is clear from this example that a family can become impoverished as a result of caring for a child with life-threatening, serious, or chronic diseases.

Employment

Simply being employed rather than unemployed provides some benefit. However, there is more to employment that merely having a job. We also must consider the safety and stability of the work, the pay or salary, the holidays and hours of employment, and the degree of responsibility, creativity, and autonomy experienced on the job. Many jobs involve work with dangerous substances, such as the pesticides, fertilizers, and other chemicals used sometimes without adequate safety precautions or even knowledge of the necessity for such precautions. Other work is dangerous because of susceptibility to new diseases, including health-care work, as the SARS crisis demonstrated (see www.sars.ca), or because of violence at work where, ironically,

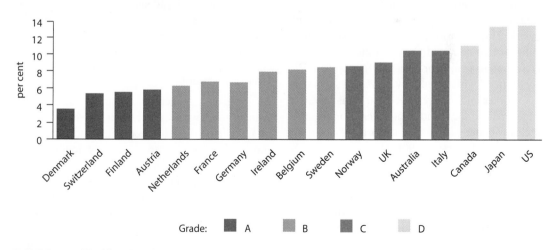

FIGURE 4.9 Working-Age Poverty

Source: How Canada Performs: Working-Age Poverty," by Conference Board of Canada, 2013, http://www.conferenceboard.ca/hcp/details/society/working-age-poverty.aspx.

health-care workers are among the most vulnerable, along with correctional officers, social service workers, and teachers. Aside from safety at work, employment stability and good wages are crucial to adequate employment. The minimum wage across the country, as of June 2015, varies from $10.20 in Alberta and Saskatchewan to $12.50 in the Northwest Territories. After the NWT, the next highest minimum wages—$11—are found in Nunavut and Ontario (http://www.retailcouncil.org/quickfacts/minimum-wage). Consider, for example, how much one has to pay for a one-bedroom apartment in your community and calculate how much of the income of a person collecting minimum wage must go to housing. Or think about the number of students and others you know who have more than one job in order to make ends meet.

Barbara Ehrenreich, a noted author and social critic with a Ph.D. in biology, in *Nickel and Dimed: On (Not) Getting By in America*, documents her trying to get, and then live on, minimum-wage jobs in several different states in the United States. She points out that having to live on minimum wage can happen to anyone, and most students know this very well. She also shows how difficult it was for her to get a job and then how impossible it was to distinguish herself and her unique abilities and training no matter where she found work. As she says, "Several times since completing this project I have been asked by acquaintances whether the people I worked with couldn't, uh, tell—the supposition being that an educated person is ineradicably different, and in a superior direction from your workday drones. I wish I could say that some supervisor or coworker told me even once that I was special in some enviable way—more intelligent, for example, or clearly better educated than most. But this never happened" (Ehrenreich, 2001: 8).

Work and its absence are significant determinants of health and illness. Occupation is also an important predictor of health through the mechanism of income because the most important determinant of income is employment, although there are those who live on investment income or pension income and are not dependent, or not entirely

dependent, on the paid labour force. So, what is a good and healthy job aside from one that is stable and provides an adequate income? Adequacy and stability of income are of significance. However, the quality of work life is also important (yet understudied). A good job offers a manageable workload, and flexibility and autonomy in the execution of the workload. Being able to decide what to do and when in order to accomplish goals, which the worker takes a part in setting, is important. Having to work to persistent deadlines established by others, particularly urgent deadlines, is often experienced as problematic. Creativity, self-expression, and self-development, possibly rare aspects of work in the paid labour force, are also important to the quality of human work life. Satisfying social relations are another aspect of what might be described as "good" work. Important as these qualities appear to be to health and well-being, very little research actually addresses such questions with respect to work in Canada (Jackson, 2009). Polanyi (2004), in reviewing research in this area, notes that topics studied include "job control" (which includes "pace, participation and control, and opportunities for personal development"), effort–reward balance, and job strain, work hours, work–life conflict, and job insecurity. All of these have been found to have links to health outcomes. Good work, according to Polanyi, is available, adequate (as to income, benefits, and rights), appropriate to training and life circumstances, and meaningful to workers. Good work is also acknowledged and appreciated.

Unemployment

As difficult, dangerous, unstable, and poorly paid as some work is, at least it provides a degree of involvement in the economy and a minimal sense of being able to contribute to one's own or one's family's well-being. As of June 2015, the unemployment rate in Canada was 6.8 per cent. This figure is considered to be relatively low in a global context today, but it had been declining over the past decade and a half until the market meltdown of 2008, when it rose rapidly for a time. This means that more than a million people in

Canada are actively looking for work. In addition, a sizable proportion of Canadian workers, such as fishers, loggers, roofers, and other outdoor workers, are intermittently or seasonally unemployed. Further, untold thousands of other people out of work are not factored into unemployment statistics because they are not actively seeking employment. Unemployment and underemployment are also differentially and inequitably distributed across such socio-demographic categories as gender, education level and type, ethnic background, immigrant status, age, and rural/urban location. Regional variations persist, with unemployment rates highest in Atlantic Canada and lowest in the western provinces. Today, as well, the youth unemployment rate is particularly high.

Education/Literacy

Education is an important resource in Canadian society. It opens doors to certain (and often safer) occupations; it increases the chances of promotion to a more satisfying occupation. Education often increases financial stability and security, job satisfaction, and choice, and may help people cope with problems of living, including those related to healthy living (atlas.nrcan.gc.ca/site/English/maps/health/nonmedicaldeterminantsofhealth/education/education_figure1.gif/image_view). People with higher levels of education are also more likely to perceive their health as very good or excellent.

Education is related to types of employment, the prestige of a person's occupation, and the level of individual income, as well as to health-related behaviours, such as eating nutritious food and driving safely, and to awareness of and access to health information. People with more formal education are more likely to work in jobs in which they have control and self-sufficiency. Jobs requiring more education also are more likely to be the jobs that are predictable from season to season and year to year and have higher social status and prestige. Such jobs are associated with self-esteem, respect, health, and well-being. Education is such a powerful predictor of income that it is sometimes used as

a proxy for income in some data analyses (Feldman et al., 2004).

The importance of early childhood education and care cannot be overemphasized (Friendly, 2009). It can set the stage for later successes in school and all other aspects of life. It is particularly important that early childhood education be available to the children of single-parent families and of poor mothers and families as a way of levelling the playing field for later educational achievement. According to Ronson and Rootman (2009), considerable evidence indicates that literacy is also a powerful predictor of income and health status. It is also likely that illiteracy limits the ability of a person to know about how to engage in healthy behaviours and to understand all sorts of health-related messages regarding exercise, disease prevention messages, early detection guidelines and the like. Imagine, for a moment, how your life would be altered if you could not read.

Housing

The number of homeless people in Canada has grown in recent decades. Current estimates of the total number of those experiencing homelessness in Canada range from a conservative government total of 150,000 to those of non-governmental organizations, which place the total at somewhere about 200,000 according to the excellent and detailed report from the Wellesley Institute (http://www.wellesleyinstitute.com/wp-content/uploads/2013/06/SOHC2103.pdf). About 30,000 Canadians are homeless any given night. Accurately enumerating the homeless is difficult since not having a fixed address makes one difficult to locate and contact. One partial measure of housing inadequacy is how many people are living in shelters across the country because they cannot afford their own apartments, rooms, or homes. Shelter "counts" provide a snapshot of only one night and vary seasonally, and cannot account for those on the streets or in other conditions of homelessness. In addition to **absolute homelessness** or being unsheltered, some people are sheltered on an emergency basis only, i.e., emergency sheltered.

SPOTLIGHT ON ETHICS

BOX 4.3   Bioethical Dilemmas

Many Aboriginal reserves lack clean, potable water. Do you think that we as a society are ethically bound to correct this situation immediately? This is not a question of research ethics but of policy. If we understand that health is in all policies, do we have an obligation to ensure that the human right to water is honoured?

The following table (Table 4.3) lists the top 10 ethical dilemmas from the point of view of bioethicists. Health sociologists might have a different list and one that would include such issues as equity in access to water because of our interest in the social determinants of health and illness. The following are all downstream ethical issues whereas sociologists are more interested in upstream ethical principles. What would be your list of the top 10 ethical issues in social and health policy today? Think of the social determinants. You might want to co-ordinate your answer with the Universal Declaration of Human Rights found at http://www.un.org/en/documents/udhr/.

TABLE 4.3   Top 10 Ethical Challenges Facing Canadians in Health Care

Rank	Dilemma
1	Disagreement between patients/families and health-care professionals about treatment decisions
2	Waiting lists
3	Access to needed health-care resources for the aged, chronically ill, and mentally ill
4	Shortage of family physicians or primary care teams in both rural and urban settings
5	Medical error
6	Withholding/withdrawing life-sustaining treatment in the context of terminal or serious illness
7	Achieving informed consent
8	Ethical issues related to subject participation in research
9	Substitute decision-making
10	The ethics of surgical innovation and incorporating new technologies for patient care

Source: Top 10 health care ethics challenges facing the public: views of Toronto bioethicists. Jonathan M. Breslin, Susan K. MacRae, Jennifer Bell, Peter A. Singer and the University of Toronto Joint Centre for Bioethics Clinical Ethics Group. BMC Medical Ethics, 2005 6:5.

There are also people who can be classified as **provisionally accommodated** (those who live in a car, the "couch surfers" who live with friends or family, and those in long-term institutions). In addition, many other people, in substandard housing or on the verge of losing their shelter, are said to be at risk for homelessness (ibid.). Housing insecurity is particularly problematic among vulnerable groups of people, including the working poor, those who are unemployed or mentally ill, lone-parent families, recent immigrants, and Aboriginal people, both on reserves and in urban areas.

Neighbourhood

Some research has found that neighbourhood characteristics, such as the degree of stability and affluence, have a powerful and independent effect on health status and may, at times, be more important to health than individual social and economic status, health behaviours, and insurance coverage (Browning and Cagney, 2003). According to Browning and Cagney, neighbourhood explains a large portion of the health gap by "race" in the US. Other research has documented that poorer neighbourhoods, assessed through both quantitative and qualitative measures, may be highly stressful and linked to both physical and mental illness (Latkin and Curry, 2003). Among the contributing factors to a disadvantaged neighbourhood are the relative lack of social support and social integration, vandalism, litter and trash, vacant housing, teenagers hanging out, burglary, drug-dealing, and robbery. Such findings underscore the significance of social cohesion and the neo-materialist explanation for the link between inequalities and health outcomes. Neighbourhood deprivation parallels health inequities (Bell and Hayes, 2012).

The chief cause of death and disease in Canada today is cardiovascular disease (CVD). The following map (Figure 4.10) shows how the incidence of both mortality and morbidity are patterned by neighbourhood in Toronto. Essentially what this map demonstrates is the powerful association between neighbourhood characteristics and the death rates from CVD. CVD is caused by a complex of factors including stress, diet, smoking, and exercise. People living in the poorest neighbourhoods are more likely to receive this diagnosis and to die as a result. Income, employment, and household data on the neighbourhoods shown in this map and study of CVD demonstrate clearly the significance of inequities in living standards to death from CVD.

Social Theory, Economics, and Health

While we have discussed each of these social conditions as if it were a singular and separable condition, in reality they operate together through individual bodies and lives and through social policies and practices. It is possible only

theoretically or in the abstract to characterize any one individual or any one policy by only one social characteristic, such as "degree of poverty." All such social categories intersect. In other words, people are gendered, racialized, employed/unemployed/poor (or not) all at the same time. Moreover, any single characteristic can exacerbate or mitigate the effects of any other characteristic.

Why are there pervasive correlations between death, disability, disease, and inequalities? Marxist analysis attempts to integrate all discrete and superficially unique explanations into a unified explanation. A substantial body of scholarship documents the relationship between the economy and health status. Beginning with the work of Friedrich Engels in *The Condition of the Working Class in England* (1985 [1845]), analysis has focused on the state and on the economy as they affect health outcomes. Engels noticed in the earliest industrialist economies the contradictions between the workers' need to sell their labour power and the capitalist factory owners' need and desire for profit. Because industrial profit was necessary to maintain factory-based production, the wages of workers were kept low and their working conditions poor. Shelter for the poor was frequently inadequate, crowded, unheated, and unsanitary. Poor hygiene and inadequate nutrition resulted in widespread contagious diseases such as tuberculosis and typhoid.

The first principle of capitalism (and especially of neo-liberalism) is that business requires profit. Profit is the bottom line. According to Marxist analysis, all capitalist states are arranged in such a way as to maximize profits. Furthermore, competition forces capitalists to maximize outputs while minimizing the costs of production. The growth of profits results in the accumulation of capital. Excess capital is invested in new or more efficient production units. New and greater profits are then realized. Increased production invokes a need to find and create new markets. When domestic markets are saturated, new foreign markets must be opened up. Profits from these markets are reinvested, and the cycle of profit, competition, accumulation of capital, investment, and expanded markets repeats

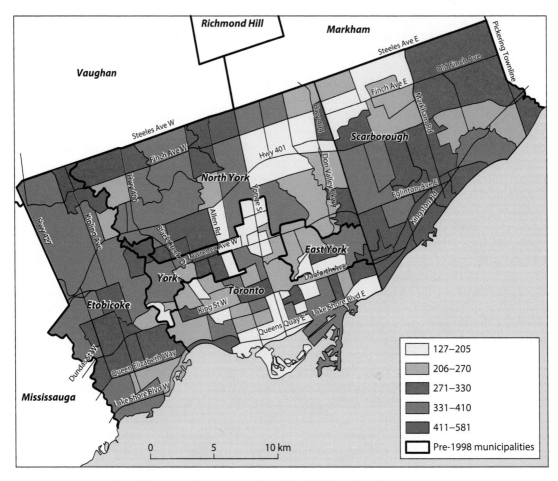

FIGURE 4.10   Crude Cardiac Arrest Rate per 100,000, by Neighbourhood

Source: Taylor, "Where you live in Toronto can increase your risk for cardiac arrest: study." St. Michael's College. January 6, 2012. http://www.stmichaelshospital.com/media/detail.php?source=hospital_news/2012/20120106_hn.

itself. All the while, the owners of capital—the capitalists—take some of the profits to live luxuriant lives, usually bolstered by substantial savings and investments. The *Christian Science Monitor*'s list of the 10 companies with the largest gap between the average salary of the worker and that of the CEO is enlightening. The gap between the CEO of Walmart and Walmart's workers is seventh on the list at $6,898 per hour for the CEO and $8.86 for the average hourly wage of the worker: the CEO's rate is 779 times the wage rate of the worker. The gap is highest at McDonald's, where the average hourly wage of the worker is $7.73 and that of the CEO is $9,247. The CEO makes 1,196 times the hourly wage of the worker (http://www.csmonitor.com/Business/2013/1212/CEO-vs.-worker-pay-Walmart-McDonald-s-and-eight-other-firms-with-biggest-gaps/McDonald-s).

When the state economy is based on capitalism (or neo-liberalism), state decisions are guided by the apparent necessity of supporting the most successful profit-making initiatives. Usually, when a choice between profitability and human need is confronted, profitability comes first. The argument is that the good of the whole—the freedom and well-being of individuals—is advanced when economic productivity and profitability prevail. Consequently, when the need for profit is the determining principle, the health needs of the population assume secondary importance. The worth of individuals in a capitalist economy is measured by their relationship to the means of production. Because of upturns and downturns in the economy, a reserve labour force is required. The reserve labour force is made up of people who are peripheral to the paid labour force and can be brought into it or dismissed from it depending on market demands. An alternative to this economic theory, proposed by a member of the wealthy class, is that a prosperous middle class drives the economy and that they should be supported by the rich providing more than minimally adequate wages for workers (Hanauer, 2014).

The more marginal the worker is in the capitalist (or neo-liberal) economy, the more easily he or she can be replaced. Occupational health and safety precautions are expenses to the capitalist owner. To the extent that the cost of such precautions threatens the level of profit, and in the absence of state legislative requirements, health and safety standards will be minimal. Indeed, less stringent health, safety, and environmental regulation is one reason why so much industrial production has shifted to developing countries in recent decades. Accidents, job-related sickness, and alienation will be most prevalent among those workers who are most marginal and most replaceable. One overriding reason for income, gender, age, and ethnic differences in health is the variation in access to safe, satisfying, adequately remunerated work. Marxist analysis provides an important explanation for inequities in health outcomes.

To conclude: good health is the outcome of access to fundamental resources. Poverty, poor nutrition, inadequate housing and transportation, and the lack of effective birth control all contribute in known ways to ill health. In a capitalist economy with a neo-liberal ideology there are significant differences in access to these life-giving resources

in respect to differences in age, gender, income, and ethnic group.

Commodification

One other contribution of Marxist analysis to understanding inequities in death, disease, and disability is through the concept of commodities or **commodification**. Commodities are objects or activities having an "exchange value." They can be bought and sold in the marketplace and can be used to acquire other things. Their value is determined by market factors such as supply and demand. Health can be seen as a commodity. Health no longer is simply the individual experience of well-being but, in a capitalist economy, is subject to supply and demand. The buying and selling of organs for transplantation into unhealthy bodies is perhaps the most blatant example of commodification. Health is purchasable for those with the money, even at the expense of the health of others. There is also a way in which health itself is an object that reflects value and worth back on the individual. In this case, health is used to indicate the productive value of the person to the society. Healthy people are thought to be "good" people. Health embodies a certain level of conspicuous consumption and a degree of much valued self-control.

Whenever a government or a corporation decides to allow the continuance of a practice that is destructive to the health of a population in the interests of financial benefits, such as taxes or profits, health is being commodified. Cigarette manufacturing is a case in point. There is absolutely no doubt that cigarette smoking is a significant cause of disability and death in Canadian society. Yet neither the cigarette industry nor the government has been willing to pull cigarettes from the market or to limit their production to low-tar cigarettes. Cigarettes are a fundamental and crucial aspect of contemporary economies. According to Doyal (1979), the state has made a deliberate decision to allow the tobacco industry to continue. The British Department of Health showed that a reduction in cigarette smoking would be costly to the state. Not only would the tax on cigarettes be lost, but the additional financial costs of caring for people longer into their old age would be the inevitable result of increased life expectancy.

SUMMARY

1. Health and illness in societies are linked to social inequities.
2. One way of conceptualizing the various inequities is through the social determinants of health.
3. The social determinants of health work through materialist processes and include the neo-materialist, socio-psychological, and life course approaches.
4. Other theorists use a different conceptual framework and have focused on social capital and its role in health outcomes. These perspectives are largely consistent with one another.
5. Morbidity and mortality are linked to political and economic systems and to particular ideologies such as neo-liberalism.
6. Among the social determinants of health discussed in this chapter are: inequality, food security, employment, unemployment, housing, and neighbourhood.
7. Social theory, economics, and health are linked. Health is sometimes treated as a commodity.

KEY TERMS

absolute homelessness
commodification
cumulative advantage theory
cumulative effects
downstream model
fundamental cause

health in all policies (HiAP)
latency effects
life course approach
materialist approach
neo-materialist approach
pathway effects

provisionally accommodated
social capital
social inclusion
upstream model

QUESTIONS FOR STUDY AND DISCUSSION

1. How can we explain the different life expectancies of racialized people, of those with different sexual orientations and identities, and of those from higher and lower social classes?
2. What is the relevance to health outcomes of the increase in inequality in Canada over the last several decades?
3. Compare a magazine that is written for an African-American audience (e.g., *Ebony, Jet,* or *Essence*) and one that is written for a mainstream audience (e.g., *Maclean's, Reader's Digest,* or *Cosmopolitan*) with respect to advertisements for health- and body-related products, such as anti-depressants, hair colouring chemicals, diet pills, and the like). Theorize your findings.
4. Critically examine your personal social determinants of health.
5. Should your university or college develop policies to encourage social inclusion? Why or why not?

SUGGESTED READINGS

Access Alliance Multicultural Community Health Centre. 2005. "A Literature Review Exploring Poverty, Housing, Race-based Discrimination and Access to Health Care as Determinants of Health for Racialised Groups." In *Racialised Groups and Health Status*, 1–16. Toronto: AAMCHC. This literature review brings together evidence from a number of small Canadian studies to offer a preliminary analysis of the relationship between health status and racialized groups, with a particular focus on poverty, housing, and discrimination.

Hanauer, Nick. 2014. "The Pitchforks Are Coming . . . For Us Plutocrats." *Politico* (July–Aug.). http://www.politico.com/magazine/story/2014/06/the-pitchforks-are-coming-for-us-plutocrats-108014.html#.VViJQ1LFtT4. An interesting alternative economic proposal by an Internet entrepreneur who labels himself a "zillionaire" and warns others of the wealthiest class that unless they provide more than barely adequate wages to narrow the income gap, they won't have time to escape in their private jets when revolution occurs.

Martin, M.C., E. Seanna, N.D. Willows, I. Colman, and A. Ohinma. 2013. "Diet Quality and Feelings of Worry, Sadness or Unhappiness in Canadian Children." *Canadian Journal of Public Health* 104, 4: 322–6. This article raises the question of whether some of the increase in the diagnoses of children's mental health issues relates to the quality of food.

Mikkonen, Juha, and Dennis Raphael. 2010. *Social Determinants of Health: The Canadian Facts*. Toronto: York University School of Health Policy and Management. A brief overview of the health impacts of the major social determinants of health in Canada.

Raphael, Dennis, ed. 2008. *The Social Determinants of Health*, 2nd edn. Toronto: Canadian Scholar's Press. Important research on the social determinants of health and interventions by policy-makers that can improve the health inequities in Canadian society.

Wilkinson, R., and K. Pickett. 2010. *The Spirit Level: Why Equality Is Better for Everyone*. London: Penguin UK. This book offers analysis and statistics on the impact of inequality on health and social issues.

5

Diversities and Health: Age, Gender, Sexualities, "Races," and Aboriginal Peoples

© Leswrona | Dreamstime.com

CHAPTER OVERVIEW

▶ Inequity in a society impacts health at the level of the individual and of the population as a whole. It affects people of diverse socially constructed identities and social statuses differently.

▶ The social determinants of health discussed in the previous chapter operate through cross-cutting or intersectional social identities and statuses such as age, life stage, gender, sexual identities, and marital status, as well as ethnic and racialized identity membership.

▶ The most significant change in life expectancy over the last century and a half has been in infant and child mortality. This factor has been important in the overall aging of the population. Age and age identity are linked to morbidity and mortality.

▶ Gender identity, marital status, sexual identity, and "race" are associated with sickness and death.

▶ Aboriginal Canadians face particular health hazards linked to the history of colonialism and the residential school system, among other factors.

▶ Explanations for differential morbidity by age include differences in income, other social determinants of health, lifestyle, psychosocial aspects of symptoms and care, and differential access to health-giving resources.

▶ Explanations for differential morbidity and mortality in men and women include all of the social determinants of health, biological factors, gendered behaviours, attentiveness to bodily sensations, ability to remember and describe health, and engagement in preventive actions.

▶ "Race" or racialized identity status is associated with poorer health, because of income, education and occupational inequalities, discrimination, and racism.

▶ Aboriginal Canadians have dramatically different life chances and higher rates of morbidity and mortality than non-Aboriginal Canadians.

▶ Political power seems to be associated with health status.

Introduction: Social-Structural Positions and Health

Socio-economic status is a fundamental cause of health disparities both because of the higher rates of illness associated with those lower on the status hierarchy or living in more unequal societies and also because of the uneven access to care and treatments (Chang and Lauderdale 2009). Moreover, all of the socio-economic (social) determinants of health discussed in the previous chapter impact people with varying identities and social-structural positions differently. We will look in more depth in this chapter at gender and sexual identities, age and stage identities, and racialized and ethnic identities and their relationships to morbidity and mortality. For example, the social determinant of health, occupational insecurity, will likely affect income differentials and this may operate differently among those identified as male and those identified as female. Occupational insecurity may also affect those who identify as gay men and lesbian women differently than heterosexually identified people. Notice the use of the term "identities" here. This idea reflects the notion that **essentialized** social statuses such as male and female as biologically given and unquestioned needs to be critiqued. Whether a person is seen by himself/herself as a male or female and in turn whether others see individuals as belonging to the gender they would like to be seen as is sometimes a very complicated issue. Until recently we, in our society, and we, as sociologists, have failed to carefully examine the complexities of various identities such as gender. Now, however, we are coming to more fully understand the pervasiveness of the social in the construction of the ways that persons act, think, feel as men or women or "trans" and so on. Sexualities, sexual

preferences, age or life course stage, and racialized identities are also being deconstructed and their health impacts studied in more depth. We will review some of the literature on the health effects of various diverse identities in this chapter.

Underlying the following analysis is the argument that the social determinants (as discussed in the previous chapter) also interact with one another either to exacerbate or to mitigate their health effects. This is an illustration of intersectionality, a theoretical framework introduced in the first chapter. We must underscore the idea that the social constructions related to gender, sexualities, life course, age, **racialization**, and Aboriginal group status are not applied to individuals and groups within society one variable at a time. Every woman, for example, as well as having a gender identity also has an age, a sexuality identity, and is racialized (or has a racial identity) both by herself and by others within the society. She will also have a certain level of income, a particular type and level of education, and so on. Therefore, it should be emphasized that we are simplifying the picture of the causes of health and illness for purposes of discussion, and readers must recognize that, empirically and theoretically, the situation is a great deal more complex in any given case. It is also important to note that there are other cross-cutting sources of inequality and status such as religious group membership or identity, occupational status, and country of origin.

Among other questions, this chapter considers the following: Are women more often sick than men? Do men and women suffer from different illnesses? Why are children in the first years of life particularly fragile with respect to illnesses? Does old age bring increasing infirmity and illness? Are the elderly over-prescribed medicines by their doctors? Do the elderly feel that their health is poor? Are racialized groups more likely to be sick and/or to die early? What is the health profile of Aboriginal peoples in Canada?

Age, Gender, and Life Expectancy

Age is associated with morbidity rates and life expectancy in both predictable and surprising ways. You have probably heard of "the grey tsunami" or "the greying of the nation." These terms point to the most obvious projected change in the Canadian population over time, as shown in Figure 5.1. This overall aging of the population and the corresponding decrease in the younger proportion of the population show especially the increase in the percentage of people over 80 years old. Population aging is expected to continue to increase significantly until at least 2036, as is the decline in the proportion of the population under 20.

The **population pyramid** is the most basic graphic method used to describe the age distribution of a population. Figure 5.2, which includes population pyramids for Canada from 1925 to 2050, illustrates the demographic shift in the population over more than a century. The rapid growth

of the older population is especially evident among women (the right side of the pyramids).

A number of explanations have been offered for this complex phenomenon. The most important factor in population aging is the overall decline in the birth rate. As people have fewer babies, there are correspondingly fewer young people. The presence of fewer young people in the population gives necessarily a greater proportion of elderly. A second and somewhat less important factor is the increase in life expectancy in Canada. Figure 5.3 shows this trend as an increase over the last 80 years of the twentieth century.

Life expectancy increases are the result of a number of changes. As we discussed in Chapter 2, first and most important is the rapid decline in the infant mortality rate. The average life expectancy for Canadians over the last 160 years or so has grown substantially. Notice, too, from Figure 5.3 that women's life expectancy has increased more than that of men. Significantly, while men, in all of the years recorded, have lived shorter lives than women, the difference between the average life expectancies of men and women has been greater in the past 25 years than at any point in history. Women's mortality rate has declined so that it is almost half the rate in 1921. The drop is not so dramatic for men. The most significant decline for both sexes is clearly in the early years of life. An important part of women's

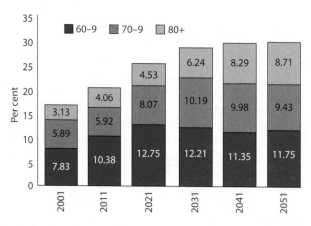

FIGURE 5.1 Population Projections for Canada, Percentage of the Population Aged 60 and over, 2001–51

Source: Commission on the Future of Health Care (2002: 22).

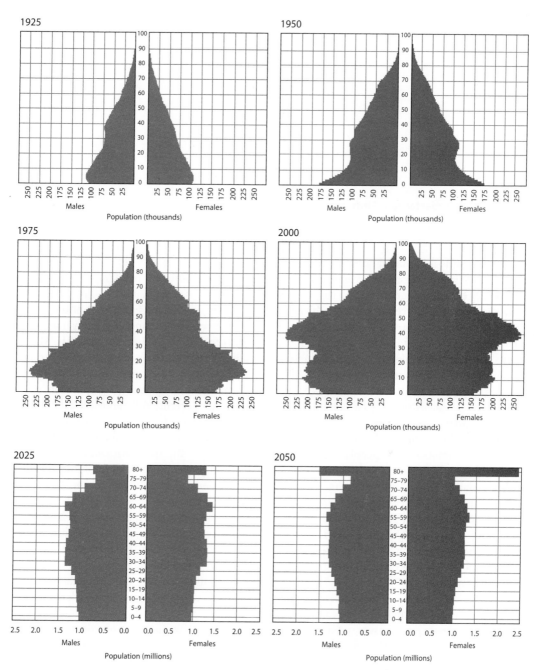

FIGURE 5.2   Population Pyramids for Canada, 1925–2050

Source: For 1925–2000: Statistics Canada, "Age Pyramid of Population of Canada, July 1, 1901–2001," www12.statcan/english/cencus01; for 2025–2050: US Census Bureau, International Data Base, "Population Pyramid Survey for Canada," www.census.gov/cgi-bin/ipc/idbpyrs.pl?cty=CA&out=s&ymax=25.

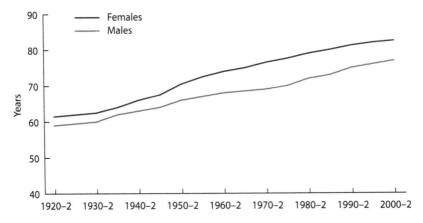

FIGURE 5.3   Life Expectancy at Birth, by Sex

Source: *Canada Year Book* (2006: 159), Statistics Canada.

increasing longevity is improved nutrition and other public health measures for pregnancy and childbirth.

Overall, though life expectancy has grown significantly over the last century and a half, some obvious questions remain. How much more is it likely to grow? Will new diseases such as Ebola or SARS, or new outbreaks of common illnesses such as pandemic influenza, seriously threaten the health of the population? Will the medical and technological advances of the past continue into the future? And if these advances do continue, can we expect that these additional years will be lived in a state of disability or will people live increasingly lengthier and healthier lives, becoming ill only in the short term just before death?

None of the causes of the dramatic decline in mortality are explicitly sex-specific, with the exception of birth control and pregnancy management. Moreover, the early and more rapid increases in life expectancy for women as compared to men have diminished since about 1978 (Nault, 1997: 36). The difference between the life expectancies of males and females is due partly to the changing sex-specific incidence of certain diseases. For instance, while the rate of heart disease has declined for both men and women, the absolute decline has been faster among men than women. Still, men are more likely to die from a variety of causes and this has been true historically.

Why, then, do men today live shorter lives than women? Several lines of inquiry might be followed to answer this question. First, the genetic superiority of women is an aspect of the explanation. More males are conceived and yet more male fetuses die (Doyal, 2003; Waldron, 1981). Males, in a number of different species, have higher death rates than females (although this is not universal). However, even if genetic predisposition plays a part in the mortality differential, it cannot be the only factor. For one thing, as Rutherford (1975) points out, the changes in the **sex-mortality differential** over the twentieth century, which continues today, could not be due entirely to genetics because genetic structures do not change that quickly. Furthermore, men are less likely to be ill. If the cause of the mortality differential were genetic, surely it would be paralleled in differences in morbidity rates for men and women.

Second, to explain this anomaly—that men are more likely to die, even though women are more likely to get sick—we must look at the causes of mortality by sex. Some of this difference in life expectancy between men and women is related to stereotyped machismo masculinities, which tend to put men more at risk than women. As Doyal says, "constructing and maintaining a male identity often requires the taking of risks that can be serious hazards to health" (Doyal, 2003: 934).

This differential is reflected in the important distinction between male and female causes of mortality during early to middle adulthood: males are almost three times more likely to die as the result of motor vehicle and other accidents and suicide (www40.statcan.ca/l01/cst01/health30c-eng.htm). Men and women are about equally likely to be victims of (reported) violent crime (http://www.statcan.gc.ca/pub/85f0033m/2010024/part-partie1-eng.htm). Men are almost three times more likely to die in any of the many wars fought around the world. Otherwise, men and women die from essentially the same causes, although at different rates and ages: cancer in general and lung

CRITICAL THINKING

BOX 5.1   Steroids, Sports, and Health

Despite the "insanely high" positive test result for synthetic testosterone reported in December 2011 for the National League's Most Valuable Player (*Toronto Star*, 2011), the crackdown in recent years on drug use in Major League Baseball, including mandatory drug testing, appears to have ended what became known as the Steroid Era in that sport, which extended from the 1990s to the 2000s. During that period, long-time home-run records were surpassed by alleged steroid-using players, and other players extended their years of peak performance with the aid of performance-enhancing drugs (PEDs). In Canada, and around the world, attention was drawn to PEDs, and to steroids in particular, when Canada's Ben Johnson, after breaking his own world record in winning the 100-metre dash at the 1988 Seoul Olympics, was stripped of his title and his world records after testing positive for an anabolic steroid. The Dubin Inquiry in 1989, headed by Ontario Justice Charles Dubin, examined the extent of performance-enhancing drugs in Canadian athletics and found that Johnson and his coach certainly were not alone. Female athletes, too, have used performance-enhancing drugs, most notoriously the East German women's swim team during the 1970s. In addition, the US sprinter Marion Jones was stripped of three gold and two bronze medals from the 2000 Summer Olympics after admitting to steroid use. Numerous recording artists, especially in rap and hip hop, as well as movie actors, also have been implicated in steroid use (McCallum, 2008). Perhaps the most egregious example of this problem of performance-enhancing drug use was cyclist Lance Armstrong, the legendary winner of seven consecutive Tour de France road races, who after years of vociferous and righteous denials had to admit on *Oprah* in 2013 that he had depended on drugs throughout his career. His defence was essentially that everyone else was using and so he had to use drugs to compete on an even playing field.

The deleterious effects of steroids are numerous. Steroid use is associated with increased violence and aggression. Steroid use is also related to megorexia—the opposite of anorexia. Megorexia involves a distorted body image and a voracious, even insatiable appetite. The steroid user then has an unattainable desire to acquire mass. Steroids are also addictive and may cause serious psychological symptoms upon withdrawal. Many physical health conditions result from steroid use, including liver and cardiovascular diseases, high blood pressure, harmful changes in cholesterol, hypertension, acne, fluid retention, and sleep disturbance. Prolonged steroid use also can lead to suicidal depression. During the Steroid Era in baseball, players often were assumed to be on steroids when their foreheads—and baseball cap size—increased from one year to the next.

In spite of the "crackdown" on the use of steroids, the problem continues. As recently as 2010 the University of Waterloo suspended its football program because steroid use had been discovered. What do you know about steroid use at your university or college?

cancer in particular, cardiovascular disease and stroke, accidents and adverse effects associated with motor vehicle accidents, chronic obstructive pulmonary disease, influenza and pneumonia, and Alzheimer's disease (www40.statcan.ca/l01/cst01/ health30c-eng.htm; www.statcan.gc.ca/pub/84-215-x/ 2011001/hl-fs-eng.htm).

The most important contributions to higher male mortality can be argued to be related to the following causes (all of which relate to the perform-ance of masculinities). The higher rate of cigarette smoking among men has had a significant and long-term impact on the sex differential for lung cancer, cardiovascular disease, and respiratory dis-eases, although this sex differential is narrowing as women have taken up smoking and the smok-ing rates of men have declined. Another import-ant contribution to the respiratory and lung cancer differential is likely linked to the higher risks of breathing toxins at men's employment venues, as discussed in Chapter 3. Men are more prevalent in the workforces of industries involving work with carcinogenic substances. It is worth noting, how-ever, that some cleaning, hygiene, and beauty prod-ucts used primarily by women in the home and on their bodies have been found to be carcinogenic and of significant risk to women's health.

Risk factors for heart disease include smok-ing, high-fat diet, overweight, and stress resulting, in part, from the performance of hegemonic mas-culinities (Rosenfeld and Faircloth, 2006). These risk factors are more prevalent among men than women (ibid.). Higher alcohol consumption among men is implicated in several causes of mortality—but chiefly accidents and suicide. Men drive more than women and less safely. About one-third of Canada's automobile accidents are associated with alcohol consumption (www.tc.gc. ca). The probability of other accidents, assaults, homicides, and suicides is increased by alcohol consumption. Liver diseases associated with alco-hol ingestion are more than twice as common as causes of death among men.

Thus, while there may be gender-based gen-etic differences, male lifestyles, including cigarette smoking, industrial employment, excess alcohol

consumption, and high-fat diet, clearly contribute to male mortality. In addition, the male procliv-ity to engage in violent, aggressive, and high-risk activities cannot be overlooked in gender-specific mortality rates. Such gendered characteristics are also implicated in the much higher suicide rate among men. Women are more likely to attempt suicide, but men, in part because they tend to choose more violent means, are more likely to suc-ceed at dying by suicide.

It is also worth noting that the health issues faced by transgendered people are much less understood, although it is evident that the stigma, discrimination, and stereotyping that are both internalized and experienced by transgendered people would tend to lead to exacerbated vulner-abilities to all manner of diseases both because of stress and because of the associated medical inter-ventions including hormonal, surgical, and other pharmaceutical treatments.

Age

Infancy and Youth

Age is paradoxically related to morbidity and mor-tality. Everyone dies, and as people live to old age they will get sick and die. That statement is obvious. What is less obvious is that infants, children, and youth are particularly susceptible to sickness and death, especially when they also are poor, of "col-oured" complexion and resultant status, belong to families headed by lone mothers, and experience other negative social determinants of health. Rates of infant and childhood mortality, accidents, and sickness are correlated with social class. Poorer mothers are more likely to give birth to undersized babies. When we think about a link between age and health, we tend first to associate aging and health decline. However, newborns are another age group whose health is of great significance to the overall health of the population. The weight of newborn babies is a "key predictor of their survival chances" (Millar et al., 1993: 26). Low birth weight, said to be less than 2,500 grams or about 5.5 pounds, is associated with physical and mental dis-abilities and infant death. Despite various types of preventive strategies, such as prenatal programs for pregnant women at high risk, the rate of low-birth-weight babies has declined only slightly, to about 6.2 per cent of live births in Canada in 2010 (http://www4.hrsdc.gc.ca/.3ndic.1t.4r@-eng.jsp?iid=4). Older mothers between 35 and 49 are more likely to have low-birth-weight babies. The average age of childbirth has been increasing over the past three decades and is now about 30 years of age for women (http://www4.hrsdc.gc.ca/.3ndic.1t.4r@-eng.jsp?iid=75). Also, mothers who smoke during pregnancy are more likely to have low-birth-weight babies. Low birth weight is associated with a number of health outcomes, including overweight and obesity in later years, which are, in turn, linked to diabetes and cardiovascular disease. Low birth weight is linked to various types of intellectual and cognitive delays that impede success in learning and in school. The first three years of life are also significant to subsequent health. During this time children's brains and nervous systems are growing and developing, and they are acquiring language and other essential skills.

Significantly, the social status of women has consequences for the health of children. This is true around the globe, as was discussed in Chapter 2, and is especially the case with respect to women in developing nations. Women's status is also important for the health of children in the developed world. Investment in women's education has been shown to significantly reduce mortality rates among children. Koenen et al. (2006) examined this relationship in the US. They defined women's status through four complex, composite indices, including women's political participation, economic autonomy, employment and earnings, and reproductive rights in 50 states. The well-being of children was measured according to the percentage of low-birth-weight babies, infant mortality rate, teen mortality, high school dropout rate, and teen birth rate. The health and well-being of children was found to be linked to women's political, economic, and social status. Other research, using a similar model of women's status, found that the health of adult men and women is better in states where women have higher status (Kawachi et al., 1999). Today in Canada approximately 36 per

cent of children living in low-income families live with a single mother; these single mothers constitute a group of mothers who live with relatively low incomes and status, on average (http://www.statcan.gc.ca/pub/89-503-x/2010001/article/11388-eng.htm).

Youth, too, are particularly vulnerable to health challenges. Young men, for instance, tend to take more risks and to be more aggressive and more stoic in the face of pain and distress (Spitzer, 2005). Thus, male youth are more likely to suffer various injuries associated with binge drinking, and to take greater risks in regard to frequent and multi-partnered sexual activity. Eighty-seven per cent of traffic fatalities among youth in Canada are young men and more than half of these deaths, according to Mothers Against Drunk Driving (MADD), involve alcohol consumption (http://www.madd.ca/madd2/en/services/youth_services_statistics.html).

The Elderly

Health problems affecting the elderly are of growing concern as the population ages. The elderly go to the doctor more frequently than young people and they are more likely to be hospitalized and to be prescribed medications. In addition, evidence indicates that the elderly are more likely to be given prescriptions inappropriately (Ferguson, 1990; Shorr et al., 1990; Brook et al., 1989). In fact, many hospital admissions result from inadequate or inappropriate drug prescriptions or utilization. The cost to the system of such preventable admissions is about $2.6 billion per year in Canada (http://www.accreditation.ca/sites/default/files/med-rec-en). Some of the problems associated with pharmaceutical use among the elderly result from the fact that the drugs have been tested on much younger people. Metabolic and other changes due to aging affect the absorption rates of drugs. Moreover, side effects from multi-drug use associated with the simultaneous treatment of several problems are particularly problematic among the elderly, not only because of the rate of drug absorption but also because of the increasing numbers of memory, visual, or motor problems, which may make taking medications, particularly multiple medications, more challenging (Tamblyn et al., 1994). Medications may be prescribed to be taken with or *not* with meals, before or after meals, with or without water or milk, at different times of the day, and so on. Managing a multi-drug regime is difficult at the best of times for the most able and fit of persons. Managing complicated scheduling is even more difficult for the elderly (especially those whose literacy is compromised) and for the elderly sick. Thus, the elderly may inadvertently use their prescribed drugs inappropriately, causing additional health problems. Falls are also a major cause of suffering and hospitalization among the elderly (www.phac-aspc.gc.ca/seniors-aines/publications/pro/injury-blessure/falls-chutes/tech/hospital-eng.php), and their probability is often increased as a side effect of medication. One in three people over 65 is likely to fall each year (ibid.), as is one in two over 80.

Almost a million Canadians suffer dementia of various kinds, including vascular dementia and Alzheimer's disease. By 2031 it is estimated by the Canadian Institutes for Health Research that 1.4 million Canadians will suffer dementia. Alzheimer's and dementia, characterized by severe cognitive and emotional deficits, increase over the life course. Alzheimer's disease (a primary degenerative disease of the brain involving progressive memory loss up to, at times, extreme disability resulting ultimately in the need for round-the-clock care) is the most common type of dementia, accounting for 64 per cent of all cases. It is more common in women than men, as 72 per cent of those with Alzheimer's are women and 62 per cent of those with dementia are women. Both conditions are expected to grow in incidence over the next decades (http://www.cihr-irsc.gc.ca/e/45554.html). Age-standardized rates of dementia among those 65 and over were 21.8 for women and 19.1 for men. This means that there are 21.8 women and 19.1 men with dementia per 1,000 non-demented population of those 65 and over (http://seure.cihi.ca/cihiweb/

HIGHLIGHTED ISSUES

BOX 5.2 Viagra

Women's health has been and continues to be an important issue. However, men's health should not be ignored. The near-epidemic of desire unleashed with the marketing of Viagra, a drug designed for the treatment of angina but that, instead, was found to produce an erection in a male with "erectile dysfunction," is one indication of how little is known about the ways that men suffer in their bodily functions. Until Viagra was introduced into the market in 1998 (soon to be followed by similar drugs, such as Cialis and Levitra), few knew of the extent of erectile dysfunction among men. Perhaps men weren't talking about it with their doctors and were thus not getting counted in morbidity figures, or perhaps this is best seen as a case of a drug in search of a problem, disease-mongering, or the medicalization of masculinity (Moynihan et al., 2002; Rosenfeld and Faircloth, 2006). One of the most dramatic example of the "overuse" of Viagra is among some men who have sex with men and use it (sometimes along with other drugs such as amyl nitrate, a "popper" that gives a burst of dizzying energy) to enhance their sexual pleasure. One recent community-based study in San Francisco found that the rate of Viagra use among men who have sex with men was 32 per cent (Chu et al., 2003). Clearly, Viagra and its counterparts are now used to enhance sexual pleasure as well as for erectile dysfunction. The success of the medicalization of sexual dysfunction among men has led to a new focus on the biology of female sexual dysfunction along with the marketing and use of pharmaceutical interventions such as those for males (Moynihan, 2003).

products/WHSR_Chap_19_e.pdf). As the population continues to age, this disease is expected to grow in significance so that the number of Canadian seniors with Alzheimer's or dementia is likely to triple by 2031 (Figure 5.3).

The elderly have more chronic conditions, are more likely to be hospitalized and medicated, and yet are still likely to self-report excellent or good health and health satisfaction. This may be because they see and evaluate themselves in relative terms in comparison with others of the same age. This finding is also true of those over 85. In a national study of Canadians over 65, a separate analysis for those over 85 was calculated (Ebley et al., 1996). Most Canadians over 85 years of age rated their health as either pretty good or very good. Furthermore, other research has shown how psychosocial factors among the elderly, such as a sense of purpose in life, a sense of control, social participation, and life satisfaction (Anstey et al., 2001; Pinquart, 2001; Ranzijn, 2001), as well as socio-economic factors, are positively related to quality of life and longevity. In 2009 about 96 per cent of Canadian seniors said they were satisfied or very satisfied with their lives (http://www.phac-aspc.gc.ca/cphorsphc-resp-cacsp/2010/fr-rc/cphorsphc-respcacsp-06-eng.php), according to an extensive 2010 report by the Chief Public Health Officer's Report on the state of Public Health in Canada.

Gender, Poverty, and Mortality/Morbidity

Women and female children are particularly likely to be ill, to die, or to be killed when they live in impoverished circumstances. Women are more likely, within their own domestic spheres, to become ill and die because they tend to take responsibility for ensuring that others are provided for when there is a relative absence of necessary foodstuffs, water, or other necessities of life. When poorer women are pregnant they are less likely to have access to the essential nutrients, social support, and prenatal care. They are more likely to live with chronic hunger and lowered resistance to various chronic and infectious diseases. This situation is true around the world (Wermuth, 2003). Women usually have the responsibility of feeding

their children. Inequalities in the valuation of men and women in all classes, but particularly among the poorest people, lead to a higher valuation of boy babies in many cultures. Sometimes this results in the intentional death of female babies or the abortion of female fetuses. There is little evidence of this occurring in Canada, but a survey of women in Madras, India, found that more than half reported having killed a female child (ibid., 2003). China, for many years, limited couples to only one child per family. This, in effect, led to the deaths of baby girls because females were less desired. In some cultures, women who are unable to produce male heirs are sometimes killed, maimed, or sent away from their families. Poor families sometimes sell their girl children into sexual slavery because they cannot support them or because they are told that their daughters will then be able to send money home to support the rest of the family. Rape is more common among poor women (ibid.), and female genital circumcision or mutilation, depending on cultural beliefs, may be considered another type of violence against women or a sign of female beauty and desirability. It causes pain, infection, disability, and sometimes death, and interferes in the possibility of women experiencing sexual pleasure when they do engage in sexual relations. This practice affects female children not only in the countries in which such practices originate but also in countries such as Canada because of the numbers of immigrants and refugees from areas of the world where this practice is accepted and where women are thought not to be marriageable because their genitals are considered "ugly" in the absence of **female circumcision**. The social policy and ethical issues raised by the desire of some immigrants to continue this practice in Canada are worthy of serious thought and discussion, not least under a nationally funded medical care system.

The conclusion that must be drawn from our research on gender differences in health is that women are more likely to suffer from a variety of illnesses than are men and that men at every age are more likely to die than are women. Which is the better measure of parity: to live longer and be ill or to die earlier? What will the future bring? Are women actually "dying to be equal," as evidenced by their growing rates of cigarette smoking, alcohol consumption, sedentary lifestyles, and increased involvement in non-traditional, high-risk, and high-stress careers? Should the Canadian medical care system support circumcision for males and females?

Transitions and the Life Course

Life course transitions offer additional opportunities for increased health as well as additional potential for stress and illnesses of all sorts. (The topic of life changes is examined in social-psychological terms in the next chapter in the Holmes and Rahe scale.) All transitions include the potential for health changes and stresses but especially transitions that occur out of the typical order or at a non-normative time. The transition that has garnered the most research is that of single teenage women embarking on a pregnancy and then on to child-rearing. The consequences of this trend are significant both for the mother and for her offspring. Similarly, young men who drop out of school before completion usually face greater economic and social challenges as they age. Young widowhood, early retirement, late childbearing, job insecurities, and educational interruptions all offer additional challenges to those that are inevitably a part of any transition. It is also important to note that while the probability of illness is increased by transitions and especially those that are out of the normative order there is always room for individuals to cope exceptionally well and to "succeed" in their lives despite difficult transitions.

The life course perspective adds to our discussion because it points out the possible variability in trajectories across place, time, social class, gender, and so on. Simply, the rich can (in exceptional cases) become poor over time and the poor can become rich. Further, growing up poor in the Great Depression or in the boom economies of the latter part of the last century would lead to different health outcomes in all likelihood (see Glen Elder's 1998 work for both an overview

of this literature and for detailed studies). This perspective is based on the very valuable but also expensive and difficult and, thus, less often undertaken longitudinal research.

Marriage

Marriage is a social status and identity that has important links to health and illness and has changed considerably over time. Married people tend to be healthier and to live longer lives. Single and divorced or separated people are more likely to become ill and to die. Nevertheless, the rates of divorce are increasing and Canadians are more likely to say that they do not want to remarry after a divorce (http://www.statcan.gc.ca/pub/89-630-x/2008001/article/10659-eng.htm). More than one-half of those divorced say they do not want to remarry. Marriage appears to offer men particular protection from illness (Robards et al., 2012). This outcome may be related to the higher social status of married men, as illness is associated with being in a subordinate position (Thoits, 2011). Whether this overall positive association between marriage and health is a result of healthier lifestyles among the married (such as healthier eating, more controlled alcohol consumption, routine exercise) or because healthier people are selected into marriage is an issue under investigation. Loneliness has been linked to ill health (Hawkley and Cacioppo, 2010). Certainly, too, the periods of transition into and out of marriage are times of heightened vulnerability to illness. Furthermore, particular types of caring, for instance, for gravely ill or disabled partners, can have negative health consequences for the carer and at times these can mitigate the benefits of marriage. Longitudinal research is needed on the impact on health of changes in the divorce rates and of the increasing proportion of single people living alone. Furthermore, the research reported so far has almost entirely focused on heterosexual couples and, thus, research on same-sex couples is needed. In addition, unhappy marriages do threaten the health of the partners as unhappy and negative emotions are linked to elevated blood pressure and heart rate and increased levels of stress hormones (Robles and Kiecolt-Glaser, 2003), among other deleterious effects.

Lesbian, Gay, Bisexual, Transsexual, and Queer Identities and Health

In the past decade or so a significant increase in research and policy development for people with non-heterosexual sexual identities and ambiguities in sex and gender identities has occurred. The rapid spread of the legalization of same-sex marriage is among the most important social forces enabling the growing public acknowledgement of sexual diversity. The openness of some prominent celebrities of diverse sexual identities, such as the television host Ellen Degeneres, has also played an important role in the "mainstreaming" of sexual diversities. However, acceptance is not universal and LGBT people continue to experience significant amounts of stigma and discrimination in some places in Canada and elsewhere in the world. "Coming out" to parents and to peers continues to be fraught for many Canadian young people. Research has shown that LGBT people have higher rates of various types of illnesses. For instance, some LGBT people struggle with mental health challenges such as depression, anxiety, and trauma (Zwiers, 2009). Gay men and lesbian women are more vulnerable to certain types of cancers, excess alcohol consumption, and cigarette smoking. Gay men are more susceptible to various sexually transmitted infections, including most seriously HIV/AIDS (Mulé et al., 2009), and lesbian women have a greater likelihood of certain problems associated with reproduction (for instance, the side and after effects of hormone ingestion sometimes used to enable artificial insemination). Bisexual, transsexual, and

---

CRITICAL THINKING

BOX 5.3   Femininity and Cancer: Look Good and Feel Better

The Look Good and Feel Better campaign was started in 1989 by the Cosmetic, Toiletry and Fragrance Association (CFTA) and the National Cosmetology Association in the United States. It has spread around the world and is ostensibly designed to help women feel better about themselves through "improving" their appearance with the use of various toiletries and cosmetics particularly when they are faced with a cancer diagnosis (Phillips, 2009). The campaign involves magazine and newspaper inserts advertising cosmetic and toiletry products and group sessions for women undergoing treatment for all kinds of cancers. The sessions are given to "makeovers" for attendees along with a gift bag of makeup products. "Much of their work rotates around a '12-step signature program' with the 12 steps being: cleanser and toner, moisturizer, concealer, foundation, powder, blush, eyebrows, eye shadow, eyeliner, mascara, lip liner and finally lipstick" (ibid., 69).

According to Phillips's analysis, however, the focus on femininity and beauty encouraged by this program has another function and that is to obfuscate the presence in the cosmetics of cancer-causing ingredients such as parabens (which has estrogenic activity; estrogen has been found to be a factor in the development of breast cancer). Further, she suggests that focusing on beauty belies the devastating effects of the disease and the greater need for learning treatments for such side effects of chemotherapy as mouth sores, nausea, and other complications. Such an emphasis also conceals the life-threatening reality of cancer and obscures the need to examine the environmental causes of cancer. This article is supported by the findings in Samantha King's *Pink Ribbons, Inc.* (2006) and evident in the film of that name.

You have probably seen the inserts for this program in a popular magazines or newspapers. Next time you do, take a more careful look, read Phillips's article, and make your own assessment.

CRITICAL THINKING

BOX 5.4   Movember

In 2003 a couple of men in Australia asked themselves what had happened to moustaches. In response, they decided to grow them and asked a bunch of their friends and acquaintances to join them. Each person was charged $10. They decided to use this adventure into face hair to raise money for charity, and inspired by the breast cancer movement they chose men's health and prostate cancer. The movement grew from 30 in 2003 to 4 million in 2013. The Mo movement has spread like wildfire around the world.

By 2013 in Canada the Movember movement had raised $572 million, $33.9 million in 2013 alone. In total in 2013, $129.6 million were raised as a result of campaigns in 21 countries around the world, including Canada, the UK, the US, Belgium, Switzerland, Austria, Ireland, and Sweden.

The Movember campaign is held every November in the involved countries. It essentially involves men supporting one another and raising funds through growing moustaches. It has become a major supporter of research and programs for men's health in general and prostate cancer and depression more specifically.

While the Mo movement is lay-based, Us TOO, another movement for prostate cancer, primarily focuses on providing education and support to those diagnosed and is heavily funded by pharmaceutical companies. As the name suggests, Us TOO was initially motivated by men who were tired of all of the attention going to breast cancer, a mostly women's disease.

These examples of gendered, disease-based fundraising lead us to ask a number of questions. Should medical research, and associated programming, be determined by the lay people? Should research direction be determined by the efficacy of a social movement? Should the "gender wars" enter into funding allocations? Should disease funding be determined by its incidence, age of the diagnosed, probability of a cure or prevention in the near future, severity of impact of the disease, or something else? Should pharmaceutical companies be allowed to contribute to lay organizations or does this inevitably lead to a conflict of interest?

These are just a few of the ethical issues raised by health-related social movements. What do you think?

---

intersex people may also have excesses in the problems noted above. Seeking health care may be more challenging for those with diverse sexual identities because of stigma and discrimination. Internalized shame and lowered self-esteem can also threaten the health and well-being of sexually diverse people. Compounding all of these problems is the lack of education and training for health-care providers about sexual diversity and the possible homophobia, heterosexism, and other stereotyped attitudes and practices to which the LGBT community is subject. Further, LGBT people are less likely to seek health care because of their own fear and discomfort resulting from anticipated discrimination.

Racialization, Ethnicity, and Minority Status

"Race," ethnicity, culture, and minority status are important factors affecting health in Canadian society and around the world. They should be defined and distinguished. "Race" is a social and political construct that has been used to distinguish people on the basis of physical characteristics such as skin colour, hair colour and texture, bone density, blood types, and facial structure. Historically, there were thought to be three broad categories of race: Caucasian, Mongoloid, and Negroid. In fact, there are no pure races and the concept is outdated.

However, the false beliefs about race continue and produce the prejudice called **racism**. "Ethnicity" refers to a common cultural background. Culture is a fundamental category for understanding similarities and differences in peoples around the world and within diversified countries such as Canada. There are numerous definitions of the concept of culture. Broadly speaking, "culture" refers to the total way of life of a group or aggregate of people. Of particular relevance to the topic of health is the idea that health is socially and, thus, culturally constructed, as are signs and symptoms of ill health, attitudes to those who are well and those who are ill, and different types of health care, among other things. "Minority status" refers to the numerical distribution of different ethnic categories of people.

The relevance of race to health is primarily due to the pervasive and systemic realities of racism experienced most egregiously by racial minorities. The constant and often invisible racism accumulates in the life experiences of all of us, particularly racialized people through **microaggressions** such as casual and seemingly minor slurs, slights, and interpersonal assumptions endemic in white privilege (Sue, 2011). These microaggressions happen so commonly that they are often outside of the awareness of the perpetrator and possibly even the recipient. Yet, they build up and are internalized and do lead to both mental and physical health problems. Microaggressions are a fundamental part of racism and the suffering it causes.

At the same time as Canadians extol our diversity and Americans articulate the value of their melting-pot society, violence against racial minorities continues. Recently, for example, a resurgence of attention has been paid to racially based police brutality and racial profiling, both of which have been documented repeatedly in both countries. As I write, protests are continuing around the United States over the shooting death of Michael Brown in Ferguson, Missouri, by a white police officer (http://www.nytimes.com/interactive/2014/08/13/us/ferguson-missouri-town-under-siege-after-police-shooting.html?_r=0) and over the mistreatment by police officers following the arrest of Freddie Gray in Baltimore, Maryland, that led directly to his death. Other forms of racism include systemic violence, racially based hate crimes, and so on. These, too, are linked to poorer physical and mental health.

While the term "microaggressions" has been used most frequently in relation to racism, it is also a part of other "isms," including ableism, ageism, sexism, and phobias such as homophobia and transphobia with their constant companions of stigma, discrimination, and prejudice. We need to understand that microaggressions weary and hurt those who are insulted and distanced and can lead to higher rates of various illness. Although less investigated, the perpetrators of microaggressions likely also are hurt and made sick by this behaviour.

For all of these reasons associated with racism, there is a close and persistent relationship between racialization, ethnicity, and class. Significant economic inequality can be attributed to differences in ethnic background. Racialized groups are more likely to be poor, homeless, or inadequately housed and to experience discrimination and barriers in access to health care (Access Alliance, 2005; Colour of Justice Network, 2007; Nestel, 2012). Ethno-racial minorities in urban centres have lower levels of income as a result of historical and continuing discrimination in the labour market (Galabuzi, 2001; McGibbon and Etowa, 2009). Among racialized groups, women and children in female-led households are more likely to be poor. Poverty is especially endemic among immigrant and refugee groups from Africa, South Asia, and Southeast Asia. Among racialized groups, unemployment rates are higher and they are over-represented in low-wage sectors of the economy as well as in unregulated and temporary work. In 1995, 35.6 per cent of people from minority racial backgrounds had incomes below the low-income cut-off (LICO) point as compared to 17.6 per cent of the general population (Galabuzi, 2004: 241).

Of those who self-identified as a visible minority on the 2006 census (in the 10 provinces only), the poverty rate (defined in this study as those whose income is below the after-tax LICO) was 22 per cent, while it was only 11 per cent for everyone overall, and only 9 per cent for those white or non-racialized persons (http://www.esdc.gc.ca/eng/communities/reports/poverty_profile/snapshot.shtml). It would not be fair to say that the poverty rate has been reduced since 1995, however, since the same study says that poverty among racialized persons has increased by 362 per cent between 1980 and 2000—other differences in methodology must be causing the reduction in reported numbers! This impoverishment of the racialized continues today and may even be a more prominent issue given the increases in racialized minority immigrant populations in Canada and particularly in the largest Canadian cities (Colour of Justice Network, 2007). Furthermore, how others view an individual has important consequences for the individual's self-esteem, stress, mental health, and well-being. To the extent that ethnicity is related to occupational status, income, and education, people of different ethnic groups will differ in their morbidity and mortality rates. Nancy Kreiger (2011) has linked the continuing poorer health outcomes of racialized peoples to the following conditions;

economic and social deprivation, toxic substances and hazardous conditions, discrimination and other types of social trauma, targeted marketing of unhealthy products, inadequate and degrading medical care provision, and degrading ecosystems in living areas. Consider Table 5.1. It shows that while visible minority people are equally likely to visit general practitioners (as white people), they are less likely to engage in early detection procedures such as a PSA test, a mammogram, or Pap smears and are less likely to be cared for by a specialist or to be admitted to hospital.

Cultural differences may play a part in immigrant and refugee health statistics and health care. Some differences arise at the clinical level, some at the level of policy, and others at the level of organizations and institutions. A new emphasis on what is called cultural competence in the practices of health-care providers and associated organizations is designed to overcome such behaviours as the unwillingness of visible minorities to engage in some health-related behaviours and medical interventions (Tuck et al., 2010; Purnell, 2000).

TABLE 5.1 Odds Ratios for the Utilization of Health Services by Members of Visible Minorities Compared with White People

Health service (sex and age, yr)	Odds ratios (95% CI)	
	Unadjusted	Adjusted*
General practitioner	1.00	1.28
Specialist physician	0.77	1.01
Hospital admission	0.65	0.83
PSA blood test (men ≥ 40)	0.54	0.64
Mammogram (women ≥ 35)	0.61	0.68
Pap smear (women ≥ 18)	0.31	0.47

Note: CI = confidence interval, PSA = prostate-specific antigen.

*Adjusted for sex, age (65 years or >65 years), marital status (married or common-law; single; others, including widowed, separated, and divorced), highest level of education (less than secondary, secondary, post-secondary), annual income (<$30,000, $30,000–$49,999, $50,000–$79,000, >$80,000, datum missing), immigrant status and length of stay in Canada (born in Canada, <10 years or >10 years since immigration), speaking English or French (yes or no), self-perceived health (excellent, very good, good, fair, poor) and number of chronic diseases (0, 1, 2, or >3). Immigrant status and length of residence in Canada are proxies of acculturation. After categorizing the study population based on immigration status (born in Canada: yes or no), we then grouped those not born in Canada into 2 subgroups (<10 years or >10 years since immigration); 1 variable, therefore, has 3 categories (born in Canada and <10 years or >10 years since immigration). In our actual modelling, we specified this 3-level variable by entering 2 yes-or-no dummy variables (immigration <10 years ago and >10 years ago) into our model; being born in Canada (or not) was the baseline variable.

Source: Quan et al. (2006: 789). Reprinted by permission of the publisher. © 2006 Canadian Medical Association.

One definition of cultural competence is "having the knowledge, understanding, and skills about a diverse cultural group that allows the health-care provider to provide acceptable cultural care. Competence is an ongoing process that involves accepting and respecting differences and not letting one's personal beliefs have an undue influence on those whose worldview is different form one's own" (Giger et al., 2007). This perspective on cultural competence privileges the dominant culture. It also privileges the dominant conventional medical care system. A broader and more useful notion is an intersectional one that includes culture along with other social characteristics such as gender, class, language, sexual identity, and so on. To be sure, there are culturally bound disorders and culturally unique healing systems (Helman, 2007), but cultural competence is more broadly about anti-oppressive health experiences and care provision. This includes interrogating a multitude of health-related concerns at once, including those associated with governing structures of health-care organizations, policy documents, human resource issues, education, and clinical practice. Such conscientious attention to diversity is increasingly important as Canada continues to increase its immigrant and refugee population in the years to come.

Immigrant Health

There were 5.4 million immigrants enumerated in the census of Canada in 2001 (Ng et al., 2005). Each year since 2001 an average of about 250,000 immigrants have come to Canada, and this immigration accounts for much of the growth in the population. This estimated number of immigrants would result in approximately 3.5 more million on top of the 5.4 million already in Canada in 2001 (minus those who emigrated). These estimates seem to be holding: in 2010, for example, 280,636 were admitted to the country (www.cic.gc.ca/english/department/media/releases/2011/2011-02-13.asp). In 2014 Canada expected to admit between 240,000 and 265,000 immigrants to Canada (http://www.cic.gc.ca/english/department/media/notices/2013-11-01.asp). Because of low fertility rates among native-born Canadians, immigration protects Canada from population decline and maintains slow population growth and contributes to economic growth. At times the population increase from immigration is much greater than that from native-born increase. For example, new Canadian residents accounted for nearly 80 per cent of the total population growth of 324,000 during a one-year period (www.statcan.ca/Daily/English/060927/d060927a.htm).

People of colour made up about 19.1 per cent of Canada's population in 2011 according to Statistics Canada. However, it must be emphasized that gathering statistics about this sensitive topic is not easy, nor are the results as valid as would be ideal. Most new immigrants arrive in the major cities of Toronto, Montreal, and Vancouver (Newbold and Danforth, 2003). By 2017 visible minorities in Toronto and Vancouver are expected to be in the majority, and by 2030 both Vancouver and Toronto are predicted to have almost or above 60 per cent of their populations representing visible minority groups (Statistics Canada, 2010). Obviously, the term "minority" will longer be relevant.

Considerable research in both the United States (Singh and Miller, 2004) and Canada (Beiser, 2005) documents the relatively good health of new immigrants. In the US, male and female immigrants live, respectively, 3.4 and 2.5 years longer than those born in the US. Even among most racialized minorities the health of immigrants is superior. For example, the life expectancy of black immigrants is substantially greater than that of blacks born in the US, at 9.4 years for males and 7.8 years for females. Moreover, most immigrant groups have had lower infant mortality and fewer low-birth-weight babies than is the case among those born in the US (Singh and Miller, 2004). With respect to major and significant causes of death such as (many) cancers, heart disease, cirrhosis, diabetes, respiratory diseases, HIV/AIDS, and suicide, immigrants to the US also fare better (ibid.). This phenomenon has been called the **healthy immigrant effect** (Beiser, 2005). The process of planning for, organizing, and executing the move for immigration demands a high level of intelligence, skill, energy, money, and overall well-being. Moreover, Canada's immigration policies favour the educated, occupationally skilled, and young. In addition, immigrants are screened for various diseases prior to being accepted to Canada (ibid.) and may be denied admissibility solely on medical grounds (www.canadavisa.com/immigration-medical-inadmissibility.html). Even after arriving in Canada in generally better health than the average Canadian, as immigrants adjust to life in Canada their health tends to deteriorate.

The situation is similar in many ways among refugees, even though, by virtue of their status as refugees, they have experienced highly stressful living conditions prior to coming to Canada (ibid.). Nevertheless, the health of refugees is somewhat poorer than that of other immigrants and they are, for example, more susceptible to infections and parasitic diseases. Tuberculosis is a case in point. This highly contagious disease has incidence levels among refugees of approximately three times that for those born in Canada. However, Canada continues to screen refugees for physical and mental illnesses so that they can be immediately treated. Furthermore, a group of doctors has banded together to demand health coverage for refugee populations (http://www.doctorsforrefugeecare.ca/).

Initially, many immigrants are relatively poor in the new country, although wider variations occur among immigrants in respect to education

---

REMEMBERING OUR HISTORY

BOX 5.5 The Great Dying

The numbers have been debated, but the most reliable recent estimate is that the New World (First Nations) peoples likely numbered between 90 and 112 million before they were devastated by the diseases and warfare that Europeans brought with them to North and South America. Not only were the Amerindians numerous, they also enjoyed good health. Before contact they may have been in better health, in some ways, than Europeans. They did not have measles, smallpox, leprosy, influenza, malaria, or yellow fever. For most, staying healthy and living well were essential tenets of their religion. Hygiene included regular bathing and the peoples of the New World kept themselves very clean. The Europeans could not help noticing the "good smells" emanating from the healthy, robust people. Apparently, they especially admired their even, white teeth and clear complexions, "something most pockmarked Spaniards, Portuguese and French had lost at an early age" (Nikiforuk, 1991: 80). At this time, the average life expectancy of Europeans was about 20 years less than that of the Amerindians. It is suggested that their good health was the result of the origins of these people, who had crossed the land bridge that spanned the Bering Strait to the New World at a time of lower sea levels. Because of the harsh cold, the diseased immigrants and their germs were killed. Only the fittest survived.

Into this context of good health the new disease smallpox entered—an unknown yet dangerous predator that spread as an epidemic until it and other diseases such as the plague and tuberculosis killed upwards of 12 million people in North America. This "great dying" occurred during about one century. Some historians rank this as the greatest demographic disaster in the history of the world.

and income than among others who are already Canadian citizens. Often, however, their academic credentials and work qualifications are not readily accepted (Ng et al., 2005). Racialized people experience discrimination in the labour market, housing, health care, and elsewhere. The unemployment rate is three times higher for university-educated immigrants than for the Canadian-born with similar levels of education (Access Alliance, 2005). According to a study by Ornstein (2006), the most severely disadvantaged people in Toronto include Aboriginals and immigrants from South and East Asia, the Caribbean, South and Central America (20 per cent of whom have incomes below the low-income cut-off [LICO]); among Arab and West Asian immigrants in Toronto, 30 per cent have incomes below the LICO, and 40 per cent of African immigrants in Toronto have incomes below the LICO.

Another way to consider the issue of the relative health of immigrants is through a comparison of their subjective reports with those of other Canadians. Ironically, perhaps, immigrants report that they perceive themselves to be healthy to a greater extent than do other Canadians, regardless of socio-economic and demographic characteristics when they arrive. However, the longer they remain in Canada the closer their self-reported health status comes to the rest of the population. As Table 5.1 indicates, they are less likely to receive screening for the early detection of various cancers and less likely to be hospitalized. They may also be less likely to receive referrals to specialists (Colour of Justice Network, 2007; Williams et al., 2011).

Aboriginal Health

History

The one minority "group" for which extensive current and historical data are available is Canadian Aboriginals: First Nations, Inuit, and Métis. The variety of terms, including the older "Indians" and "Eskimos," reflects the struggle to find a name that best reflects the history and identity of peoples whose cultures were colonized by people of European origin over the past 500 years. Some debate whether Aboriginal Canadians ought to be considered an ethnic group or not, and Canada's Aboriginal peoples are not considered "visible minorities" by the Canadian government. Those who favour the "ethnic group" designation argue that there are significant similarities among all 55 or more Aboriginal peoples—as distinguished by language, culture, and geography—and all are colonized peoples, so that together they constitute an ethnic group. Others, however, argue that simply because the cultural diversity of the Aboriginal peoples at colonization has been seriously compromised by the dominance of the state, this does not mean they can be considered one cultural or ethnic group. Regardless of which side of this complex controversy one takes, the evidence remains that Aboriginal peoples have experienced much poorer life chances, more disease, and lower life expectancy rates than non-Aboriginal Canadians (Figure 5.4). Based on Statistics Canada projections since 2001, however, Aboriginal life expectancy is anticipated to grow from one to two years per year until 2017, as projected in Figure 5.5, until it is very close to that of the rest of the population of Canada. It needs emphasis, though, that this projection will be met only if the social, economic, and political concerns discussed in the next section are satisfactorily resolved.

Demography

The 2006 Census of Canada indicated that close to 1.2 million Canadians were of Aboriginal identity, a 45 per cent increase over the previous 10 years. Of these, 698,025 were First Nations, 389,785 were Métis, and 50,485 were Inuit. These numbers are higher now, according to the National Household Survey (NHS) of 2011. According to the NHS there were 1,400,685 people with Aboriginal identity, or 4.3 per cent of the population. This constitutes an increase of about

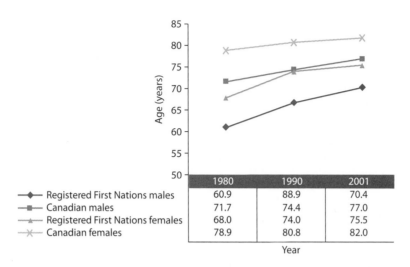

	1980	1990	2001
Registered First Nations males	60.9	88.9	70.4
Canadian males	71.7	74.4	77.0
Registered First Nations females	68.0	74.0	75.5
Canadian females	78.9	80.8	82.0

Year

FIGURE 5.4   Life Expectancy at Birth in Years, by Sex, Registered First Nations and Canadian Populations, 1980, 1990, and 2001

Source: Population Projections of Registered Indians, 2000–2021, Indian and Northern Affairs Canada, 2003; and Population Projections for Canada, Provinces and Territories, 2000–2026, Statistics Canada, 2001. Medium Assumption, pages 25–26, as cited in Basic Departmental Data 2004, Indian and Northern Affairs Canada, 2005. Catalogue no. R12–7/2003E. http://www.hc-sc.gc.ca/fniah-spnia/pubs/aborig-autoch/stats-profil-atlant/index-eng.php#a634.

20.1 per cent since 2006 as compared to 5.2 per cent for non-Aboriginal people (http://www12. statcan.gc.ca/nhs-enm/2011/as-sa/99-011-x/99-011-x2011001-eng.cfm#a1). Some of the recent growth in the Aboriginal population can be attributed to more people acknowledging their

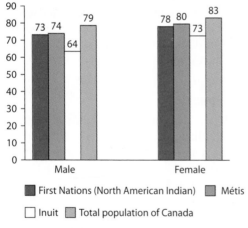

FIGURE 5.5   Projected Life Expectancy at Birth by Sex, Aboriginal Identity, 2017

Source: Statistics Canada: www.statcan.gc.ca/pub/89-645-x/2010001/life-expect-ancy-esperance-vie-eng.htm.

Aboriginal ancestry, but natural increase is the principal factor. Regardless of specific identity, Aboriginal Canadians live shorter lives than other Canadians and experience a considerably higher **birth rate**. These factors are reflected in the fact that Aboriginal communities tend to have a much greater proportion of people under 30 years old than other communities. This difference is shown in an age pyramid of First Nations and total Canadian populations (Figure 5.6). About 61 per cent of the members of Aboriginal communities are under 30 as compared to 38.8 per cent in the total population. The relative youth of the communities also reflects that the average life expectancy is shorter among Aboriginals: 64 for males and 73 for females according to Statistics Canada's estimate for 2017 (http://www.statcan.gc.ca/pub/89-645-x/2010001/life-expectancy-esperance-vie-eng.htm). These figures constitute a significant gap of more than a decade for Aboriginal men and women as compared to non-Aboriginals. In addition, Aboriginal people are more likely to die violent deaths from automobile accidents (the leading cause of death overall), as well as from suicide, injuries of various sorts, poisonings,

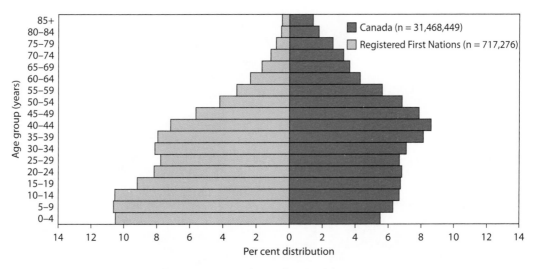

FIGURE 5.6   Age Distribution of First Nations and Canadian Populations, 2002

Source: Population Projections of Registered Indians, 2000–2021, Indian and Northern Affairs, 2002; Statistics Canada, Canadian Socio-economic Information Management System Table 051-0001.

drowning, and fires. Rates of injury also tend to be higher among First Nations in northern Ontario, for example, by a factor of 2.5 for all-cause injuries, assault (5.5 female and 4.8 male), intentional self-harm (5.9 female and 5.2 male), and by accidental poisoning (4.9 for female and 3.7 for male) (Fantus et al., 2009).

All these causes of death result from difficult and impoverished living conditions. As McCormick et al. (1997) explain, "Everywhere in Canada [Aboriginal peoples] are struggling to overcome the effects of colonialism and its associated assimilationist practices. Such effects include, but are not limited to, cultural loss, discrimination, unemployment, and poverty." Colonialism, from first European contact to the present, has had broad and devastating health effects, with epidemics of smallpox, measles, and tuberculosis killing large numbers of people repeatedly and over time. Indeed, epidemics of European diseases often preceded actual European contact, carried into communities ahead of European settlers. In the twentieth century the residential school system, reserve life,

and extensive racism have played a part in high poverty rates experienced by Canada's Aboriginal people (Shah, 2004). These levels of poverty are mirrored in high rates of morbidity and mortality. The continuing differences in income, education, employment, and housing are fundamental contributions to the poorer health of Aboriginal Canadians. Figure 5.7 shows the poverty rates for all Canadian children as compared with Aboriginal and racialized children. Table 5.2 indicates the age-standardized prevalence of selected health conditions, differences between First Nations, on and off reserve, and the general Canadian population. Aboriginal seniors are particularly vulnerable, according to the Health Council of Canada (2013). First Nations people on reserves are not receiving adequate home care and long-term care in their communities and thus many must leave their communities and live far from home in culturally foreign environments, possibly hundreds of miles away from their homes. The situation for Inuit who live in remote northern communities may be especially dire as they age.

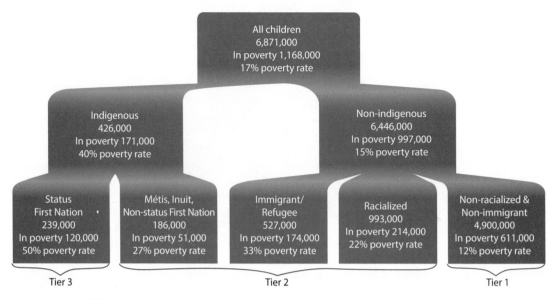

FIGURE 5.7   Child Poverty among Disadvantaged Groups in Canada

Source: David Macdonald and Daniel Wilson. Poverty or Prosperity: Indigenous Children of Canada. Canadian Centre for Policy Alternatives (2013), pg. 13.

A lack of adequate and accessible food continues to pose a significant threat to the health of the Inuit and other northern Aboriginal peoples, who historically lived on the land and sea and even today try to rely to a considerable extent on country or bush food. However, the movement away from the land and into government-designated settlements that began over a half-century ago led to dietary changes, costly store-bought foods, and lots of cheap junk food—chips, candy, pop. To counter the sedentary, welfare-reliant settlement life, Quebec for a number of years has had a Cree Hunters and Trappers Income Security Program that pays couples and couples with children to spend much of the year on the land to acquire country food for themselves and their communities (Bone, 2016: ch. 7). Yet, as game, fish, and sea mammal populations dwindle, or as these animals at the top of food chains accumulate in their systems toxic substances that have been carried in the atmosphere from Asia, Europe, and North America, or mercury from hydroelectric dam projects, they become unsafe as the basis for human diets.

Specific Indicators of Health and Disease among Aboriginal Canadians

The Aboriginal birth rate is one and a half times that of the birth rate of non-Aboriginals (www12.statcan.ca/english/census01/Products/Analytic/companion/abor/canada.cfm#2). About four times as many Aboriginal women become mothers in their teens, and the rates of both overweight and underweight babies are higher than those of other Canadian women. Further, the rates of fetal alcohol syndrome (FAS) and fetal alcohol effects (FAE) are substantially higher among the Aboriginal population. In fact, the incidence of FAS and FAE may be as high as one in five babies. Smoking rates, rates of substance abuse, problem gambling, nutritional inadequacy, physical inactivity levels, overweight and obesity, and rates of unsafe sexual practices tend to be higher in Aboriginal communities (Shah, 2004).

In addition, the incidence of various infectious diseases is considerably higher among Aboriginal people than in the general population. Cases of pertussis (2.2 times higher), rubella (7 times higher), tuberculosis, (6 times higher),

REMEMBERING OUR HISTORY

BOX 5.6   Nutrition Experiments and Aboriginal Health

Was there any compelling ethical justification for the nutritional experiments with Aboriginal people in the 1940s?

A doctor working for what was then called the Department of Indian Affairs was concerned because there was an epidemic of tuberculosis and blindness among the 300 or so Aboriginal people who lived in Norway House in northern Manitoba in the 1940s. He decided, with the approval of the House of Commons, to capitalize on this situation and to undertake experiments with nutritional supplements to see if they would improve the health of the suffering people. He chose 125 of the 300 members of the community for treatment. He followed their health over two years and noted that the vitamin supplements seemed to be associated with health improvements. This nutritional experimentation then spread to British Columbia, Alberta, Ontario, and Nova Scotia and included about 1,300 Aboriginal people. Included among the studies were keeping people on very-low-calorie diets, withholding vitamins and minerals, and denying dental care in order to observe the impacts of these strategies on the health of the people. At one residential school some children were given one-half the ration of milk to observe the influence of this on their health. Ian Mosby, a University of Guelph professor who researches the history of food policy in Canada, discovered and publicized these studies in 2014. Could this same sort of research be carried out today? Or would the research ethics boards established across the country and governing research in Canada prevent such destructive research?

The basic principles governing research with human beings (animal research ethics are also articulated in detail) are as follows:

- Respect for human dignity so that research subjects are never treated as a means to an

end and that the welfare of research subjects is paramount.
- Free and informed consent so that research participants are fully informed and understand all of the costs and benefits of taking part in research.
- Respect for vulnerable persons so that children, those who are institutionalized (e.g., in mental hospitals or prisons), and those who are for any other reasons vulnerable are to be especially protected from any possibility of harm.
- Respect for privacy and confidentiality so that involvement in research will never threaten the social and personal relations of participants.
- Respect for justice and inclusiveness so that participants in research will be invited from all walks of life, equitably.
- Balance of risk and benefit so that the risks of any research will be lesser than the benefits.
- Harm will be minimized so that researchers use the smallest samples possible and minimize the research impact as much as possible (for example, a questionnaire should use the minimum questions necessary for testing the hypotheses).

Following is a statement of contemporary research ethics principles from York University: http://www.yorku.ca/igreene/tricoun.htm. *Maclean's* magazine published a brief description and analysis of the nutrition experiments carried out on Aboriginal people: http://www.macleans.ca/general/harper-must-acknowledge-horrors-of-nutrition-tests-on-aboriginal-children-afn/. The research ethics form for undergraduates at Wilfrid Laurier University that must be completed before beginning any research under the aegis of this university can be seen at: https://legacy.wlu.ca/forms_detail.php?grp_id=1430&frm_id=3288.

and shigellosis (2.1 times higher) all are higher in the Aboriginal population. The first three are infectious diseases that are much more likely to spread among people living in crowded and inadequately hygienic living quarters. Shigellosis is a bacterial infection spread through contaminated water and food. Various dramatic differences in disease type/incidence exist between Aboriginals and other Canadians.

With respect to the self-perceived health of Aboriginal peoples (Table 5.2), they have higher body mass indexes than non-Aboriginal peoples; are more likely to perceive their mental health as poorer; and are less likely to eat fresh fruit and vegetables (which is understandable since many Aboriginal people live in the three northern territories and in the northern reaches of the provinces where the colder climate and short growing season are not amenable to fresh produce). On the other hand, overall they are only slightly less satisfied with their lives. The picture of Inuit health is somewhat different. They are less likely than all other groups to report a chronic condition, for instance, and have a much greater sense of community belonging, and their level of life satisfaction is the equivalent to that of non-Aboriginals.

Sexually Transmitted Diseases

Sexually transmitted diseases are also prevalent in Aboriginal communities. The incidence of chlamydia, for example, is almost seven times higher than the rate among other Canadians. HIV/AIDS occurrence has risen dramatically, from 1 per cent of the Aboriginal population in 1990 to 5–8 per cent in 2012, and 6–12 per cent of the new infections in Canada in 2012 were of Aboriginal people. Although they constitute about 4.3 per cent of the Canadian population, Aboriginal persons living with HIV/AIDS comprise about 10 per cent of the total Canadian cases (http://www.phac-aspc.gc.ca/aids-sida/publication/ps-pd/aboriginal-autochtones/chapter-chapitre-3-eng.php#a1). Thus, as Frideres (2011: 129) notes, "while the overall rate of HIV in Canada is stabilizing, in First Nation communities the incidence continues to grow." This is particularly significant and considered of epidemic proportions because of

---

TABLE 5.2   Health Indicators: Self-Reported Conditions and Personal Behaviours, Canada, 2013

	First Nations	Métis	Inuit	Non-Aboriginal
Self-Reported Conditions				
Adult body mass index (age 18+) of 25 or greater*	60.6	57.8	61.7	51.2
One or more chronic conditions	60.4	58.9	47.6	53.3
Perceived mental health, very good or excellent	64.2	66.2	65.8	74.5
Self-Reported Personal Behaviours				
Fruit and vegetable consumption (5+ per day)	35.4	38.0	25.7	44.2
Sense of community belonging (very strong or somewhat strong)	63.6	62.4	81.7	65.1
Life satisfaction (satisfied or very satisfied)	88.1	89.2	92.0	92.0

*The body mass index (BMI) can be calculated by dividing body weight by a function of the height. It is sometimes correlated with "fatness" and with some health problems. A BMI of 25 or higher is considered to be overweight (http://www.cdc.gov/healthyweight/assessing/bmi/index.html).

Source: Adapted from Statistics Canada, Health Indicators 2013, Canadian Institute for Health Information (2013). https://secure.cihi.ca/free_products/HI2013_EN.pdf, pp. 38, 46.

SPOTLIGHT ON ETHICS

BOX 5.7   The Case of Makayla Sault

Should the courts have taken Makayla Sault from her First Nation parents and community and forced her to have chemotherapy?

Makayla Sault, a 10-year-old Mohawk girl from the New Credit First Nation near Brantford, Ontario, was diagnosed with leukemia (acute lymphoblastic leukemia) in 2014 by the doctors at McMaster Hospital in Hamilton, Ontario. She was given a 75 per cent chance of survival and full recovery if she completed the chemotherapy treatments prescribed to take place over several years. Makayla was hospitalized for the first stage of the treatment and experienced very severe side effects in hospital. During this time in hospital Makayla thought she had received a message from Jesus telling her that her body was healed. She told her parents, both of whom were pastors, and they agreed to remove Makayla from the hospital and to pursue other types of treatments that were culturally appropriate. In response, the doctors at McMaster argued that she would die without treatment and asked the Children's Aid Society of Brant County to take Makayla into their custody so that she could receive the prescribed allopathic medical treatment. The Aboriginal community rallied behind the Sault family and supported their right to care for their daughter using "natural" treatments. The community remembered the spectre of children who had been taken away from their parents and forced into residential schools and equated forcing chemotherapy on Makayla as similar. This case went to court to determine if Makayla's parents had the right to care for their child as they saw fit or whether Makayla should be removed and hospitalized so that she would receive the scientifically well-documented medical treatment.

In what was an unusual decision the judge rejected the claim by McMaster that the child should be removed in favour of the idea that Makayla's parents had the right to choose what they considered to be appropriate care for their daughter. Makayla died less than a year later, in January 2015.

Was this a victory for Aboriginal rights or a failure to protect a child?

---

the small size of the communities and the amount of intermingling regarding both drug use and sex. Aboriginal women are especially susceptible because of the higher rates of other sexually transmitted disease, inequitable gender relations, and high-risk sexual practices (Shah, 2004). The proportion of Aboriginal peoples whose HIV is the result of injection drug use is much higher than among other Canadians. Homosexual relations, according to these data, are a much less important cause of transfer of the virus in First Nations communities although that may reflect a greater need to be "closeted."

Inequalities within Aboriginal Communities

The health of Aboriginal peoples is related to gender, class, age, and area of residence (Wotherspoon, 1994; Shah, 2004). The same factors that explain health differences among other Canadians affect the health of the Aboriginal peoples. Thus, Aboriginal people who are higher on the various social structures are more likely to have good health and, on average, the health of Aboriginal people is poorer because, on average, they have lower incomes, have less education, and are more likely to be unemployed or underemployed than other Canadians. Aboriginal people are also more likely to be incarcerated—22.8 per cent of all federal inmates are Aboriginal, and in a sample study of Aboriginal inmates, 96 per cent reported that substance use (drugs, alcohol) "was related to their current offence," 73 per cent noted a family history of residential school experience, and 88 per cent "had a family member struggling with alcohol or drug addiction issues" (Office of the Correctional Investigator, 2014).

Aboriginal people are also more likely to be homeless and to be dependent on welfare, and are disproportionately affected by housing considered inadequate, with 5.3 per cent of housing, though still in use, deemed uninhabitable. Many homes are in need of major repair (19.6 per cent as compared to 9.8 per cent in the general population). Aboriginal homes are 90 times more likely to lack potable water (9.5 per cent as compared to 0.17 per cent). They are five times more likely to lack bathroom facilities (3.2 per cent as compared to 0.6 per cent) and 10 times more likely to lack a flush toilet (5.3 per cent as compared to 0.5 per cent) (Adelson, 2005). Although these figures are dated, there has been no substantial improvement in Aboriginal housing in the meantime, as a factsheet from the National Collaborating Centre for Aboriginal Health (NCCAH) indicates (http://www.nccah-ccnsa.ca/docs/fact%20sheets/social%20determinates/NCCAH_fs_housing_EN.pdf). Clean water for drinking and cleaning is still missing on a significant number of Native reserves, and a group of Aboriginal leaders have sued the federal government for their failure to provide clean drinking water (http://www.cbc.ca/news/canada/calgary/alberta-first-nations-sue-ottawa-over-safety-of-drinking-water-1.2677316; http://www.cbc.ca/news/canada/clean-running-water-still-a-luxury-on-many-native-reserves-1.1081705).

Aboriginal people are less likely to have achieved all levels of education from grade school to university. The gap between Aboriginals and other Canadians occurs for elementary school, for high school, and for college or university. Almost one-half of Aboriginal people between the ages of 25 and 64 had post-secondary education or certification in 2011 as compared to about two-thirds of non-Aboriginal Canadians (http://www12.statcan.gc.ca/nhs-enm/2011/as-sa/99-012-x/99-012-x2011003_3-eng.cfm). However, Aboriginal children are staying in school longer than in the past. Moreover, there has been increased funding for band-operated elementary and high schools. In addition, Aboriginal programs in universities have grown, including programs for training Aboriginal

people in the professions (e.g., medicine, law, and, especially, social work), in part so that they can work in the Aboriginal community and provide services to their people. There is also a university in Regina established explicitly for First Nations people, the First Nations University of Canada (http://www.fnuniv.ca). Still, there are substantially higher rates of unemployment. Figure 5.8 shows the relative rate of employment of Aboriginal and non-Aboriginal people in Canada. Aboriginal people also face disproportionately low salaries (https://www.aadnc-aandc.gc.ca/DAM/DAM-INTER-HQ-AI/STAGING/texte-text/rs_re_brief_incomedisparity-PDF_1378400531873_eng.pdf). Unemployment, underemployment, and low incomes all contribute to the poverty of Aboriginal people, as well as to their poorer health status. As Adelson explains, "It is the complex interplay of job market discrimination, lack of education, cultural genocide, and loss of land and sovereignty that affect employment status and, ultimately, the degree of poverty faced by those who are caught in a circle of disadvantage" (Adelson, 2005: S53; see also "Fact Sheet—2011 National Household Survey Aboriginal Demographics, Educational Attainment and Labour Market Outcomes," at: https://www.aadnc-aandc.gc.ca/eng/1376329205785/1376329233875).

Self-Perceived Health and Reported Social Problems

Aboriginal people tend to define health as comprised of balance, harmony, holism, and spirituality, and individual pain, suffering, and disease, per se, do not necessarily alter this inner sense of well-being (Shah, 2004). For some Aboriginal groups, health is thought of as a "medicine wheel," which includes physical, mental, emotional, and spiritual aspects (ibid.). In this context, Aboriginal people a number of years ago reported all of the following as significant health and social problems: unemployment, 67 per cent; alcohol abuse, 61.1 per cent; drug abuse, 47.9 per cent; family violence, 39.2 per cent; suicide, 24.5 per cent; and rape, 15 per cent (Adelson, 2005). Obviously, all of these social issues constitute social determinants of morbidity and mortality. Violence is a significant problem in Aboriginal communities. Teenage

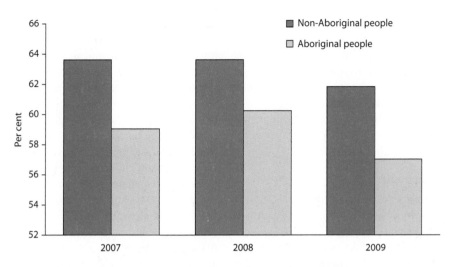

FIGURE 5.8   Employment Rate, by Aboriginal and Non-Aboriginal Population

Source: Statistics Canada, Canada Year Book 2012 (Publication 11-402-X), "Aboriginal peoples." http://www.statcan.gc.ca/pub/11-402-x/2011000/chap/ap-pa/ap-pa-eng.htm.

mothers and their children are particularly vulnerable (ibid.). As Adelson explains, citing a submission to the Royal Commission on Aboriginal Peoples, "up to 75 per cent of the victims of sex crimes in Aboriginal communities are women and girls under the age of 18 (50 per cent of those are under age 14 and almost 25 per cent are under the age of 7)" (ibid., S55). Adelson also notes, "Racism coupled with sexism leaves Aboriginal women in a highly vulnerable position" (ibid.). Aboriginal people are more likely to live with spousal abuse and substance abuse, and they are more likely to be victims of homicide. Suicide rates are high, particularly among the young. Thirty-eight per cent of the deaths among 10–19-year-olds are due to suicide; 23 per cent of the deaths among 20–44-year-olds result from suicide. The overall rate is more than twice as high as the rate of suicide for Canada as a whole (ibid.).

In 1993, one Innu community, Davis Inlet (Utshimassits), Labrador, made front-page news when several children were found in a shed, high on gasoline fumes, and suicides in the community became a critical issue. These children, in some ways, represented the results of a loss of culture. The people were one of the last groups of nomadic hunters in

North America. Until about 45 years ago they lived in tents on the Labrador–Quebec peninsula, a homeland they call Nitassinan. Then they were resettled year-round in permanent communities, the two largest being Sheshatshiu and Davis Inlet, the latter on an island 275 kilometres north of Goose Bay, where they struggled with alcoholism, glue- and gasoline-sniffing, physical and sexual abuse, and suicide. More recently, over $50 million was spent to build a new village, Natuashish, on the mainland for the people of Davis Inlet. But their former way of life was destroyed, both by their initial removal from the land to settlement and by the intrusion of hydroelectric development and mining on what had been their homeland. Their future is uncertain, as the research presented by British medical sociologist Colin Samson in his aptly titled book, *A Way of Life That Does Not Exist: Canada and the Extinguishment of the Innu*, clearly attests. Indeed, a British study led by Samson found that the Innu of northern Quebec and Labrador had the highest suicide rate in the world—a rate 13 times higher than for anyone else in Canada (McAndrew, 1999: A1; Samson et al., 1999; Samson, 2003: 227–9).

The problems continue today, not only for the Innu but on reserves across the country, as traditional land is taken away and people are reset-tled. This is not simply a problem of geography but also one of culture, a way of life and a history. Many attempts have been made to solve the "behavioural problems" such as those described above regarding the people of Davis Inlet. Many would argue, how-ever, that prevention of the problems through First Nations self-government is the only real possible direction for lasting social change.

Residential Schools

Arguably, three significant factors affecting the mental and physical health of Aboriginal Canadians are unique to their circumstance: (1) the experience of residential schools; (2) continuing questions regarding autonomy and authority in governance structures and landownership; and (3) the quality of the physical environments upon which people who live on reserves depend.

Although from a very early date there were some residential schools for Aboriginal children in New France, beginning in 1874 the Canadian state, with the help of various churches, established residential schools for the education of Aboriginal young people and their assimilation to the major-ity society. More than 100,000 Aboriginal chil-dren were taken from their homes and educated in more than 100 residential schools across the country. This practice reflected the government's desire to assimilate Aboriginals into the main-stream culture, an aim supported by the desire of Christian churches and their missionaries to Christianize the Aboriginal peoples. The strategy was to remove young people from their families and cultural roots. Most of these schools were closed by the 1970s, although the last school—in Saskatchewan—closed in 1996. The residential school era of more than a century caused immense suffering for the children and their families. Not only did the residential school experience disrupt the family life of these children, it also diminished their ability to parent when they grew to be adults (Barton et al., 2005). Many of the children lost their culture, language, and identity. Others were sexually and physically abused. Many were ver-bally and physically abused for speaking in their native language, for communicating with their brothers and sisters, for crying or for complain-ing of hunger or fear, and so on. Indeed, for older children, especially, these schools often were less institutions of education than forced labour camps, with the children expected to put in long days of labour tilling the soil, growing crops, and making repairs for the school.

In order to survive and psychologically avoid the pain, many children experienced dissociation (ibid.). Today, many residential school survivors suffer symptoms of post-traumatic stress disorder (PTSD), such as recurrent and intrusive memories, nightmares, flashbacks, sleep difficulties, anger management problems, a tendency to abuse drugs and/or alcohol, and difficulties in relationships. PTSD is associated with marital instability, educa-tional failure, and unemployment (Barton et al., 2005). Some children died from illnesses encoun-tered in the residential schools and were interred in unmarked graves. Tuberculosis was a leading cause of death. In one community, the Nuxalk Nation, 52 per cent of all deaths between 1917 and 1983 involved people under the age of 25. Most likely, many of these deaths were among children in residential schools (ibid.). In the recent past many individuals have come forward to share their stories of abuse and suffering, and there have been many lawsuits against the churches and the gov-ernment for their roles and responsibilities during more than a century of suffering.

The government of Canada, as part of the 2006 settlement for the individual, family, and community harms caused by the residential schools, established a $350-million Aboriginal Healing Fund and the Truth and Reconciliation Commission (see www.trc.ca), which in 2009 began hearing the stories of survivors and help-ing to bridge the gap between the settler Canadian society and Aboriginal cultures. The government has paid damages of about $2 billion to individuals who were wrested from their families as children; deprived of their denigrated cultures, languages, and values; and sometimes sexually or otherwise abused. The churches that ran these government schools—Anglican, Roman Catholic, United, and

Presbyterian—worked out their degree of responsibility with the federal government (the Anglican Church, for example, paid reparations of $25 million) and, except for the Catholic Church, all of the churches made formal apologies in the 1990s (Frideres, 2011: 67–70).

With many residential school survivors in attendance, the Canadian Prime Minister formally apologized in a special sitting of Parliament in June 2008, stating in part: "The Government of Canada sincerely apologizes and asks the forgiveness of the aboriginal peoples of this country for failing them so profoundly. We are sorry." Leaders of the other federal parties also presented statements of apology, and the leaders of the five major national Aboriginal organizations spoke in response. The response of Beverley Jacobs, at that time the president of the Native Women's Association of Canada, cut to the heart of this significant issue in Canadian health and society:

> Prior to the residential schools system, prior to colonization, the women in our communities were very well respected and honoured for the role that they have in our communities as being the life givers, being the care takers of the spirit that we bring to mother earth. We have been given those responsibilities to look after our children and to bring that spirit into this physical world....
>
> I want to say that I come here speaking from my heart, because two generations ago, my grandmother, being a Mohawk woman, was beaten, sexually beaten and physically beaten, for being a Mohawk woman. She did not pass that on. She did not pass it on to my mother and her siblings, and so that matriarchal system that we have was directly affected. Luckily, I was raised in a community where it has been revitalized by all of our mothers.
>
> I want to say that as mothers, we teach our boys and our girls, our men and our women equally.... It is not just about women's issues, it is about making sure that we have strong nations again. That is what I am here to say. (Hansard, 11 June 2008)

The long-term effects continue in the generations who are being born and raised now and in the future.

Environments, Governance, and Land Disputes

There are various threats to the environment, including flooding as the result of the construction of dams and hydroelectric projects, water contamination, and depletion of fisheries. One of the effects of racism is the environmental destruction of the lands of Aboriginal peoples, as corporations from southern Canada and other parts of the world, with the blessing of governments, seek profits from resource extraction and hydroelectric development in northern Canada without due consideration of what such megaprojects as the Alberta tar sands, diamond mining in the Northwest Territories and northern Ontario, nickel and gold mining throughout the provincial and territorial North, or the damming and diverting of water courses will do to environments or to the long-term sustainability of livelihoods.

These various risks are linked not only to the immediate health of the people living on reserves but also to the long-term degradation of the environment. As Beverley Jacobs noted in her response to the residential schools apology, we must ask what effects our actions and decisions today will have "seven generations from now." The ongoing environmental deterioration threatens the entire natural world, including animals, birds, plants, and people. The soils in some communities are infused with toxic heavy metals such as mercury and lead, a result of previous mining and other resource extraction activities. On at least one reserve, Aamjiwnaang, which is just south of Sarnia, Ontario, the sex ratios have been changing and the number of girl babies born is significantly higher than the number of boys. This shift has been shown to be related to a number of nearby industries that produce endocrine-disrupting chemicals linked to the functioning of the immune system, organ and tissue growth, metabolism, behaviour, and sexuality, among other things (Shingler, 2013).

REMEMBERING OUR HISTORY

BOX 5.8   The Ojibway of Grassy Narrows

The experience of the Ojibway of Grassy Narrows First Nation provides a poignant and trenchant critique of the disastrous impact the Canadian state and Canadian industry can have on a people and their way of life. It is just one example of a continuing problem. Until 1963, the Grassy Narrows Ojibwa lived a settled, traditional life, hunting and fishing on and around the English–Wabigoon River system in northern Ontario. Then, in 1963, they were relocated by the Department of Indian Affairs, so the reserve would be nearer to a road, thus, nearer to a number of services and amenities in modern life, such as schools, various social services, and electricity. Uprooting and moving the people had a tumultuous impact on their health and lifestyle. Before the Ojibway had time to adjust to this crisis, another hit. This time it was the discovery that the English–Wabigoon River system, which had been their main source of livelihood for many years, was poisoned by methyl mercury, the source of which was a paper mill at Dryden, Ontario, 170 kilometres upstream (Dickason, 2002: 394).

Before 1963, over 90 per cent of all deaths among the Ojibway were attributed to natural causes. By the mid-1970s, only 24 per cent of the deaths resulted from natural causes. By 1978, 75 per cent of the deaths were due to alcohol-induced violence directed against the self and others. Homicide, suicide, and accidental death rates soared. Child neglect and abuse grew rapidly, and numerous children were taken into the care of the Children's Aid Society and placed in foster homes. As Shkilnyk (1985: 3) says: "Today the bonds of the Indian family have been shattered. The deterioration in family life has taken place with extraordinary swiftness." Despite the good intentions of the Canadian government in relocating the people, their socio-economic conditions deteriorated. "All the indications of material poverty were there—substandard housing, the absence of running water and sewage connections, poor health,

mass unemployment, low income, and welfare dependency" (ibid.).

The Grassy Narrows Ojibway experienced too much change, too quickly. Their autonomy and cultural traditions were destroyed. Because of mercury pollution, they were robbed of their health and their means of livelihood. Difficulties continue in Grassy Narrows as a result of these historical incidents, along with newer challenges such as logging by private commercial companies. Logging is a threat to the livelihood of the people who rely on hunting for their food, health, and well-being.

Recently, in 2014, the Supreme Court re-affirmed the right of the province of Ontario to use this land for industrial logging (http://www.thestar.com/news/canada/2014/07/11/supreme_court_rules_against_first_nation_in_grassy_narrows_logging_case.html). Perhaps most telling of government attitudes, however, is the extent of inaction in regard to the mercury pollution. No remediation of the river system has ever been carried out by the federal or provincial government, although mercury levels are still rising and the earlier claim that natural processes would clean up the contamination has proven to be false (Porter, 2015). No explicit government recognition of the negative health impacts of mercury poisoning on the people of Grassy Narrows (e.g., central nervous system and brain damage, with weakness and tingling in the limbs, difficulty swallowing and speaking, and loss of motor function) has been made. There is no ongoing Canadian research on the problem, nor has there been support for the people from government—yet Japanese researchers, from 1975 to 2014, have visited the community on five separate occasions to examine the people and chronicle the effects of mercury poisoning, and 40 years ago a Japanese researcher identified numerous instances of Minamata disease, a neurological disorder caused by mercury poisoning, among the people of Grassy Narrows (Crowe, 2014).

Canadian Aboriginal peoples on reserves may suffer from isolation, remoteness, and limited power in the control of their own housing, location, education, and occupation. The negotiations over the ownership of land and the governance of reserves continue (slowly) with the Canadian government. The consequences of this lack of autonomy and authority are problematic for the total way of life and well-being of people who live with such uncertainty and with experiences of racism that lead to low expectations of others and for themselves. Self-rule is an important factor in the health and well-being of any people (www.naho.ca/inuit/english/pdf/redefining_relationships_report.pdf). Many Aboriginal people argue that their land was taken away from them through trickery in the eighteenth and nineteenth centuries, and they are seeking reinterpretation of treaties, documenting errors in land transfers, and arguing land claims cases across the country (Frideres, 2011). The government sometimes argues that the treaties were and are legal and binding and that the Aboriginal people got a "good deal." At times, though, the Canadian government has ignored its treaty obligations (for one discussion, see http://reviewcanada.ca/magazine/2014/07/paper-promises/).

Evidence increases of the potential power of organizing for change among First Nations, Inuit, and Métis, along with their supporters across the country. In response to the Conservative government's omnibus budget bills of 2012, which severely weakened environmental protection and limited assessment of resource development projects, a new movement, Idle No More, was born in November 2012. The movement was bolstered by the hunger strike of the chief of the Attawapiskat First Nation, Theresa Spence, who protested the ongoing violation of treaty rights by Prime Minister Harper and the government of Canada, and by a rapidly spreading social media campaign. Idle No More has included non-Aboriginal Canadians and, to an extent, has spread internationally. Many have great hopes for change coming from this inclusive and widespread movement in the context of the power of social media. In reaction to the significant over-representation of Aboriginal women among those who have disappeared and/or who have been murdered, the call for a national inquiry is gaining ground. Along with the 2015 final report of the Truth and Reconciliation Commission, we may be witnessing the beginnings of positive change for the health and well-being of Aboriginal peoples in Canada.

Explanations for the Health Effects of Inequalities

What is the link between inequities in the social structure and the components of health? The following simplifies and summarizes some of the explanations for health inequities according to just a few of the cross-cutting intersections of social reality age, gender, and racialized group status.

Age

People age and their bodies undergo some degeneration over time. Many kinds of chronic diseases, such as cancer, arthritis, stroke, and heart disease, seem to be associated largely with old age. Infancy, early childhood, and youth are other periods of heightened vulnerability to health challenges. This is especially true of boys, children born into poor families, and those who are underweight or overweight at birth. Certainly, biological factors are part of the explanation for age differences in mortality and morbidity. But there are social and economic causes as well. Many are correlated with the social determinants of health.

1. Infants are totally dependent on the care given by their caretakers. Whenever caregiving is inadequate because the parents are unable to provide safe, clean housing and hygienic conditions, sufficient and nutritious food, and protection from accidents, infants and children are more likely to sicken and die.
2. Youth and the elderly may be undervalued and live in an insecure state of ambiguity. They are treated neither as children nor as adults. They are especially vulnerable to social changes,

such as economic recessions or governments' withdrawal of support from certain employment sectors. They suffer from higher rates of suicide and accidental deaths.

3. Older people of different age groups or generations have lived through shifting historical and political-economic circumstances. Such events as war and economic depression have significant and long-term consequences for the health and disability levels of all age groups.

4. Historical periods have differing cultural and social norms regarding the recognition of symptoms and signs of ill health and the action to be taken to respond to them, e.g., whether to "doctor" oneself, do yoga, or go to the doctor. Any and all of these factors may result in different health outcomes.

5. Significant political and economic differences certainly exist between these different and more vulnerable age groups. Children and youth are especially susceptible to political-economic influences as they are dependent on others for their basic well-being and lack independent sources of income. It is also clear that poverty accompanies aging, particularly for women. Income disparities lead to differences in nutrition, stress levels, density in living quarters, access to transportation, and the like. Such resources affect health status.

6. Marginalized youth and children are more likely to be poor and sick and show higher mortality rates. The elderly are more likely to be poor and to live relatively isolated lives separated from family and friends. As they age, friends and important social connections disappear through death and disability.

Gender

Verbrugge (1985, 1989) and Verbrugge and Wingard (1987) made a major contribution to understanding gender differences in morbidity and mortality at the psychosocial level. Since the 1990s, however, considerable research has expanded the explanatory

power of gender differences in morbidity and mortality through the inclusion of the social determinants and social capital perspectives on health. The research literature available on the effects of differences in health outcomes and in death rates leads us to draw the following conclusions about gender differences:

1. Women are more likely to be poor and they tend to have less access to such ameliorative resources as education.

2. Women tend to be responsible for their children's and husband's home health care, including feeding and access to health-giving resources. This role may lead them to put their family members first and to give themselves fewer of these important sorts of capital.

3. Women are more likely to face various kinds of social and political exclusion. They are less likely to hold positions of political power, especially at the highest levels of government. They are also less likely to hold positions of power in large corporations and community-based organizations.

4. Women are highly vulnerable to violence at the hands of men.

5. Because of both biological factors and lifestyle, women have more illness of a mild, transitory type, whereas men have more illness of a serious type. Mild illness has cumulative effects over time, so that women suffer more bed days and disability days and are more likely to see themselves as ill than men do. When men get sick, however, it is more likely with a serious or fatal condition.

6. Women are more attentive to bodily sensations and more willing to talk about them. They tend to take more care for each episode of illness. When the illness is serious (e.g., cancer), men and women are equally likely to take action.

7. While the sexes have similar levels of ability to remember major health problems, women are better "describers" of mild problems because they are willing to talk about them. Women

are more likely to include their feelings in their descriptions of their health.

8. Women's greater attention to minor signs and symptoms and their greater willingness to take preventive and healing actions (i.e., bed rest, diet) mean that their health problems tend not to become as severe as those of men of the same age. This greater carefulness regarding their health helps women to extend their lives.

9. Hegemonic masculinities mean that men, in acting "masculine," are more likely to engage in high-risk activities such as driving drunk and driving at excessive speeds.

10. Men are more likely to engage in violent activities, from bar brawls to war, leading to injury and homicide, and men are more likely to succeed when they attempt suicide.

11. Men are more likely to be employed in high-risk occupations, such as the construction, mining, fishing, and manufacturing industries, as well as the military.

Ethnicity

A final question remains: Why are there "race"/ethnic differences in morbidity and mortality rates? The explanations offered are similar to those outlined in the above discussions on the other structural inequities. The most important additional explanation is racism, which through prejudice and discrimination may have an additional impact on the health of Canadian Aboriginal people, and on that of blacks and other visible minorities. Racism leads to bias in how people are treated in all aspects of their lives. It limits their choices and chances for jobs, education, religious expression, recreation, marriage, residence, and family.

SUMMARY

1. Illness and death rates vary, depending on social-structural conditions such as age, gender, and visible minority status.

2. Canadians are living longer today than in the past.

3. The life expectancy and the morbidity rates for men and women continue to differ.

4. Men have shorter life expectancy and women live longer but with chronic illness and disability.

5. Relative poverty is an important explanation for gender differences in health.

6. Immigrants tend to arrive in Canada in an excellent state of health, but, over time, immigrant health tends to deteriorate to match the health of native-born Canadians.

7. Aboriginal health is poorer than that of other Canadians in many different ways.

8. Schooling in residential schools, environments on reserves, and continuing governance and landownership issues with the Canadian and provincial governments have had negative health impacts.

KEY TERMS

birth rate
essentialized
ethnicity
female circumcision
healthy immigrant effect

life course transitions
microaggressions
minority status
population pyramid
"race"

racialization
racism
sex-mortality differential

QUESTIONS FOR STUDY AND DISCUSSION

1. How do age, gender, and racialization affect the health of individuals?
2. How does the overall degree of inequity in society affect the health of people at the top of the invisible social status hierarchy of the population?
3. Why and how is education related to morbidity and mortality?
4. How and why are prevention-related behaviours associated with socio-economic status?
5. What are the major challenges to the health of Aboriginal peoples? What social and health policies do you advocate with respect to this issue?

SUGGESTED READINGS

Adelson, N. 2005. "The Embodiment of Inequity: Health Disparities in Aboriginal Canada." *Canadian Journal of Public Health* 96: S45–S61. A report on inequalities in health among Aboriginal Canadians.

Barker, K. 2005. *The Fibromyalgia Story: Medical Authority and Women's Worlds of Pain*. Philadelphia: Temple University Press. This book investigates the sociological story of the experience of fibromyalgia among women today.

Barton, S.S., H.V. Thommasen, B. Tallio, W. Zhang, and A.C. Michalos. 2005. "Health and Quality of Life of Aboriginal Residential School Survivors." *Social Indications Research* 73, 2: 295–312. An evaluation of the impacts of residential schools on the health of survivors.

Fenge, T., and T. Penikett. 2014. "Paper Promises." *Literary Review of Canada* (July–Aug.). http://reviewcanada.ca/magazine/2014/07/paper-promises/. This article covers some of the ways in which modern treaties between Aboriginal peoples in Canada and the Canadian government are not being properly implemented or enforced.

Lett, D. 2010. "Police Launch Criminal Investigation into Actions of Emergency Department." *Canadian Medical Association Journal* 182, 18: 817. This brief article highlights some of the critical issues that led to the death of an Aboriginal man, Brian Sinclair, who died in an emergency room waiting for help.

McInturff, K. 2013. "The Gap in the Gender Gap: Violence against Women in Canada." *Canadian Centre for Policy Alternatives Report*. www.policyalternatives.com. A contemporary picture of violence against women in Canada.

McPherson, K., S. Kerr, E. McGee, F. Cheater, and A. Morgan. 2013. *The Role and Impact of Social Capital on the Health and Well-being of Children and Adolescents: A Systematic Review*. Glasgow, Scotland: Glasgow Centre for Population Health. A discussion of the impacts of social capital on children and youth.

Metraux, S., L.X. Clegg, J.D. Daigh, D.P. Culhane, and V. Kane. 2013. "Risk Factors for Becoming Homeless among a Cohort of Veterans Who Served in the Era of the Iraq and Afghanistan Conflicts." *American Journal of Public Health* 103: S255–61. An article that documents the role of serving in combat on later homelessness.

Tamburri, Rosanna. 2012. "Heavy Drinking a Problem at Most Canadian Universities: Report." *University Affairs*, 29 Aug. http://www.universityaffairs.ca/news/news-account/heavy-drinking-a-problem-at-most-canadian-campuses-report/. An article describing the problem of alcohol on university campuses.

Zlotozynska, M., E. Wood, J.S. Montaner, and T. Kerr. 2013. "Supervised Injection Sites: Prejudice Should Not Trump Evidence of Benefit." *Canadian Medical Association Journal* 185, 15: 1303–4. This article raises an important public health issue relating to offering services to help drug-addicted people use drugs relatively safely.

6

Some Social-Psychological Explanations for Illness

Antonio Guillem/Shutterstock.com

CHAPTER OVERVIEW

▶ Socio-psychological factors are related to physically defined morbidity and mortality. They are also linked to mental illnesses.

▶ Stress, social support, social cohesion and social capital, sense of coherence, resilience, prayer, and religiosity are related to wellness, sickness, and death.

▶ Psychoneuroimmunology is a field of study that focuses on mind/body interactions.

▶ Stress was first defined and studied by Cannon and Selye and has been developed into a complex area of ongoing research.

▶ There are a variety of new ways to observe and measure stress, including the frequently used and critiqued Social Readjustment Rating Scale (SRRS), trauma, daily hassles, discrimination, and out-of-sync life transitions.

▶ Social support is integrally related to health outcomes.

▶ The sense of coherence and resilience reflect psychological strengths in dealing with life's challenges.

▶ Religion and religiosity have an impact on health.

▶ People go to the doctor for a variety of social and economic reasons and not simply because they feel ill.

Introduction

Interpersonal relationships play a role in illness. People can die of a "broken heart." Does the repression of feelings, particularly anger, cause cancer? Can a person choose to live or die? What is stress? Is stress sometimes good for health? Does prayer help when a person is sick? Is religion of any benefit to well-being? Why do people go to the doctor? When do people choose to visit a physician rather than "carry on" or go to bed taking an aspirin? The symptoms of a head cold, backache, digestive difficulties, or influenza will send one person to bed, another to the doctor, and others to the drugstore, acupuncturist, nurse practitioner, or neighbour. What determines the personal actions that people take when they are feeling ill? These are the sorts of issues this chapter addresses. It is always important to remember that socio-psychological processes occur inside the human mind and body, and are altered by the invisible and inequitable social structure and the person's cultural context.

Evidence from a wide range of studies indicates that the mind and the body are related. Perceptions, feelings, expectations, and thoughts, for example, affect aspects of bodily functioning such as heart rate and blood pressure as well as cognition and moods. Many people visit doctors for psychosocial reasons such as stress, emotional distress (grief, unhappiness, depression), social isolation, and information rather than for strictly disease-related reasons. At times, these psychosocial difficulties become physical illnesses through biological processes. At other times they may mimic physical illness and be considered **psychosomatic** illness. Physical illness, at times, leads to additional stress, anxiety, depression, and other mental illnesses. People also choose medical answers to large existential questions and even to small aesthetic concerns such as breasts that they consider too small or too large, skin that is considered too wrinkly, skin blemishes, cosmetic issues such as the size of the nose or the slant of the eyes, or bodies that are considered too fat. They choose medicine to transform their lives, sometimes in the context of the new technologies that are a part of biomedicalization of the person (Clarke et al., 2003).

This chapter is divided into two parts. The first part deals with just a few of the many socio-psychological factors associated with illness and well-being including stress, social support, social capital, sense of coherence, resilience, religion, and prayer. The second part will discuss the processes through which people come to define themselves as ill and as needing care, and the actions they take in regard to their health when deciding to seek help from an allopathic practitioner.

Stress

Stress occurs when an organism must deal with demands much greater than, or much less than, the usual level of activity or perceived activity. As such, stress is ubiquitous. All of us are stressed to some degree. The presence of at least some stress in life is beneficial. Stressful experiences can be healthy and can fit us for positive and flexible adaptations to increased stress and sometimes more complex and intransigent stress later on. Or stress can be so overwhelming that it leads to serious illness or death. Too much change in too short a time can overtax the resources of the body.

Two prominent scientists, Cannon (1932) and Selye (1956), were involved in the early articulation and measurement of stress. Cannon suggested that health is ultimately defined not by the absence of disease but rather as the ability of the human being to function satisfactorily in the particular environment in which he or she is operating. People must constantly adapt to changes and perceptions of changes—to alterations in weather, conflicts at work, a traumatic event, failure in school, great success on the hockey team, promotion, flu germs, and so on. The body adapts to such changes by maintaining a relatively constant condition. For example, when the body becomes overheated, it evaporates moisture to help keep it cool; when confronted with bacteria, it produces antibodies. The process of maintaining a desirable bodily state (the constant condition) is called "homeostasis." The body is prepared in many ways to meet threats by adapting in ways that will attempt to continuously return it to the homeostatic state.

Cannon described the typical bodily reaction to stress as "fight or flight," and detailed the accompanying physiological changes. Somewhat later, Selye defined stress as a state that included numerous specific changes within the biological system of the organism. Stress is a general reaction that occurs in response to any number of different stimuli. Both positive and negative events can cause stress. It does not matter whether the event is the happy decision to become engaged to be married or the disappointing failure in a course in university—each requires adaptation.

Building on several decades of research on the pituitary-cortical axis, Selye proposed the General Adaptation Syndrome (GAS) as the body's reaction to all stressful events. The "syndrome" has three stages: (1) an alarm reaction; (2) resistance or adaption; and (3) exhaustion. During the first stage, the body recognizes the stressor and the pituitary-adrenal cortical system responds by producing the arousal hormones necessary for either flight or fight. Increased activity by the heart and lungs, elevated blood-sugar levels, increased perspiration, dilated pupils, and a slowing of the rate of digestion are among the physiological responses to this initial stage of the syndrome. During the adaptive stage the body begins to repair the damage caused by arousal and most of the initial stress symptoms diminish or vanish. But if the stress continues, adaptation to it is lost as the body tries to maintain its defences. Eventually, the body runs out of energy with which to respond to the stress and exhaustion sets in. The prolongation of the stress response can result in a physiological state known as "allostasis" (Lantz et al., 2005). The allostatic load, an excess of which can lead to allostasis, refers to the "wear and tear" on the body that can lead to disease (ibid.). (For a detailed examination of some of the latest research on the allostatic load consider this summary from researchers at the University of California: http://www.macses.ucsf.edu/research/allostatic/allostatic.php). During this final stage, bodily functions are slowed down abnormally or stopped altogether. The theory that ties the mind and body together in modern biological science is called **psychoneuroimmunology** (PNI). It is the study of the interrelations of the central nervous system, the immune system, and psychological processes. The immune system is chiefly located in the bone marrow, thymus, lymph nodes, spleen, tonsils, appendix, and Peyre's patches (clumps of immune tissue in the small intestine).

Continued exposure to stress during the exhaustion stage can lead to what Selye calls the "diseases of adaptation." These include various diseases with emotional, mental, and/or physical symptoms. Table 6.1 provides an example of a stress self-assessment checklist. People are not always aware that they are living under stressful circumstances.

TABLE 6.1   Stress Self-Assessment Checklist

Use the following scale for each symptom and circle the number that best applies to you.

1. Never
2. Occasionally
3. Frequently
4. Constantly

In the last month I have experienced the following

1.	Tension headaches	1	2	3	4
2.	Difficulty in falling or staying asleep	1	2	3	4
3.	Fatigue	1	2	3	4
4.	Overeating	1	2	3	4
5.	Constipation	1	2	3	4

continued

TABLE 6.1 *Continued*

6.	Lower back pain	1	2	3	4
7.	Allergy problems	1	2	3	4
8.	Feelings of nervousness	1	2	3	4
9.	Nightmares	1	2	3	4
10.	High blood pressure	1	2	3	4
11.	Hives	1	2	3	4
12.	Alcohol/non-prescription drug consumption	1	2	3	4
13.	Minor infections	1	2	3	4
14.	Stomach indigestion	1	2	3	4
15.	Hyperventilation or rapid breathing	1	2	3	4
16.	Worrisome thoughts	1	2	3	4
17.	Skin rashes	1	2	3	4
18.	Menstrual distress	1	2	3	4
19.	Nausea or vomiting	1	2	3	4
20.	Irritability with others	1	2	3	4
21.	Migraine headaches	1	2	3	4
22.	Early morning awakening	1	2	3	4
23.	Loss of appetite	1	2	3	4
24.	Diarrhea	1	2	3	4
25.	Aching neck and shoulder muscles	1	2	3	4
26.	Asthma attack	1	2	3	4
27.	Colitis attack	1	2	3	4
28.	Periods of depression	1	2	3	4
29.	Arthritis	1	2	3	4
30.	Common flu or cold	1	2	3	4
31.	Minor accidents	1	2	3	4
32.	Prescription drug use	1	2	3	4
33.	Peptic ulcer	1	2	3	4
34.	Cold hands or feet	1	2	3	4
35.	Heart palpitations	1	2	3	4
36.	Sexual problems	1	2	3	4
37.	Angry feelings	1	2	3	4
38.	Difficulty communicating with others	1	2	3	4
39.	Inability to concentrate	1	2	3	4
40.	Difficulty making decisions	1	2	3	4
41.	Feelings of low self-worth	1	2	3	4
42.	Feelings of depression	1	2	3	4

Source: Neidhardt, Joseph, Malcolm Weinstein and Robert Conry. No-Gimmick Guide to Managing Stress, Vancouver: Self-Counsel Press (1985). © 1985, 1990 International Self-Counsel Press Ltd.

Sometimes bodily and emotional symptoms are the first sign that something is amiss. Table 6.1 lists many of the warning signs or symptoms of stress that may result in subsequent health problems. A typical person will have a score of between 42 and 75 in any given month. The higher the score, the greater the likelihood of illness developing, including mental and physical illnesses.

As well as the symptoms and diseases listed, stress can also, at times, lead to death. To study such effects of stress, Engel collected 170 reports of sudden death. He discovered that the deaths usually occurred within an hour of hearing emotionally intense information, which could be either positive or negative. Of the sudden deaths, 21 per cent occurred on the collapse or death of a close friend, 20 per cent during a period of intense grief, 9 per cent at the threat of the loss of a close person, 3 per cent at the mourning or anniversary of the death of a close person, 6 per cent following a loss of status or self-esteem, 27 per cent when in personal danger or threat of injury (whether real or symbolic), 7 per cent after the danger was over, and, finally, 6 per cent at a reunion, triumph, or happy ending (Engel, 1971). One of the implications of this study is that stress, even stress resulting in death, is (often) mediated through cognitive and emotional perceptions. That is, as human beings, we have the capacity to define things as stressful or not depending on our understandings of the meanings that these things have (Pearlin et al., 2005). Women may be more sensitive to relationship stress. In strained marriages women are more likely to experience risk factors for illness, in general, and heart disease, in particular. These include such issues as hypertension, obesity at the waistline, high blood sugar, high levels of triglycerides and low levels of HDL (the good cholesterol) (Henry and Umberson, 2009). While both men and women in this study of 276 couples reported depression as a result of arguments and feelings of hostility in marriage, women were more likely to exhibit the metabolic syndrome described above and linked to heart disease incidence.

Stress is ubiquitous and can be of short, medium, or long duration. Briefly, short-term stressors arise from small inconveniences, for example, traffic jams, lost keys, or waiting for the doctor. Such things usually result in a temporary sense of anxiety. These have been called "daily hassles" (Lazarus and Delongis, 1983). Medium-term stressors develop from such things as long, cold, dark winters, a layoff from work, stress at work, or an acute sickness in the family. Long-term or chronic stressors result from such incidents or events as the loss of a spouse or the loss of a job, as well as from living in poverty or, for example, in a neighbourhood characterized by vandalism, litter, burglaries, drug deals, and vacant housing (Latkin and Curry, 2003). Chronic strains can accumulate over a lifetime through "stress proliferation" and lead to an earlier onset of morbidity and to mortality (Pearlin et al., 2005). Life transitions "out of sequence," such as becoming pregnant prior to marriage or in the teenage years or during or after menopause, can also lead to stress (ibid.).

We have discussed a brief history of the early research on stress. It is important to note, however, that this is still a very fruitful concept and an ongoing subject of considerable empirical research. There is, for example, recent work on the deleterious impact of the stress of racialization on parenting (Nomaguchi and House, 2013). This work focuses on the ways that people who are discriminated against because of their racial status respond by feeling stressed and having difficulties in parenting their children. Considerable work has also been done on the importance of understanding how people perceive, construct or understand, and subjectively interpret the stress response (Benson, 2014). For a further detailed critical analysis, examine Thoits's review paper on the concept of stress (Thoits, 2010).

One way of conceptualizing the link between events in life over the life course and subsequent stress is through the classic Holmes and Rahe (1967) life events scale. This scale considers change in and of itself to be a major source of stress. Holmes and Rahe (1967) have systematized the stress value attached to a list of life events in a scale called the **Social Readjustment Rating Scale** (SRRS).

Using extensive interviews with 394 people of varying ages and socio-economic statuses, they developed average scale values representing the relative risks of a number of specific life events. Marriage was assigned an arbitrary value of 50. The adjustment value of other items was estimated in comparison to marriage. The resulting scale itemizes 43 changes and quantifies their hypothetical impact (see Table 6.2). In general, the higher the score in a given 12-month period, the greater is the likelihood of illness. It is important to note that, while some of the events are considered negative or undesirable and others might be considered positive or desirable, they all require psychosocial adjustment and are, thus, potentially stressful.

As the scale and other related research indicate, stressors can be the result of changes in any area of life and at a variety of levels, such as: (1) the individual biological level (e.g., bacterial infections); (2) interpersonal situations (e.g., loss of a spouse); (3) social-structural positions (e.g., unemployment, promotion at work); (4) cultural systems (e.g., immigration); (5) ecological systems (e.g., earthquake); or (6) political/state systems (e.g., wars). The greater the number of stressors, and we might hypothesize the greater the number of levels of stressors, the more vulnerable a person is to the possibility of disease and emotional and bodily dysfunction.

It should be reiterated that stressors are not to be thought of as objective things that affect an unthinking organism in a consistent and objective manner (Pearlin et al., 2005). A person's evaluation of the stressful situation, the strategies available for coping, the degree of control felt, and the amount of social support experienced all mediate the impact that the stressor ultimately has on that person. As Viktor Frankl (1965) has pointed out, some people, even in the most atrocious of circumstances such as a concentration camp, have been able to use their experiences in a manner that was meaningful to them, and thus these people ultimately became stronger and healthier as a result of this most extreme of stress-filled situations. Frankl's work has been used to develop a school of vibrant, contemporary psychotherapy called logotherapy, which focuses on helping people to find meaning in their lives.

TABLE 6.2   The Stress of Adjusting to Change

Events	Scale of impact
Death of spouse	100
Divorce	73
Marital separation	65
Jail term	63
Death of close family member	63
Personal injury or illness	53
Marriage	50
Fired at work	47
Marital reconciliation	45
Retirement	45
Change in health of family member	11
Pregnancy	40
Sex difficulties	39
Gain of new family member	39
Business readjustment	39
Change in financial state	38
Death of close friend	37
Change to different line of work	36
Change in number of arguments with spouse	35
Mortgage over $10,000	31
Foreclosure of mortgage or loan	30
Change in responsibilities at work	29
Son or daughter leaving home	29
Trouble with in-laws	29
Outstanding personal achievement	28
Wife begins or stops work	28
Begin or end school	26
Change in living conditions	25
Revision of personal habits	24
Trouble with boss	23
Change in work hours or conditions	20
Change in residence	20
Change in schools	20
Change in recreation	19
Change in church activities	19
Change in social activities	18
Mortgage or loan less than $10,000	17
Change in sleeping habits	16
Change in number of family get-togethers	15
Change in eating habits	15
Vacation	13
Christmas	12
Minor violations of the law	11

Source: Reprinted from Thomas H. Holmes and Richard H. Rahe, "The Social Readjustment Rating Scale," Journal of Psychosomatic Research 11 (1967), 2: 213–18, with permission from Elsevier.

The SRRS has been used to predict illness among a wide variety of different people in North America. It has also been used in a number of cross-cultural studies that have included Swiss, Belgian, and Dutch peoples (Bieliauskas, 1982). Overall, researchers have found significant similarities among different cultural groups in their evaluation of the impact of various events. Such studies have shown the SRRS to be a remarkably stable or reliable instrument. It has also been used to "predict" illness and symptoms of distress. Holmes and Masuda's 1974 study concluded "that life-change events . . . lower bodily resistance and enhance the probability of disease occurrence." Several researchers have correlated high SRRS scores with symptoms and with illness, including major illnesses such as heart disease (Theorell and Rahe, 1971; Rahe and Paasikivi, 1971). High SRRS scores have also been found to be associated with psychological distress in a number of studies (Bieliauskas, 1982). Several researchers have used SRRS successfully to predict the onset of illness. One interesting example of this research is the study that examined the SRRS of 2,600 navy personnel prior to their departure on voyages of 6–8 months. The researchers found significant correlations between the levels of stress before the start of the voyage and the subsequent levels of disease during the voyages (Rahe et al., 1970). Thoits's (2010) review paper discusses a number of studies using the SRRS and contextualizes the importance of this measure in a historical context. Another study focuses on one group of people—the incarcerated—who have experienced significant life change, and notes the increased death rate that resulted from the many stresses and strains of imprisonment (Pridemore, 2014). Imagine for a moment, if this is even possible, about the subculture in the prison environment, and consider the myriad life changes necessitated by incarceration—not being able to see the stars at night or to walk on the grass or to choose one's food or to enter a store or restaurant or see a friend, and so many worse deprivations. The lack of stimulation in a limited and threatening environment affects the brain, and the reasons for subsequent ill health and even death become clear.

The SRRS can be critiqued for the following reasons.

1. It ignores differences in the meaning people place on the various events. There is evidence that the impact of the death of a spouse, for instance, varies depending on whether the death was sudden or occurred after a protracted period of illness.
2. Some of the events listed may be signs of illness or the results of illness, such as changes in eating habits, sleeping habits, personal habits, or sex difficulties. Thus the scale is, in part, tautological.
3. Some research has found that distinguishing between the desirable and undesirable events enhances the predictive value of the scale. Marriage is generally taken as a reason for celebration, death as an occasion for mourning. It has been argued that the stress-related effects of death are, therefore, more pronounced than those of marriage.
4. The ability to control events has been shown, in a number of studies, to be an important factor in determining the degree of stress experienced.
5. Whether stress affects the incidence of disease or merely affects behaviour during illness has been questioned. It may be that life events affect the likelihood of people reporting illness rather than affecting the disease process.
6. The SRRS asks about events that have occurred during a specified period of time. Some research has shown that the association between stress and subsequent illness or disease cannot be studied separately from the previous stress level and the history of past illnesses. Thus, experiences of the years before the time period referred to in the SRRS may also have a powerful effect on the level of stress experienced. A car accident followed by the loss of a driver's licence and a household move in the years before the designated SRRS time period might exacerbate whatever level of stress is experienced during the year of the SRRS measurements.

Large and significant life events such as marriage, divorce, and imprisonment contribute to the stress response but, as noted earlier, so do daily hassles such as a fight with a friend, having to study for a test, or even getting stuck in traffic jam (Serido et al., 2004). In fact, there is some possibility that the accumulation of daily hassles is perhaps more problematic for the individual organism than specific life events, either within the previous 12-month period as suggested by Holmes and Rahe (1967) or occurring at any time of life. Serido and colleagues, for example, compared the effects of daily hassles with those of chronic stressors and found that they had different effects on psychological distress. They argue that chronic stressors offer an "ever-present potential to erupt in ways both large and small in an individual's life" (Serido et al., 2004: 30). Daily hassles, on the other hand, actually constitute ongoing stressors that require an individual response. Further, research indicates that daily hassles and chronic stressors interact so that together they cause greater stress than the simple addition of one to the other would predict. So widely accepted has this notion of stress become that popular magazines often include their own stress tests and cures. As an example, a recent post of the website of the popular psychology magazine *Psychology Today* offered advice and warned people not to "sweat the small stuff" or the daily hassles (Riggio, 2012). Popular psychology's advice for preventing stress due to daily hassles is thinking positively, learning to relax, and giving oneself rewards.

Pearlin and his colleagues have shown how the stress response is exacerbated by repeated hardships over a life course, such as those resulting from discrimination on the basis of such socially structured issues as racialization, gender, sexual orientation, and disability. In fact, they suggest that ascribed statuses originating at birth and co-extensive throughout life, such as race and gender, usually offer the potential for repeated discriminatory and stressful

experience. Furthermore, such ascribed statuses are often enacted in a variety of contexts, such as work, school, housing, the justice system, medical care, and in commercial transactions (Pearlin et al., 2005: 209). The relative ubiquity of the potential for the stress experience, they suggest, likely enhances its impact. Moreover, the experience of discrimination at one point in time or in one life realm may prepare the person to anticipate further discrimination and lead to a relatively constant state of vigilance. The ongoing stress—and the potential for ongoing stress—in central areas of life may lead to "stress proliferation" in that chronic strain in a pivotal social role (e.g., work or school) can lead to other hardships or stressors. Thus, stress at work can spill over into stress at home, which can then affect family relationships and one's actual and perceived well-being.

Pearlin and colleagues also articulated the potential stress impact of one-time-only trauma such as rape or other sudden, violent, negative, or otherwise onerous events. Such events not only tend to accumulate in some people, especially those nearer the bottom of the socioeconomic ladder, but they may, like chronic discrimination, lead to the "creation" of associated stressors. Consider the case of rape. The woman who has been raped, as a consequence of this incident, may have to interact with the medical system, the legal system, the educational system (if she is a student), family, and friends in regard to having been raped. Any, indeed all, of these interactions may add to the stress load of the already victimized female (or the victimized male). Moreover, some sorts of stressful events seem to repeat themselves over time. It may be, for example, that adults who were abused as children are more likely to abuse others as adults.

Pearlin and colleagues also point to the stressful effects of transitional and other life events occurring at a non-normative time in a person's life. Two that occur early in life and can have ongoing implications for the rest of life are dropping out of school and becoming pregnant

TABLE 6.3   Some Examples of Indicators of Excess Stress

Physical	Psychological	Behavioural
Rapid pulse	Inability to concentrate	Smoking
Increased perspiration	Difficulty making decisions	Medication use
Pounding heart	Loss of self-confidence	Nervous tics
Tightened stomach	Cravings	Absent-mindedness
Tense arm, leg muscles	Worry or anxiety	Accident-proneness
Shortness of breath	Irrational fear or panic	Hair-pulling, nail-biting,
Tensed teeth and jaw	Feelings of sadness	foot-tapping
Inability to sit still	Frustration	Sleep disturbance
Sore back and shoulders		Increased use of alcohol
		Addictive eating

Source: Adapted from Neidhardt, Joseph, Malcolm Weinstein and Robert Conry. No-Gimmick Guide to Managing Stress, Vancouver: Self-Counsel Press (1985). © 1985, 1990 International Self-Counsel Press Ltd. pp. 5–6.

CRITICAL THINKING

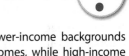

BOX 6.1   Moderate Wine Drinking Is Good for You

It's good for you! No, it's not! Yes, it is! There has been a lot of debate over the years about the benefits of moderate drinking. One study, which has tracked 4,500 graduates of the University of North Carolina since 1964, has found that wine consumption seems to be associated with good health (see Picard, 2002). This time it is not thought to be primarily because of the biochemistry of wine but rather because of the lifestyles associated with those who drink wine. Apparently, according to this recent study, those who drink wine also tend to eat less saturated fat and cholesterol, eat more fibre, smoke less, and exercise more frequently. They tend to be less likely to be overweight than those who drink beer or spirits. They tend to drink alcohol in moderation as compared to those who regularly choose other types of alcohol. As compared to abstainers, they tend to eat less red meat, more fruit and vegetables, and to be less likely to smoke. These findings are consistent across social status categories. Thus,

wine drinkers from lower-income backgrounds had good health outcomes, while high-income abstainers had poorer health outcomes.

In other studies moderate drinking has been found to be associated with a variety of better health outcomes, including lower rates of heart attacks and strokes, hypertension, Alzheimer's disease, diabetes, kidney stones, digestive ailments, Parkinson's disease, and macular degeneration (www2.potsdam.edu/hansondj/Alcohol AndHealth.html).

This controversy continues with another study and another contradictory set of findings. A more recent report of a study in the *British Medical Journal* has found that minimizing the amount of (any) alcohol consumed is beneficial and lowers the risk of heart disease and blood pressure (Spencer, 2014).

The question continues: is drinking red wine good for you or not? How much should one drink to maximize health?

while a youth (Pearlin et al., 2005: 212). In addition, people who make "disorderly transitions" are more likely to be from economically

disadvantaged families. Pearlin et al. also point out that life disruptions or events can occur on top of all of the other sources of stress, such as discrimination, out-of-sequence transition, and trauma, and then may have exacerbated consequences. Table 6.3 lists some behavioural indicators of excess stress that over time may correlate with serious illness.

Social Support

Almost all people think they understand **social support**, on an intuitive if not on a cognitive level. If you were to ask your friends whether they know the meaning of social support, you would probably find unanimous affirmation. If you were then to ask each to define its meaning, you would likely hear as many definitions as there are people. For some, social support would be defined as "a feeling that you have or don't have." For others, it would be defined as friends with whom to party. Another would define it as someone with whom to do things. Still another might see social support as having someone on side in case of an argument. Material and practical aid might be necessary components of social support for others. While living alone does not necessarily mean living without support, at times it may be so. The number of households inhabited by one person continues to grow. In 2011, 29.5 per cent of households were single-person households; 28.5 per cent lived in households with children (http://www12.statcan.ca/census-recensement/2011/as-sa/98-312-x/98-312-x2011003_2-eng.cfm). Some people who live alone are aging, having raised families and become widowed. As they age in place (at home) they may become isolated and unable to care adequately for themselves.

When sociologists attempt to measure social support, the varieties and idiosyncrasies of what "social support" means become apparent. One definition comes from the work of Cobb (1976), who thought of social support as information that would lead a person to believe (1) that he or she is cared for and loved, (2) that he or she is esteemed and valued, and (3) that he or she belongs to a network of

communication and mutual obligation. A group of researchers used this definition as the basis for a scale that was later revised and subjected to a number of uses (see Turner et al., 1983). The scale asks people to describe themselves in comparison to others with respect to the amount of social support they feel they have. It is an essentially subjective measure based on each person assessing his or her felt degree of social support. It includes both social support in the sense of a person's feeling of being loved and esteemed by others, and social support as an experience of being part of a "network" of people.

This definition of social support emphasizes the subjective perception of the respondent. Others have considered social support as something that can be objectively measured—social support exists to the extent that a person can count on others to offer specific services such as cooking, cleaning, snow shovelling, or transportation when the need arises. Among the mechanisms through which Thoits (2011) deems support exerts social influence are control comparison, purpose and meaning, self-esteem, belonging, sense of control, and companionship. The degree of social support is demonstrated in the reliability and extensiveness of the actual aid supplied. The degree of social support perceived may also reflect the subjective feelings of the individual. In a further refinement, others have pointed out that different kinds of "support" are desired and expected from different "kinds" of others. That is, people may expect different things from their friends than from their spouses or kin. Whether or not the network is made up of people who know each other may also affect the experience of social support.

A number of studies have examined the impact of social support on health outcomes (Thoits, 2011). The *Journal of Health and Social Behavior*, a major American journal in the field of the sociology of health and illness, has published numerous articles concerning social support in a variety of situations. In recent years such articles have addressed all of the following:

the health consequences of being unemployed; self-assessments of the elderly; occupational stress; mental health; psychological well-being; primary deviance among mental patients; life stress; psychotropic drug use; psychological distress and self-rejection in young adults; adolescent cigarette smoking; health in widowhood in later life; teenage pregnancy; social support among men with AIDS; and depressed patients. This list gives some idea of the range of situations in which social support has been shown to act or to be lacking. It is also worth emphasizing that the health benefits associated with social support

are not limited to those who receive it: those who provide support can benefit as well.

Some researchers have emphasized that social support has a direct relationship to health so that the person who has support is less likely to become ill. Others have noted that adequate social support can minimize the harmful effects of stress on a person's mental or physical health. These two notions are compatible with one another: social support may have both direct and indirect effects on health (Thoits, 2011).

In 1973, Gove analyzed causes of mortality and noted that married people tended to live

---

HIGHLIGHTED ISSUES

BOX 6.2   Uncertain Identities, Support-Seeking, and Health Risk

We have discussed the frequency of smoking in society today. We have talked about the ways that peers, cigarette taxes, advertising, cigarette package warnings and families contribute to smoking rates. We have also, but only briefly, talked about some of the serious health consequences of smoking. Taking another tack, Martyn Denscombe (2001) has used the symbolic interactionist perspective to understand the meanings of smoking to young people who do smoke. While the rates of smoking among adults have been declining over the last 30 years or so, young people continue to begin to smoke, particularly young women, despite aggressive government anti-smoking campaigns. Clearly, government campaigns are less effective than tobacco industry advertising campaigns or peer group influence. A number of researchers have investigated the increase in smoking among young people. Among the explanations put forward are peer pressure, feelings of immortality, stresses of adolescence, addiction to smoking occurring from "just trying it," susceptibility to advertising, influence of parents and older siblings, low self-esteem, and "fun."

The explanation Denscombe investigates is "uncertain identities among young people."

He argues that uncertainty—the postmodern condition—is particularly endemic and problematic for a number of reasons. As a result of interviewing and conducting focus groups with young people, he describes the ways in which cigarette smoking is used to develop and maintain a desired identity. The following is a list of identity-related motives given by young people about why they smoke:

- to look grown up
- to look cool
- to look hard
- (among girls) for girl power
- to be in control

Denscombe concludes that smoking can be seen as a way to enhance self-image, self-empowerment, and self-affirmation. The tobacco industry through its advertising plays on insecurities by linking smoking to female beauty, empowerment, liberation, and health, according to the World Health Organization (www.who.int/tobacco/wntd/2010/tob_ind_marketing – women/en/index.html). What about you? Do you smoke? If so, do any of these explanations fit you and your experiences, either personally or in your observations of others?

longer. Analysis of the dates of death of famous people (Phillips and Feldman, 1973) showed that death rates declined just before a significant occasion, such as a birthday, wedding, or Christmas celebration—an occasion on which these people would have the opportunity to reaffirm social ties with the group of significant others. A very large study (Beckman, 1977) charted the lives of 7,000 people over a period of some nine years; during that period 682 of the 7,000 people died. After controlling for a variety of socio-demographic and risk factors, the data revealed that those who died tended to lack social ties (family, church, informal and formal group associations). Beckman concluded that isolation and the lack of social and community networks likely increase vulnerability to disease in general. Recent research continues to investigate the links between social support and death (and illness). For example, the study by Yang and colleagues notes that one biological mechanism for the association is inflammation, which is said to operate differently in males and females (Yang et al., 2013).

One study that made an effort to move beyond the correlational connections between social support and health outcomes is based on interviews with teenage mothers during pregnancy and then after childbirth. The purpose of this study was to investigate the impact of social support (Turner and Avison, 1992). These researchers examined the impact of social support on what has been argued to be a very important indicator of the health of a population—infant birth weight. Consistent with their hypothesis, the researchers noted that pregnant teenagers who received more support from family, friends, and partners had higher-birth-weight babies. The level of social support positively affected not only birth weight but also the psychological health of the new mother. This research also found that socio-economic background influenced the relationship between social support and the health outcomes of mothers and their infants. Social support was especially helpful to young women with lower-class backgrounds, although it was not unimportant for those from higher socio-economic backgrounds. In conclusion, it is well established that in a variety of situations a supportive social network can reduce mortality and morbidity over time (see, e.g., Cheng and Chan, 2006; Poortinga, 2006).

The relationship between social support and specific diseases such as cancer, hypertension, and heart disease has also been examined. A number of studies have reiterated the relationship between cancer and the loss of a marriage partner (LeShan, 1978). Relationships have also been discovered between the incidence of cancer and other indicators of social connections. For example, the greater the religious cohesion, e.g., among Mormons, the lower the incidence of cancers (although it is important to note here that there are many differences in lifestyle and diet exhibited by Mormons). While the studies neither establish a causal connection nor explain all of the variance, there seem to be sufficient grounds to pursue further research on

TABLE 6.4   Some Hypothetical Explanations of Health Differences among People of Different Socio-economic Status

Material Resources	Lifestyle	Social-Psychological Resources	Family/Community
Housing	Smoking	Stable, secure employment	Stability/integration into family and community
Food	Drinking	Supportive relationships	Supportive mutual-aid relationships
Clean water	Exercise	Education	Decision-making authority
Clean air	Sexual safety	Coping abilities, emotional stability	Privacy
Access to necessary immunization, drugs, and medical care	Risk-taking	Sense of coherence, sense of efficacy	

the potential association between social connections and longevity as well as different disease states (Cornwell and Waite, 2012).

Professor David Spiegel, a psychiatrist and researcher at Stanford University Medical School, set out to refute the notion that the mind could be used to affect the outcome of disease. He observed 86 women with breast cancer for 10 years. To his surprise, he found that women who took part in group therapy and who had been taught self-hypnosis lived twice as long as those who had not (Spiegel et al., 1989). Subsequent research has repeated this finding, although not consistently. The promise of such research has proven to be so great that a new field, psycho-oncology, examines the psychological aspects of getting and surviving cancer and includes a now classic text, *Handbook of Psychooncology* (Holland and Rowland, 1989; see also Lerner, 1994: 139). According to Lerner, "Social support is . . . one of the most important and interesting categories which psycho-oncologists address" (ibid., 14). A recent systematic review of a number of studies of the role of social support in cancer longevity found sufficient evidence of the association in the case of breast cancer (there was an adequate number of valid studies) and less support for the link with other cancers. The authors note that considerations such as the extensiveness of the disease at diagnosis, the treatments offered, and the site of metastasis were important intervening variables (Nausheen et al., 2009). Clearly, there is room for a great deal of additional research on this topic.

A number of questions remain. What are the mechanisms through which support operates? How does social support affect health? Does support influence the interpretation of stressful life events? Are people who feel supported likely to feel that they can manage to cope with the sudden death of a spouse because they believe that others will listen and continue to care? Does social support have different meanings among people of different social categories, such as the elderly, minority populations, or the poor? Can stress lead to the destruction of

potentially supportive relationships at times? Do those lower on the social ladder, lacking relative power, also experience a daily lack of social support in their interactions with mainstream and powerful social institutions such as churches, schools, and health clinics? The mechanisms through which social support affects health need to be further studied and clarified.

Recently, social support has also been studied as social capital or **social cohesion**. In regard to experience at the level of the individual, however, "social support" still seems to be a very useful concept. However, when we consider the ways in which societies, neighbourhoods, towns, work groups, and so on are organized to offer support, or not, the alternative terms—"social capital" and "social cohesion"—are most relevant (McPherson et al., 2013; Vyncke et al., 2013). This has been a very important new direction in research. Indeed, a substantial body of empirical literature documents a link between social capital and health. According to Poortinga, there are three complementary ways of thinking of social capital; *bonding, bridging,* and *linking.* Bonding refers to horizontal ties among similar people in a social grouping. Bridging involves links across different social groups who are not necessarily similar. It also incorporates perceived levels of social justice, solidarity, and mutual respect. Linking refers to vertical interactions across formal and institutionalized power structures in a community. All three are thought to be important in health outcomes (Szreter and Woolcock, 2004). Another useful distinction is between objective and subjective components of social capital. This refers to the fact that social capital is both perceived and structural. The former refers to feelings of support, connection, trust, and the like and the latter to actual links observed, for instance, in membership or leadership in an organization (Poortinga, 2006). Social capital is seen to have both direct benefits to individuals and indirect benefits through organizations.

Social connections prevent isolation. Hawthorne (2006) suggests several different beneficial dimensions offered by social relationships, friendships, and social connections. They include being able to share feelings and intimacies with a significant other or others; being able to relate to another regarding whatever it is that a particular relationship provides; being able to ask for emotional or instrumental/practical support when it is needed; having a social network within which to give and receive social support; and not being isolated from others and not being alone. What do you think are the most important advantages of social cohesion or social capital? Does your university or do your classes encourage social cohesion? Does group work lead to social cohesion? Think for a moment about the up- and downsides of social cohesion in your life at present.

CRITICAL THINKING

BOX 6.3   Bullying and Cyberbullying

Not all social and human interactions are supportive. One particularly problematic type of interaction, according to studies of schoolyards and workplaces, is increasingly prevalent. Bullying has been known to cause stress, illness, and even, in some cases, death by suicide. Since bullying has been defined as a problem there have been a number of studies of its incidence and discussions of social policies that may limit it. One useful website (www.bullying.org) offers a number of "facts" about bullying. It is dedicated to helping those who bully and who are bullied know that they are not alone and that there are ways to get help. This site defines bullying as "a conscious, wilful, deliberate, hostile and repeated behaviour by one or more people, which is intended to harm others." It includes physical violence, threats, exclusion, and verbal attacks. The website suggests that bullying is not about anger but contempt: "a powerful feeling of dislike towards someone considered to be worthless, inferior or undeserving of respect." A new kind of bullying, called "cyberbullying" is a particularly pernicious development, as hateful and hurtful taunts through social media such as Facebook can spread quickly, and extend far beyond a small group of young people in a schoolyard. There are several recent Canadian examples of young people committing suicide as a result of their online experience of being bullied. In the world of cyberbullying, bullies can come from anywhere and be of any age or gender. Amanda Todd, a teenager from British Columbia, for instance, committed suicide as the result of being bullied by a man from Holland, it is alleged (http://www.cbc.ca/news/canada/arrest-of-dutch-man-in-amanda-todd-cyberbullying-rekindles-family-anguish-1.2622226). Apparently, the video of Todd's torment has been seen at least 30 million times around the world. More recently, 13 young men who were students in dental school at Dalhousie University were suspended from clinical practice because they had developed a Facebook page on which they made sexually explicit comments and threats of sexual assault and otherwise sexually harassed some of their female student colleagues. There was a strong outcry across the country and within Dalhousie University over this incident (see, e.g., Rush, 2014).

A recent international study of bullying involving more than 200,000 children ages 11–15 from 40 countries found that countries with established anti-bullying campaigns had the lowest rates of bullying. Canada ranked in the middle: twenty-first for boys and twenty-sixth for girls in bullying rates. What can be done? What are some of the links between health and bullying? Do you have a bullying story to tell—one in which you were the bully or the bullied? Are bystanders ethically responsible for bullying, too? Should bystanders be punished as bullies if and when they are caught?

CRITICAL THINKING

BOX 6.4   How Does Racism Work to Hurt People?

A great deal of research documents the many ways that discrimination hurts adults. It has been shown to cause psychological distress, depression, low self-esteem, anxiety, and declines in physical health. Are these effects the same in adolescents and children who experience racism? What are the consequences of growing up as a person who is a member of a stigmatized and stereotyped ethnic minority? It makes sense to suggest that the impact of racism is even greater on children than on adults because young people are at the stage of developing their identities and understandings of what it means to be a member of an ethnic group. Perceived discrimination may interfere with the ongoing internalization processes because of the difficulties of identifying with a group one sees being rejected and hated.

Whitbeck and his colleagues (2001) studied 195 Amerindian children in Grades 5–8 on three different reservations in the Upper Midwest of the United States. Although this study is based in the US there is no compelling reason to believe that the processes differ in Canada. They found that the experience of prejudice and discrimination had significant consequences for the

development of Amerindian adolescents. Being perceived as different from others and being rejected by the majority groups during early adolescence may lead to self-hatred, anger, delinquency, and substance abuse. Beginning substance abuse behaviours early compounds the difficulties associated with altering them and may seriously impede later life chances. Children who use substances are more likely to drop out of or fail at school and to have problems getting along with other people, including peers and family members. These are among the adaptations to discrimination that can accumulate and severely limit opportunities later in life. Other research has documented links between perceived racial discrimination and hypertension, birth weight, sick days, respiratory illnesses, anxiety, depression, and psychosis (McKenzie, 2003).

What can be done? Do you have any experiences with discrimination and prejudice? Have you felt critical or disparaging of people because of their ethnicity or visible minority status? Can you remember where and how that feeling started? What maintains your feelings of ethnic superiority, ethnic confidence, ethnic insecurity, or ethnic inferiority?

Sense of Coherence

Antonovsky reversed the usual questions we have been asking about what sorts of psychosocial factors cause illness. Instead, he asked: How do people stay healthy? Rather than look at the deleterious effects of such things as the lack of social support and the consequences of stress, Antonovsky focused on the positive and beneficial. Citing evidence from many studies, he argued that a **sense of coherence** or a belief that things are under control and will work out in the long run is a crucial component of the state of mind that leads to health. People who have good or excellent health, all things being equal, are

likely to have a strong sense of coherence, which is defined as follows:

> . . . A global orientation that expresses the extent to which one has a pervasive, enduring though dynamic feeling of confidence that (1) the stimuli deriving from one's internal and external environments in the course of living are structured, predictable, and explicable; (2) the resources are available to one to meet the demands posed by these stimuli; and (3) these demands are challenges, worthy of investment and engagement. (Antonovsky, 1979: 19)

The "sense of coherence" concept draws attention to the fact that the extent to which a person feels that he or she can manage whatever life has in store is an essential factor in health (see Richardson and Ratner, 2005). It is important to note that this socio-psychological factor is also associated with compromised mental health and various physical illnesses. Furthermore, it is a robust concept and a number of studies have found it to be an important mediator of good health (Ericksson and Lindstrom, 2006).

There are three components to a sense of coherence. The first is *comprehensibility*—the basic belief that the world is fundamentally understandable and predictable. Such a belief in the comprehensibility of the self and of human relationships is absolutely essential for coping. People with a high sense of coherence feel that the information they receive from the internal and external environment is orderly, consistent, and clear. People with a lower sense of coherence tend to feel that the world is chaotic, random, and inexplicable. A person with a high sense of coherence feels that his or her actions in the past have had the expected consequences, and they will continue to do so in the future. The student who knows how hard to study or how many drafts of a paper to make in order to get the desired A or B (or, heaven forbid, C) grade is someone with a high sense of comprehensibility.

The second component of the sense of coherence is *being able to cope*. The person with a sense of coherence understands what the world expects and feels that he or she has the ability and the resources necessary to meet whatever is demanded. Not only does the student know what is necessary to get an A, B, or C grade, he or she feels able to obtain the desired grade.

The third component of a sense of coherence—*meaningfulness*—refers to the motivation to achieve a desired outcome. This component depends on the extent to which life makes sense, has a purpose, and is worth the effort. The student values learning, and the grade achieved is important because grades and education have a purpose to play in life's satisfactions and goals.

The student with a high sense of coherence, when confronted with an unexpected (and seemingly undeserved) failure, does not give up in bitterness and disgust but rises to the challenge: he or she questions the mark, takes the course again, or takes a different course. In other words, the student with a high sense of coherence would be able to explain the failure to himself or herself, and would be willing and able to take action to improve the grade, believing that such action would have the desired outcome and that the whole process of learning and being examined is meaningful. Not surprisingly, an aspect of the sense of coherence—perceived control—is associated with socio-demographic variables.

All of these aforementioned socio-psychological issues—stress, social support, social capital, social cohesion, and sense of coherence—appear to operate on the body through the immune system. For an extensive overview of the research in psychoneuroimmunology that is accessible to social scientific understanding, see Kaplan (1991) and Lerner (1994). Research in this area is ongoing and some of the results of studies can be found in the journal *Brain, Behavior, and Immunity*. One recent example investigated the positive role of

Dancing, singing, and other forms of artistic expression have been shown to reduce stress, a key indicator and force on individual health and well-being. Choosing to go dancing rather than (for example) staying home and worrying about looming deadlines can seem like a poor choice to some observers, but may be a sign of resiliency—choosing coping mechanisms that improve well-being in the face of difficult situations.

Source: iStock/kzenon.

music in well-being (Fancourt et al., 2014) through an examination of 63 published studies. Others have documented the benefits to health and well-being of other arts such as dance, painting, creative writing, journalling, and drawing.

Resilience

Resilience is another important socio-psychological concept that helps us to understand variations in illness that arise from differences in individuals at the psychosocial level. Similar to a sense of coherence, resilience is a positive trait that aids individual adaptation. People with a high degree of resiliency are able to respond to challenges in ways that are helpful to their own well-being. Resiliency can mean the difference between responding to a life event (for example, car accident, loss of a loved one, serious diagnosis) in ways that enable the person to carry on, feel well (enough) eventually, maintain overall good health, and set and achieve goals. Resilience can be seen as an asset or a resource to assist with readjustment after a difficult event. "Those who thrive under adversity (e.g., poverty, maltreatment, loss of a parent) exhibit engagement in processes described as resilience" (Liebenberg et al., 2013: 131). This example from the many studies of resiliency focuses on young people and found 12 factors to be a valid measure of resiliency in youth.

1. I know where to go in the community to get help.
2. Getting an education is important to me.
3. I try to finish what I start.
4. I have people to look up to.
5. My parents/caregivers know a lot about me.
6. My family stands by me during difficult times.
7. My friends stand by me in difficult times.
8. I have opportunities to develop skills that will be useful in later life.
9. I am treated fairly by my community.
10. I feel I belong at my school.
11. I enjoy my cultural and family traditions.
12. I am able to solve problems without hurting myself or others.

Religion and Health: Theoretical Views

About 90 per cent of the peoples of the world are involved in some sort of spiritual practice (Koenig, 2009). Religion and religiosity, which are central features of culture and cultural difference, are associated with both physical and mental health. Durkheim's studies of suicide were the first to investigate sociological aspects of this relationship. His concern was with the degree of integration into a social group as well as the regulation of behaviour provided by religious affiliation. According to the National Household Survey of 2011 there were 108 different religious groups (including atheists, agnostics and non-affiliated) in Canada (www12.statcan.gc.ca/nhs-enm/2011/dp-pd/dt-td/Rp-eng.cfm?LANG=E&APATH=3&DETAIL=0&DIM=0&FL=A&FREE=0&GC=0&GID=0&GK=0&GRP=0&PID=105399&PRID=0&PTYPE=105277&S=0&SHOWALL=0&SUB=0&Temporal=2013&THEME=95&VID=0&VNAMEE=&VNAMEF=). Today, to a significant extent and building on Durkheim, researchers have investigated a variety of components of religious affiliation in relation to various aspects of health. According to Ellison's (1991) review, religion has been theorized to enhance well-being in four ways: (1) social integration and support; (2) personal relationship with a divine "other"; (3) provision of systems of meaning; (4) promotion of specific patterns of religious organization and personal lifestyle. First, religion may increase social integration through friendship and social ties entered into on a voluntary basis. It can provide a social support network available in a crisis, regular community celebration of ritual events, normative social control regarding behaviour associated with good health (such as dietary and drinking norms), and interpersonal and business ethics and norms. Second, a personal relationship with a divine other may involve frequent prayer and meditation, as well as identification with a supreme being or with various benevolent figures from religious texts. Third, the personal system of meaning is an explanatory framework through which believers can understand themselves, their personal relationships, their work, and personal crises, tragedies, and joys, indeed, the whole "round of life," including birth, life, death, and life after death. The fourth component refers to ways in which church membership may provide direction and support for patterns of behaviour such as church attendance and family mores, as well as other patterns having to do with such health-related activities as dietary restrictions.

Religion is also a type of coping behaviour, according to Koenig (2009), that helps people make sense of reality. It can help people make sense of suffering, provide a feeling of control over things that seem out of control, and enhance communal relations and mutual support. As a part of the evidence he points to studies indicating that 90 per cent of Americans managed or attempted to manage the stress of 9/11 (Koenig et al., 2001) by turning to religion. Bible sales increased by 27 per cent within one week. Sixty per cent of Americans attended a religious memorial service. Religious involvement has also been linked to better mental health, enhanced coping with stress and less depression, anxiety, and substance abuse (Koenig, 2009). It should be mentioned that religious experiences are not always beneficial to mental health; the Jonestown cult history of ill health, suicide, and murder culminating in mass suicide in 1978 provides the most outstanding recent case in point. The joining of religious ideals to rationalizations for warfare is inevitably deadly.

Some medical care providers have begun to include discussions of spirituality in treatments for people with both physical and mental health issues. Some psychiatric researchers, for instance, are exploring the possible benefits of training people in forgiveness, gratitude, and altruism—characteristics of personalities considered to exhibit excellent mental health—to improve health outcomes (Baetz and Toews, 2009). So seriously are some medical care personnel taking the links between health and religion that they are proposing that all Canadian physicians should receive required training in spiritual health care as a part of medical school (Miller, 2013). A number of medical schools in the US have already integrated courses on spirituality into their curricula.

In *Suicide*, Durkheim explained the protective and destructive effects of various forms of integration and regulation with respect to the suicide rate. In particular, he examined the results of too little integration or too much integration into the social group of which the individual was a part and the corresponding rates of egoistic and altruistic suicide. He also examined too little regulation and too much (normative) regulation and the corresponding tendency for anomic or fatalistic suicide. In *Elementary Forms of Religious Life*, Durkheim moved beyond the focus on the integrative and regulative functions of society and religion and examined such other topics as the division of time and space into the sacred and the profane and the impacts of ritual and group worship on the collectivity. These ideas need further study.

Religion and Health: Empirical Study

It has been nearly 150 years since Benjamin Travers remarked that he had never seen a case of cancer of the penis in a Jew, and almost that long since Regoni-Stern first observed that Catholic nuns in Verona, Italy, were at significant risk for breast cancer yet significantly protected against uterine cancer (Levin and Schiller, 1987: 9). The history of the empirical study of the relationship between religion and health is a long, circuitous, and complex one. Religion and religiosity have a wide variety of components, such as denominational adherence and interaction with the divine. Health outcomes, too, have been investigated in a variety of ways, such as the increase or decrease in specific diagnosis (e.g., heart attack), overall morbidity and mortality, and health risk factors such as smoking. Among the control and intervening variables considered are ethnicity, class, and religious density in a specified geographical area. But what aspect of religion contributes to health? What pathways relate these two to one another? Levin (1993: 5) has reviewed over 250 studies. Regardless of the definitions of the independent variables (various religious factors) or the dependent variables (e.g., specific diagnoses or overall morbidity and mortality), the results across all of the studies found that the greater the intensity or degree of religious involvement of the individual, the better the health. Levin's review of this literature concluded that nine hypotheses have been investigated.

1. *Behaviour.* The relationship between religion and health results from health-relevant behavioural prescriptions, including limiting alcohol consumption, dietary patterns of abstinence and fasting, and not smoking.

2. *Heredity.* The genetic pools of certain religious groups, particularly the most conservative and the smallest, tend to be concentrated. This may lead to greater or lesser health. For instance, Tay-Sachs disease seems to be more frequent among Eastern European Jews. Sickle-cell anemia is more prevalent among members of the predominately black National Baptist Convention in the US than among those of the predominately white Southern Baptist Convention. In this case the difference is likely attributable to the genetic inheritance of the two groups.

3. *Psychosocial effects.* Involvement in a congregation of religious adherents provides a sense of belonging; receiving and giving social support—sometimes of a fundamental type in food, clothing, and shelter, but even in regular leisure-time activities—promotes better health. This type of investigation corresponds to the tradition of research that has independently demonstrated the benefits of good and supportive social relationships, perhaps through buffering the negative effects of stress and anger through psychoneuroimmunological pathways.

4. *Psychodynamics of belief.* The beliefs of adherents to particular denominations may engender a sense of hope, purpose, peace, and self-confidence, on the one hand, or guilt and self-doubt, on the other. Such beliefs may be associated with health benefits or decrements. For example, the "Protestant ethic" could provide the epistemological and theological foundation for the internal locus of control. So-called type A individuals are competitive, achievement oriented, easily annoyed, and time urgent, in contrast to easy-going type B people.

5. *Psychodynamics of religious rites.* The practice of regular, recurrent public and private rituals, such as church attendance, daily scripture reading, and prayer, moderate anxiety, dread, and loneliness and establish a sense of being loved and accepted.

6. *Psychodynamics of faith.* It is possible that belief in a God and an ordered universe may operate as a placebo. For example, "various scriptures promise victory or survival to the faithful. The physiological effects of expectancy beliefs such as these are now being documented by mind-body researchers" (ibid., 10).

7. *Multifactorial explanations.* It is likely that the relationship between religion and health is due to a combination of the factors listed and to hypotheses that have not yet been considered.

8. *Super-empirical explanations.* The preceding hypotheses are social, psychological, and biological. It may be that the best hypothesis is one for which concepts and measurement tools are not yet available. Consider, for example, the beliefs of ancient and contemporary religious traditions in a universal life force or "energy." To date, this largely mysterious idea has been dismissed by the Western researcher. In the future, empirical observations may be available to further understand this "energy" or life force.

9. *Supernatural influence.* Another possible explanation is supernatural, "in other words, a transcendent being who exists fully or partly outside of nature chooses when and why to endow and bless individuals with health or healing, presumably on the basis of their faithfulness" (ibid., 11). Such a hypothesis, by definition, cannot be studied.

At an ecological rather than an individual level, the degree of concentration or density of a religious group is another component of the religious influence on health that has been examined. Areas with a higher concentration of religious groups have been shown to have different morbidity and mortality rates than areas that are similar in all regards but lack religious density. For example, Fuchs (1974) compared the mortality rates of two similar western states: Utah, where there is a very high concentration of Mormons, a religion that, among other things, prohibits cigarette smoking, alcohol, and caffeine, and Nevada, a more secular state, which has relatively high rates of alcohol and cigarette smoking. There were also important differences in marital, family, and geographical stability in these two states. The death rates for cirrhosis and for cancer of the respiratory system were higher in Nevada. At the county level, the impact of religious concentration and denominational affiliation on cancer mortality rates has also been examined, controlling for demographic, environmental, and regional factors known to affect cancer mortality. The findings noted the cancer-protective effects for all inhabitants of living in a densely religious area, perhaps the result of diminished exposure and increased social disapproval of cancer-causing behaviours. Contradictory findings, though, are demonstrated in the following study. Very conservative states tend to have higher rates of teen pregnancy (Strayhorn and Strayhorn, 2009), which may lead to a number of health problems both in the teen mother and in her offspring. The moderating variable in this case may be a decreased probability of using birth control. Nevertheless, it does indicate a situation in which religiosity may be linked to poorer health outcomes. Still, very religious people more often see themselves as and report that they are healthy than do less religious people, according to a recent Gallop Poll (http://www.huffingtonpost.com/2012/02/21/religion-and-health_n_1290740.html).

Studies have been done on the relationship between religious and spiritual practices and health. Overall, the evidence seems to suggest that there is a moderate protective effect (Koenig et al., 2001). A wide variety of outcomes, including those related to both mental and physical health (as well as outcomes from specific diseases) have been included in these studies. We still do not understand the actual mechanisms for the effects. For instance, the relative importance of private religious and spiritual practices as compared to attendance at public religious events such as church services is not well understood. There appear to be gender differences in the impact on health of religious and spiritual practices (Maselko and Kubzansky, 2005). Perhaps surprisingly, Maselko and Kubzansky (2005) found that while weekly public religious activity was significantly associated with health and well-being, the relationship was stronger for men than for women. That is to say, men seemed to get more health benefit from weekly church attendance than women and this was linked to denominational adherence. It appeared in this study that men's well-being increased from attendance at Roman Catholic services, but that of women decreased. The authors hypothesized that this might be related to the use of male language for God and church members alike and the imagery suggesting that God is male (ibid.). Another explanation might be that men tend to be more socially isolated and thus the shared participation in Mass may be of greater benefit. Another study found that weekly attendance, but no more, was associated with decreased anxiety and depression. The explanations for this positive effect of moderate church attendance were sense of meaning, interpersonal and self-forgiveness, among others (Sementhal et al., 2010). Other scholars have looked at the consequences on health of switching denominations. Sheitle and Adamczyk (2010), for instance, compared switching from "high-cost" (theologically restrictive and culturally exclusive) religious groups such as Latter-Day Saints and Jehovah's Witness and less demanding mainstream denominations and found the benefits of staying in these high-cost groups were highly protective as compared to others. Being a member of a high-cost group has the potential to provide support and solutions for many if not most of the uncertainties of everyday life, but only as long as the person remains a member and perhaps only as long as he/she continues to believe in those teachings.

Prayer and Health

Prayer for health is as ancient as civilization. Lately, under the modern positivistic scientific paradigm, a number of studies have been published establishing that prayer effects changes in human beings as well as a number of other biological systems or organisms, including cells, fungi, yeast, bacteria, plants, single-celled organisms, and animals (Targ, 1997). It doesn't matter whether the prayer includes the laying on of hands or if the "prayer" and "person prayed for" are geographically separated, even by a wide distance and with or without intervening barriers. How does this work? Some people think the space-time continuum has not been adequately defined by science. Some people think scientists cannot investigate whether or not God heals through prayer because, by their definition, God is outside (some would say inside, too) and greater than human senses—God is infinite and perfect. Human powers of observation and measurement are flawed and finite. Thus, we cannot "study" God empirically. Still others contend that we do not adequately understand all of what our physical senses are capable of perceiving and that some people have learned how to extend the common ways of using their perceptual senses. But is there some empirical force, energy, or information whose effects, emanating from prayer, can be studied? Prayer is believed to be "communication" with the deity, the Creator, who "answers" the petitioner. Healing in this context is the response of God, including to the requests of people.

Prayer has been investigated as a natural phenomenon with some interesting results. Levin and Vanderpool (1989) have reviewed empirical studies and found a positive link between religion and health. This link may be empirically explained as the result of (1) making behavioural adjustments, including dietary restrictions such as fasting as a way to "move into prayer"; (2) knowing that one is being prayed for may, in and of itself, lead to a feeling of being supported; (3) knowing that one is being prayed for and praying for oneself and others may be comforting and result in changes in the immune system; and finally (4) simply a belief in prayer may lead to well-being.

The most cited study of prayer and healing was done by Randolph Byrd at the San Francisco General Medical Center in 1982–3 (Lerner, 1994: 128). A devoutly religious yet scientifically trained medical doctor, Byrd set out to investigate the effects of prayer on healing by looking at the health effects of being prayed for among 393 cardiac patients. He randomly assigned the patients to two groups and assigned people from nearby evangelical and Catholic prayer groups to pray for patients in the experimental group. Those randomly assigned to the control group were alike in all respects at the beginning of the study. After the prayers, the experimental group was healthier in the following ways: (1) the need to be ventilated or intubated; (2) the need for antibiotics; (3) the frequency of cardio-pulmonary arrest; (4) the frequency of congestive heart failure; (5) the frequency of pneumonia; and (6) the need for diuretics. In this double-blind situation, prayer by distant and unknown others was effective in improving the outcomes of cardiac patients.

Another study, with parallels to Byrd's, is a double-blind clinical investigation of post-operative patients that also documented psychological and physical improvements. In this study, 53 males who underwent hernia surgery were divided into three groups. The first group received a pre-recorded tape with suggestions for a speedy recovery. The second group experienced distant healing during the surgery by a healer who was concentrating on the individual and sending him/her healing thoughts (prayers), and the third group was a non-intervention control. The group receiving distant healing/praying was more likely to experience recovery than either of the other two groups (Targ, 1997: 75). Other studies have noted the effectiveness of distant healing for various physiological measures, such as electro-dermal activity, heart rate, blood volume, and relaxation (ibid.). Music, imagery, and touch (called MIT therapy) have been found to have a positive impact on the health of people in cardiac care (Krucoff et al., 2005). Brown (2012), a professor of religious studies, has studied the phenomenon of intercessory prayer (prayer for others) and found some evidence of lasting healing. The conclusion we must come to, then, is that empirical research on the effects of prayer can be done and that more research needs to be done to demonstrate the empirical effects of prayer on health.

The Illness Iceberg

The distribution of illness in a population has been described using the simile of an **illness iceberg** (Last, 1963; Verbrugge, 1986). The image implies that most symptoms of disease go largely unnoticed by the people who have the symptoms, by health-care practitioners, and by epidemiologists interested in measuring the incidence and prevalence of disease. Illness goes undetected for a number of reasons. First, people often explain away or rationalize physical changes in their bodies in ways that seem to make sense and therefore do not require a medical explanation. Sudden or extensive weight loss and a long-standing cough that doesn't seem to get better both can be signs of very serious illness. They are, however, easily explainable in lay terms: "I've been too busy to eat" or "if it would only stop raining my cough would go away." In the second place, some signs of latent illness develop slowly over a long period, so that the patient is not alerted to them. High blood pressure and cholesterol buildup in the arteries are two examples. Some of these diseases can only be detected by clinical tests such as X-rays, CAT scans, and blood and urine tests.

Practitioners, too, are limited in what illness they can detect. Some diseases that are not observable through any specific clinical measures can be diagnosed only by a myriad of complex tests, plus symptoms described by the patient and some element of luck or art. Also, practitioners are often limited in their ability to detect illness because their patients do not provide sufficient information. Epidemiologists face all of the obstacles described above. In addition, epidemiologists frequently rely on a wide range of data collection strategies (as discussed in Chapter 2 online), all of which are subject to various limitations of validity, reliability, recall, response rate, truth-telling, and the like.

In the face of such ambiguity and variability in the recognition and acknowledgement of signs and symptoms of illness, what are the processes that lead some people to decide to do something about them and others to ignore them?

Why People Seek Help

What makes you decide to go to the doctor? Do you go when pain becomes severe? Is it when your symptoms interfere with your responsibilities at home, school, or work? Do you try to avoid going to the doctor? When you feel cold or flu symptoms do you generally just go to bed early or take a day or two off work? Do you go to the local drugstore to buy something from the shelf? Or do you go to a naturopath, chiropractor, nutritionist, allopathic physician, acupuncturist, or other therapist? The processes by which people come to notice signs they think may be symptomatic of illness, the kinds of attention they pay to these signs, and the action they decide to take are all a part of the study of illness behaviour. Whether someone seeks help and what kind of help is sought are the result of complex social and psychological determinants.

The first stage of illness is the acknowledgement or notice of symptoms or signs. Sometimes symptoms are noticeable as little more than a minor behavioural change, such as tiredness or lack of appetite. Some common symptoms, such as a cough, cause only a mild discomfort; others may cause a searing pain. Sometimes symptoms are noticeable as measurable physical anomalies such as a heightened temperature or an excessive blood-sugar reading. Other times, illness is not experienced until it is diagnosed after a medical examination.

People with similar symptoms may respond very differently to them. One may go straight to the doctor; another may "let nature take its course", even with severe symptoms. Although early responses may be quite variable, they will make sense within the context of the social, cultural, economic, and psychological conditions of each person.

An early study, "Pathways to the Doctor" (Zola, 1973), was based on interviews with more than 200 people at three clinics. For each person it was the first visit for that particular problem. According to Zola's analysis, the decision to seek treatment was based on a great deal more than the mere presence of symptoms. Rather, this decision was associated with one or more of the following:

1. occurrence of an interpersonal crisis;
2. perceived interference with social or personal relations;
3. sanctioning by others;
4. perceived interference with vocational or physical activity; and
5. a kind of "temporalizing" of symptoms (or thinking that they will go away in time).

Mechanic (1978) proposed that seeking help depends on 10 determinants:

1. visibility and recognition of the symptoms;
2. the extent to which symptoms are perceived as dangerous;
3. the extent to which symptoms disrupt family, work, and other social activities;
4. the frequency and persistence of symptoms;
5. amount of tolerance for the symptoms;
6. available information, knowledge, and cultural assumptions;
7. basic needs that lead to denial;
8. other needs competing with the symptoms;
9. competing interpretations that can be given to the symptoms once they are recognized;
10. availability of treatment resources, physical proximity, and psychological and financial costs of taking action.

Mechanic and Zola take somewhat different points of view. In particular, Mechanic acknowledges the relevance of the symptoms themselves—their severity, perceived seriousness, visibility, frequency, and persistence—and the knowledge, information, and associated cultural assumptions people use in determining whether or not to take action. In Zola's 1973 model, "symptoms" per se are not discussed; their place in the "ongoingness" of life of the individual is examined.

Medical treatment has certain costs. In Canada most treatment, whether visiting the doctor's office or the emergency room or being treated in hospital, is essentially free (paid for through the taxation system). However, there are other costs, including time off work, transportation to and from medical help, purchase of pharmaceuticals, the anxiety of waiting for results, and paying for babysitting or child-sitting arrangements. All of these and others can be viewed as constraints within which the theories above must operate. Furthermore, since these studies were published some significant social changes have developed that affect the amount of doctor-visiting, including direct-to-consumer advertising of drugs and the many health websites on the Internet. People can use the Internet to find a diagnosis for the symptoms they may experience. While a risky process, Internet advice can forestall doctor and other health-care visits or may increase the demand for doctoring. In addition, some people go to the doctor after they have read about or seen an advertisement for a new treatment or a new disease. Some diseases may even have an element of attractiveness to some people, as they seem to be so associated with camaraderie, fellow-feeling, and even popularity (high incidence). Thus, certain people may search for the possibility of a diagnosis. The Movember movement, for example, has highlighted prostate cancer as a possible diagnosis for men of a certain age for whom early and continued testing is recommended. Such positive campaigns can increase the probability that people will go to the doctor for examination. The results of the breast cancer movement can also be seen in the widespread attendance at mammography screening despite the equivocation regarding effectiveness. There are also new categories of people who visit the doctor, such as those who want to be "better than well" and better than "normal." Those who choose mood-altering drugs and cosmetic surgeries might fit into this aspirational category (see Chapter 7).

SUMMARY

1. Stress is a process that occurs in response to demands that are either much greater than or much less than the usual levels of activity. Historically, the bodily reaction to stress has been termed "fight or flight" by Cannon. Later, Selye suggested that the General Adaptation Syndrome (GAS) is the body's reaction to all stressful events. It has three stages: an alarm reaction, resistance, and exhaustion. Exposure to stress in the third stage can lead to "diseases of adaptation."

2. Some researchers have developed scales to measure degrees of stress.

3. Several factors affect the amount of stress experienced. One important factor is social support, which has been seen to be a buffer against the degree of stress experienced.

4. Social capital and social cohesion are linked to health outcomes.

5. People are more likely to stay healthy when they have a feeling of comprehensibility,

manageability, and meaningfulness in their lives and are able to develop a sense of coherence and a belief that things are under control.

6. Religion and prayer have been associated with healing both historically and, more recently, empirically.

7. The first stage of illness is the acknowledgement or notice of symptoms or signs. What people do about the illness, how illness is experienced and handled or treated, is called "illness behaviour." Illness behaviour varies according to the individual's social circumstances. Factors that lead an individual to seek treatment include the occurrence of an interpersonal crisis, the perceived interference with social or personal relations, sanctioning by others, the perceived interference with vocational or physical activity, "temporalizing" of symptoms that have continued "too long" or develop "suddenly" and "unexpectedly," and the availability of treatment resources, physical proximity, and psychological and financial costs of taking action.

KEY TERMS

illness iceberg	resilience	Social Readjustment Rating Scale
psychoneuroimmunology	sense of coherence	social support
psychosomatic	social cohesion	stress

QUESTIONS FOR STUDY AND DISCUSSION

1. Assess yourself with regard to all of the socio-psychological variables that seem to be related to health status. What changes can you make now to improve your health?

2. Design a study to measure the sense of coherence of students at your university.

3. Critically evaluate the studies examining the relationship between prayer and health.

4. What do you estimate to be the proportion of the contribution of each of the various factors said to be associated with going to the doctor, as outlined by Mechanic and Zola?

5. Define, describe, and critically analyze ideas associated with the illness iceberg.

SUGGESTED READINGS

Albrekt Larsen, C. 2013. *The Rise and Fall of Social Cohesion: The Construction and De-construction of Social Trust in the US, UK, Sweden and Denmark.* Oxford: Oxford University Press. A comparative discussion of the changes in the levels of social cohesion in several developed societies.

Cohen, P., et al. 2006. "Current Affairs and the Public Psyche: American Anxiety in the Post-9/11 World." *Social Psychiatry* 41: 251–60. A review of some of the socio-psychological impacts of the 11 September 2001 terrorist attacks on the United States.

Doidge, N. 2007. *The Brain That Changes Itself: Stories of Personal Triumph from the Frontiers of Brain Science.* New York: Penguin. A book that through a variety of stories demonstrates how people (and their brains) can change.

Fancourt, D., A. Ockelford, and A. Belai. 2014. "The Psychoneurological Effects of Music: A Systematic Review and New Model." *Brain, Behavior, and Immunity* 36: 15–26. A review paper investigating the role of music in health.

Liebenberg, L., M. Ungar, and J.C. LeBlanc. 2013. "The CYRM-12: A Brief Measure of Resilience." *Canadian Journal of Public Health* 104, 2: 131–5. This article explains in concrete empirical terms one way to measure (and understand) resilience.

Thoits, P.A. 2010. "Stress and Health: Major Findings and Policy Implications." *Journal of Health and Social Behavior* 51, 1 (Supplement): 41–53. A review of the literature on stress and health.

Thoits, P.A. 2011. "Mechanisms Linking Social Ties and Support to Mental and Physical Health." *Journal of Health and Social Behavior* 52, 2: 145–61. A review of the literature on social support and health.

7 The Experience of Being Ill

Monkey Business Images/Shutterstock.com

CHAPTER OVERVIEW

▶ Illness is experienced in subjective and personal terms, although the personal experience is socially constructed and contextualized according to all of the cultural, social determinants and socio-psychological discourses related to the issues we have discussed thus far.

▶ Disease and sickness need to be understood as socially constructed and distinct from one another but influenced by the circulating discourses and practices.

▶ Among the variety of popular personal and individual discourses of illness are the following: illness as choice, as carelessness or failure, as despair, as secondary

gain, as a message of the body, as communication, as metaphor, as statistical infrequency, and as sexual politics, as aspirational, as potential, as candidate, and as survival.

▶ The insider's view of living with illness over time (chronic illness) describes it as involving a great deal of emotional, ontological, and philosophical work, along with the management of, among other things, treatments, symptoms, side effects of various treatments, and health-care providers.

▶ Illness, sickness, and disease are linked recursively to self and identity.

Introduction

What is it like to acknowledge for the first time symptoms of a potentially serious illness? For instance, how do men feel and how do they talk to themselves and to others upon first noticing a lump in a breast? How do women manage to cope with a diagnosis of myocardial infarction? How do people manage who feel awful but cannot get a diagnosis, such as some people with chronic fatigue syndrome, fibromyalgia, or environmental sensitivities? What is it like to be told that your child has epilepsy, Tay-Sachs disease, or Down's syndrome? What is it like for the doctors, the nurses, the siblings, and significant others? How do people talk to themselves when they learn that they have cancer, diabetes, or AIDS? How do people manage the uncertainty surrounding a diagnosis of HIV/AIDS and the possible or probable future prognosis of illness? How do people tell their significant others once they have received a diagnosis from the doctor? And how, then, do family members and significant others manage the news? How are such mild and self-limiting diseases as the flu or a cold understood in the whole context of the lives of people? These are the sorts of questions that might be asked about the experience of illness.

The purpose of this chapter is to describe and explain something of the socially constructed experience of being ill in Canadian society. Most published sociological research to date and that which we have examined so far in this text assumes that the object of sociology is the observation of the institutions and structures of society and of individual interpretations of these forces through their psychosocial dynamics. Both the social and personal levels constrain and influence people's thoughts, feelings, beliefs, and actions. This view prevails in most of the articles published in all the major North American journals of sociology. Chapters 2 through 6 in this book have been written largely in these traditions of positivist, conflict, feminist, intersectional, and anti-racist points of view, using quantitative and "objective" data about social phenomena to provide description

and causal explanations. These five chapters do not examine the processes whereby these external "objective" forces come to be integrated into the social actions (thoughts, feelings, beliefs, and behaviour) of human beings. Nor do they offer explanations or descriptions of the meanings and interpretations that people give to these factors. Analysis of discourse has been largely absent in these chapters of the text.

Chapter 7 is written in the interpretive tradition: it draws attention to the meanings, discourses, and world views of human beings in relation to illness, sickness, disease, and death. The chapter examines the subjective reality, the consciousness of people making and finding meaning in interactive and social contexts. The analysis in this chapter is at the individual level. However, it must be emphasized that a person's views are constructed in the context of a particular society and by a particular place at a unique point in time in that society. They are the shifting results of accepting and resisting circulating social discourses related to power/knowledge. Meanings and identities are constructed from social interactions in specific social, political, economic, and historical contexts. Meanings and identities reflect a person's position in the social structure and that person's relationships and experience. Cultural attitudes to illness vary. Definitions of health and illness vary over time, from place to place and diverge depending on such things as medicalization, biomedicalization, culture, social class, racialization, gender, ability/disability, sexual orientation, and the like.

Illness, Sickness, Disease, Survivor and Aspirational Health

It is of fundamental importance to distinguish among disease, illness, and sickness. **Disease** is that which is diagnosed by a physician; it is usually believed to be located in specific organs or systems in the body and curable through particular biomedical treatments. Disease is most obviously constructed within the powerful discourses of medicalization and biomedicalization. **Illness**, by contrast, is the personal experience of the person who acknowledges that he or she does not feel well or as well as possible. While illness is affected by the discourses of medicalization it is also heavily influenced by the individual's social context and such characteristics as gender and racialization. What a person considers to be "normal well-being" reflects the social group within which norms are forged and maintained. **Sickness** refers to the social actions taken by a person as a result of illness or disease, such as taking medication, visiting the doctor, resting in bed, or staying away from work. Patients "feel illness" and "act sickness"; physicians "diagnose and treat disease." Aspirational health—the health that improves and enhances one—results from a confluence of medicine, malleable bodies, new technologies, and, possibly, optimism about what medical interventions might deliver. These first three concepts are classic and need to be understood within the contexts of the theories of medicalization that will be discussed fully in the next two chapters. At this point, however, I want to draw your attention to new phenomena that arise in the context of biomedicalization (Clarke et al., 2003). The use of medicine to change one's identity and improve or enhance the self leads to the notion of **aspirational health**. Others result from technological change and powerful mass media representations and include (1) living with the statistically or genetically predicted expectation of disease, i.e., being a **patient-in-waiting**, (2) being a **survivor** of a disease, or (3) being in remission and seen by others as an **illness candidate**.

Sickness, disease, illness, and anticipatory enhancement or aspirational health and patient-in-waiting, surviving, and illness candidature may be independent of one another, which is confirmed by the fact that people can feel ill and act sick and yet not visit a physician. People can act sick without having a medical diagnosis, as when a student complains of having flu in order to get an extension for an essay or an exemption from an examination. A physician may tell people that they are not ill and

ought not pretend to be sick. This type of situation may arise when a person is experiencing sleeplessness from the stress of final exams and, thus, feels ill but does not have a medical condition. A person may have an illness diagnosed as a disease by a physician. Such a diagnosis legitimizes sick role behaviour. In this case, sickness, illness, and disease may occur together. Now, though, people often seek medical intervention or medical care not because they have a medical pathology or even an anomaly but because they want to improve themselves in some way or another. Bodies, cognitions, and moods all are seen as mutable at the hands of the medical profession. Sometimes people live in fear of disease because they are only surviving or because genetic tests have predicted illness for them in the future.

Figure 7.1 clarifies the relationships among illness, sickness, disease, and medicine for self-improvement. Illness, sickness, disease, and the desirable way to be a human being all are socially constructed experiences. People do not experience or talk about their illnesses or their ideal bodies and moods in a social or cultural vacuum. Everything that people feel, say, think, and do about their illnesses and body/mind aspirations is culturally and socially mediated. For example, a sore back conjures up one set of meanings, ideas, and actions when it happens to a person with bone cancer. A sore back conjures up a different set of meanings, ideas, and actions when it happens to a world-class skier just before the Olympics. In fact, noticing that a part of the body, such as the back, is sore is only possible within a particular social-cultural context and its resultant language categories. Small breasts have a certain value for a female runner or swimmer and another for a person who wants to be a Hollywood star. In respect to moods, sadness, for example, elicited one sort of discourse as an inevitable part of life situations prior to the development of the popular anti-depressants known as SSRIs (selective serotonin reuptake inhibitors) and another much more widely accepted medicalized meaning as pathological when SSRIs became readily available (see, e.g., Metzl and Angel, 2004; Clarke and Gawley, 2009). More recently, what had begun years ago as "sadness" has turned to a discourse of

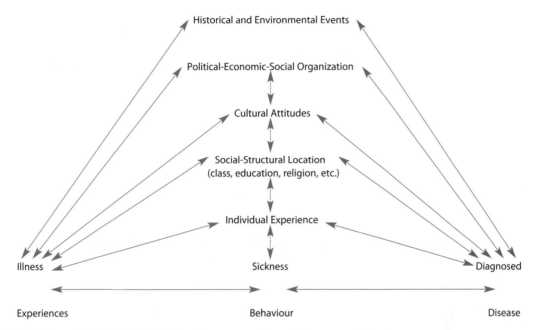

FIGURE 7.1   A Model of the Relationships among Illness, Sickness, and Disease

anger and desperation as some people have discovered the vast array of physical and behavioural side effects, including addiction to SSRIs that can lead to suicide. Numerous self-help websites and blogs are devoted to trying to help people break free of these drugs (see, e.g., www.topix.com/forum/drug/effexor; www.paxilprogress.org/; fiddaman.blogspot.com).

Sickness behaviour is socially mediated. Whether a woman goes to the hospital at the first sign of labour or does not go until she is ready to deliver, or delivers at home with a midwife or doula, depends in part on cultural influences. Old Order Mennonite women, according to the nurses in the obstetrics department of a local hospital, often have their babies on the way to the delivery room because they tend to wait through several stages of labour before travelling slowly in buggies to the hospital. According to the same source, women from some other ethnic backgrounds usually enter the hospital at the first sign of contractions and, once there, are likely to engage in long, protracted, painful, and "noisy" labour.

Disease, too, is a socially and culturally mediated event. Doctors make their diagnoses from a complex mix of socio-cultural, historical, economic, medical, scientific, technological, and clinical data, and in the context of their own age, specialty, class, gender, and ethnocultural circumstances. That death, too, is socially mediated was described first by Sudnow (1967) and later by Timmermans (1998) and then others. Nordquist (2006) studied the effect of patient insurance availability on the interpretation of do-not-resuscitate (DNR) orders of doctors. He found (in the US) that doctors were more likely to write DNR orders for people who lacked private insurance. Thus, doctors were implicitly valuing life in economic terms. Extended life was available for those who could pay for it. Li and Arber (2006) have studied how palliative care nurses, in doing the emotionally invested work necessary to nurse the dying, constructed the moral identities of dying people as "credible" or troubled. This, too, played into how dying patients were treated. McInerney (2006) has studied media discourses of death with particular focus on the "requested death movement" (i.e., "right to die movement") in the Australian press, and Shoshana and Teman (2006) have examined the construction of death through another medium—television—in the series *Six Feet Under*. These last two references are based on qualitative and interpretive media analyses and reflect evidence that media both mirror and influence everyday social practices even in the case of our understandings of death. Death is medicalized and even monitored by the medical care system in Canada today as this recent study of the performance status and symptom displays of dying patients shows (Seow et al., 2011). When celebrities die, their way of "handling" death can become a media lesson for everyone on how one ought—and more often how not—to die . . . the

moral and the immoral way to die (Frith et al., 2013). Dying of a drug overdose, as Phillip Seymour Hoffman or Heath Ledger did, becomes glamorous, perhaps not desirable but notable and understandable in our celebritized culture. Of course, as sociologists we need to critique this media portrayal of the "normative" way of dying.

Outrageous Acts and Everyday Rebellions is the title of a witty satire by Gloria Steinem (1983) illustrating how illness, sickness, and disease may also be sociological or, in this case, gendered determinations. Steinem suggests, for example, that beliefs

HIGHLIGHTED ISSUES

BOX 7.1   Social Value of the Patient: Death, Psychiatric Patients, and Children

David Sudnow (1967), in what has become a classic text, described in great detail, as the result of lengthy participant observation at two US hospitals, how the "presumed social value of a patient" affected the type of death-care the patient received. For example, poorer people, less "functioning" people, and people who were deemed less "valuable" because of "race"/ethnicity or age were given less aggressive treatments in general hospitals. Timmermans (1998) has reinvestigated the question of whether or not and how a patient's social worth continues to be a factor in the type and quality of treatment received. In particular, Timmermans examined how the use of resuscitation technologies may have altered or be reflected in this finding. How do health-care practitioners "make sense of engaging in a practice with the small chance of saving lives and the potential to severely disable patients" (ibid., 469)? Apparently, in the face of controversial options, the health-care practitioners continue to distinguish between people on the basis of their "social viability" or on their ability to contribute to society (according to the doctor's set of values) and on the basis of attempting "to avoid a lawsuit." In sum, "in the liminal

space between lives worth living and proper deaths, resuscitative efforts in the emergency department crystallize submerged subtle attitudes of the wider society" (ibid., 471). The economic value of a life also is of fundamental significance in the legal establishment of the amount owing in the case of a wrongful death.

Children by this legal accounting are worth substantially less (in terms of compensation) than adults, particularly adult males at the peak of their earning capacity. The social evaluations of psychiatric patients also affects the types and quality of treatment they receive (Lincoln, 2006). Some psychiatrists, concerned citizens, and children's rights advocates argue that children are essentially the victims of ongoing and dangerous experiments when they are diagnosed with mental illnesses in the absence of valid and reliable diagnostic criteria and then prescribed medications even in the absence of knowledge of their safety (Whitaker, 2010; Breggin, 2014). The question of whether this treatment is the result of the negative economic value of children begs to be asked in this case. Do we need more robust ethical guidelines when it comes to the well-being and even the basic human rights of children and mentally ill persons?

CRITICAL THINKING

BOX 7.2 Prozac

One of the most interesting public debates in recent years is the debate over "personality-changing" drugs such as Prozac (Kramer, 1993). The miraculous nature of this particular drug's effects on a wide variety of symptoms, coupled with its under-recognized side effects, has led to its widespread use. Still, there is disagreement about the ethics of prescribing or refusing to prescribe a drug reputed to make people feel "better than well." The availability of Prozac raises the question of whether people ought to take drugs that change their very selves (personalities) if they want to do so. Prozac's wide availability also raises the question of whether doctors should have the right to prescribe or withhold this powerful "feel-good" drug.

To what extent should we be able to choose to enhance or suppress moods and cognitions by buying a medication or some other intervention? If we agree that people have the right to choose how they want to feel and see the world we have to ask who should pay for such "cosmetic" pharmacology? Is this something that medicare should cover through all of our taxes—or not? Under what conditions, when, and for whom might this use of taxes be acceptable? In your experience have you observed that using anti-depressants is one way for women to "do" femininity, just as drinking excess alcohol is sometimes a way for men to "do" masculinity? How else is medicine sometimes enlisted to aid in "doing" gender?

HIGHLIGHTED ISSUES

BOX 7.3 Social Anxiety Disorder

Social anxiety disorder (SAD), along with a number of other types of anxiety disorders, is increasingly diagnosed in Canada and around the world (Dowbiggin, 2009; Horwitz and Wakefield, 2012). It is largely subjectively defined by the sufferer who feels that his SAD is disproportionate and causes significant distress or impairment according to the DSM-5 (http://www.dsm5.org/Documents/Social%20Anxiety%20Disorder%20Fact%20Sheet.pdf). In fact, in 2002 the World Health Organization indicated that anxiety was the most common mental health concern around the globe. There are a number of different and competing explanations for this. On the one side are commentators who point to the increasing stress of the modern world, economic and

other sorts of competitiveness, and the spread of risk consciousness. Life is harder. Less social support is available. There is more to fear, according to this view. On the other side are those who argue that the increase in this and in many other "popular" mental illnesses such as depression is a result of the claims-making advertising to doctors and patients of the pharmaceutical industry. Now that drug treatments are available, detractors argue, markets must be found. In this context pharmaceuticals are widely advertised as if they are able to mitigate all sorts of anxiety and other suffering. Social anxiety in this view is just pathologized and medicalized shyness or normal situational sadness that has been captured by pharmaceutical marketing.

about menstruation are socially determined: if men menstruated rather than women, menstruation would have very different meanings and consequences. First of all, if men menstruated, it would be a laudable, dramatic event, symbolic of strength and manhood. Men would compete with one another about how large their "flow" was, how long it lasted, and whose blood was the brightest. Menstruation would be celebrated ritually as a recurring reminder of the power of masculinity. To prevent problems such as cramps and premenstrual syndrome (PMS), billions of dollars in research money would be spent. Doctors specializing in menstruation would be thought to hold the most prestigious specialty and would be the most highly paid and desired of medical positions. Sanitary napkins and tampons would be free. Epidemiological research would demonstrate how men performed better and won more Olympic medals during their periods. Menstruation would be considered proof that only men could serve God and country in war, in politics, or in religion (ibid., 338). How far-fetched do you think that spoof is?

That illnesses are linked to identities and to political and social issues is well described by Klawiter (1999). Klawiter studied the variations in self-understandings and social identities constructed by breast cancer activists in the San Francisco Bay area over time and with respect to the advocacy/support group they joined and worked with. Three constructions of breast cancer causes and relevancies were distinguished by the three distinctly different social movements organized in the interests of three fundamentally different (and even contradictory) goals, including (1) raising funds for traditional breast cancer research that focuses on conventional treatments such as chemotherapy and radiation, (2) advocacy for and supporting ethnic minority women and other marginalized women's groups and women's health in general, and (3) protesting the multitude of potentially health destructive cancer-creating industries and the countless potential environmental causes of breast cancer. The first was represented by the Race for the Cure, which focused on research and cure through biomedicine. They valorized heteronormative identities and promoted early detection through

mammographic screening for all. Those who had cancer were called "survivors." They were enlisted to stand together and advocate for more and better conventional research and treatment. The second, the Women and Cancer Walk, emphasized support for the broader women's health movement along with other women's cancers. It explicitly included multicultural feminist issues, challenged the focus on survival alone, and critiqued the assumptions of equality and heteronormativity. This group expressed opposition to institutionalized conventional medicine and promoted social and economic equality, beginning with gender equality. The third group was called the Toxic Tour. Their focus was on environmental activism to change the environmental conditions and, thus, the preventable causes of breast cancer. Cancer was represented as "the product and source of profit of a predatory cancer industry" (ibid., 121).

King (2006) has taken ideas about the social meanings and constructions of breast cancer movements in a different direction. In *Pink Ribbons, Inc.: Breast Cancer and the Politics of Philanthropy*, King argues that breast cancer has become the model for the extensive growth of cause marketing among corporations in the neo-liberal modern states. Just as fundraising for breast cancer research and treatments has increased exponentially in the last several decades, so has neo-liberalism. Breast cancer activism, she argues, serves to de-responsibilize governments for health care and corresponds to a diminution in the roles governments are taking in health care and health-related research. That breast cancer concerns relate both to sexism and breasts is also consequential and of great benefit. Both of these facts contribute to its popular place in social marketing in a sexist and heteronormative social world. King's analysis is chiefly relevant for the first group above, exemplified by the Race for the Cure, the largest and most widely known of the movements. Aided by the support of many corporations who "pink" a multitude of products (including a pink gun!) to expand sales and contribute to breast cancer research simultaneously, this foundation was started in 1980 and has been enormously successful. It had raised $1.5 billion by 2010 for conventional medical care (http://www.pjstar.com/x1685418888/U-S-House-honors-Nancy-Brinker).

Cultural Variations in the Experience of Being Ill

In all societies and cultures people experience illness, pain, disability, and disfigurement. Sorcery, the breaking of a taboo, the intrusion of a disease-causing spirit into the body, the intrusion of a disease-causing object into the body, and the loss of the soul all are seen as possible causes of disease in a cross-cultural context (Clements, 1932). All these explanations, except for the intrusion into the body of a disease-causing object, involve the supernatural or magic in an attempt to understand illness. Westerners tend to see illness as empirically caused and mechanically or chemically treatable. Although there often is a significant moral component to an explanation for certain diseases in the Western world, immorality is not usually viewed as the immediate cause. In most of the non-Western world, non-empirical explanations and cures for disease seem to dominate: illness is seen as a combination of spiritual, mental, and physical phenomena.

The experience of pain appears to vary from one social and cultural group to another (see, e.g., Jackson, 2003). In a classic study Zborowski (1952) compared patients hospitalized in a New York City hospital and found that patients differed dramatically in how they experienced pain. Those from Jewish and Italian backgrounds responded emotionally to suffering and tended to dwell on their painful experience with great demonstrations of anguish. He also noted a difference in the attitudes of each of these groups to discomfort. Italians saw pain as something to be rid of and were happy once a way to relieve their pain was found. Jews were mainly concerned with the meaning of their pain and the consequences of their pain for their future health. "Old Americans" and the Irish, by contrast, reacted stoically. The different attitudes to pain were reflected in distinct behavioural and emotional responses of people from different ethnic groups. What is the ideal response to pain in your cultural or ethnic group?

What is viewed as disease or health varies from society to society. Disfigurement or illness may or may not be seen as normal among one culture or another. "Afflictions common enough in a group to be endemic, though they are clinical deformities, may often be accepted as part of man's natural condition" (Hughes, 1967: 88). Notions of health and disease also depend on age, gender, socio-economic status, and numerous other social conditions, as we have discussed previously.

Disagreement is widespread over which states of physical being are desirable and which are not. Among some people, an obese woman is an object of desire; others define obesity as repugnant or even as a symptom of emotional or physical illness. Among many Canadians today, obesity is considered a medical condition with associated treatments, symptoms, tests, and risk factors (www.obesitycanada.com). For some, small breasts constitute a medical problem. There are many examples of how health and illness understandings depend on value and moral judgements (Clements, 1932; Hughes, 1967; Turner, 1987; Foucault, 1973). Moreover, notions of mental health also vary widely from cultural group to cultural group, as a perusal of the academic journal *Culture, Medicine and Psychiatry* demonstrates. It is clear that, for many people, health and religion, the natural and the supernatural, are often closely related.

Popular Cultural Conceptions of Health, Illness, and Disease

The following sections describe a number of popular conceptions of health and illness.

Illness as Carelessness and Failure

Contemporary neo-liberal health promotion is built on the assumption that individuals are responsible for staying well and that it is individual carelessness and failure that causes (most) illness. Therefore, individuals are held accountable for smoking cessation, losing weight, drinking alcohol only moderately, using condoms, and pursuing early cancer detection through mammograms, prostate-specific antigen (PSA) tests, PAP smears, submitting to the HPV vaccine, and the like. When individuals fail to stay well, the medical system intervenes. The medical care system is based on aggressive intervention once a disease has been detected. The assumption is that the earlier the detection the better. To be a good citizen and a moral person is to be a healthy person. To be ill is to be a victim and often a victim of one's own weaknesses (e.g., lung cancer in the case of an individual who smoked). People are advised to change their behaviour as individuals as if such change is sufficient or even possible for all. This idea ignores the social constraints that people live under because of, for example, the neighbourhoods in which they live, the presence or absence of parkland nearby, the level of air pollution due to the industries in the neighbourhood, the choices of food (and their costs) at the local supermarket or convenience store, and so on.

Illness as Choice

Some believe that illness is a choice. We choose when we want to be ill, what type of illness we'll have, how severe it will be, and how long the illness will last. Because the body and mind are connected, illness is a result of thinking and feeling as well as of biological bodily processes. We give ourselves illnesses to take a break from the busy obligations of everyday life. We choose to be ill to allow for "time out" from our routines: to rest, to take stock, to escape, and to withdraw. A host of research in fields such as psychoneuroimmunology and psychosomatic medicine attests to the prevalence of this belief, on both theoretical and empirical levels. A great deal of work has been done on the mind–body interaction in the case of cancer, in particular. Several physician writers have addressed mind–body relationships in various ways. For an overview of several of the most popular, consider the work of Chopra (1987, 1989) and Dossey (1982, 1991) or any of Dr Andrew Weil's books (Weil, 2011). In fact, there is a new name for

medicine that is holistic and takes the body/mind and spirit seriously as necessary parts of treatment: integrative medicine. Integrative medicine is intentionally inclusive of both allopathic (conventional) medical systems of understanding and treatment and also complementary and alternative models (see the following website for further information http://www.drweil.com/drw/u/ART02054/Andrew-Weil-Integrative-Medicine.html).

Oncologist Carl O. Simonton and his colleagues were among the earliest contemporary "popularizers" of the role of the mind in both sickening and healing the body of cancer. They argued that cancer is a disease that arises from a sort of emotional despair. Simonton's book, *Getting Well Again*, is full of examples of people who come to recognize, with the help of the psychotherapeutic skills of Simonton and his staff, that their cancer has been, in a sense, a personal choice. Once a patient understands the reason for the choice of cancer as a way of coping with a personal problem, he or she can confront the problem on a conscious level and, thus, seek a cure (Simonton et al., 1978).

Simonton's method includes a number of techniques. One of the best known is the systematic use of imaging—conjuring up mental pictures of cells. For example, people are directed to imagine their cancer cells as black ants and their healthy cells as knights in shining armour. The hypothesis is that the more powerful the imaging of the anti-cancer forces, the more likely it is to be effective in ridding the body of the disease. Effective imaging may, it was believed, result in one of the following outcomes: increased longevity; moderation of symptoms, including pain; increased sense of well-being, autonomy, and control; improved quality of life; and even, at times, remission of the disease.

Imaging may be the most dramatic of the techniques used to combat cancer "psychologically" and to choose to get well. Numerous other methods are being used around the world by psycho-oncologists, including, but not limited to, yoga, meditation, journalling, art, and group and individual psychotherapy. The effects of all of these techniques on quality of life, longevity, and the disease itself are under investigation. The point to be made here is that within this model of health/illness an important part of healing (along with medical interventions) and of improving the quality of life is taking responsibility for one's state of health and choosing to try to do something about it. There is considerable ongoing research on the general topic (Schofield et al., 2006) of mind–body interactions in cancer outcomes and well-being with cancer. According to a systematic review of the evidence in some 329 trials of psychological interventions for cancer, one has reason to believe in the possible health benefits of individual and group therapy, informational and educational interventions, guided imagery, and cognitive-behavioural therapies for people with cancer (ibid.). A recent pilot study of the use of yoga also noted that "the initial findings suggest that yoga has significant potential and should be further explored as a beneficial physical activity option for cancer survivors" (Culos-Reed et al., 2006). A number of other mind/body approaches to cancer treatment are being explored, including acupuncture, mindfulness, and Tai Chi, as a part of integrative medicine (Abrams and Weil, 2009). One of the medical oncology authors of a recent book suggests that usual medical treatment for cancer (chemotherapy, surgery, and radiation) functions to get rid of the weed (that is, cancer) while integrative medicine maintains and enhances the soil so that health will flourish (Abrams and Weil, 2009).

Illness as Despair

Closely related to the idea that illness reflects choice is the idea that illness reflects and results from a sort of despair. Lawrence LeShan (1978), a psychotherapist who counselled and then studied cancer patients, came to the conclusion that common types of emotional experience among the majority of cancer patients predated the development of the disease. Examples of these emotional experiences include long-standing, unresolved grief over the loss of someone close, such as the death of a mother or father in childhood, childhood loneliness or isolation, the loss of someone close in adulthood, and the loss of a job. For

LeShan's patients, understanding their grief and expressing feelings of sadness and anger became pathways towards being healed.

Norman Cousins's work, which formed the basis for his book, *Anatomy of an Illness as Perceived by the Patient*, is the foundation of another similar and popular approach to illness, health, and healing. This book, a long-time bestseller translated into many different languages and "must" reading in a number of medical schools throughout the world, tells the story of the author's reaction to and healing from a severe and potentially fatal case of ankylosing spondylitis, a degenerative disease of the connective tissues in the spine.

Cousins's story of his "miraculous" recovery focused on three aspects of his "systematic pursuit of salutary emotions" (Cousins, 1979: 35). The first was his partnership with his doctor. Cousins, for many years the editor of the popular American literary magazine *Saturday Review* and a renowned peace activist, asked his doctor to engage in a collaborative partnership. The physician had the traditional armaments to offer. Cousins had done some reading about how healing could be affected by the power of positive thinking and by massive doses of vitamin C. Because he found the hospital forbidding, noisy, and thoroughly unhealthy, Cousins asked his doctor to treat him in a nearby motel. The second important component of his recovery was that his doctor agreed to his request for enormous intravenous doses of vitamin C, in which Cousins, having done considerable research on his own, believed. The third aspect of his rehabilitation strategy was laughter. Cousins had books of jokes and cartoons, tapes, and old film comedies brought to his room for his enjoyment. Laughing deeply relieved his pain and generally made him feel better. As he says, "It worked. I made the joyous discovery that ten minutes of genuine belly laughter had an anesthetic effect and would give me at least two hours of pain-free sleep. When the painkilling effect of the laughter wore off, we would switch on the motion-picture projector again, and, not infrequently, it would lead to another pain-free sleep interval" (ibid., 39). As he was interested in demonstrating the credibility of his experience,

Cousins instituted some small experiments. He found that each episode of laughter decreased the level of inflammation in his connective tissues. Five years after recovering from this disease, and having achieved some renown in the area of holistic health (he was appointed senior lecturer at the School of Medicine, University of California at Los Angeles, and consulting editor of *Man and Medicine*), Cousins suffered a serious heart attack. Rehabilitation resulted in another book, *The Healing Heart* (1983), in which he further developed his arguments regarding the importance of positive emotions in maintaining and achieving health that he had first elaborated in *Anatomy of an Illness*. Cousins's work is based on the idea that the mind and body are a single entity; positive change in one, for example, in the body by the use of pharmaceuticals such as vitamin C, or in the mind by mood elevation through laughter, can lead to healing. A related movement for well-being, laughter yoga, was begun in India in the mid-1990s by a physician, Madan Kataria. Today, laughter yoga numbers thousands of laughter clubs throughout the world devoted to enhancing health by "laughing for no reason." Research on happiness, laughter, and health continues. See, for example, the review paper by Bennett and Lengacher (2008) and Weil's work (2011). As discussed above, integrative medicine takes seriously the link between the body and the mind and the spirit. See for further information the website of the Arizona school established by Dr Weil (http://integrativemedicine.arizona.edu/index.html). In just one empirical example, Lockwood and Yoshimura (2014) found humour of help in social and psychological well-being during recovery from cardiovascular disease.

Illness as Secondary Gain

Sometimes illness has definite benefits. Do you remember the last time you were conveniently sick on the day of a big test for which you had not had time to prepare? Small children quickly learn to complain of sore tummies when they do not really feel like going to church, to school, or out to play. Illness may provide an opportunity or permit someone to behave in ways he or she would like to but otherwise would feel constrained from doing.

Or, illness may allow someone to meet needs that would otherwise go unmet. The benefits of illness are as varied as people's illnesses. To illustrate: Brett was a high school guidance counsellor and history teacher who had also taken on the job of basketball coach and was supervising set-building for the school play. Brett was married and had two preschool children in daycare while he and his wife Lucy worked. Lucy was required to do a great deal of travelling in her job as a buyer for a large department store. Brett was often responsible for driving the kids to and from daycare, as well as for feeding and bathing them. He hadn't expected so much responsibility; he had been raised to assume that his wife would handle the children, the house, the cooking, and most of their domestic life.

He felt trapped. On the one hand, he supported and applauded Lucy's success and realized that if she was really going to "make it" in her business of choice she would have to continue at her present pace for three or four years. On the other hand, he frequently felt overwhelmed by his responsibilities. The day his doctor diagnosed mononucleosis, Brett was secretly relieved. At least now he had a way out.

The question of **secondary gains** has been explained in a more systematic way in research on welfare mothers (Cole and Lejeune, 1972). In this case the focus was on whether and in what situations mothers on welfare would be likely to claim that they were ill. The researchers hypothesized that illness could be seen as a legitimation, or acceptable explanation, for failure. Being on welfare was thought by a substantial number of welfare recipients to be the result, and also a continual reminder, of a personal failure. This being the case, women on welfare would be likely to look for a rationalization and legitimation for their situation. Indeed, the researchers found that women on welfare who felt that they had little hope of changing their status were more likely to use illness as their explanation for being on welfare than women who hoped or expected to move off welfare. The point here is that sometimes claiming illness seems to be a better choice and to provide a greater level of reward than the other available options. In such a case illness can be thought of as providing secondary gains. Another postmodern version of this situation may be the claim of illness in order to get a day away from work or for some other personal advantage (Davidhizar, 1994) or just to use the available sick leave. This strategy even has a popular name—"taking a mental health day."

Illness as Uncertainty

A major concomitant of disease in modern society is its chronic nature. People who live with chronic diseases live in a state of uncertainty and the possibility of or the belief that they are at risk. Because of the prevalence of disease remission or chronicity, some have said that we live in a remission society (Drew, 2003; Frank, 1997). This is a psychological place where people are perhaps better but never cured. You have probably heard the phrase "the five-year survival rate." Notions such as this reflect the fact that many people who have had a serious diagnosis or a problematic early detection number, say, an elevated level of PSA (prostate-specific antigen), understand what it means to live with uncertainty. McKenzie and Crouch (2004) investigated uncertainty in the lives of people living with cancer and found that the perception of being at risk can cause ongoing suffering and a feeling of emotional dissonance from "ordinary" others. The fear of a relapse, they argue, leads to a painful discordance or alienation from ordinary life as most people experience it. Living with uncertainty may be one of the most difficult aspects of the trajectory of this disease. L.E. Miller (2014) describes how seeking and managing information are ongoing, and comprise one of the basic aspects of coping with cancer that continue long after the end of active treatment.

As many as one person in 900 between the ages of 18 and 35 is a survivor of childhood cancer. Drew (2003) investigated the narratives of long-term survivors of childhood cancer and noted how much work they had done to reconstruct or redefine themselves and imagine a personal future. To manage everyday uncertainty and lack of supportive networks, many people with a variety of diagnoses are turning to the Internet to offer and receive social support. There has been a great deal of research on illness experience using these sorts of data (see, e.g., Seale, 2006; Pitts, 2004). The Internet (including blogs, listservs, chat rooms, and discussion groups) appears to be a very rich source of narratives about surviving and coping with all sorts of mental and physical illnesses and conditions. In the case of chronic fatigue syndrome (CFS), a highly uncertain and even contested diagnosis (Bulow and Hyden, 2003), attempts to develop meaning, clarity, and certainty have even resulted in a school in Sweden for people with CFS to learn about what to expect from their illness.

Illness as a Message of the Body

At times, within the homeopathic perspective, illness is viewed as an expression of a unique person at a particular point in time and engaged in a special set of circumstances. Illness is also the expression of a whole person—body, mind, and soul. Illness and health are not polar opposites: both exist in a person continuously in a state of dynamic equilibrium. From this perspective symptoms are not signs of illness but indications that the person is responding to a challenge and is engaging in what is called a "healing crisis." The healing crisis (or the symptom) is a manifestation of what has been happening for a time but has been repressed and therefore unnoticed. Fever, rash, inflammation, coughing, crying, sleeplessness, and tension are revelations of a deep disturbance of the whole person. Such symptoms are valuable, however, because they allow the person to acknowledge the crisis and to seek help. The role of the healer is to support the person emotionally and spiritually and to enhance the natural recuperative powers of the physical body through the administration of minuscule amounts of natural medications that are known to create the symptoms the individual is presenting (see Chapter 13 for a more complete discussion of homeopathic and naturopathic medicine). This popular perspective and the next to be discussed, illness as communication, are consistent with psychoneuroimmunological research (see, e.g., Kemeny, 2007).

Illness as Communication

People communicate through words and by signs and by body language. People also send messages through the way their bodies are functioning. Illness sends a message that one part of the body is alienated from the "self." The body expresses the soul. Some even say that illness expresses the soul more impressively than health, in the same way that a good caricature expresses essential aspects of a personality more clearly than photographs taken in a studio situation (Siirla, 1981: 3). Ideas such as these may be considered relevant in integrative medicine, in complementary and alternative medicine, and in holistic medicine.

Through particular sets of symptoms or particular kinds of illnesses, people convey messages about themselves. A woman with breast cancer may be saying that her need and desire to nurture has been frustrated. Since the breast is important in mothering, feeding, and soothing, it becomes the most appropriate symbol for communication about frustrated nurturing. Thus, a person's needs may be expressed through illness. "If these [needs] cannot be expressed in a realistic, 'healthy' form, symbolic organ language takes over" (ibid., 8).

In this view, different diseases express different frustrations. Rheumatism, a disability that affects the muscles and the joints, may express the frustration of a person who once liked to be very active, but who had to limit his or her activities and then developed joint pain, stiffness, and inflammation in the joints and muscles. Cold symptoms, such as runny nose and sneezing, may result from a frustrated desire to cry. All illnesses can be examined as attempts by the body for expression that otherwise cannot be expressed or are frustrated or repressed when illness is viewed as an attempt to communicate to the world about one's existential situation.

Illness as Metaphor

Related to the suggestion that illness is communication is the idea advanced by Susan Sontag that illness is metaphor. Illness communicates when it is taken to be conveying a particular message for a person at a special point in his or her life. Illness as metaphor suggests that cultures bestow symbolic meanings on various illnesses. In Sontag's view metaphors are most likely to be related to illnesses that have no clear or obvious cause or treatment. The two examples that she examines in some depth in *Illness as Metaphor* (1978) are cancer in the twentieth century and tuberculosis in the nineteenth century. In 1988 she examined the metaphoric meanings of AIDS. Her basic argument is that the metaphors attached to diseases can be destructive and harmful. They frequently have punitive effects on the patient because they exaggerate, simplify, and stereotype the patient's experience. Metaphors may function as stigma or to reinforce stigma. They may serve to isolate the person with the disease from the community. Metaphors often imply adverse moral and psychological judgements about the ill person. They have perpetrated the view, for example, that cancer is a form of self-betrayal, a repression of the true desires of the person. A study of the portrayal of HIV/AIDS in popular magazines in 1991, 1996, and 2001 has shown how HIV/AIDS continued to be seen in the context of ongoing homophobia despite the ostensible focus in the Canadian and American media on transmission among heterosexual men, such as the former professional basketball star Magic Johnson. An ongoing emphasis polarized descriptions of the guilty victims as compared to the innocent victims of HIV/AIDS (Clarke, 2006). It is my impression, though, that with the spread of same-sex marriage and the declining levels of homophobia fuelled by the organizing and educating by the LGBTQ and Pride movements, this bias is likely no longer the case. Another study of the portrayal of HIV/AIDS in mainstream media is overdue.

A different study of magazines over the same time period (Clarke et al., 2007) found that most articles about heart disease were directed at men and depicted heart disease as if it were gendered. For men, heart disease was described as almost inevitable and as a badge of successful manhood. Its experience and treatment were described in terms both mechanical and aggressive, and its origin as the result of individual lifestyle choices that could be changed by the individual himself. In comparison, women's heart disease was portrayed as something of which to be ashamed, especially since diagnosis conflicts with the role of "caregiver." Women were described as ignorant, emotional victims with pathological bodies, especially after menopause. Depression, too, is associated with metaphors. In the eighteenth century, British writer Samuel Johnson called his depression "the black dog," as did British Prime Minister Winston Churchill in the twentieth century, and today the Black Dog Institute in Australia focuses on depression, and an award-winning crime novel about a detective suffering from depression is titled *Black Dog*. Sometimes, too, disease names are used as metaphors for something else. For example, we have all likely heard the phrase that terrorism is "the cancer of the nation." Schizophrenia, too, is sometimes used as a metaphor, for instance, "the weather is schizophrenic" was found in a study of metaphors in newspapers in the United Kingdom (Chopra and Doody, 2007).

Media Images of Cancer, Heart Disease, and AIDS

One study of the way cancer, heart disease, and AIDS have been portrayed in the mass print media illustrates how diseases come to have unique meanings, metaphors, and cultures associated with them. Disease is seen as much more than a mechanical failure—as a physiological pathology. This research is based on media that are now dated. Consider whether you think these images and metaphors have any currency today. Think, too, about movies and television shows you may have seen depicting people with different diseases. Can you offer any working hypotheses about media representations of cancer, heart disease, or HIV/AIDS currently? Table 7.1 portrays the findings. This study is presented for historical interest and to stimulate you to think about the ways in which the current portrayals of these diseases might be similar and/or different.

The moral worth of the person with cancer was attacked by the invasion of an evil predator so fearsome it is not even to be named, but fought as a powerful alien intruder that spreads secretly through the body. The person with cancer was not offered much hope of recovery. By and large, the media portrayed cancer as associated with extremely nauseating chemotherapy, surgical mutilations, excruciating suffering, and finally death. To some extent the person with cancer was held to be blameworthy because the cancer could have been detected early through timely medical checkups that would have initiated early medical intervention such as mastectomy (breast removal) or would have prevented the disease through practising positive emotions (Ehrenreich, 2009). It must be emphasized that the characteristics of the portrayal of cancer have changed to some extent, and that change is especially true of breast cancer. There is a great deal of uncertainty about the cause of cancer. There are numerous putative causes. They are usually described as the result of individual lifestyle decisions. Again, then, it is the individual who is ultimately culpable.

The media description is radically different when the disease is a heart attack. The heart attack is presented as an objective, morally neutral event that happens at a specific time and place and causes a great deal of pain. Heart disease, by contrast, was portrayed in optimistic terms. Not only were there very clear and precise steps to be taken to prevent it but when it occurred it could have been treated in a variety of mechanical ways, including using technology to replace parts of a malfunctioning cardiac system. Heart disease did not affect the whole person or the moral being of the person. It "attacked" one part only. Heart disease was an "outsider" that could be repelled through quick, decisive action and the use of medical marvels. The person with heart disease might have experienced acute fear and pain, but the period of recovery was likely to be dominated by optimism about a cure, replacement valves, pacemakers and other new technologies, and a resolve to (easily) change the lifestyle habits that led to the disease in the first place.

The person with AIDS was portrayed as a diseased person and as somewhat morally repugnant,

TABLE 7.1   Images of Cancer, Heart Disease, and AIDS

Cancer	Heart Disease	AIDS
Cancer is described as an evil, immoral predator.	Heart disease is described as a strong, active, painful attack.	Little is said about the nature of the disease; much is said about the moral worth of the victims of the disease.
Euphemisms such as "the Big C" are used rather than the word "cancer."	Heart disease, stroke, coronary/arterial occlusion, and all the various circulatory system diseases are usually called "the heart attack."	Acquired immune deficiency syndrome is called AIDS. The opportunistic diseases that attack the weakened immune system are often not mentioned.
Cancer is viewed as an enemy. Military imagery and tactics are associated with it.	The heart attack is described as a mechanical failure, treatable with available new technology and preventable with diet and other lifestyle changes.	AIDS is viewed as an overpowering enemy, as epidemic and as a scourge.
The whole self, particularly the emotional attitude of the person and the disease, is subject to discussion. Because the disease spreads and because the spread is often unnoticed through symptoms or medical checks, the body itself becomes a potential suspect.	It occurs in a particular organ that is indeed interchangeable with donor organs.	It is described as affecting the immune system and as resulting mostly from immoral behaviour and connotes "shameful sexual acts" and drug abuse (needle sharing).
Cancer is associated with hopelessness, fear, and death.	A degree of optimism prevails about the preventability and the treatability of the disease.	It is associated with fear, panic, and hysteria because it is contagious through body fluids, primarily blood and semen.
Prevention through early medical testing is advised.	The heart attack is described as very preventable. Suggestions for lifestyles that will prevent it are frequently publicized.	Prevention is advertised as possible through monogamous sexual behaviour or abstinence, and by avoidance of unsterilized needles and drug abuse.
There are innumerable potential causes listed. They range from sperm to foodstuffs to the sun.	There is a specific and limited list of putative causes offered again and again.	Initially the causes for AIDS were general: being homosexual, a drug user, or a Haitian.
There is little consideration of the socio-political or environmental causes, e.g., legislation that could limit smoking.	There is little mention of socio-political causes.	There is little mention of socio-political causes.
There is much uncertainty about cause.	There is certainty about cause.	There is uncertainty about cause.

a victim who was essentially powerless in the face of this scourge. He (usually a male in the developed world although equally male and female in the developing world) was described as hopelessly doomed and isolated from potentially significant sources of emotional support such as lovers and family members. The disease itself was described in mechanical and biomedical terms. The media did not dwell on the painful or debilitating symptoms of the disease. They did not focus on the inevitable terminal stages of the disease, on death itself, or on the mortality rate. Rather, they focused on the fear of contagion and the uncertainty about the causes of contagion. The person afflicted with AIDS was stigmatized because of the connection with a deviant lifestyle and the racialization often associated with HIV/AIDS because of the media link made to Africa, where the incidence is so much higher and where the virus was known to have existed since the 1920s in non-human primate populations (https://en.wikipedia.org/wiki/History_of_HIV/AIDS). He or she may have been isolated and abandoned because people are afraid of the contagion that might result from being close. This fear of being close affected not only the close friends and significant others of the person with AIDS, but also more distant others such as medical personnel. The media portrayal of HIV/AIDS today is considerably different because the causes and means of transmission are well known and pharmaceuticals have made HIV a fairly well-controlled chronic condition in Western society. As homophobia has decreased, so has the stigma associated with HIV/AIDS abated somewhat, especially in the North American context (see, for instance, follow-up articles by Clarke, 2006, and Clarke et al., 2006).

These images of cancer, heart disease, and AIDS were drawn from selected Canadian and American magazines—Newsweek, *Time*, *Maclean's*, *Good Housekeeping*, *Ladies' Home Journal*, and *Reader's Digest*—over a 20-year period. Think about whether this analysis fits your understanding of the mass print media stories that you have read on disease. These magazines are the highest circulating magazines in North America. However, they are not the only magazines with a mass circulation available in North America. Little research has been done on the impact of such media depictions on people in society.

More recent studies of the media portrayal of both prostate and testicular cancer have found them to be described as if they were "masculine" diseases, and descriptions of them are encapsulated in stereotypically masculine contexts such as

sports, competition, money, and sexuality (Clarke, 1999a; Clarke and Robinson, 1999). By contrast, breast cancer (although it also can occur in men) was described as a woman's disease and related to stereotypically female behaviours and attitudes, such as emotionality and a preoccupation with appearance (Clarke, 1999a). Cancer in general is still widely associated with fear (Clarke and Everest, 2006).

Illness as Statistical Infrequency

From this point of view illness is a mathematically infrequent state of mental or physical malfunctioning. When a transient condition, no matter how uncomfortable, is prevalent among a group of people, it is usually not considered pathological. Illnesses such as the common cold and common flu are so widespread as to be considered largely unimportant (it is clear that they are not taken seriously because few research dollars are allocated to investigating them).

Illness as Sexual Politics

Many feminist thinkers have analyzed the ways in which disease can be seen as sexual politics. Reissman (1987) has written a theoretical/empirical review of the medicalization of women's bodies and lives with a focus on medicalized childbirth, reproduction and contraception, premenstrual syndrome, "beauty," and mental health and illness. Currie and Raoul (1992) discuss "women's struggle for the body" in the face of culturally and historically entrenched bodily constraints and restrictions. From the feminist perspective the constraints and limitations of gender roles are associated with the conceptualization and the subsequent diagnosis of various diseases. For example, Ehrenreich and English (1978) document how the "mysterious epidemic" experienced in the nineteenth-century by middle- and upper-class women was the outgrowth of the conditions that characterized their lives. The journals and diaries of women of the time give hundreds of examples of women whose lives wasted away into invalidism. The symptoms included headache, muscular aches, weakness, depression, menstrual difficulties, and indigestion.

The diagnoses were many: "neurasthenia," "nervous prostration," "cardiac inadequacy," "dyspepsia," "rheumatism," and "hysteria." The diseases were not fatal. They frequently were treated with potions containing opium, which may have caused or exacerbated the symptoms. They usually lasted throughout a woman's life until her death. In the present day, several common diseases particularly reflect gender politics. For women, one of these is depression. Depression is associated with "just being a woman" and experiencing many of the stages that are a part of the lives of women. Take, for instance, those women's conditions relating to reproduction such as the menstrual cycle, pregnancy, and post-pregnancy. All of these have been accorded a new disease label in the DSM (*Diagnostic and Statistical Manual of Mental Disorders*). For example, post-pregnancy in particular has been **pathologized** (conceptualized as problematic and/or needing medical treatment) and accorded the new labels and new treatments as was discussed in chapter one under feminist theory. It seems that with the discovery of the SSRI anti-depressants the breadth of suffering related to just being a woman has grown exponentially along with extensive marketing (http://www.cwhn.ca/en/print/node/26773). Another illness applied stereotypically to females is fibromyalgia, although it can occur in men as well. Fibromyalgia is considered a woman's disease (Barker, 2005) and thought to reflect something of the position of women in society. The lack of an effective pharmaceutical or other treatment may reflect gender politics as it determines the possible legitimacy of the contested illness (Barker, 2011).

The feminist analysis explains that these (popular) diseases provided an appropriate role for women in the middle and upper classes. Many of these women were utterly dependent on their husbands, and their sole purpose in life was the provision of heirs. Household tasks were left to domestic servants. Hired help cared for children. The wife's job was to do precisely nothing—and thus to stand as a symbol to the world of her husband's financial success. Medical ideology buttressed this view of the appropriate role of middle- and upper-class women with the theory of the conservation of energy. This belief was that human beings had only a certain amount of energy available to spend over their lifetime. Since the primary functions of women of these classes were procreation and decoration, it behoved them to save all their vitality for child-bearing and not to waste any in studying or in doing good works. Such activities would drain energy away from the uterus, where it was needed, into the brains and limbs, where it served no good purpose.

Contemporary feminists have suggested that the eating disorders bulimia and anorexia nervosa are logical expressions of women's role today (Currie, 1988a). Eating disorders can best be understood, in this perspective, as the internalization of conflicts that result from the prevailing contradictory images of women. Anorexia is almost exclusively a disease of adolescent women, particularly those from middle- and upper-middle-class backgrounds, and occurs primarily in modern Western capitalist societies. Some have applied traditional Freudian psychoanalysis to these disorders and have attributed their causes to a fear of sexuality and an attempt to avoid the implications of their femininity. Others have explained the symptoms from a family systems perspective as a result of mothers who overprotect and overidentify with their daughters. Daughters differentiate from mothers and become separate individuals, in this perspective, by rebelling and refusing to eat. Several feminist authors have argued that eating disorders constitute a protest by women against the contradictory images of women as independent, competent wage earners and as sexual objects who earn only a portion of male salaries in work that is devalued because it is done by women (ibid.).

During two discrete periods in the twentieth century—the 1920s and the 1980s and 1990s and into the twenty-first century—anorexia was a notable problem. During both of these periods, equality of opportunity for men and women was being stressed. These were times of expanded educational and employment options for women. They were also times of contradictions. In theory, choices for women were expanding; in practice, they earned only a fraction of men's incomes. Furthermore, women were and continue to be notoriously underrepresented at all levels of the political process—municipally, provincially, and federally. Nor have their domestic responsibilities declined. Inadequate subsidized child care and excessive domestic responsibilities mean that women who work outside the home also have full-time jobs inside the home. Yet a woman's identity is still tied up with her appearance. In these circumstances eating disorders, as Orbach (1986) claimed, can be seen as a women's "hunger strike."

Illness as Aspiration

These postmodern uses of medicine enlist doctors and chemicals to make one "better" and "happier" through such interventions as cosmetic surgery to straighten the nose, enlarge or reduce the breasts, or reshape innumerable other aspects of the body (and psyche). Interventions such as surgery for physical changes may be augmented with pharmaceuticals for changes in moods or cognition. For instance, surgical sex changes may be accompanied by hormone treatments; anti-depressants may be sought for happiness or for enhanced happiness (Elliott, 2003). In these cases the idea is to use medicine not just to return the self to a "normal" or non-diseased state but to improve the body and the mind through the new technologies of medicine to reach a "new and better normal." Such medicine is transformative and not merely restorative. Even basic marks of identity can be changed. Faces can be "lifted" or even transplanted, as was done for a French woman, Isabelle Dinoire, who had been mauled in the face by her dog. She said she had the surgery as she was desperately trying to save herself after she had tried to commit suicide (http://www.bbc.com/news/magazine-20493572). In this case the transplant was intended to repair injuries; but now the technology has been tried and proven, can discretionary face transplants be far behind? Altering the face through a product such as Botox is already one of the most popular of cosmetic medical interventions. It is advertised on the following highly respected Cleveland Clinic website as one of a number of "noon hour" procedures (http://my.clevelandclinic.org/services/cosmetic_surgery/hic_cosmetic_surgery_today_and_in_the_future.aspx). The most popular cosmetic surgery in the US in 2014 was breast augmentation as women sought the perfect size, shape, and "perkiness."

In this advertisement for plastic surgery, a haggard witch gives up on her brewing and crawls to the surgery table in desperation before emerging as a happy, beautiful, young woman. The idea being sold in this ad is that plastic surgery can make you even better than you were before—can "make fairy tales come true."

Source: ZEA BBDO/Antonio Aponte.

Apparently 330,631 breast augmentations were done in Canada alone in 2012 (http://www.surgery.org/consumers/plastic-surgery-news-briefs/2012-statistics-cut-cosmetic-surgery-1050547).

Cosmetic surgery and other cosmetic medical enhancements are a significant component of medical care today. A whole new field of medicine called "anti-aging medicine" seeks to help people live longer and to look younger along the way. "Anti-aging medicine is the pinnacle of biotechnology joined with clinical preventive medicine. The specialty is founded on the application of advanced scientific and medical technologies for the early detection, prevention, treatment and reversal of age-related dysfunction, disorders and diseases." One of the very popular cosmetic anti-aging interventions is "filler" of various kinds (http://www.canadianliving.com/style/beauty/botox_restylane_or_juvederm_which_is_right_for_you.php). The most widely known is Botox. Although Statistics Canada does not maintain figures on the frequency of its use, apparently 142,374 people used Botox in 2005 and 126,554 used other fillers (ibid.). It is most commonly used by women (83.5 per cent) and by people between the ages of 35 and 50. It is also used by people as young as teens (ibid.). The *Vancouver Sun* describes the case of a 25-year-old woman who, expressing the ease of use, calls her-self "bo-jacked" (http://www.vancouversun.com/teens+twenty+somethings+turn+Botox+forever+look/7002991/story.html). Although it is impossible to get exact numbers for all of the various types of cosmetic intervention, the point remains that a new kind of medicine and a new illness identity have arrived: aspirational health and aesthetics. See the website for the American Academy of Anti-Aging Medicine (http://www.a4m.com/) for much more information about this phenomenon.

Illness as Potential or Patient-in-Waiting

The idea of illness as potential is perhaps best understood today in the context of the notion of the risk society where risk is seen as a ubiquitous, inevitable, and increasing consequence of modern life with its reliance on science and technology (Beck, 1992; Giddens, 1999). Consequently, we live in a state of uncertainty about all of the ways we and our loved ones can come to harm, be sickened, and experience accidents and violence. The underlying issue is that uncertainty and ongoing anxiety have become the expected "normal" in the conscious-ness of the modern person (Horwitz, 2013). Major accidents, even nuclear accidents, according to Perrow (1999), are considered "normal." They are anticipated, at some time or another. Medical error is so common that numerous studies and policies and news reports are directed to understanding and preventing it. (See Schwappach, 2010, for one example of this type of work written by one of the foremost researchers in the area of medical error.) Hospitalization is considered to have its own dan-gers and hospitals are thought to be an unsafe places. They may generate their own set of diseases, as when a patient admitted for a fracture from a fall catches hepatitis B on the ward. "Iatrogenic ill-ness" is illness that is inadvertent. It is caused by side effects or as an after-effect of medical treat-ment. Furthermore, interactions of patients with one another or with doctors and other health-care workers can sometimes cause psychosocial harm. Thus, engagement with the medical care system presents its own set of potentialities for illness.

In these contexts illness is an ongoing risk or possibility. Health promotion advertisements and media stories surround us. We are told to watch out for numerous potential dangers in our food, water, environment, pleasure pastimes, and so on. In a sense, everything about modern life brings with it a risk of illness or accident (see the relatively new jour-nal *Health, Risk & Society*, which covers this topic from various perspectives). Now, however, we are adding to the notion of the uncertainties of chronic illness a new idea, which is living with uncertainty without illness but under the ever-present possibil-ity of succumbing to one disease or another. The potential for illness dogs us in another way in this Internet age. No sooner does a person think of a possible "symptom" than he or she can look it up on the Internet and find it is a part of a syndrome or a disease that may need treatment. There was a time when interns were "expected" to develop the symp-toms of one disease after another as they studied them in medical school and in patients. With mil-lions of health/medical sites and as the widespread use of these sites has expanded, the potential for perceived and potential illnesses in the people who consult them has grown exponentially.

Medical and genetic advances have also altered the landscape of illness and disease. There is a new category of patient—the patient-in-waiting. It is now possible to know definitely that a person will be diagnosed with a disease. Huntingdon's, for example, is a very serious genetic disease with physical and mental health components. It doesn't usually begin until a person turns 40 or so. It is a genetic disor-der. Offspring of someone with Huntingdon's have a 50 per cent chance of being diagnosed. However, one can have a genetic test that will tell whether or not the person will be diagnosed. Until the disease processes become overt, the person is a "patient-in-waiting" (Timmermans and Buchbinder, 2010).

Illness Candidates

From a slightly different perspective—that of out-siders to illness—it appears that people have ideas about what sorts of people are likely to succumb to what sorts of diseases. This tendency to assign the likelihood of a personality or type of person being diagnosed with a particular type of disease has been called "lay epidemiology." Lay epidemiology may be an aspect of making sense of who gets ill and who doesn't. It is a way to psychologically to cope with uncertainty. "Using explanatory models allows individuals to account for, and make sense of, poor health" (MacDonald et al., 2013: 575). You may have engaged in lay epidemiology if you spotted a person who smelled as if he/she had been smoking and immediately thought of lung cancer. Or perhaps you have thought of the highly tanned person as a candidate for skin cancer. The widely accepted coronary candidate is the middle-aged overweight man. One of the problems with lay epidemiology is that it may lead people who fit outside the cultural mould for candidacy to neglect signs and symptoms of disease because their personal characteristics don't seem to fit. One example is the case of Kerri Lee Brown, a 39-year-old woman who was a health and wellness journalist and editor of the fitness magazine *Oxygen*. Although her symptoms of pain in her arm (although as she says, it was her right arm) and utter exhaustion were very severe, she failed to go to the emergency room for medical tests because she thought of herself as an unlikely candidate for a heart attack. Eventually, Brown sought help and tests indicated that she had already had a heart attack. Consequently, she has changed her lifestyle and is aware that she has ongoing risk factors. She says, "Even today, I still can't believe what's happened, it's been such a huge wake-up call" (2013: 150). In a related health surprise, it has been found that marathon runners run higher risks for heart attacks (http://www.active.com/articles/new-study-cites-link-between-marathon-running-and-some-heart-attack-factors). In a different example but one that reflects the same processes at work, men with breast cancer are diagnosed at later stages than women because they tend to explain away the symptoms. This neglect can lead to a poorer prognosis (Block and Muradali, 2013).

Illness Survivors

The concept of "survivors" refers to the fact that many diseases are considered not ultimately curable but only in remission. In a remission society some people—for example, those who have once received a cancer diagnosis—can be treated and can live as though they are well, all the while knowing they are at a heightened risk for a return of the disease. The possibility that surviving childhood cancer may lead to a new kind of diagnosis is exemplified by the survivors clinics at and near major cancer hospitals around North America and in the Western world. Considerable research is conducted on the probability of surviving various types of childhood cancer and for how long (see Mariotto et al., 2009, for one example).

The next section of this chapter moves from a consideration of models of illness in contemporary society to some empirical analyses of the experience of illness from the perspective of the subject.

The Insider's View: How Illness Is Experienced and Managed

Most sociological analyses of illness have treated it as an objective phenomenon measured by questionnaires and by biophysical or clinical tests. From this perspective the varieties of personal experiences are irrelevant. What matters is the explanation of the incidence and prevalence of various types of disease. However, in keeping with the arguments and traditions noted in the work of people such as Weber, Husserl, Schutz, Blumer, Mead, Cooley, Simmel, Garfinkel, and Goffman, and other interpretive and social constructionist thinkers, some researchers have turned their attention to the symbolic meanings and the social constructions of illness in the context of people's everyday experiences. These researchers focus on analysis of the experiences of illness at the individual level. It must be emphasized, however, that individual attitudes must always be set in a social context at a particular place and at a particular point in time.

Analyzing illness at the individual level has a long and noteworthy tradition in the sociology of medicine and the sociology of health and illness. One of the first published studies, mentioned earlier, was that of Mark Zborowski (1952, 1969), who compared the understandings and meanings of pain among Jewish, Italian, and "Old American" ethnic groups in New York City. Erving Goffman's *Asylums* (1961) described the experience of hospitalization from the perspectives of the mental patients or inmates and from that of the staff. Later, Goffman (1963) examined stigmas associated with illnesses and other "unusual or abnormal" conditions.

Roth (1963) describes his own experience of hospitalization for tuberculosis. Myra Bluebond-Langer (1978) describes the world of children dying of leukemia and the experiences of their parents, their nurses, and their doctors. Her work is particularly instructive in illustrating the control and spread of information. Bluebond-Langer documents the children's extensive, detailed knowledge of their conditions, the next stages in their diseases, the probable side effects of various medications, and which medications they were likely to be given, even when parents and hospital staff would attempt to shield them from this information. David Karp, a sociologist who experienced serious depression and published several books based on interviews with others as well as on his own experiences, is another scholar to whom one can turn to learn about this "insiders' perspective" more fully (see, e.g., Karp, 1996). Sorrel King (2009) has written a book about how her daughter Josie died as the result of medical errors. She also documents her powerful reaction, and her founding of an advocacy organization, the Josie King Foundation, dedicated to eliminating medical error in the United States (www.josieking.org).

More recently, sociologists have turned to narrative descriptions of illness experience, including emotional experiences. Marianne Paget, a sociologist whose work was the study of medical error, was coincidently the subject of medical errors. The series of errors made by different physicians were ultimately responsible for her death. Before she died, however, she wrote of her experience in *A Complex Sorrow*, which includes a play text. As she says:

It was while attending the first trial [for medical negligence/malpractice] in late 1987 that I began to experience back pain. Eight months later, I learned I had cancer. Almost simultaneously, I learned that the errors made in my diagnosis had jeopardized my life. I was told that my condition was incurable. (Paget, 1993: 5–6)

Such interpretive and **phenomenological** writing is becoming more frequent in a postmodern sociology of the body, emotion, and health and illness, but it represents a significant and reflexive move from studying others' meanings to studying one's own as Arthur W. Frank does so compellingly in *At the Will of the Body: Reflections on Illness* (2002).

Strauss and Glaser (1975) studied the impact of a number of different chronic illnesses and noted that people with such illnesses and their family members had to face a variety of common concerns. Although the study is dated it remains relevant today. Strauss and Glaser distinguished all of the following issues: (1) preventing and managing medical crises; (2) managing medical regimens (taking medications, administering needles, physiotherapeutic exercises); (3) controlling symptoms and preventing symptom eruption; (4) organizing and scheduling time (including necessary rests and treatments) efficiently; (5) preventing or coping with social isolation; (6) dealing with uncertainty and adjusting to changes during the course of the disease; (7) normalizing social and interpersonal relationships; (8) managing stigma; and (9) managing knowledge and information. Each of these will be discussed in turn.

Crisis management requires constant vigilance on the part of the ill person and those who are taking care of him or her. A diabetic, for instance, must continually monitor blood-sugar levels and weigh and measure food intake and insulin levels. Such monitoring may not be completely accurate, nor are the results entirely predictable. A reaction to an imbalance may be infrequent, but it is a constant possibility.

Managing medical regimens is often a complex matter. The physician tells the patient to take a certain number of pills or to have injections at certain intervals. The patient often adapts and adjusts the quantity or frequency to a level at which he or she feels comfortable. Most medications have side effects. The patient must learn to balance the need for the medication with the need to be free of side effects.

The control of symptoms is a related issue. This involves managing the medical regimen daily, hourly, or even more frequently so that a crisis does not erupt. It also involves taking enough medication to prevent a crisis but not enough to cause intolerable side effects. Minor symptoms may lead to changing some habits; major symptoms may require major lifestyle changes.

Organizing and scheduling time can be important in many chronic diseases because available time is almost always limited. Time is needed to manage the required medications, to visit doctors and hospital, to change clothes or apparatus, to cope with restrictions, to be able to move about, and so on. Often the symptoms, too, such as migraine headaches and herniated disk backaches, require that the ill person drop the daily routine in order to go to bed to cope with the pain.

Preventing or coping with isolation and trying to maintain social relationships when the person can no longer do what "normal" people do is another never-ending struggle. Sometimes people restrict their friendships to others who have the same problem and, therefore, understand. The ubiquity of self-help groups for most chronic diseases attests to the importance of social relationships with similarly disabled people, and perhaps, also, to the isolation felt by these people.

Another underlying experience that seems to be common among people with a variety of chronic illnesses is *uncertainty*, which affects every stage of illness, beginning with the diagnosis and ending with cure, confirmation that the illness is chronic, or death. Most chronic illnesses have variable and unpredictable prognoses. Cancer is perhaps the archetypal disease of uncertainty. Its very cure is measured by the diminishing probability of recurrence one, two, three, or more years after the initial diagnosis and treatment. As noted above, uncertainty is an almost inevitable aspect of living in the risk society—but it is exacerbated after a serious diagnosis.

Uncertainty also prevails during the stages of treatment, of spread of the disease, and of resurgence or remission. Under such circumstances, it is difficult to *normalize social relationships*—to make plans for the future, to be considered and consider oneself a reliable friend, companion, spouse, parent, or worker when faced with a disease with an unknown prognosis.

People who have once experienced a heart attack may distrust their bodies for a long time. They may avoid work and exercise and radically alter their lifestyle. They may feel unable to count on being alive in six months or a year. Because a heart attack frequently occurs without warning, those who have had a heart attack may lose the ability to take their bodies for granted. Yet this ability is often the prerequisite for life satisfaction.

Managing stigma is another issue the chronically ill must face. The sociological use of the term "stigma" originated with the work of Goffman (1963), who examined varieties of social interactions that were impaired by people's identity problems. Goffman designated a stigma as an attribution that discredits the value of a person. Goffman distinguished between the effects of stigma that are known only to the person involved and those that are known to others, and analyzed various strategies designed to handle the stigma in each case. The discredited person, whose deviant stigma is known to others, is challenged to "manage impressions" when interacting with others in order to maintain acceptable relationships. The discreditable person whose stigma is not known has another problem to contend with: he or she must manage information to hide the stigma and prevent others from discovering it. Many chronic illnesses carry stigma that can radically affect both the sense of self-identity and interpersonal relationships for, as Cooley has said, the way that we see ourselves is related to (1) our imagined idea of how we appear to others, (2) our imagined understanding of how others view us, and (3) our resultant feelings of pride or mortification. Even cities can experience disease-based stigma, as with the SARS outbreak in Toronto in 2003. For a period of time people were warned by the World Health Organization to avoid the city. Toronto lost millions in tourist dollars. Chinese restaurants, by association with the stigma of the disease originating in China, lost customers and money. Some Torontonians and visitors stayed away, fearing transmission of the virus because of its (relatively) high incidence in China and the presence of visitors from China in Toronto's Chinese districts.

Schneider and Conrad (1983) emphasize the importance of the stigma of another disease—epilepsy. Epilepsy may imply disgrace and shame. Borrowing a term originally used by the homosexual subculture, people with epilepsy are living "in the closet." This means that, like gays and lesbians, those with epilepsy have frequently tried to manage their perceptions of being different by isolation and concealment. "Coming out of the closet" is a political move by gays and lesbians intended to end their shame and isolation, and to empower and instill pride in people who formerly have felt stigmatized. People with epilepsy and their families have evolved a number of techniques designed to manage information about epilepsy and to come out of the closet. Rather than being entirely closet-bound, people with epilepsy go in and out through a "revolving door" (ibid., 115). Some people can be told, others not. Some can be told at one time but not at another. People with epilepsy have been denied drivers' licences, jobs, and even housing. Some people with the disease, therefore, have learned to hide their diagnosis when filling out application forms or applying for jobs, or when first meeting new people. Managing the anxiety that surrounds the concern about when and whom to tell is an ongoing problem.

People with epilepsy have also developed ways of telling—as therapy and as prevention. Sometimes telling others from whom the epilepsy has been kept secret has therapeutic consequences. It can be cathartic, for example, when a person has kept up a close friendship over a period of time, all the while keeping the truth of epilepsy secret. Telling can also serve preventive purposes. Sometimes this occurs when epileptics believe it

likely that others will witness their seizures. They may hope that the knowledge that the seizure is due to a defined medical problem and that there are clear ways to deal with it will prevent other people from being frightened.

People with epilepsy have frequently said that these negative social attributions were often more difficult to manage than the disease itself. A superlative account of the processes through which mutual denial of a stigmatized disease is maintained on a verbal level is found in the work of Bluebond-Langer (1978) on children with terminal leukemia. She devotes considerable detail to documenting how doctors, nurses, and parents practised mutual "pretense" to provide the "morale" for the continuation of hope through often painful and debilitating treatments. Although they all knew the children were dying, they all agreed not to acknowledge this fact. Meanwhile, the children knew in astonishing detail how long they were likely to live.

There are times when the lack of evidence that a disease exists elicits negative attributions. People with psychosomatic illness may be viewed as malingerers. Because the symptoms of multiple sclerosis can grow and then regress, people with this disease may not seem ill, and friends and acquaintances may complain that they are poor sports or "just psychosomatically" ill: "Knowing that I did have the disease was a great relief, but despite this I could not really believe it for some years to come. Other people could see nothing wrong with me and I feared that they regarded me as a malingerer" (Burnfield, 1977: 435).

Managing knowledge and information about the disease and its probable course and effects is crucial in the successful adaptation to chronic illness. In *Having Epilepsy*, Schneider and Conrad document the ways in which knowledge is a scarce and valuable resource in coping with epilepsy. Frequently, children with a diagnosis of epilepsy are kept in the dark about the name of the disease, about its duration, and about how to manage it. Often, parents are "shocked, embarrassed, fearful, and ashamed" that their children have epilepsy, or they are afraid that their child will be ostracized when the diagnosis is made known. Hiding it from the child, according to Schneider and Conrad's findings, is often a source of resentment in the child and leads to greater disability and dependence in the future. As one woman said, talking of her parents, "I mean, they, the fact that they had never told me and couldn't cope with me, I felt was a total rejection of a child by that parent" (Schneider and Conrad, 1983: 86–8).

Two other paths in the work on the experience of chronic illness need to be highlighted. The first is the work of Corbin and Strauss (1987) on the BBC chain and the second is the work of Charmaz (1987) on the struggle for the self. Each brings to the literature a fresh focus on understanding the experiences of chronic illness. Corbin and Strauss consider that the essential social components of this experience involve what they call the **BBC chain**—*biography*, *body*, and *self-conception*. By this, they point out that all who suffer from chronic illness are confronted, through their bodies (and their illness-related constraints, pains, freedoms, change, and so on), with challenges to self-concepts and to personal biography (i.e., the detailed story that the individual tells oneself about his or her life). The point here is that as the body is changed, so, too, are integral parts of the person—the self and the self-story in historical and future context.

Charmaz focuses on one aspect of the chain: the self. She argues that when individuals live with the ambiguities of chronic illness they develop preferred identities that "symbolize assumptions, hopes, desires and plans for the future now unrealized" (1987: 284). Moreover, coping with or managing chronic illness requires a balancing of identities and abilities through what Charmaz thinks of as a hierarchy of preferences. In her studies of people with various types of chronic illness she observed a tendency for people to have a hierarchy of preferences (or levels) for identity. In particular, she suggested a hierarchy beginning with, as a first choice, a "supernormal" identity and ending with, as last choice, a "salvaged" identity. Table 7.2 portrays the hierarchically arranged preferred identities of the chronically ill and describes their meaning.

This new focus on the self has also been described by Arthur Frank (1993), based on his analysis of published, book-length illness narratives. His research uncovered three typical change narratives: (1) the rediscovery of the self who has always been; (2) the radical new self who is in the process of becoming; and (3) the no-new-self assertion. Frank, a sociologist who survived two very serious illnesses in his late thirties, a heart attack and then cancer, has written an insightful book about his illness experiences (1991). He has done so from his point of view as a sociologist, and the book is a wealth of sociological theorizing based on bodily and health-related experience.

TABLE 7.2	Identity Preferences
Supernormal Identity	Persons seeking this identity try to do everything even better than those who are "normal."
Restored Self	Persons seeking this identity try to be like they were before the illness.
Contingent Personal Identity	Persons in this category try to achieve the above two identities at times, but also recognize ongoing, limiting rules.
Salvaged Self	Persons seeking this identity try to attain some parts of their previously healthy selves.

SUMMARY

1. Disease is an abnormality, diagnosed by a doctor, in the structure and function of body organs and systems. Illness is the personal experience of one who has been diagnosed by a doctor or who does not feel well; it involves changes in states of being and in social function. Sickness is the social actions or roles taken up by individuals who experience illness or are diagnosed with a disease. All are socially mediated.

2. The cultural and popular meanings of illness in contemporary society are widely varied.

3. Life experiences of individuals as they encounter illness and responses to their illness, such as stigma, are of interest to sociologists.

4. Uncertainty is another central experience among the ill.

5. Managing medical regimens is another issue for those who are chronically ill.

6. The media, including the Internet, are essential in understanding illness experiences today.

KEY TERMS

aspirational health
BBC chain
disease
illness

illness candidate
pathologized
patient-in-waiting
phenomenological

secondary gains
sickness
survivor

QUESTIONS FOR STUDY AND DISCUSSION

1. Describe a situation in which you experienced illness, sickness, and/or disease and consider the tensions among the three aspects of the experience.

2. Provide examples of five of the several popular conceptions of illness.

3. Examine a popular magazine for discussions of illness, disease, and sickness. What images of diseases are evident?

4. Look for 10 websites on a disease or cause of death and disability of interest to you. What meanings are assumed and portrayed?

5. Do you think the images of heart disease, cancer, and AIDS described in the research discussed in the chapter are still relevant today? What might be the relevance of the portrayal of disease, illness, or sickness for the individual and family experience of the disease?

6. Do you suffer from or do you know anyone who has a chronic illness? Do the challenges articulated in this chapter reflect your understanding of the experiences that you or this other person have?

SUGGESTED READINGS

Ehrenreich, B. 2009. *Bright-Sided: How Positive Thinking Is Undermining America*. New York: Metropolitan Books. Critical analysis of the negative effects of the culture of optimism.

Elliott, C. 2003. *Better Than Well: American Medicine Meets the American Dream*. New York: Norton. This book describes how more and more of us are using "medicine" for self-enhancement.

Geise, R. 2013. "The Mainstreaming of Mental Health." *The Walrus* (Mar.): 30–9. A brief critical commentary on the notion of mental health.

Horwitz, A.V., and J.C. Wakefield. 2012. *All We Have to Fear: Psychiatry's Transformation of Natural Anxieties into Mental Disorders*. New York: Oxford University Press. A book about the expansion of and meanings of "anxiety."

Klawiter, Maren. 2004. "Breast Cancer in Two Regimes: The Impact of Social Movements on Illness Experience." *Sociology of Health and Illness* 26, 6: 845–74. Illustrations of the experience of breast cancer in two different time periods.

Paget, Marianne A. 1993. *A Complex Sorrow: Reflections on Cancer and an Abbreviated Life*, ed. Marjorie L. Devault. Philadelphia: Temple University Press. Both emotionally moving and intellectually challenging, this book tells the story of a medical sociologist whose own misdiagnosis led to an early death.

Weitz, Rose. 1999. "Watching Brian Die: The Rhetoric and Reality of Informed Consent." *Health* 3, 2: 209–27. Weitz's work exemplifies a new type of sociological method called autoethnography. In this paper she discusses her personal reactions to a serious accident of a family member.

Sociology of Medicine

The next eight chapters consider issues in the sociology of medicine. Rather than investigating and discussing the causes of death and disease, how they vary across different parts of the social structure, by social-psychological proclivity, or the experiences of sickness, illness, and disease, as has been done in the previous chapters, here we examine the ways that medical practitioners and scientists define illness and sickness as disease and how medical services are organized around those definitions. It needs to be understood that the definitions, the knowledges, and the discourses of the medical profession and related social forces are also imbricated in the everyday understandings of all of the various others outside of medical functionaries. Thus, what you and I think of as illness and wellness are in large part determined by the medical discourses developed by various medical and health experts. This is not just medicine from above or from below but medicine as it is internalized and made normative in our everyday world. This is the working of power/knowledge in our daily lives within the realms of medical diagnoses and care. In the next chapters we will also look at the medical care system in Canada, with a focus on doctors, nurses, complementary and alternative health-care provision, and the pharmaceutical industry. We finish this section with a critical examination of the impact of globalization on health and medical care around the world.

Chapter 8 highlights the social construction of medical knowledge. Starting from the premise that all we know, understand, and believe about the world is related to the social-structural and cultural environments in which we grow up and live and the relevant circulating discourses, the chapter analyzes how medical knowledge is related to the historical, social, cultural, and structural backgrounds of physicians and research scientists, as well as to the social organizations of which they, and all of us, are a part. This chapter also examines briefly how the social characteristics of patients affect the diagnostics and decisions of doctors. It demonstrates that medical treatment is not an objective higher order of reality that stands above the real-world machinations of human beings; rather, it is entirely integrated into that world and is socially constructed through circulating discourses.

Chapter 9 is a historical overview of the place of medicine as a world view and practice

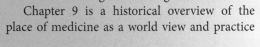

of relevance to human social behaviour. It also looks at some of the processes of medicalization through which the medical profession gained the power to define an increasing amount of human behaviour as within its realm of responsibility for diagnosis and treatment. The ways in which the doctor can be seen as a moral entrepreneur are discussed. The powerful forces of biomedicalization fuelled by technological change, pharmaceutical and other related major industries, and strong advocacy organizations of citizens are described. These processes are all accelerated by the Internet, social media, and e-medicine. Chapter 10 also takes a historical approach, examining the history, origins, and some of the current issues facing the Canadian medical care system. Some of the impacts of this system on the work of the doctor, on the disease profiles of the population, and on death rates are considered. Chapter 11 looks at allopathic medical practice as a profession. It discusses medical education in the past and today. Medical mistakes and how they are handled, malpractice, medical markets, and medical subcultures are discussed.

The next three chapters examine participants other than doctors who are involved in providing health care. Chapter 12 looks at the history and the work of nurses and midwives in their social contexts. It also examines some of the challenges currently facing nurses and midwives in their practice in Canada today. Chapter 13 briefly describes and analyzes the growing importance of various complementary and alternative practices related to health and health care. It describes in somewhat more detail the philosophies and work practices of chiropractors and naturopathic doctors. Where Chapter 13 explores some of the medical practices on the "periphery" of organized health care in Western society, Chapter 14 describes and critically analyzes activity at the "core" of Western allopathic practice—the medical-industrial complex, a significant reason why medical costs have continued to soar in Canada, the United States, and throughout the Western world. The chapter pays particular attention to the pharmaceutical industry, the major industry in this complex about which there is a growing body of research.

Finally, Chapter 15 looks at health care from an international perspective, with a focus on the work of the World Health Organization and extensive case studies of the health systems of the United Kingdom (a national universal system paid for out of the public purse), the United States (a primarily private, insurance-based system), and Brazil (a constitutionally established public system that could continue to extend its coverage and become akin to the British system or could veer towards the private-pay system of the US). In addition, the critical impacts of the economic and political forces of globalization are considered as they relate to the attempts to provide equitable health care in South Africa.

Part III covers some of the subject matter traditionally studied in a course in the sociology of medicine. However, it discusses neither hospital structures and functioning nor the place of hospitals in society today. This is just one of the enormously important topics regarding health care that we have had to leave out. This is largely because much more sociological research on these topics needs to be undertaken in Canada and elsewhere.

8

The Social Construction of Scientific and Medical Knowledge and Medical Practice

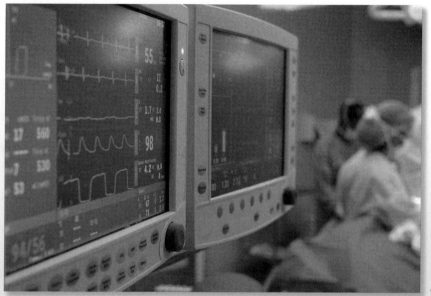

fivepointsix/Thinkstock.com

CHAPTER OVERVIEW

▶ Both medical practice and scientific knowledge are products of the societies in which they occur. They also are affected by history, economics, politics, and numerous other social forces.

▶ The modern and Western medical model of disease is only one of many possible ways of understanding the attitudes and behaviours that are labelled as "disease."

▶ The medical model encompasses a number of value judgements. There is a gap between scientific values and the work of science and that of the doctor.

▶ Technology has powerful impacts and has the capacity to change other aspects of social life

experience and identities. Technological discoveries often result in social and practice changes, even before their medium- and longer-term consequences are fully understood.

▶ Medical science and practice are infused with cultural understandings, biases, and stigmas, such as those pertaining to gender role stereotypes.

▶ Medical knowledge is accepted and rejected by different parts of the population at different times.

▶ Doctor–patient communication reflects broader social structure and cultural issues.

Introduction: The Sociology of Medical Knowledge

Is scientific knowledge universally true? Is scientific knowledge objective? Medical knowledge is based on science, but is influenced also by human, cultural, and social factors. This complex of values makes choosing among possible diagnoses and treatments complicated for patients and for medical practitioners. For example, after a cancer diagnosis patients, at times, along with their doctors, have to decide whether to use chemotherapy and/or radiation or to do visualization, botanicals, immunotherapy, or something else. The evidence as to which approach is the best, when, why, and how, is confusing and contradictory. Within medicine, debates prevail about the "reality" of some diseases such as chronic fatigue syndrome, which some people believe is just a "yuppie flu" experienced only by spoiled middle-class and upper-middle-class women. Here in the next sections of the book, we discuss questions such as the following: Do allopathic doctors have a "better" theory of medicine than chiropractic or naturopathic doctors? Does the introduction of a new technology, for example, pharmaceuticals, the CAT scanner, or MRI equipment, occur as the logical final stage of a process of rational decision-making, including cost–benefit analysis and an evaluation of the efficacy and efficiency of the new technology? Or are such decisions influenced by, among other things, the profit motive? Do medical science and practice reflect problematic cultural attitudes, such as racism, sexism, and homophobia, or are they a neutral and dispassionate endeavour?

This chapter will investigate the sociology of medical science and medical practice. To say that there is a sociology of medical science is to say that it is reasonable to examine how medical and scientific knowledge are discourses and also can be seen as determined, created, and constructed by social conditions or by using Foucault's ideas such as the productive link between power and knowledge. It is worthwhile exploring how medical science affects or constructs social conditions and

how the social and the scientific/medical worlds are frequently mutually reinforcing. Moreover, in the tradition of conflict theory, we can ask whose interests a particular form of medical knowledge, organization, and practice serves. The symbolic meanings and constructions of medical science and practice are also relevant topics for discussion.

The argument of this chapter is as follows. "Science" is not perfectly objective and universally true. It is produced by humans. It has resulted in "institutions" and discourses that have become embedded in wider social structures and maintained and resisted through processes of negotiation by some actors who live in a particular time (history) and place (culture, society, social strata) and by the associated disciplinary bodies of knowledge and practices. Medical practice is based on aspects of this socially constructed science and is also influenced by other social forces, such as the particular social characteristics of the medical care labour force and the socio-economic backgrounds from which the members of the labour force have been drawn and within which they continue to live at any given historical time period.

Medical and Scientific Knowledge: Historical and Cross-Cultural Context

Positivism, the model of science on which medicine is based, is described by attributes such as objectivity, precision, certainty (within a specific degree of error), generalizability, quantification, replication, and causality. Its search is for a series of law-like propositions designed to explain the operation of the body, the operation of medicine, the causes of disease, and the optimum methods of cure and management. These formal characteristics portray science as if it is superior to other ways of perceiving the human body in the world. Science, in this view, is outside of culture and social structure; therefore, the subjects of its study, the methods of studying human subjects, the findings from study and their interpretations, and the publication and dissemination of scientific knowledge should follow the same course and be true everywhere and at every time in history. Medicine and medical practice are similarly valorized. However, there are many reasons to challenge these assumptions.

A number of social theorists and researchers have demonstrated that beliefs regarding scientific objectivity are problematic. Kuhn (1962) has described the historical development of science and how the methods, assumptions, and even the very subject matter of science are infused with cultural categories. In *Madness and Civilization* (translated into English as *History of Madness*) Foucault describes the different understandings of and ways of "treating" those called "mad" in various societies (2006) over a long period of history. Freund, McGuire, and Podhurst (2003) have specified the value assumptions of contemporary medicine as mind–body dualism, physical reductionism, specific etiology, machine metaphor, and regimen and control.

Mind–body dualism is said to have begun with Descartes, the philosopher who effectively argued for the concept that "mind" or "spirit" is separate from the body. Descartes's writing and thinking became possible in a historical context of increasing secularization, which allowed for his belief in the separation of the body from the soul/mind. Not until Christian doctrine determined that the "soul" could be sent heavenward after death, without the body, could the notion of a non-spiritual human body following death make the cadaver "acceptable" for scientific investigation. Foucault (1975) describes the changes in the eighteenth and nineteenth centuries that allowed the physician to view the patient's body directly through the "clinical gaze," and not merely indirectly through the patient's verbal, subjective descriptions. Technological inventions such as the stethoscope gave physicians direct access to bodily functioning. With a stethoscope the doctor could observe, categorize, and explain the patient's body (or a part of the body) without the conscious awareness or involvement of the patient. Dissection of cadavers opened up a new world of speculation surrounding the patient and of

medical language for description and explanation. Such inventions further entrenched the distinction between the soul/mind and the body as they made the body a precisely describable and observable empirical entity.

Physical reductionism emphasizes the physically observable at the expense of other aspects of the individual, such as the subjectively experienced mental, sensual, and emotional. It also leads to a disregard for the social, political, and economic causes of ill health. The modern notion of the body as a group of potentially pathogenic organs made visible through technologies such as MRIs, CAT scans, and X-rays illustrates this reductionism.

René Dubos (1959) was the first to write that the **doctrine of specific etiology** is another characteristic of modern medical science. The primary assumption of this view is that each disease is thought to be the result of a particular pathogen or malfunction. It developed from the discoveries of nineteenth-century researchers such as Pasteur and Koch, who noted the specific effects of particular micro-organisms on the body. It has led to an exaggerated emphasis on the discovery of a "magic bullet" to cure one specific disease after another. Dubos notes that this emphasis is overly restrictive because it ignores the fact that the very same micro-organisms may assault any number of people but only a certain proportion of these people respond by becoming ill. It is also problematic because it has tended to ignore how a treatment for one disease may lead to side effects that may cause other diseases. It can also be associated with ignoring subjectively described symptoms such as fatigue (e.g., chronic fatigue syndrome) and pain (fibromyalgia) that lack "objective" medical measurement by available tools designed to see organ pathologies and whose symptoms may change frequently.

The **machine metaphor** for the body emphasizes discrete parts, such as individual organs, and their interrelationships with other discrete parts. This idea has led to medical specialization (e.g., cardiology, otolaryngology, urology, gynecology) and to highly skilled types of interventions such as the removal and replacement of parts of the body, including the heart, kidney, liver, blood, bone marrow, limbs, patches of skin, and even the face.

Finally, **regimen and control** are outgrowths of the machine metaphor. They assume that the body is to be dealt with, fixed, and continually improved. Not only strictly medical procedures but even health promotion policies imply that the body is perfectible and under the control of the individual through such actions as exercise and diet, and by maintaining healthy habits, such as not smoking and consuming alcohol only moderately. An emphasis on control through such things as the correct number and spacing of medical checkups as well as the use of early detection technologies reinforces this notion of the medically perfectible body. The burgeoning field of cosmetic surgery is just one significant outcome of this perspective. Stein has noted how Western, particularly American, medicine has adapted to such American cultural values. As he says:

> disease conceptualization and treatment are embedded in the value system of self-reliance, rugged individualism, independence, pragmatism, empiricism, atomism, privatism, emotional minimalism and a mechanistic metaphor of the body. (Stein, 1990: 21)

In an expanded analysis of the foundations of the medical model, Manning and Fabrega (1973) articulate the elements of what they call the biologistic view of the body. The biologistic view of the body includes the following tenets: first, organs and organ systems, and their specific functions, are identifiable and observable as discrete entities; second, the normal functioning of the body goes on pretty much the same for everybody unless disturbed by injury or illness; third, people's sensory experiences are universal; fourth, disease and experience of disease do not vary from one culture to another; fifth, boundaries between self and body and between self and others are obvious; sixth, death is the body's ceasing to function; and seventh, bodies should be seen objectively to be treated medically.

HIGHLIGHTED ISSUES

BOX 8.1   Do You Know What Causes HIV/AIDS?

What do you think causes HIV/AIDS? What do you do to prevent becoming infected? North American children and adults have been exposed to information about the transmission of HIV in schools and through doctors, public health initiatives, and the mass media. We have been advised to avoid sexual intercourse, to not share needles with an infected person, to accept for transfusion only blood that has been screened and determined to be clear of the HIV virus, and to prevent conception or to intervene in pregnancy or childbirth if infected because the virus is transmitted to the fetus or infant through bodily fluids. Most of us have heard of the new anti-viral drugs used to maintain life and extend life expectancy in the presence of a diagnosis of HIV/AIDS.

During 2002 in South Africa, 21,000 cases of child rape were reported to the police. A one-week-old baby was raped. Her mother changed her diaper only to find bruising around her genitals and bloodstains on the diaper. This baby was the youngest child in this series of child rapes, said to be motivated by the alleged belief among some people in sub-Saharan Africa that sex with a virgin cures AIDS (*Toronto Star*, 2002; Meel, 2003). More recently, the then president of South Africa, Thabo Mbeki, denied the existence of AIDS. He advocated a "healthy diet" and dietary cures such as garlic, beetroot, and vitamins (news.bbc.co.uk/2/hi/africa/4482007.stm) for the treatment of symptoms. His influence is said to have caused 300,000 deaths from AIDS (Boseley, 2008). This is one important illustration of the way that beliefs uninformed by science may have deleterious effects on health.

Sociological research provides critiques of all of these assumptions about science and medicine. First, being able to observe organs and organ symptoms depends directly on the extant epistemological and ontological discourses, the tools available for measurement, theories of the person and the body, and the type and sophistication of technology in a given culture (see Foucault, 1973, for a treatment of the historically changing discourses that allowed the modern clinical gaze and particular modern ways of seeing the patient and the disease). For example, the psychoneuro-immunological system has just been "discovered" and methods are now being developed to study it. Awareness of the possibilities of research on the body/mind connection is, in part, the result of the re-establishment of the relationship between mind and body that has come from the Eastern medical tradition, including meditation, and the discovery that the brain is "plastic" (Doidge, 2007) and that neural pathways can be reconstructed following such injuries as stroke. Second, it has become clear that much of the research on the "normal" person has been on the male person. Thus, less is known about the functioning of the female body (except her reproductive function) with respect to a whole range of disease categories including heart disease. Third, cross-cultural, anthropological, and linguistic studies have shown how people's experiences can be articulated only from their available language. Fourth, cross-cultural research has shown that what is considered "disease" in one culture may be accepted as "normal" in another. Fifth, contagious diseases such as AIDS demonstrate anew that the boundaries between people are not impermeable but vulnerable. Sixth, the definition of "death" is now very problematic because of the possibility that, for instance, respirators and defibrillators can keep people alive even when they are "brain-dead." Seventh, perhaps bodies should be seen objectively, but that is an impossible value to achieve. The values implicit in the medical model and in the biologistic view of the body reflect particular cultural histories, biases, and predispositions. Medical science and practice are not objective, are

not consistent across the discipline, and are not necessarily superior to other treatments and social practices.

Medical Science and Medical Practice: A Gap in Discourses

A significant gap frequently occurs between published biomedical research and the scientific treatments documented by such research and the actual daily practice of medicine (see Montini and Slobin, 1991). To try to minimize the distance between researcher and practitioner, the National Institutes of Health in the United States, through the Office of Medical Applications of Research, began in 1977 to convene Consensus Development Conferences (CDCs). The Canadian government and medical associations have a similar ongoing process for developing agreement between science and practice called evidence-based medicine or evidence-based practice (see, e.g., from McGill University: muhc-ebn.mcgill.ca/EBN_tools.htm). The Cochrane Collaboration is perhaps the best-known organization to provide systematic reviews of evidence about various medical issues (http://www.cochrane.org/).

The goal of the movement has been to bring together practitioners and researchers, to inform practitioners of the latest scientific findings, to inform scientists of the practical issues facing practitioners, and to work towards the development of timely, national standards of practice. Unfortunately, a number of obstacles to the immediate integration of research findings into medical practice exist. Montini and Slobin have shown how various differences in the work cultures of clinicians and researchers may play a role in limiting their amalgamation. These limitations relate to distinct value differences between researchers and practitioners, including: (1) certainty versus uncertainty; (2) evolutionary time versus clinical timeliness; (3) aggregate measures versus individual prescriptions; (4) scientific objectivity versus clinical experience; and (5) constant change versus standards of treatment. We now examine each of these limitations in more detail.

(1) *Certainty versus uncertainty.* Doctors' work involves patients who want and need immediate and certain responses. Scientific work does not depend on or even expect *certainty*; rather, *probability* is the focus of laboratory science. Time-related concerns are considerably different in those two contexts. The practitioner needs at least enough certainty to make decisions about caring for a particular patient at a specific point in time. By contrast, the scientist works within a world of probabilities—thus, uncertainty—in a time frame determined by funding, the nature of the investigation, the parameters of the experimental paradigm, the intrinsic limitations of equipment, the training and abilities of the researcher, imperatives embedded in the research institution, and so on.

(2) *Evolutionary time versus clinical timeliness.* Science does not progress by proof so much as by failing to disprove. Caution is always implied in drawing conclusions. Scientific truth develops in incremental stages as more and more hypotheses are disconfirmed. However, the clinician must make timely decisions in response to the expressed and observed needs of individual patients.

(3) *Aggregate measures versus individual prescriptions.* While the scientist, in working with probabilities, deals in aggregates, the practitioner must deal with the suffering individual. Again, because of the immediacy of the sufferer, clinicians are forced to rely on what they are learning from their experience and are finding to be "tried and true" in their practice. They may be uneasy about relegating a given individual to a clinical trial or a new treatment, the outcome of which is unknown and will likely remain unknown for a considerable period of time.

(4) *Scientific objectivity versus clinical experience.* The scientist tries to control all variables in the interests of objective and generalizable findings. The clinician, in contrast, is faced with a unique individual reporting subjectively experienced symptoms that the clinician cannot control and needs to deal immediately with the patient.

(5) *Constant change versus standards of treatment.* The researcher is aware of continuous change in research findings as new hypotheses are put forward and supported or rejected. The clinician must practise medicine under the direction and with the support of practice standards but must also make assumptions that current knowledge is "good enough" and its implementation will be beneficial to the patient. The doctor has to assume that current treatments will be helpful and have a longer "shelf life" than frequently changing scientific hypotheses on the frontiers of medical developments.

The idea of **evidence-based medicine** (EBM) has been growing in influence in medical practice (www.cebm.utoronto.ca/intor/whatis.htm). Evidence-based medicine involves using statistical and other evaluative techniques for the meta-analysis of scientific literature related to all manner of potential medical diagnoses in order to inform continually the everyday practice of medicine. The goal is that a patient's care be based on the most up-to-date, valid, and reliable medical/scientific information, rather than on the practices long in use. Further, EBM assumes that the best evidence is gathered and assessed through systematic and thorough means. Doctors need up-to-date knowledge because textbooks quickly become outdated; experts may be wrong and medical journals too prolific to allow any individual practitioner to stay current. In addition, doctors often are rushed in their everyday work. Now, however, as a result of the Cochrane Collaboration (see www.cochrane.org), physicians can access timely reviews of the best evidence published in refereed scientific journals for many of the medical issues they face. There are many limitations to EBD including the fact that published research may not be representative of the best research, partly because of the time it takes to undertake and then publish research. Some populations are under-studied (e.g., women, racialized groups, and people sick with more than one disease concurrently). When researchers are funded by private corporations such as drug companies, published findings may be restricted (by the terms of the grant) to those who support the use of the intervention financed by the company in question (see, e.g., the case of Nancy Olivieri, at: www.healthcoalition.ca/nancy-gm.html). Furthermore, not all evidence is accessible because negative findings often are not publishable.

Medical Technology: The Technological Imperative

New medical technologies continue to be developed, manufactured, distributed, and employed. Among the new technologies are cardiac life-support, renal dialysis, nutritional support and hydration, mechanical ventilation, organ and stem cell transplantation and various other surgical procedures, pacemakers, chemotherapy, MRIs, CAT scans, and new, more powerful antibiotics. The question that we ask here is: What is the relationship between medical science and this evaluation process that culminates in the use of new technologies? Available evidence suggests that practitioners tend to adopt new technologies before they are evaluated and that they continue to use them after evaluation indicates they are ineffective or unsafe (Rachlis and Kushner, 1989: 186). The power of new technologies has been called the **technological imperative**. The numerous people who are made sick or who die as the result of the technological imperative can be found in the statistics for medical error in Canada and the United States. In Canada, the Canadian Institute for Health Information along with Statistics Canada reported that up to 24,000 Canadians die annually from medical error (http://www.cbc.ca/news/technology/medical-errors-killing-up-to-24-000-canadians-a-year-1.514758). Not all of these are the result of new technologies or of improperly used technologies, but some are. Drugs that are introduced into the market or that stay on the market despite accumulating negative evaluations are cases in point. For example, the acne drug Diane-35 (a hormone-secretion modifier designed for birth control) is said to have killed 11 Canadian women and to have caused serious and minor side effects in hundreds of others (see Chapter 14).

The adoption of new medical technologies is vulnerable to social variables and has been shown to be related to four social forces (Butler, 1993): (1) key societal values, (2) federal government policies, (3) reimbursement strategies, and (4) economic incentives.

(1) Among key societal values, a number of social commentators have described the love affair of North Americans with new technology of all sorts. Enthusiastic optimism rather than realistic caution typifies our attitude to new technology. While we have yet to understand all of the possible constraints to freedom, privacy, and democracy created by the Internet, plus other threats that may easily result from global electronic communication, it already exists and is in widespread use. Some people are protesting that we don't yet know enough about the long-term effects of "wireless" technologies to use them as widely as we do, even among children in their schools. For example, the effects of the use of cell phones have not been precisely determined, but an extensive WHO review of studies reports evidence of increase in glioma (a malignant tumour that begins in the brain or spine) and schwannoma (acoustic neuroma), a non-malignant brain tumour (http://www.cnn.com/2011/HEALTH/05/31/who.cell.phones/index.html). Is this a situation calling for the precautionary principle? The development of other new and related technologies often precedes considerations of and safeguards for possible deleterious health and social impacts.

(2) In the health area, the federal government, through such bodies as the Canadian Institutes of Health Research, the Heart and Stroke Foundation, and the National Cancer Institute of Canada, quietly funds biomedical research. Taxation policies, free-trade agreements, support for education and science, and other federal incentives encourage the discovery of new technologies. Our national medical care system fosters growth and expansion of the use of medical technologies immediately upon their development. However, such undertakings have not always proven desirable or fruitful. While Butler's study is based in the US, there is no reason to assume that Canadian legislation provides greater safeguards, and, in

fact, available evidence indicates that in some situations, e.g., the thalidomide disaster of the 1950s and 1960s, Canadian regulation may be more lenient. The policies regarding post-market surveillance of the effects of the introduction of new technologies in Canada is hotly debated in the House of Commons (see http://www.cma.ca/multimedia/CMA/Content_Images/Inside_cma/Submissions/2012/Senate-Pharmaceuticals-Oct2012_en.pdf).

(3) and (4) While there are no definitive studies of the costs of new technology, a variety of studies taken together suggest that 20–50 per cent of the annual increases in health-care costs during the past 25 years or so are the result of progressive innovations in medical technology, including pharmaceuticals. A few new technologies appear to save lives and costs. Most new technologies are expensive and may be ineffective or lead to negative side effects; however, they add costs to the medical care system whether or not they work. A great deal of controversy is expressed about the ethics of including cost-effectiveness in health-care provision; thus, this conversation has been less likely to occur in Canada (see, e.g., Donaldson et al., 2002). As long as the medical-industrial complex is even partly guided by privatization and the profit motive, the development and dissemination of medical technological innovations will result, in part, from market principles rather than from planned, rational, health-benefiting, and evaluated strategies for change. Consider this example: babies weighing as little as one pound can now be kept alive at a cost of, at times, millions of dollars per baby through neonatal intensive care for several months, and then continuing care for those babies and children who may have ongoing medical and other health, educational, and social needs. By contrast, a low-technology approach to preventing low-birth-weight babies that would include feeding pregnant women nutritious diets and maintaining minimal equitable socio-economic standards—via, for instance, a guaranteed annual wage for all—is a much more cost-effective and efficient strategy for a healthy citizenry—but this prenatal support has yet to be implemented.

An example of the tendency to first adopt new technologies and evaluate them later is electronic fetal monitoring. Designed for use with high-risk births, the fetal monitor was to provide doctors with information regarding the health of the fetus during labour. If a fetus showed dangerous vital signs the physician could actively intervene in the labour process by, for example, performing a Caesarean section. Electronic fetal monitoring (EFM) was initially made available in the 1960s. By the 1970s EFM and ultrasound were widely available in most hospitals. By the 1980s, 30 per cent of all obstetricians had EFM in their offices to detect prenatal problems. Rapidly, EFM became a standard monitoring device, even for low-risk situations. Its widespread use was associated with an increase in the diagnosis of prenatal problems. The Caesarean section rate, at 4.5 per cent of all births in 1965, rose to 16.5 per cent by 1980 and 24.7 per cent by 1988. In 2001–2, C-sections accounted for 22.5 per cent of all in-hospital deliveries in Canada. By 2005 the rate of C-sections had risen to 26 per cent (www.research.utoronto.ca/behind_the_headlines/what's-behind-canada's-rising-c-section-rate/). Studies of this phenomenon have found that the rate varies substantially by region, ethnicity, socio-economic status, and availability of insurance for payment. According to the Canadian Institute for Health Information in 2010–11 the C-section rate for first-time C-section was 18.1 per cent and for subsequent births by C-section the rate was 82.3 per cent (http://www.cfhi-fcass.ca/SearchResultsNews/11-05-06/d91308d2-962d-43c6-be19-39825706e542.aspx).

Despite the rapid growth in the use of electronic fetal monitoring, randomized, controlled trials undertaken since 1976 have failed to demonstrate benefits of EFM in comparison with simpler methods of monitoring, such as the stethoscope. Moreover, EFM leads to certain risks for fetus and mother. The safety of ultrasound still remains to be completely established. In addition, there is substantial agreement that the use of new technology is a major driver for the increase in the costs of health care. Other important examples of the introduction of a new technology prior to evidence of its safety and value are (1) the withdrawal in 2004 of Vioxx, the highly popular drug for the pain of arthritis, because—after it had been sold and used by millions of people—it was found to be associated with "an increased risk of 'serious thrombotic cardiovascular adverse events'" (www.vioxx.com) and (2) the marketing of hormone replacement therapy (HRT) to millions of women prior to the testing of its negative effects, such as heart disease, breast cancer, and strokes. The use of some anti-depressants, not only among young people, has been linked to an increased rate of suicide (www.alertpubs.com/anti-depressants_and_suicide.htm; Whitaker, 2010: 306).

McKinlay and McKinlay (1981) developed a model—the seven stages in the career of a medical invention—that could be used to explain the social forces involved in the dissemination of new medical technologies before they are adequately tested.

- Stage 1: A promising report.
- Stage 2: Professional and organizational adoption.
- Stage 3: Public acceptance and state (third-party) endorsement.
- Stage 4: Standard procedure and observational reports.
- Stage 5: Randomized controlled trial.
- Stage 6: Professional denunciation.
- Stage 7: Erosion and discreditation.

The most important point is that evaluation, which is purported and believed to be the bedrock of scientifically based treatment innovations, occurs at stages 4 and 5, long after the introduction and widespread use of a medical invention. The new concept of "disease-mongering" introduced in the *British Medical Journal* (Moynihan et al., 2002) explains the tendency to active intervention as the result of the profit motive of pharmaceutical companies. **Disease-mongering** is the corporate construction of new diseases for the sole purpose of business profits, "extending the boundaries of treatable illness to expand markets for new products" (ibid., 886). Further, Moynihan et al. note that alliances between pharmaceutical companies, doctors, and patients are encouraged to frame

new conditions as widespread, debilitating, and severe. In their argument they documented three case studies. The first involved the medicalization of baldness around the time that Merck developed a hair-growth drug. Merck sponsored news articles emphasizing the extensiveness of the problem of baldness and the severe level of suffering that people experienced as the result of baldness. The company suggested that panic and emotional difficulties were associated with baldness. In addition, the company sponsored the founding of a new International Hair Study Institute. Thus, baldness came to be considered a treatable "disease." The second included the pathologizing of mild digestive symptoms into the disease "irritable bowel syndrome" as a part of the marketing of a new drug by GlaxoSmith-Kline. The third condition, introduced into the public and medical consciousness at the time of the development of an anti-depressant by Roche, was social phobia, which has been called "medicalized shyness" (see, e.g., www.thecommentfactory.com/popping-pills-for-shyness-100/). Most recently, the highly reputable Berkeley Wellness report underscored how ADHD drugs are sometimes over-prescribed. Certainly, the wide differences in different countries and in different geographic parts of the same countries suggest that there is more at work in the prescription of ADHD drugs than objective science would merit (http://www.berkeleywellness.com/self-care/preventive-care/article/adhd-disease-mongering; Whitaker, 2010). In fact, ADHD has been shown by some researchers and clinicians to be an ear-based condition that can be treated without drugs but with high-frequency sound (e.g., Doidge, 2015: 280–302; Bérard, 1993: 18–37).

Perhaps two of the most interesting historical examples of disease-mongering in the interests of profit are from the nineteenth century: the diagnosis of **drapetomania**, which caused slaves to run away from their masters, and **dysaethesia aethiopis**, which referred to poor work habits among slaves. The first can be seen as an instance of a diagnosis used to serve financial interests because slaves could be costly to own and, thus, slave owners stood to lose money whenever a slave ran

CRITICAL THINKING

BOX 8.2   Are the Costs of Immunization Greater Than the Benefits?

Countless websites are devoted to providing information and trying to organize against universal and multiple disease immunization. A sizable number of people link such problems as the growing incidence of autism and Asperger's, along with diabetes and Crohn's disease, to side effects of vaccinations. The Canadian Health Services Research Foundation (CHSRF) has published a rebuttal to these fears. Following a thorough review of the published literature, the CHSRF declares that immunizations are among the safest of modern medical interventions (www.chsrf.ca). The Foundation compares the effects of diseases such as tetanus, from which 1 in 10 infected people die, with the side effects of the vaccine, from which 1 in 5 experiences swelling or discomfort and 1 in 20 experiences fever. The CHSRF also notes that when a sizable majority of a population is immunized (otherwise known as "herd immunity") they provide a level of protection even to the non-immunized.

The latest issue facing people in the developed world is the mandated or government-supported vaccination against cervical cancer and other diseases via the vaccine for the human papillomavirus (HPV) to be given to young women as children before they are sexually active or can give informed consent. At this point in time, the ethics of such a vaccination program are being debated. It has been approved

for sale in Canada and has been made available in many other countries (www.phac-aspc.gc.ca/std-mts/hpv-vph/hpv-vph-vaccine_e.html). In some states in the US, government funding is already available and the uptake of the vaccine swift; but in others the debate continues and is vociferous (ibid.). In Canada, as of 2006, the Gardasil vaccine had been approved for females and males of ages 9 to 26 and, as of 2010, a similar product, Cervarix, was approved for ages 10 to 25 (www.phac-aspc.gc.ca/std-mts/hpv-vph/fact-faits-vacc-eng.php). All provinces and territories have implemented publicly funded programs. The safety of these vaccines is questioned by many doctors (www.americanchronicle.com/articles/view/231729). In the United States alone, more than 20,000 vaccine-related adverse reactions had been reported to VAERS (Vaccine Adverse Events Reporting System) since the vaccines were released for use. These injuries included 93 deaths, 372 post-vaccination abnormal smear tests, 411 life-threatening events, 8,661 ER visits, 2,118 hospitalizations, 4,382 non-recovery from injury, 702 victims left disabled, and 252 women suffering spontaneous abortions/stillbirths after the vaccine. As VAERS reporting represents only a fraction of the incidents, these figures may stand for the tip of a much more deadly and damaging iceberg. What are the pros and cons of government-mandated vaccinations?

away. Similarly, slaves who had poor work habits were costly to their owners. Calling these actions "diseases" reinforced the moral superiority of the owners and justified the actions they "had" to take to return the slaves home or to demand better work (Freund et al., 2003: 197).

A study comparing the approval for commercial use of two drugs in Japan and the US demonstrates the potential role of social and

political pressure to adopt or not adopt new drugs irrespective of drug safety and efficacy information (Hollander, 2006). The two comparison drugs were Viagra and an abortion pill in the US and Viagra and a birth control pill in Japan. In both Japan and the US, Viagra was shepherded through the drug approval processes within six months. In the US the abortion pill was approved 17 years after related research was first allowed and four years after application was made for distribution. In Japan, the birth control pill was approved for use 35 years after the first application for approval was made. Ostensibly, drug approval is linked to drug safety and efficacy and is the result of scientific investigation. However, Viagra has been associated with heart attacks, irregular heart rhythms, stroke, chest pain, and increased blood pressure. On the other hand, the side effects to the mother of the abortion medication and the birth control pill appeared to be minor and included cramping, nausea, vomiting, and bleeding. The most serious side effect required a blood transfusion. Clearly, then, other factors were at play in the adoption of these drugs in Japan and the US.

In another example, a tonsillectomy is a very common surgical procedure, yet there is considerable variation in its use from geographic area to geographic area and from hospital district to hospital district. The proper treatment for tonsillitis is debatable. One of the ways this debate is resolved appears to be along the lines of specialty preferences. For instance, pediatricians tend to favour recurrent use of antibiotics to control tonsil flare-ups, whereas otolaryngologists are more likely to prefer the surgical procedure and to remove the infected or inflamed organ. It appears that the ideology of the specialty is buttressed by scientific research based on clinical trials and published in specialty research journals tending to favour one procedure over another. Although it may seem that economics might drive the preferences for action chosen by each different type of specialist, even in jurisdictions where physicians are on salary these specialty group differences remain. These findings suggest that the need to believe in one's own procedure may reflect more than material interests: it may reflect the need to protect and promote the hard-earned skills necessary for the long-run success of the specialty (Chow, 1998). One implication of this conflict in treatment procedures is that the knowledge base of doctors is much greater in their own specialty and they may, at times, be myopic with respect to looking at all of the alternative treatments. A specialist should not be expected to be able to offer an evaluation of the exact health

costs and benefits of different types of treatments (based on different specialties), even though this would likely be in the interest of the health of the patient and the costs to the health-care system.

Medical Science Reinforces Gender Role Stereotypes

Scientific medical knowledge is portrayed as an objective, generalizable, and positive accomplishment. Yet, what is taken to be objective medical science has been shown to reflect fundamental cultural and social-structural beliefs (Clark et al., 1991). Normative categories of social relations, in fact, have infused medical conceptions. Findlay (1993) studied the 10 most highly circulating texts in obstetrics and gynecology in the 1950s in Canada, as well as a representative selection of academic articles from five major obstetrics/gynecology journals and from the *Canadian Medical Association Journal*. Her research showed that, a half-century ago, physicians' descriptions and understandings of the female body guarded and reflected family values. The scientific and medical publications emphasized the importance of separate spheres for men and women, of stable marriage and family life, and encouraged fertility among women (who were assumed to be white and middle-class). Findlay noted that the essence of the "normal" woman during this time period was portrayed as if she ought always to be potentially fertile. Women's bodies were described largely with respect to fluctuations in their hormones and menstrual cycles. They were described as living to reproduce. As Findlay reports, one influential obstetrician/gynecologist explained: "The desire for children by the normal woman is stronger than self-interest in beauty and figure, stronger than the claims of a career, [while] in the man it is less intense" (Jeffcoate, 1957, in Findlay, 1993). By contrast, the abnormal woman was defined as one who had sexual or reproductive problems.

The women's movement of the 1960s and beyond has focused on eliminating such prejudices. However, women still are seen as reproductive bodies and viewed as largely responsible for birth control and for accepting or refusing sexual intercourse. Women continue to be used for experimental treatments in regard to their reproductive systems. For example, as discussed in Box 8.2, the vaccination against the human papillomavirus (HPV) has recently been approved for use in Canada and is being advertised as a cervical cancer preventative despite the fact that the safety and efficacy of the vaccination over the long term are yet to be determined. Also, considering that HPV is a sexually transmitted disease, the initial rationale for excluding boys and young men in trials and utilization is not clear. The consequences of HPV to males may be as severe (predominately genital and anal warts and genital and throat cancers) as the consequences to females (cervical cancer; cervical cancer with metastases). However, the infection of males can lead to the infection of more females.

Other sorts of preventive actions could be taken without this vaccine (www.cwhn.ca/resources/cwhn/hpv.html). Nevertheless, preteens in Europe and across North America are now being injected with the HPV vaccine.

Emily Martin's *The Woman in the Body* (1987) also instructs us about gender biases in medical conceptions of women's bodies and their functions. She demonstrates how culture shapes what biological scientists see. One interesting illustration of her thesis is how assumptions about gender infuse descriptions of the reproductive cycle and its elements, such as the egg and sperm. For instance, the female menstrual cycle is described in negative terms. Menstruation is said to rid the body of waste, of debris, of dead tissue. It is described as a system gone awry. By contrast, while most sperm are also "useless" and "wasted," the life of the sperm is described as a "feat." The magnitude of the production of sperm is considered remarkable and valuable. Whereas female ovulation is described as a process where eggs sit and wait and then get old and useless, male spermatogenesis is described as continuously producing fresh, active, strong, and efficient sperm. While the eggs are swept and drift down the fallopian tubes like flotsam, sperm

actively and in a "manly" and machismo fashion burrow and penetrate.

There is evidence, as well, of stereotyping regarding hegemonic masculinities. For instance, they have long been seen as risk factors (e.g., risk-taking of males has been seen as the cause of their higher incidence of automobile accidents and homicides) and are now being medicalized (Rosenfeld and Faircloth, 2006). Erectile dysfunction is a case in point. Medical definitions of erectile functioning link the performance of masculinity to the ability to "accomplish" (Loe, 2006: 31) an erection. Baldness, too, has been medicalized (http://www.plosmedicine.org/article/info%3Adoi%2F10.1371%2Fjournal.pmed.0030146), and according to Moynihan (2006) there is another recently discovered new disease called "motivational deficiency disorder" otherwise known as "laziness" or maybe "extreme laziness." In another example, attention deficit hyperactive disorder (ADHD) is a frequent diagnosis for children and young people that functions to control their behaviours, particularly in school. What has been less documented is the fact that the diagnosis of ADHD, and the subsequent prescription of Ritalin for its treatment, serves as a medicalization of boyhood because the vast majority of prescriptions (approximately 75 to 80 per cent) are for young boys because of their "disruptive" or "boyish" behaviours in classrooms (Hart et al., 2006).

The recent development of pharmacogenetics—the study of how drug response depends on genetic makeup (Helman, 2007)—has led to the targeting of drugs to specifically racialized groups. For instance, in 2005 a heart drug was approved by the US Food and Drug Administration (FDA) for the treatment of heart failure among African Americans. The success of the Human Genome Project in mapping the genetic makeup of human beings is making it possible to design drugs with a more exact fit to genetic makeup. These developments raise important ethical debates. Some argue that such precisely targeted medical interventions, in a racist society, could be used to reinforce and even act on racism or against other marginalized groups. It is possible to imagine the "discovery" of a disease that leads to consequent

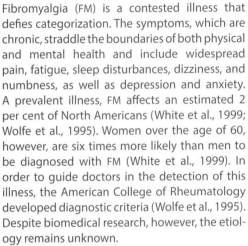

HIGHLIGHTED ISSUES

BOX 8.3   A Feminist Interpretation of Fibromyalgia
by Michelle Skop-Dror

Fibromyalgia (FM) is a contested illness that defies categorization. The symptoms, which are chronic, straddle the boundaries of both physical and mental health and include widespread pain, fatigue, sleep disturbances, dizziness, and numbness, as well as depression and anxiety. A prevalent illness, FM affects an estimated 2 per cent of North Americans (White et al., 1999; Wolfe et al., 1995). Women over the age of 60, however, are six times more likely than men to be diagnosed with FM (White et al., 1999). In order to guide doctors in the detection of this illness, the American College of Rheumatology developed diagnostic criteria (Wolfe et al., 1995). Despite biomedical research, however, the etiology remains unknown.

The mystery about causation contributes to FM's reputation as a controversial and illegitimate illness. According to the medical model, if an illness cannot be seen in test results, then it is not real: it is psychosomatic (Cunningham and Jillings, 2006; Sylvain and Talbot, 2002; Webster, 2002). FM also lacks credibility due to the hierarchy of mainstream medicine, which privileges acute diseases—affecting major organs and requiring invasive interventions—over those considered chronic or psychiatric (Album and Westin, 2008). Skepticism about FM is further compounded by the discrepancy between the appearance of people who may look well and their subjective accounts of severe functional impairment (Barker, 2002).

FM is often labelled a modern-day form of hysteria (Webster, 2002). A gendered illness, hysteria was historically associated with the fragility of female nerves, repressed sexual desires, and the "bad influence of the uterus" (Foucault, 1964: 138). It was "a ruse of the body," a manifestation of the social malaise plaguing privileged upper-middle-class women (ibid., 148). Consequently, it can be argued that the meanings bestowed on hysteria, and by extension on FM, are shaped by biases about gender, sex, and class. Fused with moral values, these illnesses are reputed as afflictions of lazy, weak, and entitled women.

Moral judgements are not only passed because FM is gendered, but also because it is chronic. People with chronic illnesses are considered morally suspect because they deviate beyond the parameters of the socially acceptable sick role (Parsons, 1951). In order to assume the sick role, people must first be assigned a diagnosis based on medical consensus. They may then be temporarily pardoned from their social responsibilities. Since FM is chronic, however, they may require prolonged absences from work, as well as a significant amount of assistance with household duties. Consequently, they may encounter resentment from informal support networks because our culture often believes that lifestyle modifications signify a flaw in character or a poor work ethic (Cunningham and Jillings, 2006; Sylvain and Talbot, 2002).

Source: © Michelle Skop-Dror. Reprinted by permission.

stigmatization and isolation in only one "race" or marginalized group. Furthermore, the genetic makeup is subject to alteration, which is how species evolve; targeting the genes of individuals is a way of interrupting evolutionary processes that have been underway for millennia and are far more complex than is yet known.

The Sociology of Medical Practice

Just as medical/scientific knowledge is a social product with social consequences, so, too, is the everyday practice of medicine. Have you ever left your doctor's office only to realize that you had forgotten to tell or ask him/her about something? Have you ever left the office unclear about what the doctor has said about your problem/disease, your medication, or something else? Have you ever felt that you "couldn't get a word in edgewise" in a conversation with your physician? Have you ever seen a sign in the examining room to the effect, "Please restrict your visit to one symptom or medical problem"? Have you ever asked for a second opinion or been skeptical about a doctor's diagnosis?

Considerable evidence demonstrates that the day-to-day practice of medicine is profoundly affected by social characteristics of patients and doctors. First, with regard to patients, there is evidence that physicians tend to prefer younger patients and to hold negative images of elderly patients. Elderly patients tend to be seen as both sicker and less amenable to treatment than younger patients. The older patient, "far in excess of actual numbers, represents the negative idea of the unco-operative, intractable, and generally troublesome patient" (Clark et al., 1991: 855). Elderly patients are significantly more likely to be treated with digitalis, tranquilizers, and analgesics, regardless of their actual diagnoses (www.chrsf.ca). The elderly are over-treated, in general (Hadler, 2011), particularly when they spend their last days, weeks, or months and then die in hospital.

Physicians' attitudes and actions in regard to racialized characteristics reflect those of the wider socio-cultural context of which physicians are a part. For instance, several US-based studies have demonstrated that black patients tend to be referred to specialists less often, are treated more often by doctors-in-training, are more likely to be placed on a ward, and are admitted less frequently to hospital except when they are involuntarily hospitalized for mental health problems. Black patients also tend to receive less aggressive workups and interventions. Differences have been documented in the way that physicians treat patients of different class backgrounds. For example, patients with poorer backgrounds are likely given poorer prognoses and less state-of-the-art treatment (see Chapters 4 and 5 for a more detailed discussion of racialization, class, and health). The social characteristics of

physicians themselves, including gender, age, professional training, education, and form of practice, have also been shown to influence their work.

Cultural Variation in Medical Practice

In an intriguing study, Lynn Payer (1988), a journalist, travelled and visited doctors in several countries: the United States, England, West Germany, and France. To each doctor she presented the same symptoms. She also examined morbidity and mortality tables and read medical journals and magazines in each country. Using this casual and commonsensical method, Payer found strong cultural differences in diagnostic trends and patterns that seemed to reflect fundamental differences in history and culture. Diagnoses and treatments varied widely from country to country, even under allopathic medical care. "West Germans, for instance, consume roughly six times as much cardiac glycoside, or heart stimulant, per capita, as do the French and the English, yet only about half as much antibiotic" (Payer, 1988: 38). In general, Payer found that German doctors were far more likely to diagnose heart problems than doctors in other countries. English physicians, by contrast, are characterized as parsimonious. For this reason, Payer describes the British as the accountants of the medical world. They prescribe about half of the drugs that German and French doctors prescribe and perform about half of the surgeries of American doctors. "Overall in England one has to be sicker to be defined ill, let alone receive treatment" (ibid., 41). By contrast, the Americans are spendthrift and aggressive. They have a tendency to take action even in the face of uncertainty. They do not, however, focus on a particular organ. Among the French, most ills are ultimately attributable to the liver.

Payer argues that these patterns reflect the German emphasis on the heart—on romance, in literature and music, for instance; the French focus on the pleasures of eating and drinking; the English have a preoccupation with rationalizing the national medical care system; and the American emphasis is on getting things done and getting on with it. Payer's work suggests, in broad strokes, something of the relationship between culture and medical practice. More cross-cultural research needs to be done and more is being undertaken (see, e.g., Lakoff's 2004 work on the links between anti-depressant use and the economic crisis in Argentina).

Class and Resistance to Medical Knowledge

One way that lay people in the US interpret, accept, or resist "medical knowledge" is described in relation to a cancer education project developed for a white, working-class, inner-city area that was known as a "cancer hot spot" because of the relatively high rates of cancer mortality (Balshem, 1991). The problem was believed by the local inhabitants to be largely the consequence of air pollution from nearby chemical plants and occupational exposure of those who worked in the plants. With this belief system in mind, the community rejected "health education" about nutrition and cancer. To illustrate the resistance, Balshem, who was working as a health educator at the time, describes the aftermath of her slide show and talk about the cancer prevention possibilities of a diet that is high in fibre and low in fat. Immediately after this talk Balshem asked if there were any questions. She was met with silence. Then she raffled off a hot-air popcorn maker. People responded warmly, with pleasure. After that, there was silence again. The meeting adjourned and the subtext of the silence emerged. One person talked about her old neighbour (93 years old) who ate whatever she liked and was still alive. Another teased Balshem: "You mean your husband will eat that stuff; mine sure won't." Still another confessed that the people in the room liked their kielbasa (spicy sausage) too much to eliminate it from their diets. Finally, Balshem was invited to their next church supper for some really good eating. Balshem describes the meeting finale as follows:

Then, the social climax: I am offered a piece of cake. The offerer, and a goodly number of onlookers, can barely restrain their hilarity. Time stops. Then I accept the cake. There is a burst of teasing and laughter, the conversation

becomes easier, the moment passes. We eat, pack our equipment, and leave. (Ibid., 156)

While the general atmosphere of these meetings was amiable, the explicit health messages were ignored or indirectly criticized as impractical and as being of less importance than things such as pleasure, family feeling, and "human" nature in the pursuit of health. To the participants the environmental causes identified by the people who lived there were the obvious culprit and cause of cancer.

To understand the community and its responses, Balshem engaged in survey research, long open-ended interviews, and focus-group research strategies. One of the findings was that the community members had sharply contrasting attitudes towards heart disease and cancer.

The causes and treatments of heart disease were both fewer and considered more responsive to lifestyle alterations. Cancer, by contrast, was described as the result of a horrible fate. It was seen as caused by almost everything in their environment. Many of the respondents directly denied the dominant scientific discourses regarding cancer causation and prevention. In particular, there were direct denials of smoking and of fat as cancer-causing agents. By contrast, no one questioned the standard scientific discourses about the prevention and causation of heart disease. Balshem called this response "resistance" and explained that:

maintaining a rebellious consciousness is part of constructing a valued self, valued community, valued life, in a subordinate class environment. Self and community, valuing and supporting each other, process myriad insults, betrayals, and frustrations. Local belief and tradition, it is asserted, are superior, as is local insight into the workings of authority and hegemony. (Ibid., 166)

For an abundance of reasons, class and community solidarity proved to be more important than expert health knowledge, beliefs about disease causation, and prevention strategies.

Despite the power of "medicalization from above," there is always resistance, or as Cornwell (1984) says, "medicalization from below." Calnan and Williams (1992) demonstrate another type of resistance to medical thinking and hegemony. They studied lay evaluations of the trustworthiness of doctors with respect to nine specific medical care issues. In particular, they asked whether or not laypersons would unquestioningly accept medical opinion with regard to the following nine interventions: (1) prescription of antibiotics; (2) hernia operation; (3) operation for bowel cancer; (4) prescription for tranquilizers; (5) hip replacement operation; (6) hysterectomy; (7) heart transplant; (8) test-tube babies; and (9) vasectomy. Their findings indicated that in only one case, antibiotics, would the majority of respondents accept medical intervention without question: 54 per cent said they would accept antibiotics without question. Yet even here, 41 per cent said they would only accept the doctor's recommendation for antibiotics with an explanation. Moreover, the views of the public regarding all interventions varied according to gender, class, age, and health categories.

Calnan and Williams note that in making their decisions respondents were guided by certain fundamental values of their own. A good intervention was characterized in the following ways: as life-saving rather than life-threatening; as enhancing rather than diminishing quality of life; as natural rather than unnatural; as moral rather than immoral; as necessary rather than unnecessary; as restoring independence rather than promoting addiction/dependence; and as giving good value for money rather than being a waste of money.

The lay population knows that medical knowledge does not form a consistent whole. Nor do the different conceptions of medical knowledge necessarily complement one another: "The medical world is a melting pot of contradictory theories and practices, controversies and inexplicable phenomena about which doctors and lay people are in constant debate" (Bransen, 1992: 99). For example, after decades of encouraging women to examine their breasts for suspicious lumps and to have regular mammograms, the medical profession has begun to withdraw those recommendations. The detection rate of cancer by these techniques is so small as to be negligible. Furthermore, false positives and costly exploratory surgery have levied a significant toll (www.theglobeandmail.com/news/opinions/opinion/cures-for-cancer-at-any-cost/article2250126/?utm_medium=Feeds%3A%20RSS%2FAtom&utm_source=Home&utm_content=2250126). Controversy still swirls around whether the potential side effects from mammography testing are worth the few cases of breast cancer that are found early enough for treatment to make a difference, as this review of 25 years of mammography use indicates (Miller et al., 2014). Similarly, the usefulness of PSA testing in men has been called in question. HRT was first heralded as the new wonder drug for the prevention of breast cancer and then later found implicated in other diseases.

Patient groups are organizing to seek their rights in Canada and around the world. The World Health Organization has spent a good deal of time considering what universal health-related rights should be (see www.who.int/genomics/public/patientrights/en for a discussion of this issue in a global context). Table 8.1 provides an indication of how the role of the patient has changed from one of passivity to one of action and co-action with the health-care provider(s). Clearly this is an idealized version and it reflects neo-liberalism while obfuscating the critical lens through which we as sociologists view power/knowledge discourses. Consider critically analyzing the hidden consequences and causes of the new model. Ask to what extent this model fits your experience. Do you think patients should have rights as patients? What do you think these rights ought to be? Box 8.4, from an organization focused on cancer patients, lists some patient rights and responsibilities. Do you agree or disagree with these assertions? Do Canadians generally have these rights? Do you have examples of either the support of these rights or their neglect/impossibility from your experience?

CRITICAL THINKING

BOX 8.4   The Eight Key Areas of the Patient's Bill of Rights

Information for Patients
You have the right to accurate and easily understood information about your health-plan, healthcare professionals, and health-care facilities. If you speak another language, have a physical or mental disability, or just don't understand something, help should be given so you can make informed health-care decisions.

Choice of Providers and Plans
You have the right to choose health-care providers who can give you high-quality health care when you need it.

Access to Emergency Services
If you have severe pain, an injury, or sudden illness that makes you believe that your health is in danger, you have the right to be screened and stabilized using emergency services. You should be able to use these services whenever and wherever you need them, without needing to wait for authorization and without any financial penalty.

Taking Part in Treatment Decisions
You have the right to know your treatment options and take part in decisions about your care. Parents, guardians, family members, or others that you choose can speak for you if you cannot make your own decisions.

Respect and Non-Discrimination
You have a right to considerate, respectful care from your doctors, health-plan representatives, and other health-care providers that does not discriminate against you.

Confidentiality (Privacy) of Health Information
You have the right to talk privately with health-care providers and to have your health-care information protected. You also have the right to read and copy your own medical record. You have the right to ask that your doctor change your record if it is not correct, relevant, or complete.

Complaints and Appeals
You have the right to a fair, fast, and objective review of any complaint you have against your health plan, doctors, hospitals, or other health-care personnel. This includes complaints about waiting times, operating hours, the actions of health-care personnel, and the adequacy of health-care facilities.

Consumer Responsibilities
In a health-care system that protects consumer or patients' rights, patients should expect to take on some responsibilities to get well and/or stay well (for instance, exercising and not using tobacco). Patients are expected to do things like treat health-care workers and other patients with respect, try to pay their medical bills, and follow the rules and benefits of their health plan coverage. Having patients involved in their care increases the chance of the best possible outcomes and helps support a high-quality, cost-conscious health-care system.

Source: www.cancer.org/Treatment/Findingandpayingfortreatment/understandingfinanciala ndlegalmatters/patients-bill-of-rights.

Medical Knowledge Becomes Popular Knowledge

Magazines, newspapers, and audiovisual media have long been important as sources of health-related information and attitudes in modern mass societies. These channels are currently being surpassed, however, by information available through the electronic superhighway. This trend has been dubbed e-scaped medicine (Nettleton, 2004) and m-medicine, that is, mobile-medicine or mobile-health (Lupton, 2012). Daily updates of scientific/medical news are available through the Internet, where there are probably billions of pages of information available at the click of the mouse. Some websites are affiliated

TABLE 8.1   The Patient's Changing Role

Old Model	New Model
Defer to provider's authority	Share responsibility for own health
Be passive: be fixed by provider	Be active: self-manage health and condition (provider supplies expert coaching, support, and sometimes direction)
Share history, when asked	Share goals, history, values, beliefs, and preferences; if necessary, be assertive
Follow provider orders	Decide what to do with support from provider
Rely on provider to solve problems	Seek provider support for solving problems
Learn about condition from provider	Learn from provider; inform self; scan environment for new information
Respond to provider questions about progress during clinical encounters	Keep track of own progress between visits; share during visits
Don't worry about medications (it's all in the medicine cabinet)	Share responsibility for keeping medication list up to date

Source: www.newhealthpartnerships.org/provider.aspx?id=202.

with major medical institutions or disease-related charities such as the Heart and Stroke Foundation and the Canadian Cancer Society. Many of these are professionally run and present dominant discourses that are widely considered to be scientific, valid, reliable, and current. Others are full of invalid and unreliable information. Privacy and confidentiality are not always protected. Some sites are outdated. Some represent various commercial interests. Some reflect the concerns of special interest groups. For example, if you investigate any number of disease-specific websites for sponsorship you will notice that pharmaceutical companies are often behind-the-scenes financial supporters. The extent to which this "pharma"-sponsorship biases the information available in favour of one drug or another is under investigation. A related investigation examined direct-to-consumer (DTC) advertisements, which are legal in the US and said to be highly regulated as to safety information. However, the research has found that DTC advertisements "exaggerate benefits and downplay risks" (www.chsrf.ca). Thus, the information varies in accuracy and accessibility. People interpret information according to their own culture and socio-economic, gender, age, educational, and psychological characteristics.

Studies of health information on the Internet paint a fairly pessimistic picture of its validity and reliability. One study set out to find out how people use the Internet by establishing a website to provide information about cardiology. The researchers found that users were seeking information "correctly," that is, 95 per cent of those who asked for information asked pertinent questions (Widman and Tong, 1997). Another study evaluated information regarding pharmaceuticals. Here the researchers found that about 50 per cent of the information provided was correct and another 50 per cent was incorrect; 10.4 per cent of the errors were potentially harmful (Desai et al., 1997). In an evaluation of the quality of information regarding how to detect and manage childhood fevers, researchers found that only about 10 per cent of the websites providing information on childhood fevers adhered closely to recommendations in peer-reviewed guidelines (Impicciatore et al., 1994). Clearly, these are issues of concern to those who use the Internet for health information. Another study, this one of breast cancer sites (Hoffman-Goetz and Clarke, 2000), found inadequacies with respect to the validity and reliability of information, the presence of references, dated information, dead-end sites, lack of acknowledged ownership, security and privacy protection, widely different reading levels from site to site, and the dominance of the English language.

To date the Internet is open, free, and unregulated. Debates flourish about whether this is the best strategy in the long run. Some researchers and institutions are working to develop indices and software that would provide organization, guidelines, and maps for users. In the meantime, however, technology leads social change and people are running to catch up! At the same time, different people use different types of media, and people use different media for distinct types of information.

Moyer and her colleagues (1994) evaluated, over a two-year period, the accuracy of scientific information as it went from original research/ medical sources to the various mass media, including newspapers and women's, science, and health magazines. They began with 116 articles in the mass media. Of those, 60 included traceable citations. There were 42 content-based inaccuracies including misleading titles, shifts in emphasis, treating speculation as fact, erroneous information, omitting other important results, omitting

qualifying information, over-generalizing findings, and inaccuracies in personal communications. Women's magazines had the highest percentage of inaccuracies in traceable citations, at 88 per cent. "Quality" newspapers had the fewest inaccuracies, at 25 per cent.

Furthermore, readers typically misunderstand at least some of the information they receive through the mass media. Yeaton et al. (1990) surveyed a small sample of college students regarding their understanding of popular press articles on health issues such as surgical alternatives for breast cancer, drug treatment for congestive heart failure, use of starch blockers for weight reduction, dietary cholesterol, heart disease, and skin transplants for burns. The overall rate of misunderstanding was 39 per cent. The fact that this level of misunderstanding exists among college students raises serious questions about the accessibility and quality of the health information accessible to the average citizen. If media-based information is both inaccurate (to an extent) and misunderstood (to an extent), we have to wonder about the quality of the health information that exists among the general population.

CRITICAL THINKING ?

BOX 8.5 Looking for Health Information on the Internet

One of the most popular uses of the Internet is to look for information about health, disease, and treatments. There are more than a billion sites dedicated to various health matters, including sites on specific diseases, related goods and services, hospitals and health-care organizations, chat rooms, and online support groups. With such a myriad of possibilities, how can one be assured of access to good, valid, and confidential information? What criteria should be used to assess health information? How can you be sure to avoid sites comprising conflicts of interest? Many librarians, health-care professionals, and interested lay people have developed strategies and checklists to be used in evaluating articles on the Internet.

The code established by the Health on the Net (HON) Foundation (www.hon.ch/) is one indication that a website has been evaluated and found trustworthy. The HON code requires that sites that receive this seal of approval include the following: (1) information is to be provided by a trained professional; (2) it is to be confidential; (3) references are to be given where possible; (4) information is clear; (5) contact addresses are available; and (6) the advertising policy is transparent and shown on the site. Additional concerns include that the explanation of an adequate privacy policy should be clear and that there should be no advertisements. Examine several health websites to assess their value.

HIGHLIGHTED ISSUES

BOX 8.6   Mental Illness

There are three major approaches to the socio-logical study of mental illness. The first is paral-lel to an epidemiological approach. It examines the correlations between various social statuses such as gender, income, education, ethnicity, and religious affiliation and the incidence and prevalence of various diagnoses of mental ill-ness. For example, such studies have found that women are more likely to be diagnosed with depression and men with alcohol and drug dependency. Such research also has found that the general population rate of mental illness has been relatively stable over a number of years. Correlational analysis, it must be noted, does not necessarily reflect a causal connection. In fact, consideration of the likely direction of caus-ality from mental illness to income has given rise to different theoretical perspectives—the "social selection" perspective and the "drift" explana-tion. The social selection perspective suggests that the presence of mental illness in a person leads that person into downward mobility through such things as the inability to hold a job, finish school, or manage to maintain a suc-cessful marriage. Mental illness in a parent tends to lead to a lower socio-economic position for the offspring or a "drifting" down the social status hierarchy. A social causation explanation examines the ways that aspects of the social structure lead to mental illness. Thus, poorer people not only tend to have more stress in their lives but they also tend to have poorer resources for dealing with stress. The relevance of these theories seems to depend, in part, on the diag-nosis. Schizophrenia, for instance, seems to have a significant genetic component.

The second perspective in this field of sociol-ogy is that of labelling theory. Here the focus is less on predicting and explaining rates of mental illness and more on the meaning and social con-struction of mental illness, an interpretive per-spective. Mental illness is considered a category or label that has been devised for and attached to people whose behaviour does not conform to everyday norms and yet is not usually crimin-ally deviant. The concept of "residual deviance" captures the meaning of this view of mental ill-ness. This theory suggests that all of us at times act in ways that violate norms. Only when such violation is very noticeable or persistent, or occurs among less powerful people is it labelled as a "mental illness." The labelling and the treat-ment of such people, this theory suggests, tend to reinforce the behaviour and the assessment of the individual as mentally ill. Once the label has been applied it is exceptionally difficult for others to separate the individual from it.

The third direction of sociological investiga-tion, what might be called "a stress approach," attempts to explain variations in the rates of mental illness by variations in the source, amount, and type of stress in people's environ-ment. Stress has been associated with a variety of psychosocial manifestations of distress and mental illness such as depression. This perspec-tive also examines how mediating variables, such as self-esteem and social support, along with social-structural variables, such as gender, age, education, and income, have been investi-gated as part of the complex causation of mental illness. The question, of course, is whether stress per se caused the behaviours variously labelled as mental illness or whether stress exacerbates an underlying condition. The shifts in behav-iour by any one individual along a continuum of overlapping symptoms suggests the latter explanation is the more likely, i.e., that stress intensifies symptoms of a problem common to all or most types of mental illness.

In Canada, as elsewhere in North America, one of the most significant changes in mental health policy has been the widespread deinsti-tutionalization of the mentally ill. Institutions specifically for the mentally ill have existed for centuries. By the 1950s institutions in the United States and Canada were housing unprecedented numbers of mentally ill people. Then, because of the development of pharmaceuticals to suppress the symptoms of depression and of psychosis and to save money, many of these institutions were closed and former inmates were forced to live in the community. Along with deinstitutionalization came a corresponding increase in patients' rights, including the right to refuse treatment. However, deinstitutionalization occurred too rapidly to ensure an adequate level of support in housing, prescription drug-taking, and sociability, among other things. Among the tragic results of the process of deinstitutionalization has been the rapid growth in homelessness, although it must be strongly emphasized that people are homeless for many reasons besides mental illness, such as unemployment or underemployment, housing policies, and the extremely high cost of housing rentals in some cities.

Doctor–Patient Communication

Doctor–patient communication reflects the broader social structure and culture. It also reflects the particular characteristics of both patients and doctors. Physicians and patients each embody their own particular social spaces as carriers of culture and structure. In a study based on ethnographic fieldwork that entailed joining the surgical ward rounds at two general hospitals, Fox (1993) examined the communication strategies used by doctors to maintain authority and power in their interaction with surgical patients. When patients tried to ask questions, such as why they felt the way they did, how soon they would feel better, and when they could go home, the surgeons tended to ignore them. Instead, the surgeons maintained verbal and other sorts of control by focusing on the success of the surgery with respect to the specific goals of surgery (e.g., absence of infection, minimal scarring) and its specific outcome. Fox demonstrates that ward rounds can be understood as a systematic strategy entered into by surgeons to capture and maintain their discursive monopoly. By keeping the discussion focused on surgeon-centred themes, the doctors allow patients few opportunities to introduce their own views, concerns, or worries.

One area of social life around which there is a great deal of ambiguity and ambivalence is sexuality. On the one hand, sexual relations are more openly discussed, portrayed, and symbolized in all of the mass media today than in the past. Acknowledgement of the pervasiveness of sexual activity outside of the bounds of monogamous marriage is widespread. Accompanying the "liberalization" of sexuality, and particularly of women's sexuality, is the belief that a satisfactory sex life is an important part of a satisfactory life as a whole. Yet, many are still ambivalent about sex and many still believe it to be a shameful duty to be kept secret. Today, people are more likely to consult doctors when dissatisfied with their sexual functioning (Weigts et al., 1993). Sometimes, women's dissatisfaction with their sex life seems to be hidden behind complaints about physical functioning, including such things as vaginal infections and pain during intercourse (Stanley and Ramage, 1984).

It is useful to understand how such ambiguity and ambivalence are manifest in personal relations and in talk between doctors and their female patients. One study of doctors' and patients' talk showed constructions of sexuality were managed in the doctor's office quite "sensitively" so as to reinforce gender stereotypes about the "shame" and "mystery" surrounding female sexuality (see Table 8.2). The strategies used to discuss such "delicate" matters are best characterized as delay, avoidance, and depersonalization. Reflected in the talk and in the silence is the construction of the "delicate and notorious" character of female sexuality in the context of the possible discourse with an often more powerful and male doctor (Weigts et al., 1993).

Sociological discussion of "talk" is not trivial. It is important both theoretically and practically. "Delicacy"—or the shame and privacy norms

TABLE 8.2   Doctors' Strategies for Talking about Sex to Patients

Strategies	Device
Delaying	• delaying discussions of sex • refraining from answering "sensitive" questions • acting agitated in the context of delicate terms
Avoiding	• using vague, indirect, and distant terms • avoiding certain delicate terms • using pronouns
Depersonalizing	• avoiding personal references • using definite articles
Tuning/Adapting	• adopting and repeating patients' use of pronouns and their omission of delicate terms

Source: Adapted from Weigts/Hontkoop/Mullen, "Talking Delicately: Speaking about Sexuality during Gynecological Consultation", *Sociology of Health and Illness* 15 (1993), 4.

passing as "delicacy"—with respect to sexuality, particularly female sexuality, is a major factor in unwanted pregnancies, sexually transmitted diseases, and the transmission of the HIV/AIDS virus in heterosexual populations. To the extent that women remain unable to talk clearly and confidently about their sexuality, about their genital and reproductive health, and about birth control and health and safety devices such as condoms, they may be more likely to be unable to refuse unwanted and/or unprotected sex. In a context in which there is a high prevalence of STDs and STIs (sexually transmitted diseases and sexually transmitted illnesses) and unprotected sex by teens and young people, often with several partners and without protection (www.statcan.gc.ca/daily-quotidien/080820/dq080820c-eng.htm), it is important that sexually active people feel comfortable asking for regular STD and STI checkups. Good websites are devoted to prevention and early signs of infections (e.g., www.phac-aspc.gc.ca/publicat/std-mts/index-eng.php). Moreover, popular magazines for women, in particular, are full of information about prevention (Clarke, 2010).

One important aspect of doctor–patient interaction is the emotion regulation of patients and doctors. Some aspects of emotional display are expected or at least allowed among patients. Crying, withdrawal, and even modulated anger are appropriate emotions for patients to display when

A doctor is expected to emotionally regulate, and not break neutrality, when talking to patients—no matter what their personal feelings may be about the issue. Doctors also employ language and visiting strategies with patients to ensure that they maintain verbal control. Treatment decisions may subconsciously be affected by the patient's age, race, and socio-economic class. Treatment choices may also vary by culture. In all of these ways, the interaction of doctor and patient is subject to socialization.

Source: Burlingham/Shutterstock.com.

receiving bad news, for example. Doctors, however, are expected not to show such emotions even when they are frustrated, disgusted, or angry. Talcott Parsons thought of this as a part of the affective neutrality that doctors were taught to show to patients. One recent study examined the effects of emotion regulation among doctors on their patients (Kafetsios et al., 2014). Patients' satisfaction was found to be dependent on the emotion regulation (or suppression of emotion) displayed by their doctors. Evidently, emotion work is an important part of the skill set required for good medical practice and patient satisfaction. Doctors join other service workers in selling their emotional labour as a part of how they work (Hochschild, 1983). This suppression of emotion can be detrimental to the life and job satisfaction of doctors.

SUMMARY

1. Medical knowledge is socially constructed. It reflects cultural values and social-structural locations. It has varied historically and cross-culturally.
2. Some of the specific values of contemporary medicine include mind–body dualism, physical reductionism, specific etiology, machine metaphor and regimen, and control. Sociological research provides a critical overview of these medical assumptions.
3. A large and significant gap exists between the findings of biomedical research and the implementation of the consequences of these findings in medical practice. The values of medical scientists and medical practitioners are, in many ways, at odds with one another.
4. Available evidence demonstrates that new technologies are usually adopted (even widely) before their safety and effectiveness have been ascertained.
5. Medical science has been infused with cultural and gendered stereotypes such as those described by Emily Martin.
6. Research shows that medical practice, too, is infused with cultural stereotypes, including those that pertain to age, gender, class, and race.
7. One cross-cultural study of medical practice by Lynn Payer offers provocative evidence of cultural differences in diagnosis and treatment.
8. Significant class differences exist in public understanding and acceptance of medical knowledge.
9. Lay views of medical practice vary according to gender, class, age, and specific health categories.
10. Media information about medical knowledge is frequently inadequate or inaccurate.
11. Medical doctors employ various discursive strategies in an attempt to maintain control over their own definitions of reality in the face of patient questioning.

KEY TERMS

disease-mongering
doctrine of specific etiology
drapetomania
dysaethesia aethiopis

evidence-based medicine
machine metaphor
mind–body dualism
physical reductionism

regimen and control
technological imperative

QUESTIONS FOR STUDY AND DISCUSSION

1. Find examples of mind–body dualism, physical reductionism, the doctrine of specific etiology, the machine metaphor, and regimen and control in an online medical journal, such as the *British Medical Journal* or the *Canadian Medical Association Journal*.

2. Do a search of a major newspaper over a period of at least one year and compare and contrast the understandings put forward of the vaccine for HPV.

3. What are the advantages and disadvantages of the widespread availability of health-related information on the Internet for the doctor and for the patient?

4. What social, institutional, and organizational forces in the current way that medical care happens might tend to promote poor communication between patients and doctors in the hospital?

5. Consider the attitude in your own family to medicine and doctors. What are its characteristics and to what are they related?

SUGGESTED READINGS

Beck, U. 1992. *Risk Society: Towards a New Modernity*. London: Sage. The classic statement of the risk society.

Foucault, M. 1979. *The History of Sexuality. An Introduction*, vol. 1. London. Allen Lane. The first volume of a three-volume study, which introduces the term "biopower" as a means of governing of populations.

Giddens, A. 1999. "Risk and Responsibility." *Modern Law Review* 62: 1–10. A brief but excellent overview of some important issues in thinking about the "risk society."

King, Samantha. 2006. *Pink Ribbons Inc.: Breast Cancer and the Politics of Philanthropy*. Minneapolis: University of Minnesota. A critical look at cause-marketing in the case of breast cancer.

Moynihan, R. 2006. "Scientists Find New Disease: Motivational Deficiency Disorder." *British Medical Journal* 332: 745. A commentary on disease-mongering.

Rose, N. 2003. "Neurochemical Selves." *Society* 41, 1: 46–9. A commentary on identity in a psycho-pharmaceuticalized society.

Timmermans, S., and M. Buchbinder. 2010. "Patients-in-Waiting: Living between Sickness and Health in a Genomics Era." *Journal of Health and Social Behavior* 51, 4: 408–23. An article that considers some of the effects of genetic testing on social relations and identities.

9

A Brief History of Medicine and the Development and Critique of Modern Medicalization

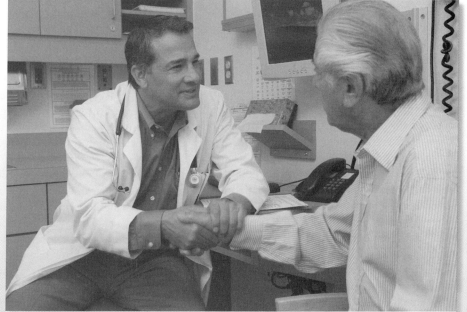

Ronnie Kaufman/Getty Images

CHAPTER OVERVIEW

▶ Amid growing tensions Canada has become more medicalized in many ways over the last century and a half.

▶ Over the last 30-plus years the processes of medicalization have come to involve biomedicalization as well.

▶ Medicine, as treatment for illness, has a very long history in the world.

▶ Hippocrates, a Greek physician from the era before Christ, can be considered one of the founders of what has become the Western, or medicalized, view of illness, disease, and related treatment. The Hippocratic oath of ethical practice is still used today.

▶ The process of medicalization has, in many ways, paralleled the process of secularization. Medicine and religiosity or spirituality, over time and across cultures, have often overlapped They both deal with matters of life and death.

▶ Important critiques have been made of medicalization as a cultural, socio-economic, philosophical, and technological system.

▶ The contemporary physician can be seen as a moral entrepreneur.

▶ Medical definitions of reality are powerful and have widespread consequences.

▶ Whether doctors are increasing or decreasing in power is a matter of debate.

Introduction

What is the social reaction to behaviours, feelings, and bodily functioning that are not "normal"? One response to what have been called social problems or might be constructed as aberrations of the preferred or ideal way of being is medicalization and, more recently, biomedicalization. We have discussed the processes by which people notice signs and call them "illness" rather than "immorality" or just "inconvenience." What are the processes by which doctors recognize some of these signs, label them as symptoms, and provide a diagnosis? Medical diagnostic categories change over time and may differ in different locations. Illness experiences change, too. What are the relationships among medicine, law, and religion? In what sense is medicine an institution of social control? To what extent have medicine's powers of social control been increasing over the past century while the power of institutional religion has declined in Canada? When do medicine and the law overlap or conflict? Is there a way that biomedicalization buttresses and is reinforced by social inequalities? Men's and women's bodies are medicalized in gender-specific ways. Some people resist medicalization. Others seek it. Why are medicalization and biomedicalization such powerful forces today? What are the origins of our contemporary medical care system? To what extent is the practice of medicine a science? To what extent is it an art? These are the sorts of questions addressed in this chapter.

Medicine and illness are intertwined; they are not necessarily co-extensive. Today the definitions and diagnoses of illnesses are made primarily by the medical care system and increasingly the powerful effects of the pharmaceutical companies and other private industries in the field of health care. Both the mass media and the World Wide Web play important parts in the social construction of disease and illness. The signs or symptoms that people pay attention to, and those they ignore, are largely determined by medical and pharmaceutical definitions of illness and wellness or normality and abnormality. These processes are often **mediated** through the mass media and the Internet. The expectations people have of their bodies, and the way they sometimes communicate by being ill, also depend to some extent on categories of disease available and are defined by the culture and power of the medical care system. Medicalization and biomedicalization provide dominant perspectives in the power/knowledge nexus overlaying other possible ways of understanding the world, our bodies, and our needs. Medicalization is a powerful cultural force and narrative infusing language, behaviour, and attitudes, in fact, affecting our total world view.

Some people experience their bodies and minds in ways they consider to indicate medical conditions or illnesses that doctors are not able or willing to diagnose. For example, sufferers frequently experience chronic fatigue syndrome long before they are able to find a clear diagnosis and medicalization (for further discussion of this issue, see Clarke and James, 2003; Dumit, 2006). Multiple sclerosis is notoriously difficult to diagnose because it lacks clear markers and symptoms, and at times mimics normal, though perhaps exaggerated, behaviour, such as periodic stumbling and slurring of words. Alzheimer's cannot be definitely diagnosed except through autopsy after death. Some conditions develop with so few symptoms in the early stages that the seriousness of the disease is not perceived; the rare autoimmune disease of Goodpasture Syndrome, which attacks the lungs and kidneys, and cervical cancer are two such conditions. At other times, medical diagnosis precedes a person's awareness of a physical problem. High blood pressure, for instance, is often detected only by medical tests, not by any physical sensations experienced by the person. The point is that sometimes what is defined as a deviant, unusual, or unacceptable feeling, behaviour, or attitude is also seen as a medical problem. Sometimes the problem may also fall within the realm of religion and/or of law. For instance, AIDS is viewed as a disease by the medical care system. It has also been seen as evidence of sin by some churches, in a homophobic focus on the "immoral" sexual behaviour of the diagnosed person. Because HIV/AIDS is contagious,

AIDS patients may also be subject to legal controls. At times criminalization and medicalization constitute competing discourses. For example, the prisons, including juvenile facilities, incarcerate a disproportionate percentage of people who suffer symptoms of mental illness and a high percentage have language and communication disabilities as well as significant deafness (e.g., Myers, 2000: 175; LaVigne and Van Rybroek, 2011).

Ashley Smith, the young woman who choked (herself) to death while being watched by the prison guards at the Grand River Correctional Institution for Women in Kitchener, Ontario, is a case in point. That her the death was ruled a homicide by the inquest points to the view of the courts that she was not able to make a good decision for herself because of her (undiagnosed) mental illness (http://www.theglobeandmail.com/topic/Ashley-Smith).

The spread of medical definitions of reality can be seen in many places today. Perhaps one of the best examples is the case of mental illness. "Diagnostic inflation" is a particular problem in the case of mental illness (Kudlow, 2013). *The Diagnostic and Statistical Manual of Mental Disorders* (DSM) is the "bible" or dictionary of mental illness. It lists all of the diagnoses considered acceptable in the medical profession and lays out their symptoms in lists. This type of empirical clarity was intended to provide consistency in diagnosis. It has been useful for monitoring and determining costs in the case of third-party payment for services by insurance companies and governments. The first edition of the DSM was published in 1952. It was 130 pages long and included 106 mental disorders; although this first edition had little impact on the practice of psychiatry, it was useful in the effort to quantify the incidence of mental illness.

In the 1960s and 1970s the question of the definition of mental illness became increasingly fraught and divisive. On one side were the Freudian psychoanalysts who believed that mental illness was the result of deep internal conflicts stemming from the inadequate resolution of the various developmental stages of childhood. As such, it was counterproductive, in the view of the Freudians, who then dominated psychiatry in North America, to label and to delimit symptoms as the DSM did without paying attention to the causes in early childhood—the etiology, as they believed. In psychoanalysis the purpose of psychotherapeutic treatment is to uncover the childhood causes of neuroses and through self-knowledge and insight into those causes find healing. "Talk therapy" is the preferred method of treatment. On the other side were those who thought mental illness was ultimately biological and progress in understanding and treating it would be parallel to the biological observation and measurement of observable pathology, primarily in the brain. The past was considered to be unimportant. Detailed descriptions of specific symptoms and the ways they were patterned together and observable in brain lesions were thought to be the fundamental building blocks of specific cures for pathologies. Ultimately, specific symptoms and sets of symptoms would be linked to specific, underlying biological aberrations.

In 1980 another revision of the DSM (made by a group of expert psychiatrists working together to try to come to agreement and to represent the different types of suffering they saw in their practices) was published. It was to be a compromise between the two positions and the two understandings of mental illness, and to accommodate these viewpoints it was much longer and more detailed. The DSM-III was 494 pages long and had 265 diagnostic categories. The DSM-IV (1994) was 886 pages long and included 297 disorders. The most recent DSM (2013) is "about the same length" but has added new diseases and removed others (http://psychcentral.com/blog/archives/2013/05/18/dsm-5-released-the-big-changes/). It results from a group process in which the committee charged with the revision posted the revision online three times. In response they received about 13,000 letters suggesting changes, amendments, and so on, plus thousands of other e-mails and messages. Apparently every comment was read and many ideas included before the committee finalized and published it. Still, there have been very public disagreements about the final product from some quarters. Critics say that now it contains a disease for everyone and a drug treatment for most of us (http://www.dsm5.org/about/pages/faq.aspx).

A Brief History of Western Medical Practice

At the beginning of written history, the medical practitioners in the Tigris-Euphrates and Nile valleys were also priests. Illness was regarded as a spiritual problem, a punishment for sins or for violations of the norms of society by such acts as stealing, blaspheming, or drinking from an impure vessel (Bullough and Bullough, 1972: 86–101). In Egypt under Imhotep, the Egyptian pharaoh who built the stepped pyramid, medicine began to receive some separate recognition. At this time, however, the medical functionaries' roles, by modern Western standards, were strictly curtailed. Medical practitioners could treat only external maladies. Internal illnesses were firmly believed to result from and to be treatable through supernatural intervention.

Modern Western medicine appears to have been derived primarily from Greece in the fourth and fifth centuries before Christ and from medieval Europe. In both time periods, the tie between the body and the spirit, the physician and the cleric, was strong. Early Greeks erected temples in honour of Hygeia, the Greek goddess of healing, and those who were ill sought treatment in these temples. Sometimes the sick simply slept in them in hope of a cure. Sometimes temple priests acted as physicians and used powers of persuasion and suggestion to heal. Early Greek physicians viewed their calling as holy or sacred.

One of the most important Greek physicians of the time, Hippocrates, perhaps best illustrates this view. He proposed the Hippocratic oath, still relevant to the practice of physicians today. The first sentence of the oath illustrates both the sense of calling of the physician and the dedication to the gods that medical practice involved:

I swear by Apollo Physician, by Asclepius, by Health, by Panacea and by all the gods and goddesses, making them my witnesses, that I will carry out, according to my ability and judgements, this oath and this indenture.

The oath further states: "But I will keep pure and holy both my life and my art" (Clendening, 1960: 1, 5). The Hippocratic oath, with the injunction, "First, do no harm," contains prohibitions against harming the patient, causing an abortion, or becoming sexually involved with a patient. It considers that words spoken by a patient to a doctor are to be kept confidential and treated as "holy secrets." Nevertheless, Hippocrates and the Greek physicians of his time and somewhat later also were distinguished by their efforts to secularize the concept of disease by making its treatment not the concern solely of priests and its focus not simply on the supernatural. They began to make medicine a practice based on repeated, systematic, empirical observation. Through this conscientious focus on method, "Hippocratic medicine achieved a level of excellence never again attained in the subsequent two thousand years, and surpassed only in the twentieth century" (Lewinsohn, 1998: 1262).

The idea of balance that dominated Hippocratic medicine in the fourth and fifth centuries before Christ persists today in a variety of forms. Returning to health after a stressful event is thought of as returning to balance—to homeostasis. To Hippocrates, health depended on a harmonious blend of humours (fluids)—blood, phlegm, black bile, and yellow bile—that originated in the heart, brain, liver, and spleen, respectively. Sickness resulted from an imbalance in any of these four humours. Symptoms reflected this lack of balance. Treatment relied largely on the healing power of nature and on the use of certain diets and medicines to return the organism to balance and its natural order.

There were two types of practitioners, each catering to a different social class. Private physicians cared for the aristocrats. Most large towns, partly for the prestige of having a doctor and partly to serve those who needed medical care, retained public doctors. Both the public and private physicians tended to cater to the wealthier classes.

The poor and the slaves usually received an inferior quality of medical care from the physician's assistant (Rosen, 1963).

The Greek period is considered to have culminated in the work of Galen (AD 130–201). His discoveries were influential for almost two thousand years after his time. Working with the principles of Aristotelian teleology, he thought that every organ had a purpose and served a special function. But Galen's greatest contributions were his anatomical and physiological works (his knowledge of anatomy was based on dissections of pigs and apes) and his systematic and logical speculation (Freidson, 1975: 14).

When the Roman Empire collapsed, medicine and other sciences fell into disrepute and religious scholarship developed greater prominence. Conflict emerged between two modes of thought: the spiritual and philosophical, in which truth was deduced from accepted religious principles without any reference to the real world, and the empirical, in which truth could only be inferred from evidence based on observation in the real world. Medicine lost much of the scientific analysis and empirical practice developed by the Greeks. Religious dogmatism limited scientific advances by prohibiting dissection and by forbidding independent thought, experimentation, and observation. The only knowledge deemed acceptable was that found in ancient texts and approved by the Church. For medieval Christians, disease was (again) a supernatural experience, as well as a physical experience. Secular medicine and public health measures were criticized as signs of lack of faith. The Church, its liturgies, and its functionaries were believed to be the source of healing; sinning was believed to be the source of illness.

The Church influenced the practice of medicine. It also influenced its organization. Medicine was taught in the universities by rote and faith, and by memorizing the canons of Hippocrates, Aristotle, and Galen. The clergy practised medicine, but they were not allowed to engage in surgery or to use drugs. These two forms of physical treatments were left to the "lower" orders. Barber-surgeons treated wounds, did other types of surgery, and cut hair. Even lower in status than barber-surgeons were the apothecaries, who dispensed medicines. Hospitals were taken over by religious orders, thus coming under the control of the Church.

Medicine did not progress much during the medieval period. However, epidemics of disease and death led to certain new methods of inquiry that were instrumental in the later development of scientific medicine. Faced with a horrendous death rate such as that during the bubonic plague—the Black Death is said to have taken one-third of the population of Europe in the fourteenth century—people began to raise practical, empirical questions about disease. In the first place, it was clear that the plague was contagious from person to person. Second, not all people succumbed to the plague. Questions about the background differences of those who did and who did not fall ill seemed relevant. The bases for quarantine, germ theory, and the case history were laid.

By the eighteenth century, scientific medicine was becoming distinguished from religious practice and folk medicine. Available medical knowledge was organized and codified. Many new medical discoveries were made. The universities, particularly in Western Europe and Scotland, became centres of exciting medical advances in research and treatment. New tools, such as forceps and the clinical thermometer, were invented. New medicines, such as digitalis, were made available. Edward Jenner demonstrated the value of the smallpox vaccine. At the same time, the popular climate was confused by competition among various types of healing. People visited shrines or used the services of a variety of alternative healers. Medical research was inadequately financed, lacked facilities, and had no specialties; the few practicing doctors were overworked.

The modern separation of medicine and the Church is the result of a number of social processes. The secularization of the human body as an object of science was a part of this process. A doctrinal development that paralleled the philosophical discussions of Descartes—the changing Christian doctrine of the separation of the body and the spirit that came to be called the Cartesian duality—resulted in autopsies being allowed. If the body was no longer the house of the soul, then the integrity or wholeness of the body after death was no longer of great importance. Institutional secularization occurred, too, as the Church became separated from the state. Through these processes clearer distinctions were forged among "disease," "deviance," "crime," and "sin."

Growing belief in the potential power of science and the emphasis on individual rights and freedoms contributed to the development of modern secular medicine, too. In the nineteenth century, particularly the last half, an enormous number of new discoveries occurred, as did many dubious attempts at healing:

> The medical literature of those years makes horrifying reading today: paper after learned paper recounts the benefits of bleeding, cupping, violent purging, the raising of blisters by vesicant ointments, the immersion of the body in either ice water or intolerably hot water, endless lists of botanical extracts cooked up and mixed together under the influence of nothing more than pure whim, and all these things were drilled into the heads of medical students—most of whom learned their trade as apprentices in the offices of older, established doctors. (Thomas, 1985: 19)

In fact, most of these remedies did more harm than good, with perhaps the exception of morphine and digitalis. Biology moved from the level of the organ to that of the cell, and both physiology and bacteriology were studied at that level. Germ theory emerged. Surgery grew in sophistication along with asepsis and anaesthesia. Table 9.1 outlines some of the most important discoveries in the history of allopathic medicine.

Medicalization: A Critique of Contemporary Medicine

Medical science became increasingly influential during the period that urbanization, industrialization, bureaucratization, rationalization, and secularization developed. Medical institutions began to increase their powers as agencies of social control. More and more types of human behaviour began to be explained in medical terms. It has been argued that as the medical system's powers of social control increased, so, too, did the religious institutions' powers of social control decrease. Behaviours once viewed as sinful or criminal are now more likely viewed as illnesses. Alcohol addiction is a case in point. There was a time when drinking too much, too frequently, was seen as a sign of moral weakness, i.e., a sin. Today, however, alcohol addiction is often seen as a medical problem. Treatment centres for the "disease" are located in hospital settings, and treatment frequently includes medications and is under the control of the medical profession. Madness, too, has gone through many different definitions and treatments over the time period (Foucault, 2006) as distinctions between normality and abnormality have shifted. Unhappiness has, for some, become a disorder (Geise, 2013). Small breasts, too, are thought by some to require surgical intervention and enlargement for the "self-esteem" of the patient.

It is important to note that medicalization would not have been possible were it not for the acceptance of the Cartesian duality: the separation of the "whole person" from the body. This separation allowed for the medical gaze (Foucault, 1973) as it imbricated the possibility of seeing the person as a body with discrete organs, with a skeleton, and so forth. These could be seen from the outside (and later, through new technologies, on the inside) by medical experts. As the individual came to be seen as a collection of parts so, too, did doctors have things to say about the various parts and their working together. Today these processes might be called biological reductionism and the separation of the mind and body from the spirit. In the context of these epistemological changes a new set of truths or discourses about the normal and abnormal person and the body emerged. These discourses have affected not only the patient in the clinic or doctor's office but also the understanding of the whole population as being made up of people with varying degrees of normality and abnormality

TABLE 9.1   Making Medical History: A Timeline

−400	−300	100s
• Hippocrates separates medicine from religion and philosophy, treats it as a natural science	• Anatomy and physiology develop in Alexandria	• Asclepiades brings Greek medicine to Rome; bases treatment on diet, exercise, baths, massage

100s	200s	400s
• Ancient medicine culminates with Galen; his influence will last until Renaissance	• Growing Christian religion emphasizes healing by faith	• Fabiola founds first hospital in Western world at Rome

700s	800s	900s
• Arabs develop pharmacology as a science separate from medicine	• Monk-physicians treat the sick in infirmaries attached to monasteries	• Influential medical school founded at Salerno, Italy; students include women

1000s	1200s	1300s
• Arab physician Avicenna writes the *Canon*, textbook used in medieval Europe	• Thomas Aquinas describes medicine as an art, a science, and a virtue • Human dissection practised at Bologna	• Urine sample first used in diagnosis • Black Death kills one-third of Europe's population; medicine powerless to stop it

1500s	1600s	1700s
• First attempts to restrict right to practise to licensed and qualified doctors • Advances in anatomy and surgery as influence of Galen wanes	• William Harvey discovers circulation of blood • Descartes conceives of body as machine and sees medicine as part of developing modern science • Hôtel-Dieu in Quebec City founded, first hospital in Canada • Use of microscope leads to new discoveries	• First successful appendectomy performed • Guild of surgeons formed in England separate from barbers, with whom they had been joined • Advances in scientific knowledge begin to be reflected in medical practice • Edward Jenner proves value of vaccination in preventing smallpox

1800s	1810s	1830s
• Medical specialties begin to develop	• René Laënnec invents stethoscope	• Theodor Schwann shows all living structures made of cells

1840s	1850s	1860
• Inhalation anaesthesia techniques developed • Edwin Chadwick brings about public health reforms in England	• Nurses led by Florence Nightingale save thousands in Crimean War • Dr Elizabeth Blackwell founds New York Infirmary for Women	• International Red Cross founded • Joseph Lister introduces antiseptic surgery • Gregor Mendel discovers law of heredity • Louis Pasteur shows that diseases are caused by micro-organisms

continued

TABLE 9.1   *Continued*

1870s	1800s	1890s
• Robert Koch discovers tubercle bacillus	• Otto von Bismarck introduces first state health insurance plan in Germany (1883) • Sigmund Freud begins to develop psychoanalytic method (use of hypnosis begins in 1885; psycho-analytic method per se is intro-duced in 1896) • Founding of Johns Hopkins hospi-tal in 1889 and its medical school in 1894 introduces systematic medical education in US	• Malaria bacillus isolated • Wilhelm Roentgen discovers X-ray
1900s	**1910s**	**1920s**
• The hormone adrenalin is isolated • Flexner Report leads to reform of medical education	• Influenza epidemic kills millions worldwide	• Banting and Best produce insulin for use by diabetics • Iron lung invented • Alexander Fleming discovers penicillin
1930s	**1940s**	**1950s**
• Norman Bethune of Canada introduces mobile blood transfusion unit in Spain, continues work in China	• Use of antibiotics becomes widespread • World Health Organization founded	• J. André-Thomas devises machine needed to take over heart func-tion for performing open-heart surgeries. • Discovery that DNA molecule is a double helix provides key to gen-etic code • Jonas Salk develops polio vaccine • Ultrasound first used to monitor fetus during pregnancy
1960s	**1970s**	**1980s**
• First state health insurance plan in North America successfully introduced in Saskatchewan despite doctors' strike • Michael DeBakey uses artificial heart to keep patients alive during surgery • Christiaan Barnard per-forms first heart transplant	• Smallpox eliminated from earth • First baby conceived outside the womb born in England	• Cyclosporin allows entire organ transplantation • Nuclear magnetic resonance makes possible more accurate diagnosis • A new disease, AIDS, will kill millions (to this time of writing); no cure or vaccine in sight

TABLE 9.1 *Continued*

1990s–2015
Substantial progress in Human Genome Project
Development of antibiotic resistance
International public health efforts to mitigate spread of infectious diseases such as SARS and avian flu
New awareness of medical error and systematic attempts to eradicate it
Rise of e-scaped medicine via the reliance on the World Wide Web
Consumer advocacy for disease recognition develops and spreads, often with the help of the Internet
Direct-to-consumer advertising of pharmaceuticals expands their use
Spread of biomedicalization through the increase in new technologies such as the Human Genome Project, growing rates of organ transplantation, and pharmaceuticalization

Source: Adapted from *Compass* (May 1988): 10.

that could be measured and observed and then, through public health directives, made to behave in certain (medically determined) desirable ways.

Medical institutions, including hospitals, extended-care establishments, pharmaceutical companies, and manufacturers of medical technology, have grown in importance. A large part of the gross national product is spent on health care. Some thinkers call this process medicalization or **biomedicalization**. One definition of medicalization, from the work of Zola (1972), is that it is a process whereby more and more of life comes to be of concern to the medical profession. Zola portrays medicalization as an expanding **attachment process**, with the following four components:

1. the expansion of what in life is deemed relevant to the good practice of medicine;
2. the retention of absolute control by the medical profession over certain technical procedures;
3. the retention of near-absolute access to certain areas by the medical profession;
4. the expansion of what in medicine is deemed relevant to the good practice of life.

In this view, the first area of medicalization is the change from medicine as a narrow, biological model of disease to a broader concern with the social, spiritual, and moral aspects of the patient's life. As well as bodily symptoms, the entire lifestyle of the patient may now be considered of concern to the doctor. For example, some physicians now routinely include in their patients' case histories questions about eating habits, friendships, marital and family relationships, work satisfaction, and the like.

The second component is the retention of absolute control over a variety of technical procedures. A doctor is permitted to do things to the human body that no one else has the right to do. Doctors are responsible for surgery, prescription drugs, hospital admittance, and referral to a specialist or another doctor. Doctors are the gatekeepers to numerous associated services and provisions.

The maintenance of nearly absolute control over a number of formerly "normal" bodily processes, and indeed over anything that can be shown to affect the working of the body or the mind, is the third component. Zola argues that the impact of this third feature can be seen by looking at four areas: aging, drug addiction, alcoholism, and pregnancy. At one time, aging and pregnancy were viewed as normal processes, and drug addiction and alcoholism were seen as manifestations of human weakness. Now, however, medical specialties have arisen to deal with each of these. Zola illustrates this point with a discussion of the change in the view and treatment of pregnancy. He points to the pivotal importance of the management of childbirth for the growth of medical power.

> For in the United States it was barely 70 years ago when virtually all births and their concomitants occurred outside the hospital as

well as outside medical supervision … but with this medical claim solidified [to manage births] so too was medicine's claim to whole hosts of related processes: not only birth but prenatal, postnatal, and pediatric care; not only conception but infertility; not only the process of reproduction but the process of sexual activity itself. (Zola, 1972: 77)

The last component is the expansion of what in medicine is seen as relevant to a good life. This aspect of medicalization refers to the spread of

the inclusion of a wide variety of social problems and behavioural anomalies as medical problems. Depression, ADHD, obesity, criminality, and juvenile delinquency are among those "problems" that were once linked to the moral/religious realm and are increasingly seen as amenable to medical definition and treatment.

Ivan Illich's Critique of Medicalization

Ivan Illich offers another useful definition and critique of medicalization in *Limits to Medicine* (1976). His argument is that contemporary medical

---

SPOTLIGHT ON ETHICS

BOX 9.1   Top 10 Ethical Issues in Health Care

TABLE 9.2   Top 10 Ethical Issues in Health Care According to Toronto Bioethicists

Rank	Scenario	Score
1	Disagreement between patients/families and health-care professionals about treatment decisions	113
2	Waiting lists	102
3	Access to needed health-care resources for the aged, chronically ill, and mentally ill	89
4	Shortage of family physicians or primary care teams in both rural and urban settings	82
5	Medical error	76
6	Withholding/withdrawing life-sustaining treatment in the context of terminal or serious illness	56
7	Achieving informed consent	43
8	Ethical issues related to subject participation in research	40
9	Substitute decision-making	38
10	The ethics of surgical innovation and incorporating new technologies for patient care	21

Source: Top 10 health care ethics challenges facing the public: views of Toronto bioethicists. Jonathan M. Breslin, Susan K. MacRae, Jennifer Bell, Peter A. Singer and the University of Toronto Joint Centre for Bioethics Clinical Ethics Group. *BMC Medical Ethics*, 2005 6:5.

These rank-ordered issues in bioethics focus on who has the power to determine controversial medical decisions: patients or doctors, patients or their family members (1, 9); what is fully informed consent (7); how to decide who gets care and who doesn't in the context of limited resources for care (2, 3, 4, 6); when to engage in medical intervention in the face of new and often very expensive and unproven technologies (10); determining responsibility and compensation for medical error and preventing error (5), and the safety and protection of patients involved in clinical trials and other biomedical research (8). Do you have any experience with any of these ethical issues? Can you find an example of each issue? What principles do you think need to be applied in any one of these issues?

practice is *iatrogenic*, that is, it creates disease and illness even as it provides medical assistance. Three sorts of **iatrogenesis** are isolated and explained.

> [It is] clinical, when pain, sickness, and death result from the provision of medical care; it is social, when health policies reinforce an industrial organization which generates dependency and ill health; and it is structural, when medically sponsored behaviour and delusions restrict the vital autonomy of people by undermining their competence in growing up, caring for each other, and aging. (Illich, 1976:165)

Clinical iatrogenesis, that is, injury and/or disability that results directly from the work of the doctor, nurse, or other medical care provider in the hospital or in the clinic, is the first problem addressed by Illich. Addictions to prescribed drugs, the side effects of prescribed drugs, harmful drug interactions, and suicide resulting from prescribed medication are specific examples of clinical iatrogenesis. Thalidomide, prescribed in the 1950s and 1960s in West Germany, Canada, and elsewhere to women with a history of miscarriage, resulted in untold tragedy when numerous children were born without limbs. DES (diethylstilbestrol), again prescribed (in the 1950s) to women with obstetric problems, has been found to result in thousands of cases of ovarian and cervical cancer in the daughters of those who used DES and in other cancers in their sons. Unnecessary hysterectomies have caused extensive emotional, marital, and other social problems for the women who have undergone this procedure, as well as for their family members and significant others. Silicone breast implants have been found to be associated with numerous and various deleterious health outcomes. Today, millions receive chemotherapy, radiation, and/or surgery as treatment for a variety of cancers. However, such treatments are often felt by the patients to be more painful and debilitating than the disease itself. Those for whom a cure is effective may feel that the cost is worth the pain. On the other hand, those who are not cured, and whose lives can be extended for only a limited period, may regret having submitted

to such treatments as chemotherapy. The spread of HIV/AIDS and hepatitis C through blood transfusions from Canada's blood supply, along with the development of antibiotic resistance, are two of our most recent widely known examples of clinical iatrogenesis. The rise in hospital-acquired infections and numerous medical errors is another impetus for critical thinking among the populace. The Canadian Institute for Health Information estimates, based on a survey of Canadians, that one in four Canadians is affected by a medical error. O'Hagan and his colleagues (2009) based an estimate on the self-report of patients and found that one in six Canadian patients said they had experienced a medical error of one sort or another. This amounted to approximately 4.2 million Canadians who were given the wrong drug or the wrong dose, the wrong report, the wrong surgery, and so on. These are just a few of the troubles that occur in an over-medicalized clinical and hospital practice. Many more examples will be discussed throughout this book.

In the developing world, poor sanitation, unsafe drinking water, malnutrition, and insufficient and/or dangerous birth control measures are the major health problems. However, large parts of the health budgets of poor nations are spent on tertiary level care for the few or drugs that do little to alleviate any of these problems. Substantial expenditures for pharmaceuticals by less-developed countries minimize and prevent expenditures for clean water, the development of a good agricultural base, and the promotion of safe and inexpensive birth control devices and practices.

Social iatrogenesis is evident in the impact of medicine on lifespan. Medical and technological intervention begins at birth and ends with the care of the aging and dying. There are medical specialties to deal with pregnancy and childbirth (obstetrics), childhood (pediatrics), adult women (gynecology), adult men (urology), the elderly (geriatrics), and the dying (palliative care). The presence of medical specialists to deal with various normal stages of the human lifespan is symbolic of the trend towards the medicalization of life and the increasing addiction of modern people to medical institutions.

The most onerous example of medicalization is the growing dependence on medical interventions in Western industrialized societies. The huge growth in spending on medical treatment, on hospitalization, and on pharmaceuticals is just one example. The success of medicalization has played a part in the generation of the "risk" society (Beck, 1992). "In this view, risks are increasingly globalized and generalized in ways which are seen as out of the individual's control, bolstering the social and political significance of scientific institutions and expert knowledge represented by, for instance, medicine" (Howson, 1998: 196). Who in modern society is not aware of the myriad risks associated with just living? Air, water, and land pollution compete with fatty diets, botulism and dangerous bacteria in food, pesticide residues, excess alcohol consumption, and even sunshine as things we have to "watch out for." Public health policies are frequently based on "prevention," which is a form of early detection. Examples leap easily to mind, such as screening for breast, cervical, testicular, and prostate cancer. Such surveillance increases the development of "risk consciousness." Avoiding risks of disease and maintaining health have become moral imperatives (Lupton, 1993; Howson, 1998).

Considerable evidence suggests that pharmaceuticals are often prescribed to people for social and psychological problems. Women consistently receive more prescriptions for mood-altering pharmaceuticals such as tranquilizers and antidepressants than men do. Women in the middle and older age groups are at highest risk. Over a period of some 19 months in Saskatchewan, researchers noted that one in seven of the population received a prescription for diazepam (the generic name for Valium). Yet research has found that the majority of those who used tranquilizers explained that they needed the Valium because of a variety of societal, familial, and occupational demands and expectations rather than for a physical need (Tone, 2009). As noted in Chapter 8, Metzl and Angel (2004) have documented how SSRIs (antidepressants) have invaded more and more aspects of women's lives as these aspects became diagnosable as depression. Women's very bodily shape and appearance have become medically diagnosable by plastic surgeons who recently instituted a new disease category—small breast syndrome. Cosmetic surgeons now offer designer vaginas. Naomi Wolf in *The Beauty Myth* (1991) says that medical discourse tells women that "beauty" is equivalent to good health. We discussed the expansion of the medicalization of women's moods in the case of reproduction in the first chapter (Godderis, 2010).

By *structural iatrogenesis* Illich means the loss of individual autonomy and the creation of dependency. The responsibility for good health has been wrested from the individual and the community as a result of the imposition of the medical model by the prevalence of medical institutions and medical practitioners. Pain, suffering, disease, and death are important experiences for all human beings. They can encourage the development of service, compassion, and connectedness with others. But medical bureaucracy and technology minimize the possibilities for the fertile development of family and community-based models of care. The medical model and its institutions usurp individual initiative and responsibility and thus destroy humanitarianism and spiritual development. In sum, in Illich's view, we rely excessively on medical care, and this overdependence has many destructive consequences for people and their communities. To correct this problem he advocates the deprofessionalization and debureaucratization of medical practice, and the maximization of individual responsibility. Self-care, autonomy, and self-development should be the guiding principles.

Navarro, a leading Marxist critic of medicine, takes issue with Illich's explanation of medicalization. Whereas Illich's main foe appears to be the bureaucratic organization and growth in the numbers of medical practitioners and medicine-related industry, Navarro (1976) argues that medicine is a mere pawn in the hands of a much greater power—the power of the state directed through the dominant class. The health industry in the United States is neither administered nor controlled by medical professionals. The same situation prevails in Canada. Members of the corporate class (the owners and managers of financial capital) dominate in health and other important spheres of the economy. The upper middle class (executive and corporate representatives of large and middle-sized enterprises and professionals, primarily corporate lawyers and financiers) have major influence in the health delivery sector of the economy through the pharmaceutical and medical device industries, medical insurance companies, and medical organizations providing related health-care service delivery. Doctors themselves are often invested in these quasi-medical corporations. Together these groups may comprise less than 20 per cent of the health-care providers, yet they control most of the health institutions. The majority of those involved in health care (about 80 per cent) have no control over either the production or consumption of health services.

David Coburn is one of Canada's foremost medical sociologists. He argues that while the power of the state has been more or less visible at various times, the state has had and continues to have considerable power in the determination of the degree of medical dominance. The process of state–professional activities, he notes, has been altered by universal health care. Once the state began to finance health insurance plans, the relations between it and medicine and other health occupations changed. The state began to "directly affect medical dominance through its attempts to rationalize health care" (Coburn et al., 1997). The numerous debates among doctors and nurses and the provinces and federal government attest to the conflicts that continue in these arenas. Medical organizations, however, are influenced and constrained not only by state policies but also by the public at large and their wishes. At the same time, conventional medical dominance may be declining, because of the growth of its competitors in the complementary and alternative medical field and an increase in power of the state: "We argue that the state in Ontario is increasingly controlling both the context, and more indirectly, the content of medical care. Physician fees, incomes, number and modes of representation have all been affected" (ibid., 18). (See Chapters 11 and 12 for sustained discussions of this topic and Chapter 15 for a discussion of the globalization of medicalization.)

The Medicalization of Human Behaviour

Conrad and Schneider (1980) have contributed to the debates about medicalization. In one example, they analyzed the impact of the medicalization process in a number of areas, including mental illness, alcoholism, opiate addiction, delinquency, **hyperkinesis**, homosexuality, and crime. In all of these situations they attempt to show how medicine is increasingly an institution of social control. Their research on hyperkinesis (now called ADD or attention deficit disorder and ADHD or attention deficit hyperactivity disorder) provides one specific illustration of the process of medicalization.

Hyperkinesis (ADHD) is a relatively new "disease" that has been "discovered" over the past three-quarters of a century or so. It is estimated that it now affects between 3 and 10 per cent of the population of children. Although its symptoms vary a great deal from child to child, typical symptom patterns include some of the following: excess motor activity, short attention span, restlessness, mood swings, clumsiness, impulsiveness, inability to sit still or comply with rules, and sleeping problems. Most of these behaviours are typical of all children at least part of the time. In fact, all of these behaviours are probably typical of all people at least once in a while. Conrad and Schneider have explained the processes by which these "normal" behaviours became grouped and categorized as indicators of "disease." They argue that hyperkinesis was "discovered" for a number of social reasons.

The first step was the discovery in 1937 by Charles Bradley that amphetamine drugs had a powerful and calming effect on the behaviour of children who had come to him with learning or behaviour disorders. Only later, in 1957, were the "disorders" to become a specific diagnostic category—hyperkinetic impulse disorder. A national task force in the US, appointed to deal with the ambiguities surrounding the diagnosis of the disorder and its treatment, offered a modern name: "minimal brain dysfunction" (MBD). In 1971, Ritalin, a new drug with properties similar to those of amphetamines but with different negative side effects, was approved for use with children. Soon afterwards, Ritalin became the drug of choice for children with hyperkinesis or minimal brain dysfunction. MBD became the most commonly diagnosed psychiatric problem of childhood. Special clinics to treat hyperkinetic children were established, and substantial research funding became available for those studying the problem. Articles appeared regularly in mass-media periodicals in the 1970s, and many teachers developed a working clinical knowledge of the diagnosis. In short, once the drug to treat the disorder was synthesized, produced, and made available, MBD became a popular disease around which a great deal of lay knowledge and activity was organized. Since that time ADD and ADHD have grown in incidence around the world and have been linked to gender, social class, pesticide use, female teachers, classroom structure and curriculum, among other things (see Rose, 2006).

Three broad social factors aided the social construction of hyperkinesis as a medical problem. These same forces have continued and grown as MBD became ADHD and the diagnosis became more common: (1) the pharmaceutical revolution, (2) trends in medical practice, and (3) government action (ibid., 157). First, the pharmaceutical revolution has been marked by a great number of drug-related success stories, such as penicillin's success as a widely effective antibiotic and the controlling effects of psychoactive drugs in a variety of mental illnesses. Such early "successes" encouraged hope for the potential value of medications in many areas of life. Now MBD has become ADHD with the help of similar forces, including the powerful effects of advertising in the mass media, on the World Wide Web and directly to doctors result in what has been termed the **pharmaceuticalization** of society (Abraham, 2010). Second, as the mortality rate from infectious diseases in children has decreased, the possibility for concern with less-threatening disorders has emerged. Medical practitioners and, in particular, paediatricians began to seek other sorts of problems in children that they could work on and treat. In this process they began to pay more attention to the mental health of children and to child psychiatry. This effort has continued under the forces of the pharmaceuticalization of medical practice. Third, government publications, task forces, conferences, and the actions of concerned parents, along with the activities of the pharmaceutical companies, reinforced the legitimizing of ADHD as a new diagnostic category to be managed

by the medical profession. The points made in this analysis are several. First, the behaviour labelled "hyperkinetic" existed long before the diagnosis. Indeed, such behaviour was, and is, widespread throughout the population. Second, the popularizing of the diagnosis corresponded to its recognition as a "pharmacologically treatable" disorder. Third, the expansionist project was aided by the entrepreneurial behaviours of government and the drug companies, along with the Association for Children with Learning Disabilities, based in the United States. To conclude, medicalization is seen, in this example, as a process by which common behaviours become codified and defined as entailing certain symptoms that are best managed through medical interventions (see Rose, 2006).

The link between social problems and health issues was articulated by Conrad and Schneider (1980) as a process of medicalization that included five **sequential stages**. The first stage involved the definition of the behaviour as in some way deviant from the normative expectations and as problematic. The second stage involved prospecting for a medical angle or perspective on the newly discovered problem behaviour. The medical diagnosis emerged. Often a confirmatory study or a new and effective treatment is developed to reinforce the new diagnosis. In the third stage the medical legitimacy is reinforced and medical moral entrepreneurship continues by the development of other medical interventions and treatments, further research, the mobilization of citizen groups for support and advocacy, and the like. Subsequently, as the legitimization continues and new specialties may develop, the state and health insurance companies accept the reality of the diagnosis. The final stage is the institutionalization of the diagnosis as a "fact," and investments in new treatments and, further research is funded and widespread acceptance occurs. It is important to note that there may be some flexibility in these stages and some moving back and forth over time.

In the "Shifting Engines of Medicalization," Conrad (2005: 3) argues that the notion of medicalization has not changed from its earlier incarnation. "The essence of medicalization became the definitional issue: defining a problem in medical terms, usually as an illness or disorder, or using a medical intervention to treat it." What have changed, though, according to Conrad, are the causes of the continuous growth in the tendency of medicine to define aspects of life as relevant to it. Instead of focusing on the drivers noted above (doctors, social movements, and other interest groups), Conrad argues that medicine is now more rooted in the pursuit of commercial and market interests. Medical doctors are still the gatekeepers in the system but they are subservient to larger social and economic forces, which he pinpoints as biotechnological innovations, especially in the realms of pharmaceuticals and genetics along with increased consumer power and organization and managed care. By "managed care" Conrad is mainly referring to the expansion of health maintenance organizations (HMOs) in the US and other health-care insurance corporations that will be discussed further in Chapter 15.

Contemporary medicalization processes have become a great deal more complex in the past half-century or so and debates about the encroaching powers of medicine and medicalization continue. Foucault was one of the most important theorists to add to the debates with his focus on medicalization as a central discourse in the demarcation between the normal and abnormal and the pathologization of that which was not widely considered to be abnormal. Medical discourse was used as a bludgeon, a tool that, through its dominating and reflexive knowledge/power discourses, infused the identity of the modern person. Through this introjection or internalization of discourses people learn to govern themselves and see themselves as well or as not in keeping with disciplinary knowledges (medical knowledges) and through **technologies of self**. In this context people have, through circulating discourses, come to think of themselves as bodies existing in health or illness and in need intervention. For example, with respect to feelings of sadness people have come to think of themselves as depressed because of their neuro-chemistry or neuro-chemical selves (Rose, 2003). These technologies of self, internalized to some extent by us all, are used to govern the self in the interests of the prevailing medical power/knowledges.

Adele Clarke and her colleagues (2003) have built on some of Foucault's ideas and also on their observations of some of the changes in the political economy of the past 30-plus years. They have changed the descriptive term from "medicalization" to "biomedicalization" because of the development of a number of complexities in the landscape pertaining to health, illness, and medicine. As background to a discussion of biomedicalization we need to think about some of the large socio-economic and political forces that have accelerated in the last half-century and particularly in the last 30 years across the developed and western world. "Neo-liberalism" (as discussed earlier in the text) is the term often used to refer to these large socio-economic and political changes. Neo-liberalism has had a profound effect on the processes of medicalization and neo-liberalism has been supported in turn by the encroaching forces of biomedicalization.

Neo-liberalism is composed of five fundamental rationalities of "good governance" including: (1) minimal government intervention in the "free" working of the economy and markets under advanced capitalism (or for the benefit of those who suffer because of the unequal social order created by what is called "economic progress"); (2) a belief in the fundamental power (for good and for growth) of the market; (3) a focus on identifying risks associated with economic development and managing these risks; (4) promoting and relying on the idea that individuals are essentially responsible for their own fate; and (5) accepting inequality as an inevitable consequence of these views (Ayo, 2012).

In this context we are interested in governmentality (Foucault, 1991). Governmentality refers to the ways that people become themselves through engagement with discourses that surround them. For example, how do people develop the sense that they are, and indeed must be, masters of their own fate in order to be good citizens of neo-liberalism? Or, how do individuals govern themselves so as to become health-conscious subjects and adopt **healthism** as a crucial part of identity (Crawford, 2006)? We are also interested in the links between the rationalities of neo-liberalism and trends in health and health care as exemplified by biomedicalization. Medicalization theory emphasizes the growth of medical perspectives in understanding human life, throughout the life span and over an expanding range of body parts, types, and functioning. In this analysis the origins of medicalization were believed to be irreducibly associated with the growing power of medical doctors. Doctors were thought of as the gatekeepers and definers of what and who (other professional groups) belonged within their purview and that of medicine and the processes of medicalization. They were observed to be expanding their power, their esoteric knowledge, and their social distance (through income and education, along with probable sex, gender, and racialized grouping) over the population at large. Doctors were the central figures in understanding medicalization as a trend.

Biomedicalization takes into account the powerful discourses and economic and political forces of neo-liberalism, particularly through changes that are internal to the technologies (such as pharmaceutical innovation and expansion) associated with medicine. Whereas medicalization was viewed as one of the most powerful transformations of the last half of the twentieth century, biomedicalization, argue Clarke and her colleagues (2003: 162), has usurped medicalization. "Biomedicalization is our term for the increasingly complex, multisited, multidirectional processes of medicalization that today are being both extended and reconstituted through the emergent social forms and practices of a highly and increasingly technoscientific biomedicine." These technoscientific innovations depend on and encourage enormous corporate investments and neo-liberal governing principles. While most of this growth originated in the US, Canada has quickly absorbed many of the advances and adopted many of the medical innovations. Empirically, in Canada, we see the rise of various types of privatization, even in the context of the universal medical care system. The pharmaceutical and medical device companies are two centrally important institutional drivers of the increasing costs of medicare as well as out-of-pocket medical expenses in Canada. About one-third of medical care for Canadian citizens

is based on out-of-pocket expenses. Further, and highlighting the increasing importance of a medical view of reality, medicare is seen as emblematic of Canadian identity and as a symbol of good nationhood. Its meaning has spread beyond that of technical, surgical, pharmaceutical, or other medical intervention so that it infuses the culture, values, and norms of the society. Its influence can be seen on all aspects of everyday life. The culture of biomedicine has become so pervasive that it can be considered a new and growing regime of truth (Foucault, 1980: 133, as cited by Clarke et al., 2003: 163). In many ways biomedicine is not fettered by governments but under neo-liberalism is autonomous, independently powerful, and cannot be controlled.

Clarke and her colleagues (2003) document five areas in which they observe the processes of biomedicalization spreading:

1. The economic growth of privatized biomedical and technoscientific research as a proportion of the GNP along with the commodification of health-related research findings.
2. A focus on governing and stratifying population and evaluating lifestyles and behaviours with respect to their relative risk for different diseases and conditions before actual disease diagnosis.
3. Increasingly sophisticated, digitized record-keeping, interventions, evaluations, and developments in sciences, including, for instance, genetics, molecularization, cloning, genetic engineering, nanoscience, and cloning.
4. Transformation in knowledges and their development and dissemination through such publicly available means as the World Wide Web, health columns in newspapers and magazines, online support groups, direct-to-consumer advertisements, and so on.
5. Alteration in bodies through such interventions as pacemakers, cosmetic and bariatric surgery, and other individualized and customized niche-marketed medical interventions.

Let us discuss each of these in turn with a focus on their relevance to Canadian society.

The first point is that there has been an absolute growth in the amount of the GNP that is devoted to medical care over the past several decades and the focus of the expenditures has changed. According to comparative World Bank data, Canada spent 11.2 per cent of its GDP and the United States 17.9 per cent of its GDP on health care (http://data.worldbank.org/indicator/SH.XPD.TOTL.ZS) in 2011. These figures represent a change over time of 4.1 per cent annual growth rate since 2000 in Canada and 4.0 per cent in the United States (http://www.oecd.org/els/health-systems/oecdhealthdata2013-frequentlyrequesteddata.htm). Second, over the past two decades pharmaceuticals have been one of the fastest-growing components of the health-care system according to the Canadian Institute for Health Information (http://www.cihi.ca/CIHI-ext-portal/pdf/internet/DRUG_SPEND_DRIVERS_EN). When compared to similar countries this growth rate is second only to the US. Between 1998 and 2007 the annual rate of increase for drugs (outside of hospitals) was 10.1 per cent annually. This rate has slowed somewhat since the economic crash of 2008. There has been a decrease in the growth rate of expenditures for pharmaceuticals in Canada over the recent past from 4.05 to 3.3 per cent (http://www.cihi.ca/cihi-ext-portal/internet/en/document/spending+and+health+workforce/spending/release_30oct12). About one-third of medical care is now paid for privately in Canada.

The second point is the idea that the demarcation between normal and abnormal populations has continued apace. This has been accompanied by enormous efforts in the area of what is called health promotion within public health. Biomedicine can be seen in the continuing encroachment of a "risk society" mentality (Beck, 1992; Giddens, 1999) among Canadians and in various public health initiatives. We have discussed the rapid implementation of the vaccine for HPV among young girls. This is a case in point of the spread of the risk society mentality. We also see striking levels of emphasis on mammography and PSA testing even in the continuing face of ambiguity about their value for health protection. Although there do not appear to be any physical

iatrogenic effects of PSA testing, the fear and anxiety resulting when elevated levels of PSA are noted are consequential and increase suffering. Watching and waiting to see if high levels go up or down or remain the same can be a serious emotional issue for some men and their families. With respect to mammography, there is evidence that, especially with older machines, there can be carcinogenic effects of the testing alone. Furthermore, the false positives can cause suffering for the person who has to be tested and retested. A recently published 25-year review of screening mammography has found that it makes no difference in death rates from breast cancer but that it may cause harm from over-diagnosis (Miller et al., 2014). Populations are described and monitored as bodies that are at risk for one medical problem or another. The rates of obesity, for example, among children and adults of differing ages and genders are calculated and published regularly. The links between the growth in body size and various health problems, most notably diabetes, are advertised on various popular media. Still there is some debate about what constitutes obesity and at what level of overweight there may or may not be negative health consequences. Moreover, the health consequences of obesity and overweight are still debated. The spread of disease categories and pre-disease categories of risk are also evident in the case of mental illnesses as our earlier discussion of the DSM and its expansion suggests.

A recent analysis of ADHD (Hart et al., 2006) demonstrates market segmentation and has sought to show how it is actually more appropriate to think of ADHD as an instance of the medicalization of male behaviours. The authors note that ADHD is now the most prevalent type of childhood disability in North America (ibid., 132) and, further, that the use of Ritalin has grown exponentially. Its use has increased 800 per cent since 1994, and 90 per cent of this utilization has been in the US, although Canada and Great Britain are among the countries whose populations are increasingly endorsing this new disorder. Apparently, too, between 75 and 80 per cent of those for whom this drug is prescribed are male. Hart and his colleagues propose that the use of Ritalin corresponds to a perceived failure among parents (usually mothers) and teachers (usually female) to socialize boys into acceptable behaviours. Furthermore, the authors link higher prescription rates to states with higher proportions of white children, disproportionately high socio-economic privilege, and expectations of higher performance levels on standardized tests. In addition, the over-prescription of Ritalin has meant that it has become a common "street" drug—sometimes known as "kibble and bits"—and that many young people sell it or pass it on to others (http://www.drugfreeworld.org).

The third point in the argument about bio-medicalization is perhaps best and most succinctly highlighted by reference to the enormous sway of genetics today through the Human Genome Project. Bilateral mastectomies have become a treatment of choice for women with a history of breast cancer in their families and the presence of the BRCA1 or BRCA2 gene. The myriad tests to which newborns are subjected has led to the term "patients-in-waiting" (Timmermans and Buchbinder, 2010). We have discussed some of the issues involved in knowing that one will inevitably be diagnosed with Huntingdon's disease because of the efficacy of the genetic test. That there are debates over whether or not newly discovered genes can be patented suggests one of the ways that neo-liberalism is imbricated in biomedicalization.

The fourth point refers to the enormous spread of the mass media and the Internet as sites for health information and the expansion of medical jurisdiction or disease-mongering. More and more people are using the Internet for information about health. In fact, in 2009, of the 21.7 million Canadians 16 years and over who regularly used the Internet, 74 per cent of women and 66 per cent of men used it to access health information (www.statcan.gc.ca/daily-quotidien/100510/dq100510a-eng.htm). The Internet is also regularly used for getting a second opinion (Underhill and McKeown, 2008). Apparently, about 49.5 per cent of people prefer to go to the Internet not instead of, but before, consulting their allopathic practitioner (Hesse et al., 2005). On the one hand, this perhaps signals the diminution of the power of the

medical doctor per se. On the other hand, it does not necessarily suggest a reduction in the power or influence of an allopathic medical perspective. In another study, 48.6 per cent of respondents first went to the Internet for information and only 10.9 per cent went first to their allopathic physicians. Once in the medical consultation, those who sought online information frequently presented a diagnosis they had already decided on and asked for treatments that had been recommended online. Many physicians say that their work benefits from the prior research of their patients, provided the Internet information was reliable, accurate, and relevant (Murray et al., 2003a). While some doctors disagreed with the value of relying on the Internet for initial health information, fully 95 per cent of consumers believe they have found useful information on the Internet (www.hon.ch/Survey/ResumeApr99.html).

The final point refers to what in Chapter 7 we called aspirational medicine, the spread of biomedical interventions to make one's life better or, as Elliott (2004) says, "better than well." One category of intervention is "brainpower from a bottle" (Kudlow, 2013). Apparently off-label use of stimulants to enhance concentration and to enable long nights of studying or working is significant. Approximately 25 per cent of the students at some Canadian universities use such stimulants as aids to school work and exam preparation. About 10 per cent of medical students have reported that they have used stimulants off-label to improve their performance in school work. About 12 per cent of dental students admit to such use. The downside of such seemingly innocent and even, to some viewpoints, laudable use of stimulants is that those who do use them are much more likely also to use alcohol, cigarettes, marijuana, cocaine, and ecstasy and to drive recklessly. Furthermore, studies suggest that while the use of stimulants may not improve performance it does often lead to over-confidence. Such cognitive enhancement has many similarities to cosmetic surgical procedures, of which there are millions in the US and Canada in just one year. Mood-altering drugs of various sorts are relevant here, too.

CRITICAL THINKING

BOX 9.2   The Ice Bucket Challenge

The enormous success of the "ice bucket challenge"(http://en.wikipedia.org/wiki/Ice_Bucket_Challenge) can be seen as an example of medicalization and biomedicalization. The "ice bucket challenge" first came to widespread attention in North America in June of 2014 on a morning television show for the Golf Channel. It then spread increasingly rapidly when the well-known anchor of the NBC television program, *The Today Show*, Matt Lauer, received a nomination to the ice bucket challenge and did it on television on 15 July 2014. Among those later nominated and participating were former US Presidents Bill Clinton and George W. Bush, and UK Prime Minister David Cameron. Even fictional characters, including Homer Simpson and Kermit the Frog have taken the challenge, ostensibly to raise money for ALS (amyotrophic lateral sclerosis). The challenge involved nominating a person to dump a bucket of water on his or her head and then nominate three others to do the same. This was to occur via video and to be posted on social media. In the process those involved were to donate money to "ALS." This performance soon became a pop cultural phenomenon. It is estimated that it raised over $100 million in about 30 days.

ALS was first observed and distinguished in 1869 by Jean-Martin Charcot and initially was referred to as Charcot's disease. In 1939 Lou Gehrig, a highly regarded baseball player, was diagnosed and died. Since then the disease has been known popularly as "Lou Gehrig's disease." Its severe symptoms cause neuromuscular atrophy and death, usually within about five years of diagnosis. Its incidence is fairly low at about 3.9 per 100,000 people (Mehta, 2014). It occurs more frequently among men and at about 40 to 80 years of age. These figures are not entirely reliable because the definition and diagnosis of the disease is uneven and it is not necessarily reportable across the country (Mehta, 2014). In diagnostic terms it has been incompletely recognized or medicalized.

Many people argue that the ice bucket challenge was unequivocally a benefit for those suffering from this disease and for those who might be diagnosed in the future. Others argue that in the absence of serious discussion of the disease, its effects, and the lack of accountability regarding the ultimate use of the money raised, the ice bucket challenge was a trivializing, superficial, and self-congratulatory social media event.

No matter what side you might take in this debate, it is clear both that money was raised and that the profile of the disease increased—an example of the role of the Internet (social media in this case) in medicalization. What do you think of using social media to create urgency regarding the importance of a particular disease?

Source: Mehta et al. (2014).

Three other newly discovered "diseases" are premenstrual syndrome (PMS), menopause, and erectile dysfunction. Considerable medical attention—and then sociological, feminist, and other critical attention—has been paid to these. Metzl and Angel (2004) document the increasing use of Prozac, a highly popular anti-depressant, for an expanding variety of women's issues, including PMS or what is now labelled "premenstrual dysphoric disorder." McCrea (1983) documents the history of the discovery of menopause as a deficiency disease and notes several parallels to Conrad and Schneider's analysis of hyperkinesis. McCrea dates the discovery of the disease to the 1960s when a gynecologist was given more than $1 million in grants by the pharmaceutical industry. Very soon, this gynecologist was writing and speaking about menopause. He described it as a deficiency disease leading to a loss of femininity and "living decay." The diagnosis was coupled with a solution—ERT (estrogen replacement therapy). In a feminist analysis, Dickson (1990: 18) argued that the "mounting sales of estrogen are a result of the expanding concept of menopause as pathology." Still, many argue that menopause is neither a "disease" nor an experience most women pass through with difficulty. The discovery that the ingredients in the drug now called Viagra, initially developed to treat heart disease, had the side effect of causing an erection led to the marketing of the drug for the newly popularized disease of erectile dysfunction (Loe, 2006). This drug has been so successful that Viagra has become a metaphor for a bull market—a rapidly rising stock market is sometimes called a Viagra market!

CRITICAL THINKING

BOX 9.3   Uncertain and Unequal Medicalization: The Case of Brian Sinclair

In a society in which medicine is so pervasively constructed as the way to understand and deal with manifold social problems, uncertainty regarding medical care or a lack of effective available medical care can be a very serious issue. Consider Brian Sinclair, a First Nations man who died in 2008 sitting in a wheelchair in the emergency ward of a hospital in Winnipeg after he had spent 34 hours without the attention of the health-care staff. An autopsy discovered that he died from an easily treated bladder infection. Other patients and security staff had repeatedly reminded the health-care workers of the presence and increasing suffering of Mr Sinclair but they were ignored. In the end, Mr Sinclair was found to have been dead between two and seven hours before anyone noticed. The inquest attributed this tragedy to racism and a culture of indifference among some health-care staff, as well as to staff shortages.

Had any of the 17 requests and reminders from the public or security staff been attended to, Mr Sinclair could have received a prescription medication resulting in a complete cure of the bladder infection (Lett, 2010). This medical problem was contained within a social problem. What social and health policies need to be in place to prevent such a tragedy from happening again?

CRITICAL THINKING

BOX 9.4   Medical Status as Identity: Disclosing HIV Status

Should people be required to disclose their HIV diagnosis? If so, under what circumstances? The Supreme Court of Canada ruled in 1998 that if significant risk of HIV transmission was involved then individuals ought to disclose their HIV status. In 2012 the Court decided that disclosure was required if there was a realistic risk of transmission—with a caveat, though. If the HIV viral load was relatively low and if a couple engaging in heterosexual vaginal intercourse used a condom, then disclosure was not deemed to be essential.

These issues are highly contentious and a variety of viewpoints have been expressed, often acrimoniously. What do you think some of the arguments might be? Two points follow. On the one hand, some people oppose the law because they think it would likely result in people being unwilling to be tested in the first place. On the other hand are those who argue that if the law is not in place then people would be able to get away with spreading the virus from sexual partner to sexual partner or via sharing apparatus for drugs as a form of intentional malfeasance. Clearly this is an important but debateable issue. What do you think?

HIGHLIGHTED ISSUES

BOX 9.5 Disease Definition

There are a number of different, competing models of disease. Some classes of disease are virtually assertions about the cause, e.g., cut on finger; others are simply descriptions of visually obvious, technically measurable, or verbally presented symptoms, e.g., high blood pressure. Some are classified by site, e.g., diseases of the stomach; some are categories of symptoms, e.g., headache; others are the names of syndromes that include the nature, symptoms, cause, and prognosis, e.g., Tay-Sachs disease. This list of categorizations could be extended. But the point is that disease diagnosis is not a straightforward and unequivocal procedure. Diseases vary fundamentally in their certainty, ranging from the most clearly defined, e.g., major anatomical defects caused by trauma, to those of unknown etiology and variable description, e.g., multiple sclerosis. Given variability in the meaning of disease, it is not surprising that the process of diagnosis is sometimes considered to be an art rather than a science (Blaxter, 1978).

HIGHLIGHTED ISSUES

BOX 9.6 Fundamental Contradictions in the Canadian Health-Care System

There are several fundamental contradictions and paradoxes inherent in the Canadian health- or medical-care system. The first is that it does little to produce health. Instead, it provides treatment for illnesses on the basis of one person with one problem at a time. Inequity, poverty, poor or no housing, poor sanitation, inadequate education, unemployment, hazardous work, gender inequality, and other social factors are important causes of disease. They are best addressed by social and health policies involving investment in housing, guaranteed annual incomes, full employment, and the like. Investing in the medical system, in some sense, perpetuates these social problems to the extent that money is spent on the medical care or cure of the individual and not on recovery through social justice. Moreover, the dominance of the medical model of defining and solving problems individualizes social issues that might better be understood as community or government responsibilities.

The second contradiction is that medicare reinforces the historically organized dominant political interests and relationships. It supports allopathic medicine, hospitals, and the pharmaceutical industry. It also supports the relations of power and inequity in the medical system, in the medical division of labour, and in the hospital and pharmaceutical industries. In various ways, it serves to protect doctors and the prevailing ideologies of allopathic medicine. However, this structure may be harmful to patients and their families, as well as to those who work in this system.

Medicalization and Demedicalization

The link between health and illness and morality is a universal phenomenon (Freidson, 1970, 1975). Religion, medicine, and morality frequently are connected. This integration may become a problem, however, in a complex industrialized society such as ours, in which the medical and the religious institutions are separate. The official perspective is that doctors deal with physiologically evident illnesses, while the clergy and the courts deal with moral and legal concerns. The jurisdictions are believed to be distinct. Yet, the doctor is

REMEMBERING OUR HISTORY

BOX 9.7   Anti-Black Racism in American Health Care

Many of us are familiar with the Tuskegee experiments in which black American men with syphilis were allowed to go untreated, suffer, and die terrible deaths even though there was a widely accepted and effective treatment (antibiotics) available at the time. This gross neglect was justified as "necessary" for the scientific understanding of the course of untreated syphilis. Lesser known, perhaps, are the experiments designed to find treatments for fistula (a hole developing in childbirth between the rectum and vagina that allows leakage) on slave women by the revered father of American gynecology, James Marion Sims. Even today, African Americans are more likely to be recruited for dangerous clinical trials. The differences in death rates between black and non-black Americans for diseases such as breast and cervical cancers are just two of the many examples of inequity in the availability of early detection and effective medical treatments. Such racism is true in the case of mental illness diagnoses as well. According to Metzl (2010) there are repeated stories of black Americans being diagnosed under the DSM with schizophrenia because of their hostility and aggression in the face of discrimination, prejudice, and violence exhibited towards them. Thus, the Tuskegee experiments stand as an illustration of a widespread racism in diagnosis, access to medical care, and prevention and early detection of disease for black Americans that continues today.

accorded a good deal more power, prestige, and influence in our society than the religious functionary or average lawyer. This power is granted in part because the doctor's work is seen as altruistic, related to the service of others, and impartial (and potentially needed by all, even the irreligious) (see Parsons, 1951, for further discussion). In fact, however, as we have demonstrated, the doctor makes moral judgements in ever-widening spheres of life (Illich, 1976; Zola, 1972; Conrad, 1975).

Physicians tend to *act* in the face of uncertainty, to diagnose disease but not to diagnose **non-disease**, and to consider social characteristics of patients in their diagnoses and treatments of physical ailments. Thus, in a variety of ways, the doctor labels or "creates" a definition of illness for the person who consults her or him.

Some argue that demedicalization is more characteristic of contemporary society than is medicalization (Fox, 1977). Recently, evidence is mounting that the power of the medical model to determine how we think about health and illness has declined in one particular way. Other health-care providers are challenging the dominance of the physician in the medical labour force. The prevalence of the medical model's way of thinking about health, illness, and treatment has been criticized frequently. Increasing expenditures on the provision of medical care have not meant an increase in the level of good health in the population. The new disease profile, which demonstrates the prevalence of chronic illness, mitigates the pervasive power of the medical model.

Implicit in Freidson's argument about the dominance of the medical profession is the notion that it has control over (1) the content of care, (2) clients, (3) other health occupations, and (4) policy (Coburn et al., 1997). Many have argued that allopathic medicine is declining in power due to the proletarianization of the profession and the decreasing gap in education between physicians and patients (ibid., 2). Others disagree. Coburn and his colleagues have recently examined this issue and concluded that "the state in Ontario is increasingly controlling both the context, and, more indirectly, the content of medical care. Physicians' fees, incomes, numbers, and modes of representation have all been affected" (ibid., 18). This shift has occurred largely through resource allocation. The boundaries of medical practice are increasingly critically examined and constrained by the state through (1) an increased reliance on health planners, health economists, evidence-based medical practice, and epidemiologists in the conceptualization of appropriate and inappropriate medical treatments via such things as cost-benefit and health outcome measures; and (2) an increasingly legitimated critique of the scientific basis of much of allopathic medical practice. The state has been able to "cut through" dealing with an increasingly hierarchical medical profession, i.e., a profession controlled via its colleges, professional associations, and other medical elites (such as specialists, and physicians at university hospitals). While medical professionals still comprise the most powerful occupational group in the overall medical system, as compared to their own previous position they have decreased in dominance.

Williams and Calnan point to larger cultural changes that are implicated in threats to medical dominance. In particular, they are persuaded that "the lay public are not simply passive and dependent upon modern medicine, nor are they necessarily duped by medical ideology and technology. Rather, in late modernity, a far more critical distance is beginning to open up between modern medicine and the lay populace" (Williams and Calnan, 1996: 1617). Contributing to this view that, in today's postmodern society, the medicalization thesis is overstated is the growth of social reflexivity—a process through which people now think about truth(s) as relative. "[A] chronic feature of late modernity" is "a never-ending cycle of reappraisals and revisions in the light of new information and knowledge" (ibid.). As more and more people pay attention to mass media and as these media reflect constantly critical and changing views of various aspects of social and cultural life—such as science, technology, and medicine—they tend to become more knowledgeable about issues that relate to health, illness, and medical care. The experience that everything constitutes a risk for some disease or misfortune—even the sunshine now causes skin cancer—leads the populace to be cynical, uncertain, and skeptical of esoteric knowledge, science, allopathic medicine, and claims to objectivity and truth. Thus, culture may be becoming demedicalized. The experience of risk is so widespread that it generalizes beyond medical risk to all sorts of other risks in the modern world, including environmental, industrial, and other such hazards (Beck, 1992), that may outstrip the fear of personal illness in some ways.

HIGHLIGHTED ISSUES

BOX 9.8   Some Possible Explanations for the Decline of the Dominance of Medical Doctors in Canada

There are signs that the power of doctors may be declining even as other aspects of the medicalization and biomedicalization of everyday life are expanding. Some indications of the extrinsic and intrinsic explanations for this process follow.

Extrinsic

(i.e., beyond the direct control of the medical profession)

1. Changing accountability and funding in the federal–provincial relationship.
2. Changing legislative climate regarding the practice of the profession.
3. Changing status and legitimacy of other providers of health-care services.
4. Changing nature of doctor–patient relationship due to the increasing levels of education of citizens/patients.
5. Growth of a risk society and critical uncertainty about truth claims of science, technology, and medicine.
6. Changes in cultural conceptions of the body and responsibility for the body.
7. Shifts of attention to more prevalent chronic diseases.

continued

8. Shift from ethic of cure to ethic of care.
9. Growth in emphasis on spirituality and holism.
10. Growth in reliance on the Internet by health consumers.
11. Increase in advertising of pharmaceuticals and other health-related interventions in mass media.

Intrinsic

(i.e., amenable to change by the medical profession)

1. Patient/physician ratios leading to over-supply in some places and undersupply in others.
2. Fragmentation within medicine along with growth in medical elites (e.g., university-based physicians/scientists).
3. Increasing specialization.
4. Wide variations in standards of care.
5. Changing and contradictory research findings and associated treatments.
6. Increasing numbers of women and ethnic minorities in the physician supply.

SUMMARY

1. The definition and diagnosis of illness today are largely the result of the labelling activities of the medical profession. The medical profession labels "deviant" and "normal" feelings and bodily signs and symptoms, and these definitions become reality for social actors.
2. The chapter gives a brief overview of the relationship between medicine and religion through history.
3. Over the past two centuries, medicine has become a distinct discipline. Definitions of "sin," "crime," and "illness" have changed. Some criminal or sinful behaviours are now viewed as illnesses, e.g., drug and alcohol addiction, although the law may not reflect those medical viewpoints.
4. Medicalization and biomedicalization are increasingly powerful social influences.
5. The physician is not only a scientist but also a moral decision-maker or moral entrepreneur.

Medicine can legitimate the illness it diagnoses on the condition that the patient adopt the "sick role" prescribed by the doctor. Medicine defines what is deviant from health and also how the patient is to react to that definition. Illness is "legitimated deviance" insofar as it has been identified by the physician and the appropriate steps are taken by the patient to get well.
6. Doctors must make other moral decisions such as the allocation of resources, choosing between the present and future interests of the patient, and balancing the needs of the patient versus those of his or her family.
7. Medicalization leads to medical action in situations of uncertainty.
8. Medicalization can be observed in the micro-situation of physicians' controlling verbal interaction between the patient and the physician.

KEY TERMS

attachment process	iatrogenesis	pharmaceuticalization
biomedicalization	mediated	sequential model of
healthism	moral entrepreneur	medicalization
hyperkinesis	non-disease	technologies of self

QUESTIONS FOR STUDY AND DISCUSSION

1. Take one behaviour that has been seen both as moral/immoral and as wellness/disease and elaborate on the consequences of each diagnosis or definition of reality.
2. Examine a search engine for websites on a controversial "disease" mentioned in the text (e.g., ADHD). Critique the information available from the conflict or feminist theoretical perspective.
3. After examining a major national newspaper for medical stories over the past year or so, what do you think are the major challenges to medical dominance today?
4. Doctors tend to act in the face of uncertainty. Discuss with respect to your personal experience.

SUGGESTED READINGS

Canadian Health Services Resource Foundation (CHSRF). 2004. "Myth: We Can Eliminate Errors in Healthcare by Getting Rid of the 'Bad Apples.'" Mythbusters. Ottawa. A discussion and evaluation of the individualizing "bad apple" explanation for medical error instead of examining the systemic workings of the medical system.

Clarke, Adele E., Laura Mamo, Jennifer R. Fishman, Janet K. Shim, and Jennifer Ruth Fosket, 2003. "Biomedicalization: The Technoscientific Transformations of Health, Illness, and U.S. Biomedicine." *American Sociological Review* 68, 2: 161–94.

Doidge, Norman. 2015. *The Brain's Way of Healing: Remarkable Discoveries and Recoveries from the Frontiers of Neuroplasticity*. New York: Viking. The most recent bestseller by the Canadian psychiatrist who has popularized the concept of "neuroplasticity," a significant recasting of neuroscience and psychiatry that shows how the brain can heal itself and be healed through non-surgical, non-pharmaceutical, and non-psychotherapeutic interventions.

Rose, N. 2006. "Disorders without Borders? The Expanding Scope of Psychiatric Practice." *Biosocieties* 1: 465–84. A review article that examines different explanations for the increase in mental illnesses.

Timmermans, S., and M. Buchbinder. 2012. *Saving Babies: The Consequences of Newborn Screening*. Chicago: University of Chicago Press. A book about the costs, benefits, and the social impact of newborn screening.

Waitzkin, Howard. 1989. "A Critical Theory on Medical Discourse: Ideology, Social Control, and the Processing of Social Context in Medical Encounters." *Journal of Health and Social Behaviour* 30 (June): 220–39. An exposition of the "politics" of the doctor–patient encounter.

Zola, Irving. 1972. "Medicine as an Institution of Social Control." *Sociological Review* 20: 487–504. One of the earliest explications of medicalization.

10 The Social Democratic and Current History of Medicare: Privatization and the State of Medicare in Canada

THE CANADIAN PRESS/Andrew Vaughan

CHAPTER OVERVIEW

▶ The first Canadian medical "system" was composed of the various medical and religious practices of the many Aboriginal peoples.

▶ The health of early settlers to Canada was severely threatened in a number of ways.

▶ Some of the first public health measures adopted in Canada resulted from the cholera epidemic brought to Canada first in 1832.

▶ Initially, medical practitioners from widely different backgrounds competed with one another for patients.

▶ Homeopathy was the first profession to be legalized and to establish its own licensing board. Soon after, other groups did the same.

▶ The development of medicare had both supporters and detractors.

▶ Tommy Douglas played an important role in the development of medicare in Canada.

▶ Medicare has had an impact on the class-based utilization rates of medical service.

▶ Medicare has had mixed consequences for medical practice and for doctor morale.

▶ Medicare is currently, and has been in the past decade or so, experiencing significant threats to public financing as its costs have continued to grow.

Introduction

Doctors in modern Western societies have been at the heart of the great forces of medicalization. Central to their role is that they have been highly respected and seen as extraordinary—the creators and keepers of esoteric knowledge. Understanding this is essential to considering the place of medicine in modern society. But have doctors always been dominant in the provision of medical care? What is the relationship between the state and physicians and how does it affect the practice of medicine in Canada? How did medicare develop? How successful has medicare been in broadening and equalizing access to the medical care system for all Canadians? Has the change in accessibility led to changes in the overall health of the population or in the distribution of health in the population? What is privatization and is it relevant to a thorough understanding of our health-care system today? What are the implications of trends towards restructuring and downsizing the health-care system? These are among the questions that will be addressed in this chapter.

Early Canadian Medical Organizations

The first Canadian medical "system" consisted of the various medical/religious institutions of the many groups of Aboriginal peoples. Each of these groups had its own culturally unique definitions of what constituted health and what constituted illness, its own pharmacopoeia, and its own preferred types of natural and supernatural interventions. Since these peoples handed down their traditions orally, the only written accounts are from white settlers, priests, explorers, and traders. These writers tell us that medicine men or shamans were frequently called upon to diagnose and treat various types of injuries and disease. Shamans, as well as Aboriginal people more generally, developed a number of very effective botanical remedies, such as oil of wintergreen, and physical remedies, such

as sweat lodges and massages. In the following we will discuss several examples from Ontario.

In the seventeenth century, at the time of the arrival of the Europeans, the Native peoples of Ontario were divided into two linguistic groups: the Algonquian and the Iroquoian. A study of Iroquoian bones dug from a burial mound near Kleinburg, Ontario, revealed that these people (around the year 1600) suffered from such well-known diseases as arthritis, osteomyelitis, and tumours (Holling, 1981). Evidence of a hole in a skull revealed the skill of a local surgeon. Some treatments devised by the Aboriginals, when the cause was obvious, were empirical and rational. Internal conditions of unknown cause were often attributed to supernatural origins, such as (1) the breaking of a taboo, e.g., mistreating an animal or showing disrespect to a river; (2) ghosts of humans, which craved company; (3) the evil ministrations of a menstruating woman; or (4) unfulfilled dreams or desires.

Aboriginal people believed that everything in the world had a spirit or a soul, including animals, trees, rocks, the sky, lakes, and rivers. Thus, everything in the world was to be respected. In some Aboriginal cultures all young people, especially males, were expected to search for a vision or a dream as a guide through life. To achieve this goal it was customary to spend at least a week alone without food. Hungry, lonely, and full of transient concerns, the young person would generally have a vision, which was then interpreted by the medicine man or father. Medicine men were both the spiritual leaders and healers. They were able to cast out spells, predict the future, recover lost objects, diagnose and treat disease, and bring rain. Some were also magicians and jugglers.

A practical armamentarium of medicines evolved, which included treatments for widely differing medical problems, from fractures and wounds to freezing and frostbite, burns and scalding, rheumatism, arthritis, urinary problems, fevers, intestinal disorders, cancer, blood poisoning, and toothaches. Some of the herbs and plants used historically by the Native peoples continue to be used today.

Canada's Aboriginal peoples are known to have used over 500 different plants as medicines. Some were chewed and swallowed, some drunk in herbal teas, some boiled and the vapours inhaled, some infused and poured as medicine into the patient's ear. At times, plants were used only for ritual purposes. For example, thorny or spiny plants were sometimes used to ward off evil spirits or spirits of disease and death. At other times the value resided in the pharmacological effectiveness of a particular plant for a particular symptom or disease. A famous example of the use of a plant with specific and now scientifically substantiated medicinal benefit is the scraping of white bark of cedar, which is rich in vitamin C, for the treatment of scurvy. This intervention was taught to Jacques Cartier by Aboriginal people. Pharmacologically useful treatments seem to have existed for a wide

---

REMEMBERING OUR HISTORY

BOX 10.1   Canada's Cholera Epidemic

The worldwide epidemic of cholera reached Canada for the first time in 1832. Apparently some Irish immigrants, who were escaping the potato famine and the beginnings of cholera in Ireland, were infected when they set forth for Quebec City and Montreal. The boats they travelled on were built for 150, but carried as many as 500 passengers. Such crowded conditions led to unsanitary circumstances and invited the spread of the virulent and contagious disease. Cholera attacked apparently healthy people, who could die within a matter of hours or days. It erupted in a number of symptoms, including severe spasms and cramps, a husky voice, a sunken face, blue skin colour, and kidney failure as various bodily processes collapsed. Doctors could do virtually nothing to help their patients. Although there were various theories associating the disease with dirt and filth, its cause was not understood.

When the colonial government in Lower Canada realized the nature of the calamity, officials established a Board of Health with a mandate to inspect and detain ships arriving from infected ports. A Quarantine Act was passed in February 1832 and remained in effect for a year. Another Act provided a fund for medical assistance to the sick immigrants and to help them to travel to their destinations when they had sufficiently recovered.

In the spring of 1832 Grosse Isle in the St Lawrence, which was directly in the path of ships arriving from Europe, was established as a place of quarantine. All ships were stopped for inspection. Distinctions were made between ships arriving from infected and non-infected ports. Those from infected ports were required to serve a quarantine period, while the ships with ill passengers were thoroughly cleaned and those who were diseased were disembarked and treated; those who died were buried there. Some of the government actions were very unpopular because they restricted individuals' freedoms, which resulted in riots in various locations throughout the country. Crowds burned down some cholera hospitals.

Cholera invaded British North America at three other times—in 1834, 1852, and 1854. While statistics are not entirely reliable, it is estimated that as many as 20,000 people died in all the epidemics. While we have not seen cholera epidemics in Canada since the nineteenth century, they still occur on several continents where water and sanitation are not hygienic (http://www.who.int/gho/epidemic_diseases/cholera/en/). There have been a number of outbreaks in Africa, as well as a recent epidemic in Haiti. Oral rehydration salts can be used to treat the majority of people (80 per cent) when they are available.

Sources: Bilson (1980); Heagerty (1928: vol. 1); Marks and Beatty (1976).

variety of symptoms such as wounds, skin eruptions, gastrointestinal disorders, coughs, colds, fevers, and rheumatism.

The health of the early settlers in Canada was assaulted continually. Even before they arrived, immigrants, who were often malnourished to begin with, faced grave dangers from the overcrowded conditions on the boats in which they came to Canada. These densely packed quarters greatly increased susceptibility to the spread of contagious diseases. Pioneer life, too, was fraught with hazards. The winters were extremely cold, much colder than winters many of the immigrants had been accustomed to—and somewhat colder than we are accustomed to today, since the Little Ice Age extended from about 1450 to 1850, and today we are in the midst of climate change and global warming. The growing season was short and difficult. Accidents occurred frequently as people cleared the bush for timber and for farmland, roads, and buildings. Accidents occurred on the rapidly flowing waterways. The building of roads, canals, and railways was extremely dangerous. Epidemics of smallpox, influenza, measles, scarlet fever, and cholera decimated the population from time to time. Childbirth in pioneer conditions was often dangerous for both mother and child (Heagerty, 1928). Local midwives, a few doctors trained in Britain and the United States, and travelling medical salespeople performed most medical treatment. Other treatments were based on folk remedies or on mail-order medicines.

The Origins of the Contemporary Medical Care System

The origins of the type of medical practice dominant today can be traced back to nineteenth-century Canada. At that time, various kinds of practitioners were offering their services and selling their wares in an open market. Lay healers, home remedies, folk cures, and other kinds of medicines were among the medical options available to the population. Whisky, brandy, and opium were used widely as medicines, as were numerous patent concoctions. Medicine shows were common from the 1830s and 1840s.

Most of the first allopathic medical practitioners in New France were either **barber-surgeons** from France, who had received primitive training as apprentices, or apothecaries who acted as general practitioners dispensing available medicines. Barbering and surgery both required dexterity with a knife: they were handled by the same person because of the ubiquitous practice of bleeding as a treatment for a wide variety of ailments. Surgery was practised only on the limbs and on the surface of the body. Internal surgery almost always resulted in death because bleeding and sepsis were not yet treatable or preventable. Two other common treatments were purging and inducing vomiting. Among the first doctors in Upper Canada were army surgeons. There were also some civilian physicians. Homeopathic doctors and eclectics (practitioners who used a variety of treatments) worked alongside allopathic or conventional practitioners. Lay-trained midwives delivered babies in the home, and other lay-trained persons performed surgery and set bones. No one type of healer was predominant.

Although the first medical school was established in Canada in 1824, theories about disease were varied and not scientifically based. The first involvement of the state in this hodgepodge of medical practices came in 1832 because advance warning had been received of the possible arrival in Canada of immigrants with cholera. The government immediately appointed a Sanitary Commission and a Board of Health, which issued directives for the protection of the people. Infected people were quarantined. Contaminated clothing was burned, boiled, or baked. Private burials were ordered. Massive outbreaks of cholera in 1832 and 1854 necessitated the establishment of a quarantine station at Grosse Isle on the St Lawrence for ship passengers who were infected and thus not allowed to enter Canada. Both Montreal and Quebec adapted buildings as hospitals to isolate disembarking passengers who had cholera. Public ordinances, which received the force of law in 1831, prevented the sale of meats from diseased animals and appointed civil authorities to inspect dwellings for their state of cleanliness. Early public health measures primarily emphasized quarantine and sanitation. Later the government became involved in other types of public health efforts. These included the Public Health Act of 1882 in Ontario, which was soon adopted in the rest of the country; the Food and Drug Act; the Narcotics Control Act; the Proprietary and Patent Measures Act; and the establishment of hospitals and asylums.

The Early Efforts of Allopathic Physicians to Organize

In spite of the primitive state of their medical knowledge, numerous attempts were made by **allopathic doctors**, dating from 1795, to have legislation passed that would: (1) prohibit any but allopathic practitioners from practising medicine; (2) provide the allopaths with licences under which they could practise; and (3) control admittance to allopathic practice. The allopathic practitioners often had high social standing in the new colony. In the English-speaking areas, they were usually British immigrants and often ex-military officers (Torrance, 1987). Generally, they moved in the highest social circles, married into important families, stood for Parliament, edited influential newspapers, and provided care for the wealthier classes (Gidney and Millar, 1984). In small towns outside Toronto, allopathic practitioners were often among the most important businessmen, church leaders, and town politicians. In 1852 an informal group of these men established the *Upper Canada Journal of Medical, Surgical and Physical Science.*

The allopathic doctors expressed frustration with their working conditions. They claimed they were under-rewarded and under-esteemed because of the competition from "irregulars" and because of "quackery" and the disorganized state of the medical schools. Many of the "irregulars" were also educated, and because they did not engage in the heroic measures of the allopaths, such as the application of leeches, bloodletting, and applying purgatives, they were less likely to cause harm. But the allopathic doctors thought of them as uneducated, ignorant imposters who ruthlessly and recklessly administered untried, untested methods with dangerous results.

In fact, even at this time, the "irregular" doctors exhibited considerable strength and organizational skills. In 1859 **homeopathy** was the first profession to be legalized and to establish a board to examine and license practitioners. The eclectics were successful in consolidating their own board in 1861 (ibid.). Perhaps because of their relative success in organizing themselves, the homeopaths and eclectics and other heterodox practitioners were "contemptuously lumped together by the established profession as 'empirics'" (Hamowy, 1984: 63). The *Upper Canada Journal* denounced homeopathy as "so utterly opposed to science and common sense, as well as so completely at variance with the experience of the medical profession, that it ought to be in no way practiced or countenanced by any regularly educated practitioner" (quoted ibid.). Opposition to the eclectics was equally passionate. They were called "spurious pretenders" and seen as embodying a continuous and strong threat to "true science."

Competition within the ranks of the allopaths, largely between "school men" (the university-trained and affiliated practitioners) and the Upper Canada practitioners (Gidney and Millar, 1984), prevented the unified stance necessary for the establishment of standards of education, practice, and licensing. In 1850 the "school men" held more power. By 1865 they had conceded some of their authority to the elected representatives of the ordinary practitioners. In the same year (1865) these ordinary practitioners succeeded in passing self-regulatory licensing legislation. This was revised in 1869 under the Ontario Medical Act to create the College of Physicians and Surgeons of Ontario. Much to the surprise of the "regular" or allopathic physicians, both homeopaths and eclectics were included under the same legislation. Homeopaths continued to be represented by the College until 1960. Eclectics were excluded in 1874. The regulation of homeopathy today will be discussed in Chapter 13.

REMEMBERING OUR HISTORY

BOX 10.2   The Flu Epidemic of 1918

In the fall of 1918 Canada's population was about 8 million. About 60,000 Canadians had died in World War I. During the fall of 1918, between 30,000 and 50,000 people died in Canada as a result of the dreaded flu pandemic sweeping much of the world. Worldwide, according to estimates, 50 million to 100 million people died as a result of this influenza. Apparently the flu came to Canada on a troopship, the *Anaguayan*. One hundred seventy-five of the 763 soldiers on board took ill. The ship was quarantined at Grosse Isle. Yet, the disease was passed on to civilians. By the end of September it was clear that Canada had a serious problem. The epidemic spread quickly. New York and Massachusetts were hit. It spread up and down from the US into Canada and vice versa. It also spread westward along the railways and highways. It was attributed to Spain and called the Spanish flu, not because it started there but because, as Spain was neutral in the war, the Spanish press, unfettered by wartime censorship, was the first to report the virulent flu epidemic as it devastated the Spanish population.

It was unique because it tended to hit young adults and often killed them. Previously, the flu had tended to affect especially the very old and the very young. The flu epidemic attacked one in six Canadians. Schools, auditoriums, and various halls were opened as temporary hospitals. Children were left without parents. Quarantines were imposed. Public meetings were forbidden. Partly because of the impact of the flu, the need to establish a federal health authority was acknowledged. The bill to institute such a department received first reading in March 1919, and the new department became operational that fall. But quarantines did not seem to work. Many people thought that quarantine was unjust. Others just did not believe that it worked because they saw people succumbing who had

been very careful, while others, less careful, remained disease-free.

Because quarantine did not seem to work, other measures were introduced. Laws were passed to ensure that people wore masks. But the laws differed. In some municipalities those who were caring for the ill were required to wear masks. In others, anyone who was in contact with the public was expected to wear a mask. Alberta required that anyone outside the home had to use a mask. Yet masks proved as ineffective as quarantine. Rather than boiling and sterilizing them frequently, and certainly between wearings, people allowed the trapped germs to spread and multiply in the moist, warm environment inside the mask.

Most homes had their own trusted preventive measures and treatment. Mothballs and camphor in cotton bags worn about the neck were common. Travelling medical salespersons reaped profits from the salves and remedies they sold. Alcohol and narcotics were prescribed.

Losses to business were enormous. People were too sick to shop or were afraid to venture into the stores for fear of catching the disease. Many staff members, too, were off sick. Theatres and pool and dance halls suffered heavy losses. Some 10,000 railway workers were off at one time. Ice storms, blizzards, and below-zero weather had never exacted so heavy a toll as this epidemic. Telephone companies were heavily over-extended, both because people were relying on the phone rather than leaving the house and because so many employees were away sick. The insurance industry was one of those most heavily hit. Apparently some companies dealt with more flu claims than war claims. All in all, Spanish flu had an enormous effect on Canadian society.

Sources: Dickin McGinnis (1977); Heagerty (1928: vol. 1); Pettigrew (1983).

This 1869 legislation gave the practitioners, via their representatives on the College, control over the education of medical doctors. Proprietary (privately owned) medical schools were founded, but they were rapidly affiliated with universities in order to grant degrees. The power struggles between the university-based doctors and the practitioners continued.

In Lower Canada the attempts to define and limit the work of physicians were complicated by the tensions between French and English doctors. The College of Physicians and Surgeons of Lower Canada, formed to regulate practitioners, was created in 1847. In 1849 legislation was passed to allow automatic incorporation of anyone who had been engaged in practice in 1847.

The competition and infighting that characterized much of the medical care system in the nineteenth century had receded by the beginning of World War I (Coburn et al., 1983). The year 1912 marked a turning point in the position of allopathic practitioners. The Canada Medical Act, which standardized licensing procedures across Canada, was passed. Finally, by this time a patient who sought the services of an allopathic practitioner had a better than 50 per cent chance of being helped by the encounter. The passage of the Canada Medical Act followed another important event. The momentous Flexner Report, *Medical Education in the United States and Canada*, published in 1910, was sponsored by the Carnegie Foundation and the American Medical Association, financed by the Rockefeller philanthropies, and researched and written by Abraham Flexner, an American educator. The **Flexner Report** severely criticized the medical systems of Canada and the United States. It advised the elimination of the apprenticeship system, the standardization of entrance requirements to medical schools, and the establishment of a more rigorous scientific program of study. It recommended the closing of many medical schools, particularly the private schools, because they did not meet the criteria of scientific medicine.

Flexner's report radically changed medical education in the US and Canada. McGill University and the University of Toronto were the only schools in Canada given acceptable ratings. The medical schools in Halifax and London moved rapidly to become affiliated with Dalhousie University and the University of Western Ontario, respectively. Medical education began to be taught as a scientifically based, scholarly field under the aegis of universities.

The Flexner Report had a significant impact on the organization of Canadian medical education and the practice of and training for modern medicine. The report enhanced the legitimacy of science as the basis of clinical practice. It reinforced the importance of empirical science with its emphasis on observation, experimentation, quantification, publication, replication, and revision as essential to medical-scientific research. It emphasized the use of the hospital for the centralized instruction of doctors-to-be and the use of medical technology for observation, measurement, and standardization in diagnosis and treatment. By the 1920s the hospital-based, curatively oriented, technologically sophisticated medical care system that Canadians know today was firmly established.

One important side effect of the report was that the schools that were closed were primarily those that educated women and blacks. Thus, the closing of the proprietary schools further entrenched the position of white, middle- and upper-class males in medicine.

A Brief History of Universal Medical Insurance in Canada

Mackenzie King first suggested a system of universal medical insurance in 1919 as part of the Liberal Party platform; it was recommended regularly by organized labour after the end of World War I (Walters, 1982). Later, universal medical insurance was proposed at the Dominion–Provincial Conference on Reconstruction in 1945. At this time, the provinces opposed the federal initiative, favouring free-market health insurance. In 1957 the federal government introduced the Hospital Insurance and Diagnostic Services Act, which provided for a number of medical services associated with hospitalization and medical testing. The federal government was to pay 50 per cent of the average provincial costs.

In 1961, the federal government appointed a Royal Commission on Health Services. The

Commission, under Supreme Court Justice Emmett Hall, recommended that the federal government, in co-operation with the provinces, introduce a program of universal health care. The result was the Medical Care Act of 1968. Finally implemented in 1972, the new universal medical insurance scheme was to cover medical services, such as physicians' fees, not covered under the previous Hospital Insurance and Diagnostic Services Act. The scheme had four basic objectives or **principles of medicare**. (1) **Universality**. The plan was to be available to all residents of Canada on equal terms regardless of such differences as previous health records, age, lack of income, non-membership in a group, or other considerations. The federal government stipulated that at least 95 per cent of the population was to be covered within two years of the provincial adoption of the plan. (2) **Portability**. The benefits were to be portable from province to province. (3) **Comprehensive coverage**. The benefits were to include all necessary medical services, as well as certain surgical services performed by a dental surgeon in hospital. (4) **Administration**. The plan was to be run on a non-profit basis.

The Canada Health Act of 1984 added **accessibility** to make five principles. The costs for the new plan were to be shared 50/50 by the federal and provincial governments. They were also to be shared in a way that would serve to redistribute income between the poorer and the richer provinces.

Government soon faced increasing financial pressure as health-care costs grew. Physicians who felt they were not paid enough "extra-billed" their patients. When a critical level of frustration and complaint was reached, the government appointed Emmett Hall again to chair a committee to re-evaluate medicare. In 1980, Hall reported to the federal government that unless extra-billing was banned, Canada's universal health-care system was doomed. In response, but amid much controversy, the Canada Health Act, which limited the provinces' right to permit extra-billing, was passed.

The Canadian Medical Association filed a lawsuit against the federal government, claiming: (1) that the Canada Health Act went beyond the constitutional authority of the federal government; and (2) that it contravened the Charter of Rights and Freedoms by prohibiting doctors from establishing private contracts with their patients. The Ontario Medical Association, the largest and most vocal provincial group, representing about 17,000 physicians, challenged the Act in court. The Ontario government passed the Health Care Accessibility Act (Bill 94) in June 1986 in response to the federal legislation, thus making extra-billing illegal. Members of the Ontario Medical Association staged a 25-day strike in protest, but eventually had to back down when the government refused to capitulate. Public opinion was decidedly against the strike action, and many doctors went back to work even before it was officially over. There have been many other doctors' strikes across the country, from British Columbia to Newfoundland and Labrador. Doctors have protested their incomes, working conditions, and the state of medical care for Canadians, among other things. There is evidence of the dissatisfaction of some doctors with their working conditions across the country: although the average income is approximately $307,000, doctors still have to pay their overhead, such as salaries for office/clinic staff, office rent, office and medical equipment, etc. Moreover, the average income varies between $236,000 in PEI to $350,000 in Alberta (Ubelacker, 2013). Salaries also vary considerably by specialty, so that a family doctor makes much less than a neurosurgeon, for example.

Medical care has continued to be a much-heralded Canadian value, on the one hand, and a site of continuing political controversy, on the other. It is often a major issue in Canadian elections. Debates about bringing back a parallel private system, about waiting lists for major tests and surgery, and about doctor shortages, compensation, and emergency room fiascos dominate the headlines of national newspapers. A Senate study, *The Health of Canadians: The Federal Role* (the Kirby Report) (www.parl. gc.ca/37/2/parlbus/commbus/senate/Com-e/soci-e/rep-e/repoct02vol6-e.htm), was published in 2002. At the same time, the federal government commissioned another investigation into the problems in health care, which was summarized in the Romanow Report (Commission on the Future of Health Care in Canada, 2002). The Canadian Medical Association (www.cmaj.ca/cgi/content/full/173/8/901) and the Fraser Institute (www.fraserinstitute.org/commerce.

REMEMBERING OUR HISTORY

BOX 10.3   Timeline: The Development of State Medical Insurance

Germany and Western Europe introduce social welfare insurance, including health insurance, in the 1880s.

New Zealand introduces social welfare insurance, including health insurance, in the early part of the twentieth century.

Great Britain introduces national health insurance in 1948.

Canada

1919 Platform of the Liberal Party under Mackenzie King includes medicare.

1919 After World War I, organized labour begins what becomes an annual statement by the Canadian Congress of Labour concerning the importance of national health insurance, and in 1919–20 several US states pass medicare legislation that is later withdrawn.

1934 Canadian Medical Association appoints a Committee on Medical Economics, which produces a report outlining the CMA's position in support of national health insurance, with several provisos.

1934 Legislation passes for provincial medical insurance in Alberta. Government loses power before it can be implemented.

1935 British Columbia introduces provincial medical insurance legislation. Despite public support via a referendum, this legislation was never implemented because of a change in government.

1935 Employment and Social Insurance Act, including a proposal for research into the

viability of a national medical insurance scheme, is introduced.

1942 Beveridge Report on Britain's need for a National Health Service published in Great Britain—the subject of much discussion in Canada.

1945 Dominion–Provincial Conference on Reconstruction includes proposals for federally supported medical insurance. Conference breaks down in the wake of federal–provincial dispute.

1947 Saskatchewan implements hospital insurance.

1951 A Canadian Sickness Survey completed. It demonstrates income differences in the populations affected by illness.

1958 Hospital Insurance and Diagnostic Services Act passes.

1962 Saskatchewan CCF/NDP government introduces provincial medical insurance; Saskatchewan doctors' strike.

1962 Royal Commission, headed by Justice Emmett Hall, is appointed to investigate medical services.

1966 Federal legislation for state medical insurance passes.

1968 Federal legislation implemented.

1971 All provinces fully participate in medicare.

1972 Yukon and Northwest Territories included in federal legislation.

web/product_files/FraserForum-February2010.pdf) continue to advance the idea of a parallel private medical care system for Canadians who can afford to pay for extra or more rapidly delivered services and to keep down the tax costs of the system. These remain hotly debated topics across the country.

Despite the arguments of vested interests for privatized, for-profit care in hospitals, Table 10.1 shows that many studies have documented advantages to not-for-profit care in hospitals. For-profit hospitals have the advantage in only five categories,

and far fewer studies have demonstrated an advantage in those categories. In all five areas where some (or one) studies found benefit, more studies of the same topic found that not-for-profit delivery of services surpassed the for-profit hospitals. For example, with respect to cost per admission, while eight studies found that for-profit hospitals were less costly, 13 found that the not-for-profit model was less costly. By contrast, there were 14 categories in which not-for-profit hospitals had the advantage. Note, however, that fewer studies even

1977 Federal government changes the funding formula with the provinces—Established Programs Financing Act (EPF).

1984 Canada Health Act reinforces the policy that medical care is to be financed out of the public purse (penalties established for hospital user fees and physician extra-billing).

1987 Ontario doctors' strike.

1990 Bill C-69 freezes EPF for three years, after which future EPF growth is to be based on gross national product (GNP) minus 3 per cent.

1991 Bill C-70 passes to freeze EPF for two additional years before new formula (−3 per cent) comes into effect. Makes it possible for federal government to withhold transfer payments from provinces contravening the Canada Health Act.

1999 Throughout the nineties, medical care deteriorates across the country. Hospitals close; patients at times are turned away from emergency; emergency room waiting increases dramatically. Nurses, doctors, and other health-care workers strike in various actions. Evidence increases of a two-tiered medical system.

2000–3 Further debates between the federal government and the provinces on health-care funding. The provinces blame "the crisis in medicare" on the lack of sufficient federal funding and the federal government chastises the provinces for misspending. A number of investigations and reports are solicited, including the Alberta-sponsored report by former federal cabinet minister Don Mazankowski and the federal reports by Senator Michael Kirby and former Saskatchewan Premier Roy Romanow. Each report is received in a flurry of contradictory political discourse.

2005 In the *Chaoulli* decision of the Supreme Court in respect to a legal suit against the Quebec government for failing to allow private health care and thus subjecting a patient to a long wait for surgery, the Court finds that the refusal to allow private insurance for health care covered under medicare violates the rights and freedoms of the patient.

2006–15 The country continues to debate the advantages and disadvantages of a private parallel system for the provision of medical care in Canada even as the system is already partly privatized (about one-third of the system is currently for-profit) and dependent on consumers to pay some expenses out of pocket. For full coverage many Canadians already buy insurance to provide services additional to those provided through medicare, such as pharmaceuticals, a single room when hospitalized, and so on. Nor are dental or optometry services universally covered via tax revenues. In considering the advantages and disadvantages of a parallel private system the point is often argued that it would be more efficient and effective, and would provide greater access to care for the population.

in these categories found advantages for for-profit hospitals. (See also the following Mythbusters report, which again documents the superiority of not-for-profit care along a number of lines: http://www.cfhi-fcass.ca/Migrated/PDF/myth13_e.pdf).

Factors in the Development of Medicare in Canada

Today, Canada's health-care system, usually called medicare, is predominantly publicly financed and privately delivered by a combination of funds and policies established at the federal level and operational decisions executed at the level of the provinces and territories. It is considered a national system because its fundamental principles are federally based and federal funding reflects, in part, adherence to these principles. The federal government is also responsible for direct health service delivery to specific groups, including veterans, Aboriginal Canadians on reserves, military personnel, inmates of federal penitentiaries, and the RCMP. In addition, the federal government's health-related

TABLE 10.1   Organizational Performance of Acute-Care Hospitals by Ownership

Specific Measures of Organizational Performance	Number of Studies		
	Non-profit Advantage	No Significant Difference	For-profit Advantage
Measures of economic performance			
Administrative overhead	3		
Cost per admission—Operating cost			
Cost per admission—Total cost	13	11	8
Measures of technical efficiency	5	3	2
Revenues/charges per admission	9	4	
Measures of quality of care			
Mortality rate (in facility)	1	7	
Mortality rate (post-discharge)	7	9	1
Adverse outcomes (other than mortality)	5	3	3
Process measures of quality	5	1	
Regulatory violations	1		
Malpractice suits		1	
Functional improvement during admission			
Consumer satisfaction			
Measures of accessibility for unprofitable patients			
Locating in low-income areas	5		
Treating uninsured	12	6	
Treating Medicaid patients	2	4	1
Facility practices affecting indigent care	4		
Providing unprofitable services	6		

Note: The numbers in the cells indicate how many relevant studies were found for each measurement. Empty cells indicate the absence of relevant studies. An advantage indicates one type of organization performed better on the measure specified. No significant difference indicates for-profit and non-profit organizations performed equally well on the measure specified.

Source: Canadian Foundation for Healthcare Improvement, copyright 2006.

responsibilities involve such things as health protection, promotion, and disease prevention along with the drug approval and regulation. It is important to note that the system relies primarily on the services of family and general practitioners, who comprise 51 per cent of physicians practising in Canada according to the Canadian Institute for Health Information (http://www.cihi.ca/cihi-ext-portal/internet/en/ document/spending+and+health+workforce/workforce/physicians/release_15nov12), and who are essentially the gatekeepers to the rest of the system, including specialty care, hospital admission, diagnostic testing, and prescription drugs. The ratio of physicians to population in Canada is relatively low in comparison with selected other OECD countries, most of which also have public systems of one sort or another (Figure 10.1). The situation in Quebec is an exception to this arrangement.

Most hospitals across Canada are run as private non-profit corporations overseen by a community board, voluntary organization, church, or municipality. Although funded in large part by government, hospitals operate independently as long as they stay within budget.

The development of medicare over the last half-century in Canada was influenced positively or negatively by a number of significant social forces. The most important of these are: (1) the widespread movement in Western industrialized societies towards rationalized bureaucratic social organization and monopoly capitalism; (2) the spread in Western Europe and beyond of social welfare legislation in public education, old age pensions, family allowances, unemployment benefits, and medical care insurance; (3) the benefits to the medical profession in maintaining **fee-for-service**, cure-oriented, hospital, and technologically based medical practice; (4) the interests of the life and health insurance companies in perpetuating their share of a profitable market; (5) the interests of the drug, medical, and hospital supply companies in continuing to develop their increasingly profitable markets; (6) the interests of the urban labour unions

and farm co-operatives in social welfare benefits for their members; and (7) the charismatic qualities and dedication of individuals such as Tommy Douglas, who had both a position of power at the "right" time in Saskatchewan and a commitment to universal medical care. Each of these will be discussed in turn.

First, the movement towards state medical insurance in Canada must be seen as part of a widespread trend in Western industrialized nations towards rationalization and bureaucratization in the context of monopoly capitalism. It was not until the twentieth century that the work of the physician came to be highly regarded as the most effective form of medical care. With the development of antibiotics to treat bacterial infections and neuroleptic drugs to control the psychosis associated with various forms of emotional despair and mental illness, the efficacy of the doctor became firmly established in the public mind. Along with the increase in legitimacy of allopathic medicine, medical practice began to alter as hospitals changed from being institutions for the dying and the indigent into being the doctor's place of work. Medical specialization increased and medical and paramedical occupations burgeoned. All of this growth and development served to enmesh the physician within enormous technically efficient bureaucratic structures.

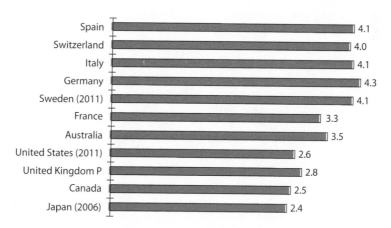

FIGURE 10.1 Practising Physicians per 1,000 Residents, 2012

Source: Adapted from OECD Health Statistics, http://stats.oecd.org/index.aspx?DataSetCode=HEALTH_STAT#, based on www.cihi.ca/CIHI-ext-portal/pptx/.../PHYSICIAN_COST_DRIVERS_EN.

Second, the introduction of medicare in Canada must be seen in the context of the spread of similar policies in the Western industrialized world. The first legislation was passed in Germany in the 1880s. By the time Britain first introduced universal medical insurance in 1912 (to be formally established as the universal National Health Service in 1948), much of Western Europe, as well as New Zealand, had already pursued this course. Talk of medicare and the passage of legislation in support of medicare (which was later withdrawn) occurred in the United States by 1919–20. From 1919 until the introduction of comprehensive state-sponsored medical care in Canada a half-century later, both federal and provincial governments made various attempts to draft legislation to implement medicare.

Third, the medical profession has had an impact on the timing and the nature of medicare.

In 1934, the Committee on Medical Economics of the Canadian Medical Association completed a report that described the characteristics of the ideal medical insurance scheme. At this time the CMA expressed support for state medical insurance provided that: (1) it was administered by a non-political body of whom the majority would be medical practitioners; (2) it guaranteed free choice by physicians of their method of payment; (3) it provided for medical control over fee scheduling; and (4) it allowed for compulsory coverage up to certain levels of income (Torrance, 1987). Following World War II, after the return of economic growth when most patients were able to pay their bills either independently or through private medical insurance, the majority of the profession opposed medicare. The strongest statement of the opposition of the doctors to state medical insurance was the 23-day strike in 1962 by about 800 of Saskatchewan's 900 physicians.

REMEMBERING OUR HISTORY

BOX 10.4   Historical Impediments to the Development of State-Sponsored Medical Care in Canada

1. The traditional division, early in the century, between the urban industrial labour force and the farmers led to the consequent inability of these two working-class groups to form a unified labour lobby in favour of medicare.
2. The strengthening and unification of the Canadian Medical Association in 1920 with the appointment of Dr T.C. Routley as leader gave the CMA a unified voice with respect to the conditions under which medicare might be acceptable.
3. The extensive representation of medical doctors in local, provincial, and federal politics and departments of health gave physicians the power to voice their individual views regarding medicare.
4. Through the British North America Act, 1867, the responsibility for health rested with the provinces.
5. Canadian Roman Catholics generally opposed state medical insurance.
6. The regional, ethnic, and occupational (labour/farmer) heterogeneity of Canadian society retarded the development of social democratic policies.
7. Private insurance companies steadily grew, especially during the fifties and sixties, and medical insurance became an increasingly common fringe benefit in collective bargaining agreements.
8. The Canadian Life Insurance Officers Association, the Canadian Chamber of Commerce, and the Canadian Manufacturers' Association repeatedly opposed state medical insurance. (Walters, 1982)

Fourth, the life and health insurance companies, through the Life Insurance Officers Association, opposed medicare. They argued that the role of the state was to provide the infrastructure for the development of such things as transportation and communication. State-sponsored medical insurance was to be limited to those who could not pay for their own policies and to assist in payment for catastrophic illnesses. The insurance companies were already making a profit and wanted to continue to do so.

Fifth, the drug, medical, and hospital supply companies and their representative body, the Canadian Manufacturers' Association, opposed government intervention in medical financing.

Sixth, the labour unions and farm co-operatives advocated national medical insurance. Except in the case of Saskatchewan, however, they did little actively to bring about state medicare.

Seventh, the importance of individuals such as Tommy Douglas cannot be overlooked. He was especially dedicated to the principle that medical care be accessible and available on a universal basis. He owed his well-being and perhaps his life to the fact that a physician operated on him without fee and saved his leg from amputation when he was a boy. Partly as a result of this experience, his personal faith based in the Social Gospel movement (he was a pastor of the Baptist Church), and, of course, because of his socialist beliefs, Douglas made medicare a fundamental plank in his CCF platform (see Box 10.5).

REMEMBERING OUR HISTORY

BOX 10.5   Tommy Douglas

Tommy Douglas is one of the most important figures in the development of a universal state-supported medical care system. He was born in Scotland in 1904 and immigrated with his family to Winnipeg when he was a boy. An incident in his own life stands out because it was often cited as having provided the motivation for his determined fight for medicare. Before coming to Canada, Douglas injured his knee in a fall. As a result of the injury he developed osteomyelitis and was forced to undergo a series of painful operations. Despite these operations, osteomyelitis recurred while he was living in Winnipeg. The doctors in Canada felt that amputation was necessary. However, while Douglas was at the Children's Hospital in Winnipeg in 1913, a famous orthopedic surgeon, Dr R.J. Smith, became interested in his condition. Dr Smith took over the case and saved his leg. He did not charge the far-from-wealthy Douglas family. As Douglas says of this experience, "I always felt a great debt of gratitude to him, but it left me with this feeling that if I hadn't been

so fortunate as to have this doctor offer his services gratis, I would probably have lost my leg."

In addition to this personal experience, Douglas was moved by the social conditions in Winnipeg in the early twentieth century. Unemployment was high. People lived with a great deal of uncertainty and were able to afford only the barest of necessities. These conditions made a lasting impact on Douglas. He was also sensitive to and strongly opposed to the discrimination and prejudice based on ethnic and racial differences that he saw around him in Winnipeg.

He acted out his commitment, first by becoming a Baptist minister in 1930 and then by becoming a parliamentarian. In 1932 he joined the Labour Party. In 1935 he was nominated as the Co-operative Commonwealth Federation (CCF) candidate for the Weyburn federal riding in Saskatchewan and was elected to the House of Commons. He was re-elected in 1940. From 1944 until 1961, Tommy Douglas was Premier of Saskatchewan, the leader of the first socialist government in Canada. He worked towards economic security for the farmer,

continued

full employment for the urban worker, and the development of natural resources. Tommy Douglas promised that socialism would provide health and social services and lift taxation from the shoulders of the people and place it upon the "fleshy backs of the rich corporations."

By January 1945, free medical, hospital, and dental care was provided in Saskatchewan for "blue card" pensioners and indigent people. Treatment for mental disorders and polio was made free to all. A school of medicine was opened at the University of Saskatchewan to increase the supply of doctors. Geriatric centres were built to provide care for the chronically ill elderly. Canada's first district-wide medical insurance program was established at Swift Current, where 40 doctors served a population of 50,000 people. This was financed by a family payment of $48 per year and a land tax. Thus, Swift Current became a testing ground for a provincial program.

By 1 January 1947, Douglas introduced the Hospital Insurance Plan. The premium at the time was $5 per person and $10 per family. At the end of 1947, the *American Journal of Public Health* stated that 93 per cent of the population of Saskatchewan was covered by the new scheme. The only exceptions were some remote northern communities.

In 1959 Douglas announced the introduction of medicare, which was to be based on five basic principles.

1. Medical bills would be prepaid and patients would never see a doctor's bill.

2. The plan would be available to everyone regardless of age or physical disability.
3. The plan would accompany improvements in all areas of health service.
4. The plan was to operate under public control.
5. The legislation was to satisfy both patients and physicians before it went into effect.

A few days after Douglas stepped down in 1961 as Premier of Saskatchewan to become leader of the newly formed federal New Democratic Party (NDP), the medical bill passed. In 1962 the Saskatchewan doctors' opposition to the government medical scheme intensified. A strike followed the announcement that the Act was in force. The strike lasted 23 days, during which time the government kept medical services in operation by flying doctors to Canada from Britain.

The Saskatchewan plan soon became the basis for a Canada-wide plan. In 1964 Prime Minister Lester Pearson announced that the federal government would give financial aid to any province that had a satisfactory medicare system. By 1969 most of the provinces were participating in the plan, with 50 per cent of the costs covered by the federal government.

After Tommy Douglas re-entered federal politics, he remained a member of the House of Commons from 1961 to 1979, first as the leader of the NDP, which had been formed in 1961 by a coalition between the Labour Party and the CCF.

Sources: McLeod and McLeod (1987); Shackleton (1975); Thomas (1982); Tyre (1962).

The Impact of Medicare on the Health of Canadians

The most important goal of medicare was the provision of universally accessible medical care to all Canadians regardless of class, region, educational level, religious background, or gender. To what extent has this goal been reached? Before the introduction of medicare a positive and clear relationship existed between income level and use of medical services. Before medicare it has been estimated that low-income groups visited the doctor over 10 per cent less often than did high-income groups. Now, however, the rates of health-care utilization across the social-class hierarchy are insignificant, if somewhat contradictory. For example, the likelihood of visiting a general practitioner was slightly higher among the poorer in 2011 (http://www.ices.on.ca/Newsroom/News-Releases/2011/Universal-access-to-health-care-is-not-enough-to-ensure). About 15.2 per cent of Canadians over 12 years of age reported that they did not have a regular doctor in 2010 (http://www.statcan.gc.ca/pub/82-625-x/2011001/article/11456-eng.htm). Men were significantly more likely than women to lack a regular doctor (see Figure 10.2). The most common reason people gave for not having a regular doctor was that they had not looked for one. Those who had looked said that they did not have a doctor because the doctors in their area were not taking new patients, their doctor had moved or retired, or there were no doctors in their area. Still, when they needed health care, people said they found the help they needed through such resources as walk-in community clinics, emergency rooms, hospital outpatient clinics, and telehealth. Although statistics regarding class differences in access to doctors in Canada are not available, it is likely that differences do exist and that poor people have a more difficult time finding a doctor in a situation of shortage and a more difficult time going to a doctor because of the associated costs of taking time away from work, transportation, availability of babysitters, and the like. While differences in access do not appear to be obviously class-based, inequities continue (Kasman and Badley, 2004). Significant differences persist in the treatment received by visible minorities in Canada as compared to white people (Quan et al., 2006). Visible minorities are more likely to have contact with a general practitioner than white people, they are less likely to be seen by a specialist, less likely to have had the early detection test for prostate cancer (the prostate-specific antigen or PSA test), and less likely to have received mammograms and Pap smears for breast and cervical cancer, respectively (ibid.). Moreover, many medical services and products (such as pharmaceuticals) require out-of-pocket expenditures that are not affordable to every Canadian. In a system that relies so heavily on drugs and yet does not insure the out-of-hospital cost of drugs, it is impossible to claim universality.

Creeping Privatization

In a sense, much of Canada's health-care system is already private. Most hospitals and long-term care

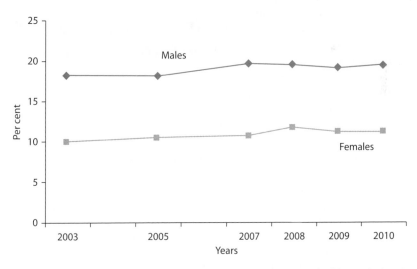

FIGURE 10.2 Percentage without a Regular Medical Doctor, by Sex, Household Population Aged 12 or Older, Canada, 2003–10

Source: Statistics Canada, "Access to a regular medical doctor, 2013." Health Fact Sheets (82-625-X). http://www.statcan.gc.ca/pub/82-625-x/2011001/article/11456-eng.htm.

institutions are owned privately. Approximately 70 per cent of health-care funds come from the public sector; 30 per cent are from the private sector (National Health Expenditure Trends, 1975–2013). This figure compares positively to the US, where about 52.2 per cent of the costs are private, but negatively to the UK, where 17.2 per cent of health funding is private (ibid.). Further, there are many new incentives across Canada for developing the private health-care sector, such as Timely Medical Alternatives (timelymedical.ca), a brokerage for private health-care services. The website indicates that it can provide speedy medical care for such procedures as knee replacement, angioplasty, gall bladder removal, CT scan, MRI, ultrasound, weight-loss surgery, cardiac bypass, cardiac ablation, and hip replacement. Most of these private services are offered in the US, although there are pockets of privatized care in Canada. The following website is one example (http://www.falsecreekhealthcare.com/). Advertised costs are said to range from the hundreds of dollars to thousands. This organization claims to have partnerships with about 20 health-care institutions across the US and Canada and to be able to negotiate an 80 per cent reduction in cost. Periodically, a well-known Canadian politician will have been found, often amid huge controversy, to have travelled to the US to receive and privately pay for medical services. Danny Williams, when he was Premier of Newfoundland and Labrador, is one recent example.

There is also some evidence of personal and celebrity bias in access to care in Canada. A 1998 survey by the Institute of Clinical Evaluative Services in Ontario of some 1,150 health-care providers indicates that 53 per cent of the hospital executives and 80 per cent of the physicians were involved in the care of a patient who received preferential access to treatment. Those most likely to have been favoured in these ways included relatives and friends, high-profile public figures, and patients and families who were well informed, aggressive, or likely to sue. Most of this preferential treatment was given for elective rather than necessary care (http://www.ices.on.ca/Publications/Journal-Articles/1998/January/ A-survey-of-provider-experiences-and-perceptions-of-preferential-access-to-cardiovascular-care-in-Ontario-Canada).

Furthermore, many costs associated with use of the allopathic medical care system are not covered. To visit a doctor, one must be able to afford transportation, take time off work, understand how to make an appointment, and speak the language necessary for making an appointment. Following the doctor's orders, including taking medications or time away from work, frequently involves costs that may not be manageable to the non-working or working poor or to those receiving unemployment or social security benefits. Homeless people are another group who often lack regular access to a doctor. As the costs of medications escalate it is noteworthy that access to prescription drugs will continue to decline. There are real consequences to this unequal access to care and treatment. For example, the death rates for people with diabetes were more than 50 per cent higher in 2012 among those with fewer financial resources (http://www.ices.on.ca/Newsroom/News-Releases/2012/Younger-low-income-Ontarians-with-diabetes-have-higher-risk-of-death).

The Impact of Medicare on Medical Practice

According to Naylor (1982), before the Great Depression, from approximately 1918 to 1929, doctors made more than four times the average Canadian salary. The Depression had a devastating effect on all incomes. In the period of recovery in the 1940s, doctors' salaries averaged about three times the national average. By 1989, with various private insurance schemes in place, doctors made about 3.7 times the average Canadian salary. Initially, medicare gave a dramatic boost to doctors' salaries. In the early 1970s doctors' salaries were approximately 5.2 to 5.5 times the national averages. Wage and price controls, which were introduced in the mid-1970s, retarded the expansion of physicians' salaries during that period. Doctors' salaries have increased in the past decade by approximately 30 per cent in Canada. Today, the average Canadian salary is about $50,000 (http://www.workopolis.com/content/advice/article/how-much-money-are-we-earning-the-average-can-adian-wages-right-now/) while that of the doctor is considerably more, even taking overhead into account. Still, however, the salaries of Canadian doctors compare unfavourably to those of US doctors.

The number of doctors in Canada grew much more quickly than the population and continues to grow. Between 1968 and 1978 the number of doctors grew by 50 per cent, the population by 13 per cent. The physician-to-population ratio has been narrowing for more than a century. In 1871, there were 1,248 citizens to every physician; by 1951 the ratio was 1:976; and by 1981 the ratio was 1:652. This trend continues, as does the increasing number of specialists. According to recent statistics, there was an increase of 5.3 per cent in the number of physicians in Canada from 1996 to 2000 (secure.cihi.ca/cihi-web/dispPage.jsp?cw_page=media_09aug2001_e). This rise was followed by a decline in numbers, but followed again by an increase. The greatest proportion of the new increase was among not general practitioners but specialists, so that today about half the doctors in the system are specialists and half are generalists (www.cihi.ca/cihi-ext-portal/internet/en/document/spending+and+health+workforce/workforce/physicians/release_15nov12.). There is a cause for concern because of the aging of the physician workforce and possibly the dispro-portionate supply of physicians in cities as com-pared to small towns and rural areas (http://www.cihi.ca/CIHI-ext-portal/internet/en/Document/spending+and+health+workforce/spending/spending+by+geography/RELEASE_15NOV12_FIG3). Only 14.6 per cent of family physicians and 2.5 per cent of specialists were located in the rural areas, where approximately 18 per cent of the popu-lation lived in 2012 (ibid.). Over- and undersupply of specialties in different locations in Canada is also a problem.

Today there are 214 physicians per 100,000 people in Canada, a ratio of 1:467. Figure 10.3 pro-vides a picture of the physician-to-population ratio

in a number of different OECD countries as com-pared to Canada. Clearly, while the number of doc-tors per population has been increasing in Canada it has still not reached the level of the average of the OECD countries. As the physician-to-population ratio changes, some areas and regions may experi-ence an excess of doctors and others an insufficient number. Supply levels impact doctors' salaries and also affect rates of surgery, prescriptions, or other necessary medical interventions, as well as unneces-sary suffering and lengthy travel or wait times to see a physician.

The involvement of the state in the practice of medicine has resulted in a number of changes in the actual work of the doctor. These include chan-ges in (1) working conditions, (2) the degree of control over patients and over other occupations in the medical field, (3) self-regulation in educa-tion, licensing, and discipline, and (4) the actual content of the work (Coburn et al., 1987). Many would say that doctors have lost independence

TABLE 10.2 Physicians per 100,000 Population by Province, Canada, 2013

Prov./Territory	Physicians per 100,000 Population
Nova Scotia	262
Newfoundland & Labrador	241
Quebec	237
New Brunswick	227
British Columbia	225
Alberta	221
Ontario	209
Manitoba	204
Prince Edward Island	190
Saskatchewan	184
Yukon	183
Northwest Territories	99
Nunavut	30

Source: CIHI, "Supply, Distribution, and Migration of Canadian Physicians, 2013,": https://secure.cihi.ca/estore/productFamily.htm?pf=PFC2672&lang=en&media=0.

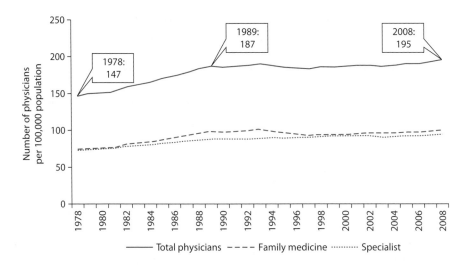

FIGURE 10.3   Physicians per 100,000 Population by Physician Type, Canada, 1978–2008

Notes:

Includes active physicians, who are defined as physicians with an MD degree and a valid address (mail sent to the physician by Scott's Directories is not returned). Includes physicians in clinical practice and those not working in a clinical practice.

Excludes residents and non-licensed physicians who requested that their information not be published as of 31 December of the reference year.

Specialist physicians include certificates of the Royal College of Physicians and Surgeons of Canada (RCPSC) and/or the Collège de Médecins du Québec (CMQ). All other physicians are counted under family medicine, including certificates of the College of Family Physicians of Canada.

Starting in 2004, specialists in Newfoundland and Labrador as well as Saskatchewan also include physicians who are licensed as specialists but who are not certified by the RCPSC or the CMQ (that is, non-certified specialists).

As of 2007, specialists in Nova Scotia, New Brunswick, and Yukon (in addition to Saskatchewan and Newfoundland and Labrador) also include non-certified specialist physicians who are not certified by the RCPSC or the CMQ.

Source: CIHI, "Supply, Distribution, and Migration of Canadian Physicians, 2008," secure.cihi.ca/cihiweb/products/SMDB_2008_e.pdf.

and power in the society, in the medical division of labour, in professional autonomy, and with their patients in the context of medicare. Charles (1976) has documented some of the ways that universal medical care insurance has altered the medical profession through increased administrative, economic, political, and social constraints. The controls of which Charles writes have increased since her publication.

With respect to administrative constraints, Charles was chiefly referring to the increased bureaucratic surveillance of the actual practice of individual physicians through the computerized account systems detailing the number of patients seen and the medical problems diagnosed in a given period of time. The government, through this bureaucratic control, became able to investigate individual doctors whose practices varied substantially from the norms. The privacy of the independent entrepreneur

was effectively eliminated through the powers of this bureaucratic and governmental surveillance.

Certain financial constraints resulted. While the salaries of physicians continued to increase under universal medical care, it was no longer possible for all individual doctors, as independent entrepreneurs, to reach the salary levels they might desire. The Quality Service Payment Formula dictated the maximum number of weekly "units" of service that could be provided by an individual physician without jeopardizing the quality of patient care.

The question of what proportion of the resources of a society should be dedicated to medical care, essentially a political concern, is the third area of constraint noted by Charles. One effect of universal medical care insurance is that physicians' fees are now negotiated between the provincial government and the provincial medical association. The government needs to keep down medical care costs and to ensure universal availability of service. It must also seek to minimize inequity among different medical care personnel within a global budget that includes hospitals and extended-care facilities, drugs, and expensive new technologies.

The final constraint noted by Charles is social. One such example is that in order to provide equitable medical care to people all across Canada, even in remote and isolated areas, governments may implement quota systems that would allow doctors to practise in a given area only if their services were needed as determined by a standardized physician-to-population ratio.

Medical practice is a source of stress for medical students, interns, and residents as well. The University of Calgary's Department of Surgery studied stress among residents in surgery in 1992, 1994, and 1996 and found that most of the residents felt that their stress level was moderate to substantial. The most important causes of stress among these doctors were consistent pressure, overload, working conditions, and an ill-defined work role (Buckley and Harasym, 1999). In the 1996 cohort (ibid., 220) the rank order of the stresses is:

1. lack of time for personal life
2. oral and written examinations
3. information overload
4. time demands of research
5. sleep deprivation
6. financial hardship
7. fear of being incompetent
8. time demands of being on night call
9. OSCAR (the hospital computing system)
10. unco-operative hospital staff
11. insecurity over future career opportunities
12. resident and staff conflicts

The changing nature of medicine and the threat of an international epidemic also are causes for concern among doctors. As Chan and Huak (2004) have noted, the SARS crisis in 2003 had serious costs beyond those for patients and families.

Many health-care workers in Toronto (an estimated 43 per cent of all diagnosed cases) became ill, and two Toronto nurses and one doctor were among the 44 deaths recorded (http://www.cbc.ca/news2/background/sars/timeline.html). As many as 20 per cent of health-care workers suffered post-traumatic stress disorder (PTSD) in the wake of SARS. Oncologists or cancer specialists are another group of doctors who experience a lot of stress because they frequently work with seriously ill patients (Rutledge and Robinson, 2004). Fully 53 per cent of oncologists in 2000 reported being emotionally exhausted. Other research estimates that about half of all practising oncologists are in advanced stages of burnout. Among the reasons cited are workloads, worry about patients, vicariously experiencing the trauma of patients and their families, and lack of self-care (ibid.).

The Impact of Medicare on Health-Care Costs

Clearly, health-care costs as a portion of GNP have increased during the period from about 1960 to the present. Figure 10.4 illustrates the continuing increase in health spending in current dollars in Canada over the period 1975–2014. It shows a cost of over $200 billion in current dollar values estimated for 2014. Figure 10.5 indicates the relative contributions of private and public expenditures from 1975 to 2014 and shows that the line for the proportion of the funding from private sources has trended upward while that for public expenditures has trended down. Since medicare's introduction, then, there has been a gradual but evident growth in the private funding of our health care and a corresponding relative decline in the public health spending.

The federal government has been withdrawing from the health-care field amid great debates with the provinces, despite the fact that the federally sponsored National Forum on Health in 1997 recommended both national home-care and **pharmacare** programs in addition to the present medicare system. The federal government, a number of provincial

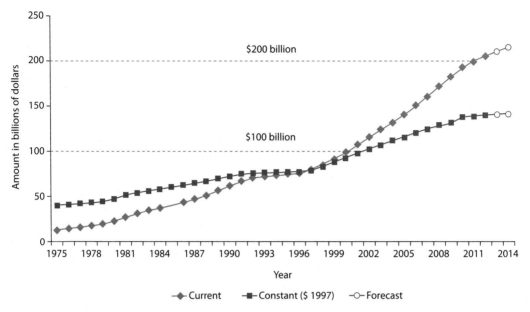

FIGURE 10.4   Total Health Expenditure, Canada, 1975–2014

Source: *National Health Expenditure Trends, 1975 to 2014*, National Health Expenditure Database, Canadian Institute of Health Information, http://www.cihi.ca/web/resource/en/nhex_2014_report_en.pdf, p. 21.

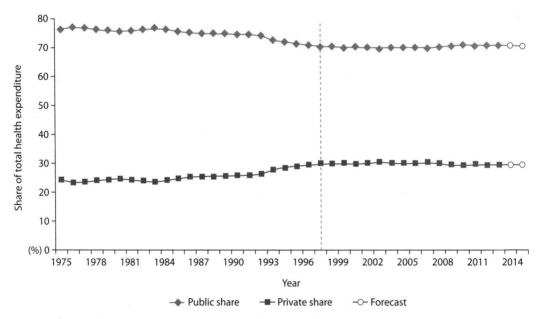

FIGURE 10.5   Public- and Private-Sector Shares of Total Health Expenditure, 1975–2014

Source: *National Health Expenditure Trends, 1975 to 2014*, National Health Expenditure Database, Canadian Institute of Health Information, http://www.cihi.ca/web/resource/en/nhex_2014_report_en.pdf, p. 33.

governments, and other organizations have studied and continue to study the "crisis" in medicare and have made various proposals. Recent examinations of the Canadian health-care situation have included the Romanow Report and the report by the Senate committee headed by Senator Michael Kirby. Some of the proposals favour an expansion of services offered universally and others favour a retrenchment of service offerings. As long as medicare is subject to the fortunes of changing political parties and their accompanying ideologies it will be vulnerable. The provinces and territories manage their own health-care systems, educational programs, and health personnel and certification. Provinces vary in respect to the number of programs provided in addition to the basic medicare services. Some, for instance, provide additional benefits, including psychologists, dentists, optometrists, chiropractors, and podiatrists, as well as home care, drugs, and general preventive services. Many Canadians pay for private insurance plans for additional services.

What is the impact of universal insurance on physician use in Canada as compared with the US? Overall, Canadians of all classes are more likely to visit a physician than are Americans. This difference is minimized but not eliminated among the elderly, who in the US have medicare available to them. However, there are no significant differences between Canada and the US with respect to hospital admission rates or length of stay. In addition, there are greater class disparities in the US than in Canada—the poor in the US have tended to visit the doctor less often, yet once they have made an initial visit they have tended to have a higher number of visits and to stay in the hospital, once admitted, longer than those of higher income status (Hamilton and Hamilton, 1993). Still, medical care on average is more expensive in both Canada and the United States as compared to other OECD countries, and Canada has a lower physician-to-population ratio than many other OECD countries, at 2.5 per 1,000 population (Figure 10.1).

Despite significant numbers of hospital closures, hospitals continue to account for the highest component of the spending, which was 32 per cent in 2001, and for 2005 hospitals accounted

for \$42.4 billion, or 29.9 per cent of total health expenditures. In recent years, spending on pharmaceuticals has climbed at an alarming rate, surpassing that spent on doctors within the Canadian system. In 1994 doctors accounted for 14.2 per cent and pharmaceuticals for 12.6 per cent, but the 2005 forecasts showed only 12.8 per cent spent on physicians as opposed 17.5 per cent on drugs (Figure 10.6). Clearly, the impact of increasing reliance on pharmaceuticals, along with the cost of drugs, is an important cost factor in the health-care system (CIHI, 2013).

The 1990s saw dramatic changes in the medical care system across the country. Elected on a platform that involved eliminating the deficit, the federal Liberal government in 1996 withdrew funding to the provinces specifically earmarked for medicare with the introduction of the Canada Health and Social Transfer (CHST), which over the next several years meant less money to the provinces but with fewer strings attached. The numbers of hospitals across the country decreased dramatically (Tully and Etienne, 1997). Between 1986–7 and 1994–5 the number of public hospitals declined by 15 per cent, and the number of beds in these hospitals was cut back by 11 per cent. The number of staffed beds per 1,000 people declined from 6.6 to 4.1. The number of outpatient visits has increased at the same time as the number of inpatient visits has decreased. More surgeries that used to include a hospital stay have been delegated to day surgery that sends the patient home to be cared for by family or friends or no one. In the context of the control of hospital costs, due to federal transfer cutbacks along with provincial decisions, many hospitals across Canada posted negative annual growth in expenditures despite population growth. In 2012 there were approximately 2.7 hospital beds per 1,000 Canadians as compared to 13.4 per 1,000 people in Japan, 4.8 in Switzerland, 8.3 in Germany, and 2.9 per 1,000 in the US (OECD Health Statistics 2014, http://www.oecd.org/els/health-systems/oecd-health-statistics-2014-frequently-requested-data.htm).

Cuts in the hospital sector may be reflected in some ill-health effects in the population. A retrospective before/after cohort study that included

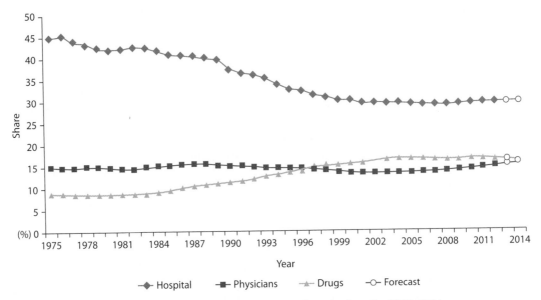

FIGURE 10.6   Total Expenditure per Capita, Selected Use of Funds, Canada, 1975–2014

Source: *National Health Expenditure Trends, 1975 to 2014*, National Health Expenditure Database, Canadian Institute of Health Information, http://www.cihi.ca/web/
resource/en/nhex_2014_report_en.pdf, p. 45.

7,009 infants born by uncomplicated vaginal delivery between 31 December 1993 and 29 September 1997 in a Toronto hospital compared the rate of hospital readmission among newborns born before and after the implementation of a supposedly cost-saving early-discharge policy. Before the early-discharge policy was implemented the mean length of stay was 2.25 days. Following the initiation of the policy the mean stay decreased to 1.62 days. Deleterious effects of the new policy were observed in the higher rate of readmissions—11.7 per cent as compared to 6.7 per cent. The most frequent cause of readmission was jaundice (Locke and Ray, 1999). As healthy infants are one of the best predictions of a healthy population, this finding warrants serious attention.

The cost of medical care, along with the provision of other social services, has been front and centre in political debates during the years since the implementation of medicare. It is fair to say that the issue is now critical—and has been dramatized by physician and nurse strikes, the closing of numerous hospitals through regionalization and debt, government caps on funding, globalization accompanied

by the political focus on the level of deficit in the government financing, the expanded free trade agreements, and a variety of other initiatives designed to restructure the provision of medical care.

Using a model of analysis focusing on the inherent contradictions in a capitalist welfare state, Burke and Stevenson (1993) provide a critique of contemporary Canadian strategies for controlling costs and redesigning health services. They argue that the political economy of health care must be studied in relation to the wider national political economy. Furthermore, they suggest, policies suffer from several biases, including (1) therapeutic nihilism (a critique of the medical model used to cut back on the various essential medical services without provision for an alternative); (2) healthism (a model that attaches health not only to medical services but also to various other issues, such as lifestyle), which can be used by the state to provide it the discursive space to claim that almost every expenditure has a health-enhancing effect and thus specific "medical" care is less important; and (3) the discourse of health promotion, which can easily be "captured by neoconservative forces to further an ideology favouring decentralization, flexibility, the intrusive state, individual responsibility, and the sanctity of the family" (ibid., 70). All of these forces have been evident in the federal government's health emphases over the past three and a half decades, beginning with Marc Lalonde's 1974 report, *A New Perspective on the Health of Canadians*.

Over the years, various proposals have been made for cutting costs. A first set of proposals includes user fees, extra-billing, co-insurance, and deductibles (suggested usually by the medical profession, often with state support). However, a number of researchers have found that such strategies do not work to control costs but rather to decrease equality of access to care, to deter use by the poor, and to redistribute the burden of paying for health care from taxpayers to sick people (Barer et al., 1979; Stoddart and Labelle, 1985).

A second set of proposals concerns controls over the supply of physicians and hospitals through limits on immigration of foreign physicians, on enrolments in medical schools, and on residency positions, monitoring of physician billing, hospital and bed rationalization and closings, decreasing budgets, and contracting out of services to the private sector. The problems associated with such provisions are that they are largely ad hoc and will, without explicit planning, inadvertently result in the dismantling of universal medical care. Table 10.3 shows the relationship between the type of funding system and service incentives.

A third set of proposals involves recognition of the increase in alternative models of health care (homeopathy, nurse practitioners, chiropractic);

TABLE 10.3   Incentives of Various Funding Systems

Funding System	Incentive
Fee-for-service	• Provide more service
Global funding	• Keep within the budget • Provide less service
Fee-for-service with hard cap, equity funding, reallocation	• Provide more service • Reduce cost per service
Capitation	• Keep people healthy • Avoid expensive service • Provide less service

Source: Closson/Catt, "Funding System Initiatives and the Restructuring of Health Care," Canadian Journal of Public Health 87 (1996), 2: 86-9. Reprinted with permission of the Canadian Public Health Association.

the introduction of alternative physician payment schemes such as medical savings accounts (MSAs), **capitation**, and salary; health promotion education; and publicly financed competition between types of health-care practitioners. Capitation is a system in which funding is given to service providers to take responsibility for the health of a specific number of people in a population, i.e., per patient annual payment to a physician. "The goal in a capitated system is to keep the population healthy so that they will not require expensive services" (Closson and Catt, 1996). There is a relationship between the type of funding system and service incentives as proposed by Closson and Catt. Even in the midst of a universal medical care system, dental and vision care and prescription drugs are private expenditures.

SUMMARY

1. The chapter provides an overview of the history of medicine in Canada. Aboriginal peoples had medicine men and shamans who used a wide variety of effective herbal remedies. Early Canadian settlers relied on a variety of treatments provided by midwives, local doctors, travelling salesmen, and mail-order dispensers

of remedies. During the nineteenth century the government started to institute public health measures to deal with cholera and to license homeopaths, allopaths, and other health-care providers.

2. The implementation of universal medical insurance in Canada, which was completed in

1972, was the conclusion of a long, uphill battle, yet that battle has continued to the present day.

3. There are several explanations for the development of medicare in Canada. Two of the most important are the movement in Western industrialized societies towards rationalized bureaucratic social organization and monopoly capitalism, and the spread in Western Europe and beyond of social welfare legislation.

4. The main goal of medicare in Canada was to provide equal health care to all Canadians, thus enhancing the general health of the population. To some extent, this goal has been reached; people in low-income groups visit physicians more often. Health, however, continues to vary by class.

5. Medicare has also had an impact on medical practice: doctors' salaries increased dramatically, but have since levelled off. The ratio of doctors to population in Canada continues to decrease. Working conditions, control over other occupations in the medical field and over clients, self-regulation in education, licensing, and discipline, and the actual content of the work have all undergone significant alterations. As well, the medical profession is now under increased administrative, economic, political, and social constraints.

6. Health-care costs as a portion of Canada's GNP have increased since the introduction of medicare. However, medicare seems to have controlled potentially spiralling costs of medical care. The greatest growth in medical expenditures until 1982 was in institutions; from 1982 to the present, the cost of drugs has represented the greatest growth in the health sector. In spite of some deinstitutionalization policies, the growth in the pharmaceutical sector is likely to continue as the population ages.

7. The cost of medical care is currently at the centre of a number of political debates regarding the provision of a universal social safety net.

8. The privatization of medical care continues to grow. Now about one-third of the cost of medical services to Canadians can be considered to be out-or-pocket.

9. The successes and failures of medicare continue to be debated.

KEY TERMS

accessibility	comprehensive coverage	portability
administration	fee-for-service	principles of medicare
allopathic doctors	Flexner Report	universality
barber-surgeons	homeopathy	
capitation	pharmacare	

QUESTIONS FOR STUDY AND DISCUSSION

1. Imagine living during the cholera and early flu epidemics in Canada. Describe how your life might have changed. Now think of and research the SARS outbreak. Do you know anyone who was directly affected?

2. Describe and critically analyze the early organizing efforts made by the allopathic doctors. Are there ways that the medical profession continues to maintain dominance in the division of labour among health-care providers?

3. Explain in detail why some forces supported the development of a nationally funded medical care scheme and others rejected it. Then discuss the arguments for and against the increasing privatization of the health-care system today.

4. How has medicare altered the heal Canadians?

5. How has medicare altered the work of doctors.

6. Debate the public/private issues with respect to medical care in Canada today.

SUGGESTED READINGS

Miller, A.B., C. Wall, P. Sun, C.J. Baines, T. To, and S.A. Narod. 2014. "Twenty-five Year Follow-up for Breast Cancer Incidence and Mortality of the Canadian National Breast Cancer Screening Study: Randomized Screening Trial." *British Medical Journal* 348. http://www.bmj.com/content/348/bmj.g366. The results of a twenty-five-year follow-up of the impact of screening on breast cancer.

Tannenbaum, C., and R.T. Tsuyki. 2013. "The Expanding Scope of Pharmacists' Practice Implications for Physicians." *Canadian Medical Association Journal* 185, 4: 1228–32. An article documenting some of the changes in the work of pharmacists now and in the future.

Ubelacker, S. 2013. "MDs' Gross Income $307,000, Report Finds." *Globe and Mail*, 22 Jan. http://www.theglobeandmail.com/life/health-and-fitness/health/mds-gross-income-307000-report-finds/article7640498/. Discussion of Canadian doctors' incomes.

Usher, W., and J. Skinner. 2012. "EMPIRE and Health Website Recommendations: Technologies of Control." *Social Theory & Health* 10, 1: 20–41. A thought-provoking piece on the power of the Internet in health.

The Medical Profession, Autonomy, and Medical Error

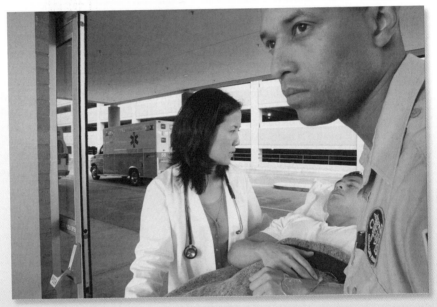

Paul Burns/Thinkstock.com

CHAPTER OVERVIEW

▶ Medical practice is considered to be a professional occupation.

▶ Three somewhat different theories of professionalization are occupation, process, and ideology.

▶ The medical profession has consolidated its position through the subordination, limitation, and exclusion of other types of health-care providers.

▶ Norman Bethune and Banting and Best are notable Canadians in the history of medicine.

▶ Medical education has changed substantially over the past few centuries.

▶ Medical students tend to be from relatively high socio-economic backgrounds.

▶ The proportion of female and visible minority medical students is increasing.

▶ Medical responsibility and clinical experience are among the values that doctors learn during their education.

▶ There are several useful critiques of contemporary medical education.

▶ Some of the critical issues in medical organization and practice today are autonomy, control, authority, technical and moral mistakes, and variations in practice norms and variations.

Introduction

Why is the occupation of the physician thought of as an ideal profession? What is it about medical practice and medical knowledge that enabled medicalization to become such a profound social force and discourse? What is a profession? How do physicians fit into the whole medical care system? Are doctors losing or gaining power, prestige, and income? Membership in a professional occupation has long been associated with a sense of high moral calling and dedication to service. Such values are not necessary, however. Doctors do not learn all that must be learned in medical school, but must continue to study and learn for the rest of their working lives. As we all do, doctors face conflicts at work. How do doctors handle mistakes or conflicts? To whom are doctors accountable? What is the place of physicians in the great narratives of medicalization and biomedicalization? These are among the issues that interest medical sociologists. The purpose of this chapter is to analyze the work of the physician as a profession and to describe the process of medical education in the context of North American society, both today and in the past. The chapter will examine the division of labour and medical practice, the issues of social control and autonomy within the profession, ideas about physicians' networks and their cultural environment, their handling of mistakes, and medical education.

The "Profession" of Medicine

The idea that medicine is a profession is relatively new. Yet, in the last century or so, the medical doctor has become the archetypal professional to the lay public and to those other occupational groups aspiring to reach the "heights" of professional status. That the status of the doctor reflects and reinforces the processes of medicalization and biomedicalization, two of the most influential discourses of the day, makes understanding it crucial to appreciating these grand projects.

There are three distinct ways to think about professions and professionalization: the trait approach, the process/power approach, and the ideological approach. Each of these will be considered in turn.

Profession as Occupation: The Trait Approach

The view of the **profession as occupation** is called the trait approach. The basis of this view is that an occupation became a profession through an accumulation of traits. William Goode (1956, 1960) thought that professions were special occupations that embodied two basic characteristics: (1) prolonged training in a body of specialized, abstract knowledge; and (2) a service orientation. Goode broke these two characteristics down further and described the traits of a profession as follows (1960).

1. It determines its own standards for education and training.
2. There are stringent educational requirements.
3. Practice often involves legal recognition through some form of licensing.
4. Licensing and admission standards are determined and managed by members of the profession.
5. Most legislation with respect to the practice of the profession is shaped by the profession.
6. The profession is characterized by relatively high power, prestige, and income.
7. The professional practitioner is relatively free of lay control and evaluation.
8. The norms of practice enforced by the profession are more stringent than legal controls.
9. Members are more strongly identified and affiliated with their profession than members of other occupational groups.
10. Members usually stay in the profession for life.

The characteristics of the medical profession in Canada today are similar to those suggested by Goode. Physicians themselves largely determine what constitutes appropriate subject matter for the study and practical experience of physicians-in-training. Medical schools have some of the most stringent admittance criteria of any educational programs. In addition to grades, many medical schools consider the personal qualities of the applicants, such as their ethical views, behaviour, self-presentation in an interview, volunteer work, ability to work with others as "team" players, leadership abilities, and, increasingly, whole-person communication skills, and the Medical College Admissions Test (MCAT) scores (www.campusaccess.com/campus_weB/educ/e4grad_mecan.hyn).The profession, too, determines licensing and admittance standards. Medicine is characterized by the relatively high power, prestige, and income of its professional practitioners. Physicians are largely controlled via various profession-managed committees and organizations, such as the College of Physicians and Surgeons. Such committees are composed primarily of practising doctors. Their own norms, incorporated in the Code of Ethics (Box 11.1), are more exacting than the law, in some ways, although they are not necessarily strictly enforced. A doctor's identity as a person is tied to his or her occupation. This affects all other aspects of his/her life, including family life. Usually, a career in medicine is a lifetime career and the occupation becomes linked to the very identity of the doctor. That doctors have their own code of ethics is just one more reflection of their claim to professionalism. The following box offers some highlights of the Code of Ethics developed by the Canadian Medical Association (CMA).

HIGHLIGHTED ISSUES

BOX 11.1   Canadian Medical Association's Code of Ethics

The CMA's Code of Ethics includes 54 statements of principle under eight different categories. The following is a small representation under just two of the categories, the "General Responsibilities" and "Responsibilities to Society."

General Responsibilities

1. Consider first the well-being of the patient.
2. Treat all patients with respect; do not exploit them for personal advantage.
3. Provide for appropriate care for your patient, including physical comfort and spiritual and psychosocial support, even when cure is no longer possible.
4. Practise the art and science of medicine competently and without impairment.
5. Engage in lifelong learning to maintain and improve your professional knowledge, skills, and attitudes.
6. Recognize your limitations and the competence of others and, when indicated, recommend that additional opinions and services be sought.

Responsibilities to Society

1. Recognize that community, society, and the environment are important factors in the health of individual patients.
2. Recognize the profession's responsibility to society in matters relating to public health, health education, environmental protection, legislation affecting the health or well-being of the community, and the need for testimony at judicial proceedings.
3. Recognize the responsibility of physicians to promote equitable access to health care resources.
4. Use health care resources prudently.
5. Recognize a responsibility to give the generally held opinions of the profession when interpreting scientific knowledge to the public; when presenting an opinion that is contrary to the generally held opinion of the profession, so indicate.

Source: Canadian Medical Association, Code of Ethics. http://policybase.cma.ca/dbtw-wpd/PolicyPDF/PD04-06.pdf.

Goode's view of professions has a number of limitations. First, it is based on an acceptance of the viewpoint or ideology put forward by the professional group itself. For example, the idea that the norms of practice are more stringent than legal controls represents an ideological perspective. The ideology of a particular occupation cannot help but be self-serving. Second, it ignores the fundamental importance of the power, not just as a characteristic but as a force behind the very ability to define the professional group. This power enables the group to maintain the prevailing ideology both internally and in society at large. Third, this analysis does not take into account the fight for changes in the profession over time. Fourth, it ignores the relationship between the profession and the rest of society— the state, the economic and political structure, and the social organization of the society. In brief, the trait approach ignores the historical development of the profession and its political, economic, and moral place in society.

Profession as Process

The second designation of profession is that it is a social construction that results from a process through which various occupational groups progress or aspire to progress over time under various conditions (see Table 11.1). Professionalization, the accomplishment of the title and status of profession as described by Goode (1960), is the goal. Wilensky's (1964) work is representative of this **profession as process** approach.

The steps to becoming a professional in this perspective are as follows: first, the members of the occupation engage in full-time work; second, they establish a relationship with a training/education program; third, they establish an association; fourth, they gain legal status; and fifth, they construct a code of ethics. This approach brings a historical perspective to the concept of the profession. It also has the advantage of showing that occupations can be seen as falling along a continuum with respect to the degree of professionalism they incorporate. Underlying this model, as well as the trait approach, is the view that the profession is a more desirable and higher calling than other occupations.

Johnson's (1972, 1977, 1982) model of the professions bridges the process and the ideology approaches in what we can call the power-analysis approach. Johnson describes professions with respect to process, too, but he focuses on how occupational groups come to think of themselves, present themselves, and fight to be identified as professions as they increase in power. He sees

TABLE 11.1 Profession as Process

	Non-Profession	**Profession**
Education	Very little, very simple concrete educational training not associated with a university.	Complex, abstract, esoteric, lengthy education associated with university.
Licensing	Anyone can call themselves a …	Profession itself determines eligibility and continuously evaluates ongoing suitability to maintain professional status.
Code of ethics	Each person for himself or herself and to his or her own benefit.	Altruism, higher calling, collectivity orientation and identity.
Association	Each person for himself or herself and to his or her own benefit.	Organized group encompassing most people actively pursuing the profession.
Peer control	State-based laws to control individual behaviour and discipline.	Professional association determines standards of education, professional activity, and disciplines members in violation.

power as the ability of the professional practitioners to define "reality" in an increasingly broad way, and even to define "the good life" for their clients.

From this viewpoint, the fundamental characteristic of a profession is the ability of the group to impose its perspective and the necessity for its services upon its clients. Professional power arises out of the uncertainty in the relationship between the client and the professional; this uncertainty stems from the social distance between the two parties. Three crucial variables determine the degree of power held by a professional group: (1) the more esoteric the knowledge base of professional practice and the less accessible this knowledge is to the lay public, the greater the power of the profession; (2) the greater the social distance between the client and the professional (e.g., when the professional is, for instance, of a higher income level and social class than the client), the greater the power of the profession; and (3) the greater the homogeneity of the professional group in contrast with the heterogeneity of the client group, the greater the ability of the group to organize and assert their power.

Subordination, Limitation, and Exclusion in the Medical Labour Force

In the process of becoming a profession and maintaining this status, doctors have also sought to restrict the scope of the work of other types of practitioners. According to Willis (1983), the allopathic medical profession achieved the level of dominance it has come to enjoy by three distinct processes in comparison with other occupational groups. The first is **subordination**. This refers to the process whereby potentially or actually competing professions come to work under the direct control of the doctors. Nursing is an example of this process, because the practice of nursing has been severely restricted and constrained so that the primary legal position of most nursing practice today is subordinate to the medical profession (see Chapter 13).

The second process is called **limitation**, and is illustrated by such occupations as dentistry,

optometry, and pharmacy. Such occupations are not directly under the control of the allopathic practitioners, but they are indirectly controlled through legal restrictions that serve the power of the medical profession. The process by which pharmacy came to be subordinate to medicine is a case in point. In the nineteenth century, pharmacists operated as primary caregivers. They prescribed medicines to patients who came to them for help, particularly to the poor and doctorless. The roles of the pharmacists and the doctors overlapped at that time because most doctors made and dispensed their own drugs. When the pharmacists in Canada became self-regulating in 1870–1, they agreed on an informal compromise with the doctors. Pharmacists gave up prescribing, and doctors generally gave up dispensing drugs.

The third process, **exclusion**, is the process whereby certain occupations that are not licensed and therefore are denied official legitimacy and tax-based financial support come to be considered "alternative" practices. The Australian example given by Willis (1983) is that of chiropractic. Chiropractors in Canada have an ambiguous position today (see Chapter 13). Perhaps a better Canadian example would be naturopaths. Because naturopathic medicine is based on a different model of science than allopathic medicine and is not yet the subject of sufficient (traditional scientific) research confirming its effectiveness, it is not considered a mainstream medical practice and its practitioners are not funded under medicare.

Significant changes have occurred in the legal status of complementary and alternative health-care practice across the country in the last few decades. In Ontario, for example, the Regulated Health Practitioners Act came into effect in 1991 and was amended in 2010 (www.e-laws.gov.on.ca/html/statutes/english/elaws_statutes_91r18_e.htm). This landmark legislation restricts allopathic monopoly. Consumers can now choose the form of health care they desire, although they may have to pay privately for such alternative services.

Profession as Ideology

An ideology is a group of descriptive and pre-scriptive beliefs used to explain and legitimize certain practices and viewpoints. Doctors pro-fess these beliefs, as Freidson (1975) implies in the title of his book *The Profession of Medicine*. Parsons (1951) adopted the prevailing ideology of professionals when he argued that a profession has the following characteristics: (1) universalism, (2) functional specificity, (3) affective neutrality, and (4) a collectivity orientation. In this view of the **profession as ideology** a physician is expected to apply universalistic, scientifically based stan-dards to all patients. Physicians are not to differ-entiate between patients or their treatments on the basis of social differences such as gender, educa-tion, income level, or race, for instance, or on the basis of other personal preferences, attractions,

or repulsions. The work of the physician is also functionally specific to the malfunctioning of the human body and mind. Functional specificity requires that the physician not offer advice to a patient on non-medical matters such as real estate or choice of a career, but restrict advice to health and disease. The doctor is expected to refrain from emotional involvement, in other words, to be affectively neutral. Finally, the physician is expected to exhibit a collectivity orientation, that is, to provide service to others out of a sense of calling to the profession and an altruistic desire to serve others. Self-interest, whether expressed in terms of financial rewards or other aspects of working conditions, is not appropriate within the ideology of medical practice.

This view is ideological—and it has served the medical profession well. Through the spread of

---

REMEMBERING OUR HISTORY

BOX 11.2 Norman Bethune

Norman Bethune, born in 1890 in Gravenhurst, Ontario, became a prominent Canadian thor-acic surgeon who served in three wars and distinguished himself as a surgeon on three continents.

Bethune came from a family with high stan-dards and widely recognized achievement. His great-great-grandfather, Reverend John Bethune (1751–1815), built Canada's first Presbyterian church in Montreal. One of his sons, John Bethune (1791–1872), became Rector of Montreal and Principal of McGill University. Two other sons, Alexander and Angus, also achieved prominence in their chosen professions: Alexander became the second Anglican Bishop of Toronto; Angus became a successful fur trader and businessman who was involved in the two great Canadian fur-trading companies, the North West Company and the Hudson's Bay Company, and later was a dir-ector of the Bank of Upper Canada. Angus's son, Norman (Bethune's grandfather), was educated

in Toronto and learned surgery in Edinburgh before returning to Toronto to become one of the co-founders of Trinity Medical School in 1850. Norman himself was one of three children of Elizabeth Ann Goodwin and Malcolm Bethune.

Bethune worked in a number of jobs, as a lumberjack and as a teacher, teaching immi-grants how to read. From 1909 to 1911 he was registered in pre-medical studies at the University of Toronto. Just before his third year of medicine, Bethune joined the Royal Canadian Army Medical Corps. After he was wounded at Ypres he returned to Canada to complete his medical degree by 1916. In 1923 he mar-ried Frances Campbell Penney with whom he had a stormy and ambivalent relationship. They were divorced and later married again. In 1927–8, Bethune contracted tuberculosis and was treated at Trudeau Sanatorium in New York. As a result of his experience of illness, Bethune developed an interest in thoracic surgery and

continued

entered practice with Dr Edward Archibald, a renowned thoracic surgeon at the Royal Victoria Hospital in Montreal. Here Bethune engaged in research on tuberculosis. During this time he invented a variety of surgical instruments that became widely used in North America.

Bethune is, however, best known for his political activities. In 1936, Bethune tried to establish a state-supported medicare system for Canadians. He organized a group of doctors, nurses, and social workers, called the Montreal Group for the Security of People's Health. Outraged at the refusal of the Canadian Medical Association to support plans for socialized medicine, he sailed for Spain at the outbreak of civil war in October 1936 to aid in the struggle against the Nationalist forces of General Franco. In Spain he devised a method to transport blood to the wounded on the battlefields.

As a professed communist, it was almost impossible for Bethune to remain in Canada. When war broke out in China, Bethune decided to help in the fight for communism. Medical treatment was needed. With funds donated by the China Aid Council and also from the League for Peace and Democracy, Bethune purchased much-needed medical supplies. He arrived in Yannarv in 1938 and quickly moved to the front lines in the mountains of East Shanxi. Travelling with the Eighth Route Army, he devoted his remaining years to fighting fascism and saving the lives of the soldiers who stood for the cause he, too, believed in. His fame reached China's political leaders. Summoned to meet Chairman Mao Zedong, Bethune convinced the leader of the need for surgical knowledge in the front lines of the Chin-Cha'a Border Region.

Bethune founded a medical school and model hospital that would later be renamed the Norman Bethune International Peace Hospital. He has a place in history's pages as a great surgeon and humanitarian. Bethune died in China of septicemia on 12 November 1939.

Sources: Gordon and Allan (1952); Shephard (1982); Stewart (1977).

Bamboo scroll painting of Norman Bethune, unknown artist. Bethune is still known as a hero in China; in 2003, when the SARS breakout in China was recognized by the government, those who went to treat the ill became known as "Bethunes."

such a view the public came to believe that doctors are "morally superior" individuals who deserve to be trusted, to dominate the practice of medicine, to hold a monopoly in the construction, maintenance, and spread of what is taken to be official "medical knowledge," to control standards for their training, and to discipline their errant members themselves. The power and beneficence attributed to the medical profession have been instrumental in the growth of medicalization.

Deprofessionalization

Widespread debate is ongoing today about the extent to which deprofessionalization or a proletarianization of medical work is occurring (Broom, 2005). Erosion of professionalism is seen in the increasing control experienced by doctors from insurance companies and government billing bureaucracies (ibid.). It occurs in the demystification of medical knowledge through widespread access to the Internet and to health information there and in other places (ibid.). A number of health and social movements, such as the women's health movement, the HIV/AIDS movement, and the breast and prostate cancer movements, also are indications of an increase in consumer power and, indeed, an increase in citizen knowledge about health matters and a decrease in medical power. More recently, the widespread citizens' response to the "liberation" treatment for multiple sclerosis (MS) demonstrates the growing power of engaged citizens rallying together via means such as online support groups and listservs and other social media for MS (liberation-treatment.com). The processes of medicalization and biomedicalization are today supported by more powerful forces than doctors' organizations (as has been described in Chapters 8 and 9).

The view that medicine is a profession that is above reproach is no longer tenable. Instead, it is challenged today in the wake of increasing costs without parallel improvements in life expectancy or health quality, mounting evidence of doctors' mistakes, growing rates of errors associated with hospitals and pharmaceuticals (www.chsrf.

ca/mythbusters/pdf/myth15_e.pdf), and media reports of individual doctors being criminally charged for sexual assault of patients. Moreover, in the wake of the "financial and debt crises," the future growth of the increasingly specialized occupations in medicine was, for a time, curtailed. During the last few decades, hospitals have been closed across the country. Home health care was to have been expanded. The federal government appears to have been increasingly supportive of what has come to be called "health promotion and disease prevention." Alternative health-care providers such as midwives have become legalized, with their own colleges, in various parts of the country (cmrc-ccosf.ca/node/19). Furthermore, midwives recently have been granted a degree of professional autonomy. Challenges to the exclusive rights of allopathic doctors to dispense medical care are evident in many alternatives. The growing autonomy of nurse practitioners challenges the exclusive knowledge of medical practice, as well. Questioning the expertise of groups and occupations such as allopathic doctors is also one telling aspect of what has come to be called the "risk society" (Beck, 1992, 1994).

Another threat to medical dominance is the easy availability, to millions of people around the globe, of medical information via the Internet. Physicians today have to deal with patients coming to their offices primed with information gleaned from the Internet. They may have already decided on their diagnosis and be visiting to demand a particular type of drug or treatment they have learned about through the Internet or other media. Interestingly, the evidence suggests that patients are not only more likely than not to get a prescription when they ask for one but also to get a prescription for the particular brand name for which they have asked (see Rochon Ford and Saibil, 2010). Nettleton calls this increasing reliance on the Internet "e-scaped medicine" (2004).

An important blow to the Canadian popular belief in the altruism of the medical profession arose at the time of the 1962 doctors' strike in Saskatchewan. A more recent and equally dramatic demonstration was the strike over extra-billing by many Ontario doctors in 1986. Still, however, in regard to public perception of ethics, a 2009 Nanos poll found doctors and pharmacists ranked more highly than 16 other professions, at 77 and 73 per cent, respectively (www.nanosresearch.com/library/polls/POLNAT-S09-T388.pdf). This percentage was higher than that for police officers, at 58 per cent, and even clergy, at 50 per cent (possibly related to the sex abuse and residential school scandals associated with some priests and churches). There are many examples of doctors and medical organizations fighting for the health and well-being of the most vulnerable around the world. Doctors Without Borders is a case in point (http://www.cbc.ca/news/canada/refugee-health-care-cuts-doctors-gave-voice-to-most-vulnerable-1.2696961).

The altruism of many in the medical profession is evident in a number of new initiatives. Doctors have become increasingly militant in their fight for what they consider to be improvements in health-care accessibility and funding. Strikes, lawsuits against the government, and limitations in access to service are among the job actions taken by doctors in British Columbia, Quebec, Alberta, and Manitoba in the latter part of the twentieth century and into the twenty-first century (Sibbald, 1998). Another recent indication of the willingness or necessity of doctors to fight for what they believe can be found in the recent Supreme Court decision in *Chaoulli*. On 9 June 2005 the Supreme Court of Canada ruled on a case in which a physician and patient sued the Quebec government after a year-long wait for hip replacement surgery. The high court struck down a Quebec law prohibiting the purchase of private insurance to cover procedures already offered within the public system. In response to the Supreme Court decision, the Quebec government asked for time to implement changes and proposed the introduction of guaranteed wait times for some procedures, such as radiation treatments, cardiac and cataract surgery, and knee and hip replacements (www.cbc.ca/news/background/healthcare/). Wait times have

improved somewhat in more recent years, and the federal government has set benchmarks for the wait times on certain procedures (http://www.parl.gc.ca/Content/LOP/researchpublications/prb0582-e.htm). Already, as documented in the previous chapter, private health-care services are widely available in Canada for those who can afford to pay for them (for just one list of available private clinics, see: www.findprivate-clinics.ca/Corporate_Health/258-0.html). More recently, doctors have organized against the federal government's refusal of medical care to refugee applicants and have been part of a movement that had the Supreme Court strike down the cuts to health care for refugees proposed by the federal government (http://www.cbc.ca/news/canada/refugee-health-care-cuts-doctors-gave-voice-to-most-vulnerable-1.2696961).

A Brief History of Medical Education in North America

After 1800, a growing number of proprietary medical schools (profit-making institutions that were generally owned by doctors who also served as teachers) began to open in North America. The quality of the education they offered was poor. They were usually ill equipped for teaching, but then medical theory was still very simple (Wertz and Wertz, 1986: 137). Bleeding, the application of leeches, and the ingestion of purgatives to cause vomiting were still the treatments of choice. At this time people were as likely to be harmed as helped by the prevalent and accepted methods of cure.

The most advanced medical training of the time was in Europe, especially France and Germany, where medical research was well supported. Louis Pasteur's germ theory, proposed in the mid-nineteenth century, had a remarkable effect on medicine and, with the new "medical gaze" (Foucault, 1973), provided the basis for the discovery, classification, and treatment of numerous diseases. By the end of the century German physicians had made significant discoveries in the world of medical science, too. Rudolf Virchow described a general model of disease development based on cellular pathology (1858), and Robert Koch discovered the bacilli for anthrax (1876), tuberculosis (1882), and cholera (1883). Because of these exciting developments in European medical science, American doctors began to cross the ocean for their education and training. Approximately 15,000 American doctors studied in German-speaking universities from about 1870 to 1914.

European training soon became a symbol of status among Americans. Those with such training were able to establish more prestigious and specialized practices than American-trained doctors. By the beginning of the twentieth century, medical research was well funded by the Carnegie and Rockefeller families. The United States began to move ahead as a leader in the development of scientific and medical resources.

Medical education, too, was radically revised and upgraded at the beginning of the twentieth century. As discussed in Chapter 10, the Flexner Report, published in 1910, reviewed medical education in the US and Canada. Sponsored by the Carnegie Foundation, Abraham Flexner visited every medical school in the two countries. Only three American medical schools, Harvard, Johns Hopkins, and Western Reserve, were given approval. The others were severely criticized and were characterized as "plague spots, utterly wretched." Flexner's observations about Canadian medical schools were very similar to those regarding the American schools. As he said:

> In the matter of medical schools, Canada reproduces the United States on a greatly reduced scale. Western University (London) is as bad as anything to be found on this side of the line; Laval and Halifax Medical Colleges are feeble; Winnipeg and Kingston represent a distinct effort toward higher ideals; McGill and Toronto are excellent. (Flexner, 1910: 325)

According to the report, 90 per cent of the practising doctors lacked a college education, and the vast majority had attended inadequate medical schools (Wertz and Wertz, 1986: 138). Flexner recommended that medical schools consist of full-time, highly educated faculty and be affiliated with a university. He suggested that laboratory and hospital facilities be associated with universities. He recommended the establishment of admission standards. Medical education, he argued, should be at the graduate school level. However, the effects of the Flexner Report were not as devastating to Canadian schools as to the American schools because Canadian medical schools had already been limited and controlled in their growth. In addition, there were far fewer proprietary schools in Canada. Proprietary schools were gradually closed, and medical education was upgraded slowly. The large American foundations donated monies to Canadian medicine and a scientifically based practice was established.

REMEMBERING OUR HISTORY

BOX 11.3   Sir Frederick G. Banting and Charles H. Best

Banting and Best are known for their discovery of how to extract the hormone insulin from the pancreas. This made possible the treatment of diabetes mellitus, a disease in which an abnormal buildup of glucose occurs in the body. In 1923 Banting was a co-recipient of the Nobel Prize for physiology and medicine for his research and the development of insulin.

Banting's interest in medicine was aroused as the result of a childhood incident. One day, while on his way home from school, he stopped to look at two men who had just begun the

continued

first row of shingles on the roof of a new house. As he watched, the scaffolding on which they stood suddenly broke. The two men fell to the ground and were badly injured. Banting ran for the doctor, who arrived in a matter of minutes. "I watched every movement of those skilful hands as he examined the injured men and tended to cuts, bruises, and broken bones. In those tense minutes I thought that the greatest service in life is that of the medical profession. From that day it was my greatest ambition to become a doctor."

He studied at the University of Toronto and became committed to his idea that insulin, a hormone secreted by certain cells within the pancreas, would cure diabetes. However, Banting's qualifications as an investigator of carbohydrate metabolism were limited. He needed an assistant.

Realizing Banting's dilemma, Professor J.J. Macleod at the University of Toronto mentioned to his senior class in physiology that a young surgeon was carrying out research on the pancreatic islets and the isolation of the antidiabetic hormone. Two students, C.H. Best and E.C. Noble, had previously been engaged in experimental studies of diabetes and had an understanding of carbohydrate metabolism as well as the specific skills required to perform the necessary tests. Both were chosen assistants for a period of four weeks each. They tossed a coin to decide who would work the first four weeks and Best won. Mr Noble never did return to assist Banting. Best became his permanent assistant. Banting and Best made a good team. Their skills complemented each other. The younger man's knowledge of the latest biochemical procedures complemented the surgical skills of the older man.

On 16 May 1921 Banting and Best were given 10 dogs and the use of a laboratory for eight weeks. Their first task was to ligate the pancreatic ducts of a number of dogs. The next step involved trying to produce experimental diabetes. Many animal rights activists argued against the use of dogs in Banting and Best's experiments. However, Banting adopted a very caring attitude towards these "assistants." He made sure the dogs were always spared unnecessary pain.

By 21 July 1921 a depancreatized dog and a duct-tied dog with a pancreas were available. Banting opened the abdominal cavity of the latter dog, removed the shrivelled pancreas, and chopped it into small pieces. This mass was ground up and saline was added. Banting and Best administered 5 cc intravenously to the depancreatized dog. Samples of blood were taken at half-hour intervals and analyzed for sugar content. The blood sugar fell and the clinical condition of the dog improved.

On 11 January 1922, after months of research to perfect the extract, Banting and Best were ready to experiment with a patient. The first patient was a 14-year-old boy suffering from juvenile diabetes. When he was admitted to the Toronto General Hospital he was poorly nourished, pale, weighed a meagre 65 pounds, and his hair was falling out. A test for sugar was strongly positive. He received daily injections of the extract. An immediate improvement occurred. The boy excreted less sugar, and he became brighter, more active, and felt stronger. This 14-year-old boy was the first of many children who were helped by the discoveries of Banting and Best.

In 1923, Banting and Professor Macleod jointly received the Nobel Prize in physiology and medicine for their investigations into and research on insulin, the active principle of the Islands of Langerhans of the pancreas and regulator of the sugar level in the blood. Macleod received this joint recognition for sharing his laboratory facilities and for finding Best as a collaborator for Banting. Macleod insisted on the verification of the initial work and the repetition of certain controlled experiments. However, Macleod did not create the serum. Banting was somewhat annoyed that Best did not receive any recognition or award for his work, so he divided equally his share of the award money ($40,000) with Best. Furthermore, Banting always assigned "equal credit" for the discovery of insulin to his friend and assistant, Best.

Sources: Bliss (1982, 1984); Castiglioni (1941); Stevenson (1946); *Academic American Encyclopedia*, vol. 3 (1980: 71); *Colliers Encyclopedia*, vol. 3 (1973: 602); *Encyclopedia Britannica*, vol. 3 (1976: 134).

By the mid-1920s the medical profession in America had clearly established itself as a leading profession. Its standards for training had been improved and were considered excellent. Medical research had reached great heights. The power of the doctor as a healer and as a scientist was widely assumed.

Medical Education in Canada Today

The first Canadian medical school, established in 1824 with 25 students, was at the Montreal Medical Institution, which became the faculty of medicine of McGill University in 1829 (Hamowy, 1984). By the turn of the century six other university medical schools had opened their doors—Toronto, Laval (Montreal and Quebec City campuses), Queen's, Dalhousie, Western, and Manitoba. From the early 1980s to the late 1990s, the number of students admitted to the first year of medical school declined. In 1983, 1,887 students were admitted. By 1997 only 1,577 students were admitted to medical schools in Canada—a 30 per cent decline in the number of first-year positions per 100,000 Canadians—in spite of population growth and aging (Buske, 1999a: 772). Since then, the number of physicians per 1,000 people has continued to grow as a result of the high rates of immigration of physicians, as well as increased medical school enrolments. Since 1997–8, first-year enrolments in Canadian medical faculties have climbed steadily: by 2004–5 enrolments had reached 2,193, in 2009 total first-year enrolment was 2,742; and in 2012–13 first-year enrolment was 2,919 (http://www.afmc.ca/pdf/Cmes2013_Enrolment-Attrition-2014-05-09.pdf, p. 11). Of the medical students enrolled in 2012–13, 56.1 per cent were female (Table 11.2).

The process of becoming a doctor requires three different steps: an undergraduate education in science and/or arts, graduate study leading to the MD, and a minimum one-year internship in which the graduate MD works in a hospital or clinic under the supervision of practising doctors. During the internship year students write qualifying exams through the Medical Council of Canada, after which a licence to practise medicine is issued by any one of the provincial medical licensing bodies. Many doctors continue after the internship to specialize in family practice or any of a number of different specialties recognized by the Royal College of Physicians and Surgeons of Canada. Today, 17 Canadian universities grant an MD degree and there are new programs around the country, including in northern Ontario and northern British Columbia (http://www.afmc.ca/pdf/CMES2013-2014-06-04-reduced.pdf).

Medical students have been and continue to tend to be drawn from middle- and upper-middle-class family backgrounds, although some medical schools are making a concerted effort to admit people whose first language is not English and who come from poorer backgrounds (www.straight.com/article-338984/vancouver/ubc-med-school-seeks-less-affluent-students). The proportion of women graduating from medical school has altered significantly: 6 per cent of all graduates in 1959 and 44 per cent in 1989 were women (Williams et al., 1993). By 1990, women comprised almost 50 per cent of all medical students. As noted above, women students now outnumber males. This trend is likely to continue, as the rates of female university enrolment in all fields, with the exceptions of math and engineering, are higher than the rates of male enrolment, according to Statistics Canada (http://www.statcan.gc.ca/pub/81-582-x/2010004/tbl/tbld1.5-eng.htm).

Medical education is both expensive and lengthy. This means that it is generally more difficult for young people from less affluent families to attend. Tuition has continued to increase with the growing privatization of universities and professional schools in particular (www.nlma.nl.ca/nexus/issues/winter_2004/articles/article_16.html). Currently, medical school tuition varies considerably from school to school and province to province, ranging from a high of over $20,000 per year at McMaster down to a low in Quebec (for in-province students) of about $3,102

TABLE 11.2   Total Enrolment in Canadian Faculties of Medicine by Sex, 1968–9 to 2012–13

Year	Men	Women	Total	% Women
1968–9	4,012	669	4,681	14.3
1969–70	4,259	795	5,054	15.7
1970–1	4,457	967	5,424	17.8
1971–2	4,690	1,162	5,852	19.9
1972–3	4,936	1,389	6,325	22.0
1973–4	5,127	1,632	6,759	24.1
1974–5	5,181	1,831	7,012	26.1
1975–6	5,167	2,042	7,209	28.3
1976–7	5,065	2,197	7,262	30.3
1977–8	5,002	2,306	7,308	31.6
1978–9	4,877	2,432	7,309	33.3
1979–80	4,810	2,537	7,347	34.5
1980–1	4,710	2,677	7,387	36.2
1981–2	4,649	2,787	7,436	37.5
1982–3	4,553	2,939	7,492	39.2
1983–4	4,433	3,051	7,484	40.8
1984–5	4,349	3,124	7,473	41.8
1985–6	4,219	3,131	7,350	42.6
1986–7	4,177	3,124	7,301	42.8
1987–8	4,059	3,147	7,206	43.7
1988–9	3,961	3,163	7,124	44.4
1989–90	3,960	3,112	7,072	44.0
1990–1	3,956	3,154	7,110	44.4
1991–2	3,959	3,169	7,128	44.5
1992–3	3,817	3,224	7,041	45.8
1993–4	3,616	3,300	6,916	47.7
1994–5	3,496	3,324	6,820	48.7
1995–6	3,276	3,358	6,634	50.6
1996–7	3,189	3,262	6,451	50.6
1997–8	3,189	3,246	6,435	50.4
1998–9	3,139	3,253	6,392	50.9
1999–2000	3,155	3,233	6,388	50.6
2000–1	3,151	3,408	6,559	52.0
2001–2	3,513	3,784	6,937	54.5
2002–3	3,216	4,176	7,392	56.5
2003–4	3,276	4,532	7,808	58.0
2004–5	3,367	4,869	8,236	59.1
2005–6	3,605	5,082	8,687	58.5
2006–7	3,828	5,323	9,151	58.2
2007–8	4,052	5,588	9,640	58.0
2008–9	4,254	5,894	10,148	58.1
2009–10	4,427	6,091	10,518	57.9
2010–11	4,592	6,261	10,853	57.7
2011–12	4,802	6,340	11,142	56.9
2012–13	4,990	6,385	11,375	56.1

Note: Includes students enrolled in *année préparatoire* at the Université de Montréal.

Source: Adapted from Canadian Medical Education Statistics 2013. Office of Research and Information Services, Association of Faculties of Medicine of Canada, http://www.afmc.ca/pdf/Cmes2013_Enrolment-Attrition-2014-05-09.pdf.

(http://www.macleans.ca/news/canada/how-much-they-pay-for-it/). Despite the high cost, applicants to medical school today exceed the available spaces (content.healthaffairs.org/cgi/content/full/22/4/71). Although doctors are well remunerated financially as compared to the average employed Canadian (Table 11.3), the attraction of gaining a medical education and becoming a licensed practitioner certainly involves more than simply making a comfortable income. In business occupations, for example, with less education (possibly an MBA) a bright and hard-working person can hope to make a lot more money.

The Process of Becoming a Doctor

The most influential and complete sociological studies of medical education were done in the 1950s and 1960s. The two most notable were the studies done at the University of Chicago by Howard S. Becker and colleagues—*Boys in White: Student Culture in Medical School* (1961)—and at Columbia University by Robert K. Merton et al.— *The Student Physician: Introductory Studies in the Sociology of Medical Education* (1957). Each in

TABLE 11.3   Average Gross Income per Physician Who Received at least $60,000 in Fee-for-Service Payments, by Type of Practice, 2012–13

	Average
Family medicine	**247,490**
Medical specialties (avg.)	**323,755**
Internal medicine	384,082
Neurology	294,258
Psychiatry	232,966
Pediatrics	269,157
Dermatology	410,451
Physical medicine	270,625
Anesthesia	335,371
Surgical specialties (avg.)	**446,138**
General surgery	394,806
Thoracic/cardiovascular surgery	480,136
Urology	441,528
Orthopedic surgery	388,308
Plastic surgery	357,024
Neurosurgery	401,491
Ophthalmology	701,143
Otolaryngology	410,591
Obstetrics/gynecology	412,798
Total specialties	**364,173**
Total physicians	**305,869**

Note: Alternative forms of reimbursement, such as salary and capitation, are not included. Based on gross payments.

Source: Adapted from Table A.5.1, Physicians in Canada, 2013, Canadian Institute for Health Information, https://secure.cihi.ca/estore/productFamily.htm?locale=en&pf=PFC2675.

its own way contributed to our knowledge of the socialization of the physician. Each explained some of the processes whereby young men (the vast majority of students were male in those days) pass through one of the most rigorous, busy, lengthy, and pressured educational programs and come to adopt the values, norms, skills, and knowledge expected of a medical doctor.

Becker and his colleagues observed and spent time doing participant observation with medical students during their years of medical education at the University of Kansas Medical School. These researchers noted that the major consequences of medical school were that physicians-in-training became aware of the importance of two dominant values: clinical experience and medical responsibility. These two dominant values then guided and directed the strategies used to manage the potentially infinite workload involved in learning all that had to be known before graduation. **Clinical experience** essentially refers to the belief that much of medical practice is actually based on the "art" of determining, from complex and subtle interpersonal cues and in interaction with the patient, the nature of the disease and the appropriate treatment. Along with clinical experience, doctors-in-training were instilled with the notion of **medical responsibility**. By this, Becker and his colleagues stressed the "enormous" moral responsibility of the life-and-death decisions that frequently confront doctors in practice.

These two values were the most important aspects of learning. They enabled the medical students to choose, from the masses of detail presented in books and in lectures, what actually had to be learned. The notion of clinical experience guided the selection of facts that had to be memorized to pass the examination. It tended to lead the students to disregard basic science and focus on classes where they were provided with practical information of the sort that was not typically found in medical textbooks. Furthermore, the focus on medical responsibility tended to produce an emphasis by the student on interesting cases that involved life-and-death medical judgements rather than on the more common and mundane diseases.

It also tended to guide the choice of specialties. The most desired specialties frequently were those with the potential of saving patients (or killing them), such as surgery and internal medicine.

Merton and his colleagues described medical education and socialization as a continuous process by which medical students learn to think of themselves as doctors and in so doing absorb sufficient knowledge to feel comfortable in their new role. Accordingly, two basic traits are developed: the ability to remain emotionally detached from the patient in the face of life-and-death emergencies, great sorrow or joy, or sexuality; and the ability to deal with the inevitable and constant uncertainty. Fox (1957) observed three sources of uncertainty. The first occurs because it is impossible to learn everything there is to learn about medicine and its practice. The second stems from the awareness that, even if the student were able to learn all the available medical knowledge, gaps would remain because medical knowledge is itself incomplete. The third source of uncertainty arises from the first two: the uncertainty in distinguishing between lack of knowledge on the part of the student and inadequacy in the store of medical knowledge.

Over time, disease and death, to the physicians-in-training studied by these researchers, ceased to be frightening, and emotional issues came to be seen as medical problems. The researchers elucidated the processes by which the students learned, in the face of enormous amounts of information, what they would be quizzed about and thus what they had to know to pass their courses and to graduate. *Boys in White* also describes the conversion of the idealism of the new student to the cynicism held by students in later years. When graduation approached, the original commitment to helping patients and practising good medicine tended to return.

These two studies are about a half-century old. Some things have changed but there are similarities. Doctors still have to work and learn within a situation where uncertainty is inevitable and, in fact, is a basic aspect of the process of diagnosis—called differential diagnosis. This means that every diagnosis essentially involves ruling out other possible explanations for the presented symptoms. Further medical knowledge is changing all the time as new studies and new technologies are developed. Keeping up with everything is impossible and doctors have to live with that sense of inadequacy constantly. Clinical experience is still important in determining each diagnosis, but this increasingly has to be done in the context of what is called evidence-based practice. This puts a powerful burden on doctors to base their decisions on more than experience. Moreover, in the context of increased specialization, doctors have to decide whether or not to refer patients to specialists or order more tests to help in diagnosis. This personal responsibility, while still a feature of medical work, takes place in an increasingly complex field of possibly fraught definition of the limits of personal responsibility and knowledge.

In addition, medical education has been shown to be sexist both in textbooks and in clinical examples used in classroom lectures (Giacomini et al., 1986; Zelek et al., 1997). In the past, an unwritten quota system governed the admittance of women into medical school (Woodward, 1999). In fact, the practice of medicine has been shown to be built around a masculine prototype (Zelek et al., 1997). A great deal of published research, the basis of medical practice, has used the male body as the norm (McKinlay, 1996). Doctors have to be aware of this and question their own gender and other biases. Sexism currently is being addressed in a variety of programs in medical schools across the country and, as noted previously, the majority of new students now are female. Increased gender equality in education, training, and research will undoubtedly follow.

Doctors did and do reflect the heterosexism of the rest of society and lesbians, gays, and bisexual and transgendered people may not always receive the most appropriate health care as a result. Lesbian and gay doctors, too, are subject to discrimination (Druzin et al., 1998). The number of "out" gay and lesbian doctors is increasing and they are organizing. This movement undoubtedly will have benefits for lesbian, gay, bisexual, and transgender

patients (LGBT) patients, as well as for other sexual minorities (www.utoronto.ca/diversity_in_medicine/glbtmeds/). Same-sex marriage and the immense success of the Gay Pride movements in Canada and around the world are among the important contributors to a more open-minded attitude of the majority of Canadians to LGBT issues. The Canada-wide association of lesbian, gay, bisexual, transgendered, and queer (LGBTQ) medical students will most likely add to the progressive thrust of the treatment of LGBTQ patients and doctors alike (http://www.utoronto.ca/diversity_in_medicine/glbtmeds/mission.htm). Teaching medical (and other) students about broader diversity issues than gender and sexual orientation continues to be a challenge.

Getting Doctored

Shapiro (1978), in one of a number of autobiographical accounts of medical school, has critically evaluated his own experiences of becoming a physician in a book entitled *Getting Doctored*. In this analysis the two most important features of medical education are the concepts of alienation and the authoritarian personality. Alienation is evident in the relationships of medical students to one another, in the relationships of doctors, interns, and residents towards one another, and in the approach of the medical student to studies, medical school, and pharmaceutical companies and other related institutions. The authoritarian personality, which breeds alienation, is experienced at most stages of medical education and, later, in medical practice. Four types of alienation are discussed: alienation of labour or productive activity, alienation from the product of labour, alienation of people's relationships with others around them, and alienation from life.

Alienation of labour is seen throughout the medical care system, from the workers at the top to those at the bottom. Shapiro provides numerous examples of alienated labour in medical school. These include: fierce competition between medical students, an enormous workload, and little direction regarding what, out of the mountains of information, is most relevant. "Students, especially in the early stages, spend extraordinarily long hours at study without any assurance that they have mastered what is necessary" (Shapiro, 1978: 29). Shapiro uses the phrase "doc around the clock" to encapsulate the doctor's experience of being tied to medical work.

Alienation from the product of labour exists when the worker does not feel that the product of his or her labour is a true reflection of his or her self and values. The way doctors learn to talk about patients and their illnesses provides some illustrations of their lack of identification with patients. Patients were called "crocks" when their complaints were believed to be psychosomatic. They were described as having "two neurons" when they were believed to be lacking in intellectual functioning or were unco-operative (ibid., 168).

Alienation of relationships, too, is repeatedly evident in Shapiro's description of medical school. One set of interpersonal strategies will be used to illustrate this. Competition is a central feature of the interpersonal interaction of physicians-in-training. Fear of failure is widespread. Students compete for rank in class. Students vie for the best internships and for the position of chief resident. Shapiro's personal critique of medicine may be idiosyncratic, but it is not unique to him.

I like this analysis for a number of reasons. It is a well-written and richly illustrated book. I like it, too, because these notions of alienation are more and less relevant to all of us, students and professors and others. Perhaps you might take a moment a think about how your life as a student suffers from certain forms of alienation.

More recently, Conrad (1998) analyzed four autobiographical studies of medical school and practice. His findings parallel those discussed previously and indicate a lot of continuity in the issues involved in medical practice and education.

- The culture of medical education discourages caring.
- Doctors' clinical perspective focuses almost entirely on the disease rather than the illness (or the suffering person).

- Doctors are not taught how to talk to patients. (Although this is changing, there is still a ways to go).
- "Medical school does an excellent job at imparting medical knowledge and technique, but it is inadequate in conveying humane and caring values." (343)
- "Technological medicine, with its disease orientation, myriad lab tests, complex interventions, and 'fix-it' mentality, pays scant attention to teaching about doctor–patient relations." (343)
- Medical students' life of long hours, sleep deprivation, excessive responsibility, and (arrogant) superiors inhibits the growth of compassion and empathy.

Medical students today experience high rates of stress and depression (Yiu, 2005). For instance, it has been estimated that about 12 per cent of second-year medical students in Canada suffer from depression, with a lifetime prevalence of depression of 15 per cent among all doctors (ibid.). Other studies report rates of depression of up to 25 per cent. The definition of depression is variable from person to person but rates are likely equivalent between practising doctors and the general population. When other types of "mental health" problems such as substance abuse are included, the rates of "mental distress" in the profession may be higher (http://www.cma.ca/multimedia/CMA/Content_Images/Inside_cma/Physician_Health_and_Wellbeing/Resources/Mentalhealthstrategy_e.pdf). Some studies have found that as many as a third of medical students drink alcohol excessively. Understandably, with the constant temptation, higher rates of addiction to prescription drugs have also been documented. The suicide rates for doctors are higher than those for Canadians as a whole, according to studies undertaken and reviewed by the Canadian Medical Association (ibid.). Medical students tend to have high personal standards for work and achievement. These traits are sometimes associated with maladaptive perfectionism and an extraordinary concern with performance. Linked to this, medical students tend not to seek help, reporting that they lack time or are afraid of a lack of confidentiality. Relying on friends and family for support, exercise, recreation, and spirituality are some of the coping strategies that were found to help doctors-in-training (as well as the rest of us!) (ibid.).

The Canadian Medical Association has recently published a systematic literature review of the mental health concerns and issues of doctors, residents, and medical students (ibid.). One set of stresses relates to the fact that doctors have to deal constantly with suffering, pain, and emotional fragility in their patients, and a fear of failure. Patients do not visit their physicians to report on how happy they are and how well they are feeling. These existential issues related to the job of being a doctor can perhaps be mediated (and the CMA does offer a list of recommendations such as a sort of "buddy system" for doctors), but they will not go away. In addition, there are the physical stressors such as long hours, overnight calls—as many as 70 per cent of doctors are on call in a given month (https://www.cma.ca/multimedia/CMA/Content_Images/Policy_Advocacy/Policy_Research/HQ_Article.pdf), and bodily stresses resulting from poorly designed work locations. The CMA points to workload, physician shortages, and monetary limitations as other constraints, and also notes, among other stressors, harassment and intimidation in training, multiple responsibilities, the difficulties of transitioning into clinical work, and fiscal management. Doctors, after all, not only need to learn to manage their own finances, but also how to run an office, with all the accounting, management, hiring, and firing this involves.

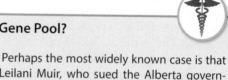

SPOTLIGHT ON ETHICS

BOX 11.4   Sexual Sterilization: Purifying the Gene Pool?

In 1928 the legislature of Alberta enacted the Sexual Sterilization Act to be overseen by the Alberta Eugenics Board. The Act was passed during the period in which eugenics was becoming a powerful idea and believed by many to be a way to purify "races" and ensure a healthy and intelligent gene pool. Mental illness and retardation, epilepsy, and even criminal behaviour and prostitution were among the conditions that were thought to be genetically transmitted. Initially in Alberta, the primary group targeted to be sterilized were "mentally disabled or defective" people. Before a person institutionalized for being mentally defective was discharged the Alberta Eugenics Board insisted on sterilization to ensure that there would be "no danger of procreation" once the inmate had left. The rationale was to mitigate the risk of the "multiplication of the evil by the transmission of the disability" (http://www.mcgilldaily.com/2014/03/the-science-of-harm/). Later, people with Huntington's, syphilis, and epilepsy were included. This legislation was finally repealed in 1972.

Perhaps the most widely known case is that of Leilani Muir, who sued the Alberta government in 1995 for sterilizing her without her consent during an appendectomy. Muir had been institutionalized in a training school at 10 years of age because she was an abused and unwanted child. She was successful in her suit, and the Alberta government was forced to compensate her financially. Subsequently, more than 700 other victims of forced sterilization sued the Alberta government, which settled these suits out of court. A National Film Board video about this is case can be found at the following site. (https://www.nfb.ca/film/sterilization_of_leilani_muir). While people with intellectual disabilities may not face sterilization today, they still face oppression and are discouraged from reproducing (http://www.cbc.ca/news/canada/edmonton/alberta-s-sex-sterilizations-re-examined-1.871749).

What are the ethical issues at play in this debate?

Organization of the Medical Profession: Autonomy and Social Control

Physicians are self-regulating. Through their organizations they decide what constitutes good medical practice, determine the requirements for training a physician, set standards of practice, and discipline colleagues who depart from these standards. The way that practice is organized, its locus of activity, and the payment modality are all affected by the regulatory power of doctors. The profession has established two major control bodies, the College of Physicians and Surgeons and the Canadian Medical Association. The federal and provincial governments recognize these organizations. These organizations attempt to define expectations of medical behaviour, to improve standards of performance, and to protect the status and economic security of their members. The Canadian Medical Association is an amalgamation of the provincial medical associations. The CMA represents physicians as a national lobby group. The provincial bodies negotiate with the respective medical care plans for fee scales and other matters of relevance to the practice of medicine. The situation is somewhat different in Quebec.

The Medical Act requires that the Medical Council of Canada be responsible for the licensing of qualified medical practitioners, for supervising what these practitioners do, and for preventing unqualified practitioners from practising (http://mcc.ca/). Thus, the provincial colleges have the power to eliminate from the register all those who are convicted of certain offences. And while practitioners may appeal the judgements of the Medical Council in court, the view of the Council is almost invariably upheld. The courts thereby have long declared that the profession is the proper judge of the actions of its colleagues (Blishen, 1969: 81).

Autonomy and power are crucial characteristics of an occupational group that claims to be a profession. Freidson (1975: 71) describes how the self-regulating doctors' institutions depend on the type of practice in which the doctors are engaged. Freidson distinguishes among doctors practising

alone, colleague networks, large group practices, and university clinics. Those who practise alone enjoy the greatest freedom from outside control. Pure forms of solo practice generally are quite rare. Solo practice, nevertheless, is lauded as the model of the ideal-typical entrepreneurial professional who is free from control: the doctor treats the patient privately and confidentially, without the interference of colleagues, insurance companies, governments, or any other outsiders. This patient–doctor relationship is described as a "sacred trust." Assurance of competence by the physician in private practice is based primarily on the assumption of adequate recruitment policies, educational programs, and licensing procedures. In fact, the ongoing day-to-day control of practice ultimately rests with the individual practitioner.

One of the primary sanctions against behaviour deemed inappropriate by professional colleagues is ostracism—by not referring patients or by denying certain privileges, such as hospital privileges. This is useful only to the extent that the particular medical practitioner depends on colleagues and hospitals for her or his practice. Specialists usually are colleague-dependent to a greater extent than are general practitioners because access to these specialists by patients can occur only through the medical referral system. The number of doctors in solo practice is decreasing. A 2001 survey by the College of Family Physicians found that 25 per cent of family doctors were in solo practice as compared to 31 per cent in 1997. The percentage dropped to 23 percent in 2007 (http://www.parkhurstexchange.com/practicemanagement/54a).

The mode of practice also relates to how doctors in Canada today are paid. About $21.5 billion, or 13.4 per cent of the health-care budget, according to 2009 figures, is spent on the services of doctors (secure.cihi.ca/cihiweb/products/National_health_expenditure_trends_1975_to_2009_en.pdf). Most receive at least some of their income from fee-for-service payments. Ninety per cent of those surveyed recently by the Canadian College of Family Physicians were paid by fee-for-service, 14.9 per cent were paid by salary, and 1.9 per cent were paid by "capitation," that is, the number of patients in the practice (ibid.). Some doctors are paid by more than one method.

Fee-for-service has been the preferred method of payment in the past because it seemed to reflect on physician autonomy. Now, however, the governments in Canada are encouraging group practice with various incentives, and doctors working in groups make as much as 30 per cent more (http://www.cfhi-fcass.ca/SearchResultsNews/10-01-01/13b5e8bb-e7c2-4544-8da5-b1aa5d9e38db.aspx). With these changes the percentage of doctors preferring fee-for-service has declined dramatically, from 50 per cent in 1995, to 28 per cent in 2004 and 23 per cent in 2007 (CHSRF, 2010; http://www.cfhi-fcass.ca/SearchResultsNews/10-01-01/13b5e8bb-e7c2-4544-8da5-b1aa5d9e38db.aspx). Group practices are also preferred by women and by younger doctors, and thus the trend towards group work ought to continue. Furthermore, work satisfaction appears to be higher in group situations (ibid.).

Today, the power and autonomy of the physician within the hospital are severely restricted. Doctors used to be the only gatekeepers to the hospital system: they determined which patients, medical colleagues, and various paraprofessionals would be admitted. Now, hospital administrators, many of whom are graduates of university-based hospital administration programs, are the pivotal figures organizing the hospitals (Wahn, 1987). Doctors now function in the hospital as the middle managers whose work is likely to be constrained, organized, and directed by the hospital administrators and observed and critiqued by the nursing staff and others below them in the hospital hierarchy. Hospital administrators are guided by different primary goals than are doctors. They are chiefly concerned about managing the organization in a rational and efficient manner and eliminating "unnecessary" services and costs so as to balance the hospital budget. This, of course, involves satisfying the goals of promoting and maintaining good, safe, and efficient medical care. But these medical goals must be met in the context of rationalizing services and balancing the interests of many specialty groups who work within the hospital.

Coburn et al. (1997) have argued that the medical profession has, in part, declined in autonomy and control via the imposition of state control. In particular, "in recent years, the state has introduced changes in the structure and functions of the self-regulatory college,

has intervened with a number of cost-controlling mechanisms—denying funding for new technologies, tightening controls on insured service, and promoting explicit guidelines for medical decision-making" (ibid., 17). The autonomy of the medical profession is a fragile and complex matter and threats to that autonomy are real. Biomedicalization theory (Clarke et al., 2003) also reflects a demise in the independence and autonomy of doctors in the face of huge for-profit organizations such as pharmaceutical and medical device companies and various types of insurance providers. Government surveillance through payment policies also constrains medical autonomy.

The Management of Mistakes

Mistakes happen to all of us. They happen both on and off the job. They are an inevitable part of life. Which student has ever received 100 per cent on all tests, essays, and exams? Which teacher has never made an error in adding or recording marks? Doctors are no exception: they also make mistakes. But when doctors make mistakes the results can be devastating—they can result in death or serious disability for the patient. One question Marcia Millman asks in her book *The Unkindest Cut* (1977) is how doctors handle their mistakes. Millman carried out her research for two years at three university-affiliated hospitals, where she was a participant-observer working with doctors at all status levels. Because these hospitals were teaching hospitals attached to universities, their standards can probably be considered above average.

Millman's work highlights three basic points. First, the definition of what constitutes a mistake is variable. In fact, the old joke that the operation was a success but the patient died has a basis in fact. Results that patients interpret as mistakes are not necessarily considered **medical errors**. And doctors in different specialties may have different understandings of what constitutes a mistake. Actions that would be considered reprehensible in an attending physician are considered permissible in an intern who is, after all, "just learning." The point here is that there is no universal standard of perfect or imperfect medical practice. Norms are worked out in practice.

HIGHLIGHTED ISSUES

BOX 11.5   Medical Practice and Errors: Part One

An interview study of 40 doctors' interpretations of what constitutes mistakes in their work demonstrated the "anguish of clinical action and the moral ambiguity of being a clinician" (Paget, 1988). Mistakes, the interviewed doctors noted, are absolutely inevitable in the work of the doctor. Mistakes are intrinsic to medical decision-making: they are essential to the experience of doctoring. Clinical practice involves risks because it requires the application of finite knowledge to specific situations. Mistakes occur often not because doctors are at fault or incompetent. Medicine by its nature is an essentially "error-ridden activity." Because of the method of interpretive understanding based on interview data, Paget was able to describe medical practice with empathy for doctors. As she says, "mistakes are complex sorrows of action gone wrong" (ibid., 131).

The doctor knows that she/he is making decisions based on some but not all of the information available. Moreover, even if the doctor has all the available information, it may not be enough to diagnose or treat a disease. Medical practice inherently encapsulates a degree of uncertainty. Yet, it usually results in, even requires, action. Paget's work enables us to see the definition of mistakes from the perspective of the practising clinician. Based on open-ended interviews and using a phenomenological approach, she shows the everyday struggles of doctors who make decisions in an error-ridden climate.

Treatments can be dangerous; the potential for deleterious results from mistakes has grown enormously. Irreparable mistakes are inevitable: they occur in spite of good intentions, good education, and care.

Second, while the designation among doctors of what constitutes a mistake is problematic, some results of medical practice are considered undesirable enough to warrant investigation. One example would be an unexpected death during surgery. When such an outcome occurs, Millman notes, doctors tend to use two mechanisms for dealing with it: (1) neutralization, and (2) collective rationalization. As Millman says:

> By neutralization of medical mistakes I mean the various processes by which medical mistakes are systematically ignored, justified or made to appear unimportant or inconsequential by the doctors who have made them or those who have noticed that they have been made. (Millman, 1977: 91)

Thus, an action that results in harm to a patient can be ignored, or it can be justified because of the intricate nature of the surgery involved or because it was the patient's fault for not informing the physician of a drug reaction. In justifying themselves, doctors may emphasize unusual or misleading clues; or they may focus on the patient's unco-operative attitude or "neurotic" behaviour. Even though "doctors may have differences and rivalries among themselves with regard to defining, blaming, and acting on mistakes, all doctors will join hands and close ranks against patients and the public." The assumption made is, "there but for the grace of God go I" (ibid., 93). In the face of mistakes, doctors will tend to band together to support one another and to explain the behaviour leading up to the "mistake" as blameless or at least as being as logical as possible given the circumstances.

The third point of Millman's work is that hospitals have instituted formal mechanisms for dealing with mistakes, for using errors as a source of education, and for investigating culpability. The Medical Mortality Review Committee, one such mechanism, met monthly to discuss deaths within the hospital and to review each death in which there may have been some possibility of error or general mismanagement. The fundamental yet unspoken rule governing such a review was that it was to be "a cordial affair." Even though the atmosphere may sometimes be slightly strained, and the individual physician whose decisions are being reviewed may be embarrassed, rules of etiquette and sociability were stringently enforced. All members of staff who had a part in the mistake used the committee meeting as an opportunity to explain to the others how each was individually led to the same conclusion. Emphasizing the educational aspect of the event rather than its legitimate investigatory nature also minimized the discomfort level.

Today in Canada a significant minority of patients (7.5 per cent) experience negative effects as a result of medical error (www.chsrf.ca/mythbusters/index_e.php). It has been estimated that between 44,000 and 98,000 people die annually in the US as the result of error (ibid.). Sometimes the error is dramatic, such as when bandages are left inside a patient after surgery or when patients are given the wrong medication. Sometimes they may be more equivocal errors. One study, for example, found that 25 per cent of people surveyed said that they had experienced an "adverse event" in either the hospital or the community (ibid.). In the past, errors were seen to be the result of individual "bad apples" who were then blamed as individuals. Now, however, error is believed to be often the result of system failures and to result, in large part, from understaffing, multi-tasking, the myriad of new equipment needing monitoring,

---

SPOTLIGHT ON ETHICS

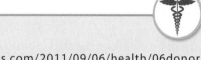

BOX 11.6 Errors in Infertility Treatments

Sperm banks and fertility clinics sometimes make mistakes or fail to adequately screen donors (blogs.wsj.com/informedreader/2007/08/08/sperm-banks-policy-may-leave-room-for-error/). One of the most obvious cases involves a situation in which black twins were born to a white couple. In another case a doctor in Ottawa apparently mixed up the sperm so that the wrong sperm was inseminated in women in four documented cases (http://www.cbc.ca/news/canada/ottawa/ottawa-doctor-loses-order-of-canada-after-sperm-mix-ups-1.1398704). A different but related concern is that there have been no limits on the numbers of times that sperm from an individual donor might be used. One person who was following up on the "fatherhood" of the sperm she used for her child found that there were 150 others who had registered online as having the same sperm donor. In other words, her child had at least 149 half-siblings (http://www. nytimes.com/2011/09/06/health/06donor.html?pagewanted=all&_r=0). In the absence of regulation the numbers of half-siblings could be very large indeed. Although some may know the number or even the name of the sperm donor, others may not, and the possibility of intermarriage and other potential problems in the future is real.

Mistakes such as these raise many ethical and legal issues. To whom should the children belong? Is maternity more important than paternity in these cases? Is maternity more important than ethnicity, in other words, should the woman who carries and bears the baby "own" the baby? Should there be a limit on how often the sperm from a particular individual can be used? There are questions, too, about the rights of the child to know who his/her father (sperm donor) and siblings are. What do you think as you contemplate these questions?

and a rushed environment. There are a number of new trends for managing and minimizing errors, including critical incident reporting (Iedema et al., 2006), electronic health records, and bar codes on medications (www.chsrf.ca/mythbusters/index_e.php). In 2007, CIHI, drawing on a variety of data sources, reviewed patient safety in Canada. The analysis estimated the frequency of a range of adverse events. Of the events examined, nosocomial infections (i.e., infections acquired in the course of health care) were most common, occurring in around 10 per cent of patients. At the other end of the scale, the least-common incident in the analysis was a fatal event due to blood transfusions, which occurred in 0.001 per cent of patients (see Table 11.4). Similarly, Figure 11.1 portrays neurosurgical errors.

Medical errors are often the result less of individual mistakes than of system failures. Among the documented systemic errors, according to Charney (2012; http://canadiandimension.com/articles/4671/) are the following:

- the profit motive or the need to make a profit to stay in business and/or to thrive;

- inadequate levels of staffing (e.g., patients hospitalized with a 1:4 nurse-to-patient ratio are 31 per cent less likely to die than those with a ratio of 1:8);
- shiftwork, which can lead to potentially dangerous consequences for patients;
- hospital working conditions (staffing ratios, work hours, ergonomics, work flow, and autonomy, for instance);
- intimidation and harassment from colleague to colleague;
- accountability and laws that may prevent some reports of errors (from fear of censure or prosecution);
- failure to report or the under-reporting of errors, which means that the systems are not as likely to be changed;
- new and complex technologies.

Technical and Moral Mistakes

Bosk's (1979) work on mistakes among doctors adds another theoretical dimension to our understanding of medical error. Bosk studied the ways surgeons and surgeons-in-training at a major university medical centre regulated themselves. He noted that the medical centre's hierarchy

TABLE 11.4   Types and Rates of Adverse Events

Event	Number Affected per Event
Adults contracting a nosocomial infection while in an acute-care hospital	1 in 10
Children contracting a nosocomial infection while in an acute-care hospital	1 in 12
Obstetrical traumas during childbirth (vaginal delivery)	1 in 21
Birth trauma: injury to neonate	1 in 141
Post-admission pulmonary embolism or deep vein thrombosis	1 in 279
In-hospital hip fracture for adults aged 65+	1 in 1,263
Foreign object left in after procedure	1 in 2,998
Adverse blood transfusion events	1 in 4,091
Fatal events definitely, probably, and possibly related to transfusion of blood components	1 in 87,863

Source: Adapted from CIHI, Quality of Healthcare in Canada: A Chartbook, Ottawa: CIHI (2007).

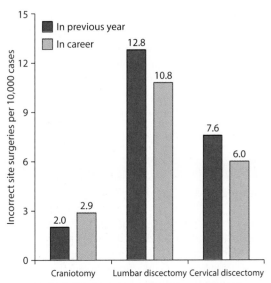

FIGURE 11.1   Rate of Incorrect Surgery Site, Neurosurgeons Survey, 2003

Source: Quality of Healthcare in Canada: A Chartbook, Ottawa: CIHI (2007). Canadian Institute of Health Information.

is structured and managed so that those at the bottom levels are more likely to have to bear the responsibility for mistakes than those at the top.

There were, he noted, two different kinds of mistakes—technical and moral. **Technical mistakes** are to be expected in the practice of medicine and, usually, colleagues are forgiven them. They are viewed as an inevitable part of medical work and are seen as having definite value in that they often motivate improvements in practice. People are expected to learn from their technical mistakes. **Moral mistakes**, however, are severely reprehensible. They constitute evidence that the physician or physician-to-be does not belong as a medical colleague (as a member of the team or as a team player). Moral errors that demonstrate an unco-operative attitude, unreliability, or a lack of responsibility towards patients are more serious. Moral errors are not as easily forgotten or forgiven because the person who made them is believed to be unsuitable as a doctor.

Practice Norms and Variations

A study by Wennberg (1984) showed that different colleague networks develop different sets of beliefs, norms, and practices regarding specific diseases and the appropriate treatment for them. Wennberg compared rates of hospitalization and surgery in the states of Iowa, Vermont, and Massachusetts and found tremendous variations from state to state and within states. He then divided the different areas into what he called "hospital markets" or hospital service areas (populations using one hospital or a group of hospitals). He found that different hospital service areas had highly variable rates of all measures of hospital and surgery utilization. For instance, he noted that the rate of hysterectomy (among all women under 70) varied from 20 per cent in one market to 70 per cent in another. The rate of prostatectomy varied from 15 per cent in one market to 60 per cent in another. Tonsillectomy rates varied from 8 per cent to 70 per cent in two different markets. In trying to explain these wide differences, he examined the roles played by (1) illness rates, (2) insurance coverage, (3) access to medical services, (4) age distribution, (5) per capita hospital bed ratios, and (6) physician–population ratios. None of these factors made a significant impact on the utilization of hospitals or surgery. Wennberg concluded that the differences must be due to subjective variations in the **practice norms** and styles of physicians in each area.

Rachlis and Kushner (1994: 5) have illustrated how the productivity and practice norms of doctors vary substantially from area to area.

For example, they note that radiation oncologists in Toronto have 50 per cent fewer patients than those in Hamilton and that those in Hamilton see 50 per cent fewer patients than those in Halifax. Part of the difference is due to research responsibilities and part to the expansionist role of radiation oncologists—from the technical (as is

---

CRITICAL THINKING

BOX 11.7   Medical Practice and Errors: Part Two

The medical system, as all systems, is mistake-ridden. However, under-reporting of mistakes is common. In the US the under-reporting is said to be 50–96 per cent per year (Lawton and Parker, 2002). This is partly because the culture of medicine in many ways reflects the capitalist economies of the West. It is a culture that emphasizes professional autonomy, collegiality, and self-regulation. Such an individualized system does not easily foster shared responsibility and the opportunity of learning from mistakes. Rather, it encourages denial, fear, and blame. In addition, the population served by doctors is increasingly litigious and numerous lawyers are ready to take medical error cases.

Estimates are that 80 per cent of the accidents with hazardous technologies are the result of human error (ibid.). This may reflect the biases of reporting. Although doctors and other health-care personnel are often at "the sharp end" of the system (ibid., 16), the failure in many cases may actually be attributable to action or inaction further down the line. It may, for instance, be due to faulty machinery. In the absence of systematic reporting of errors, improving the quality of health care is hampered.

A high proportion of patients feel unsafe. A poll in the US found that 42 per cent of the respondents disagreed with the proposition that the current health-care system had made adequate provisions to prevent medical mistakes. A further 42 per cent said that either they or a close friend had personally experienced a mistake (Vincent and Coulter, 2002). The majority of complaints stem from problems in communication. Miscommunication can lead to misdiagnosis and mistreatment. It may even lead to death. Yet, consultations with doctors average less than 10 minutes. This interval is insufficient for many patients to feel they have an opportunity to get their point across.

The medical profession has traditionally relied on the method found most unhelpful in reducing errors—"shame and blame of individuals with accusations of incompetence, unprofessionalism, and unworthiness to treat patients" (Liang, 2002: 64). The first step in changing this climate is to educate physicians regarding the appropriate focus of quality improvement systems. "Physicians cannot claim full credit for a positive patient outcome; rather, it is a team effort involving a minimum of physician, nurses, administrators, and the patient" (ibid.).

Nor should doctors take all of the blame. In the airline industry, for example, it is not only the pilot who is held responsible for the safe outcome of a flight but also the air traffic controllers, the maintenance people, the stewards, and the ground staff. The system is held accountable.

The most extreme case of medical "error" to come to light in the recent past is that of a British doctor, Harold Shipman, who was found to have murdered at least 215 of his patients and to have done so without any suspicion being directed towards him for a very long time. He was caught only when he crudely altered the will of his last victim in a way that apparently made detection inevitable. It has been suggested that the doctor was addicted to pethidine (an opioid painkiller). He may have also been addicted to murder. How did these murders go undetected for so long? How did he manage to get corroborating signatures from other doctors on certificates of cremation? Donna Cohen (2002) suggests that he was able to avoid detection, in part, because of prevalent ageism. She argues that because the elderly are more likely to die of all sorts of conditions, people tend to ask fewer questions when a death is unexpected or unexplained. All of the people killed by Shipman were at least middle-aged, 82 per cent were women, but many had been healthy. What can and should be done to prevent errors of clinical practice?

common in Britain) to whole-patient management (as is common in the US). Considerable treatment variation from one place to another exists within the Canadian medical care system. Rachlis and Kushner note the following findings: (1) a person is three times as likely to receive a tonsillectomy in Saskatchewan as in Quebec; (2) county-by-county rates for coronary bypass surgery vary 2.5 times throughout Ontario; (3) the length of stay for hospitalized heart attack patients ranges from 6.6 to 12.9 days (within just one province). Also, there are sometimes substantial differences in diagnosis and treatment from province to province in Canada (Revah and Bell, 2007). At times, this is the result of different levels of coverage for different procedures (http://www.benefits.org/coverage/health-care/public-plan/provincial-plan-coverage). Ongoing issues are also related to the differences in personal values and religion, which lead some doctors to refuse to provide certain treatments (birth control and abortion are the two most widely known of these) (http://ottawacitizen.com/news/local-news/debate-about-doctors-right-to-refuse-treatment-for-religious-reasons-re-ignited).

According to John P. Bunker (1985), such variation occurs because medicine is an art and not a science, and therefore a great deal of uncertainty is involved in the practice of medicine. Most surgery is not for life-threatening problems but for conditions of discomfort, disability, or disfigurement. Moreover, in most cases the benefits just about equal the risks. Surgery may be equally likely to improve the health, comfort, and lifespan of the patient as it is to cause an increase in morbidity. There are no clear differences in mortality rates in different hospital markets. Hospitalization or surgery rates are not correlated with declines in either the mortality or morbidity rates.

Wennberg, Bunker, and Barnes (1980) studied seven different types of surgery, including hysterectomy, tonsillectomy, gall bladder surgery, prostatectomy, and hemorrhoidectomy in Canada, the United Kingdom, and different locations in the United States. Generally, the rates were highest in Canada and lowest in the United Kingdom. The authors suggest that while such differences have enormous implications for costs, and for morbidity and mortality rates, they are not the result of malpractice but occur because diagnostic and treatment procedures are not perfect. Norms of practice develop out of colleague and network interaction. Many new and comparative studies of medical care in Canada and the US are discussed in Chapter 15.

Malpractice

One type of social control of medical practice designed to minimize errors and punish individuals for malfeasance is the malpractice suit. Malpractice insurance policies are now taken for granted as a necessity, and fees for malpractice insurance have grown substantially. Despite common misperceptions, the numbers of lawsuits against Canadian doctors have been declining in the recent past (www.chsrf.ca/mythbusters/index_e.php). The number of lawsuits peaked in 1995, at 1,415. In 2004 there were 1,083 (ibid.). The number of lawsuits continues to decrease. It was

16.1 per 1,000 members in 2004 and 9.5 per 1,000 members in 2013 according to the annual report of the CMPA (https://oplfrpd5.cmpa-acpm.ca/en/annual-report). This is a 40 per cent drop. This may be the result of a diminution in errors or of fear of reprisal in the case of initiating a suit, for example. Most complaints originate in hospitals or other health-care institutions where there are constraints on whistle-blowing on the practices of others and where there may be substantial fear of self-disclosure. The provincial/territorial licensing bodies are required by law to examine all complaints against their members that are brought to them. Still, the numbers are high: in 2004, according to the Canadian Institute of Health Information, anywhere from 9,000 to 24,000 Canadians were said to die annually as a result of medical error (http://www.cbc.ca/news/technology/medical-errors-killing-up-to-24-000-canadians-a-year-1.514758).

As a consequence of these trends, doctors are now spending hundreds of millions annually on insurance for claims of injury alone. This rate, however, is still not close to the malpractice insurance rates in the US. The Canadian doctors' "insurance company," the Canadian Medical Protective Association, which was established in 1913 by an Act of Parliament (www.cmpa.org/english/whatis-e.cfm), grew financially from a base of $24.5 million in assets in 1983 to $614 million at the end of 1992 and $2.9 billion in 2006 (www.cmpa-acpm.ca/cmpapd03/cmpa_docs/english/resource_files/admin_docs/common/annual_reports/2006/pdf/com_report-e.pdf).

The Canadian Medical Protective Association had approximately 86,000 members across Canada in 2012. According to the annual report, membership fees in 2014 vary considerably from specialty to specialty (https://oplfrpd5.cmpa-acpm.ca/documents/10179/24999/2014cal-e.pdf). The highest fees, reflecting the highest rates of legal complaint, were for physicians working in obstetrics and some surgical specialties. In Ontario, the annual fee for an obstetrician was $57,420. The lowest rates—$504 annually—were for doctors doing humanitarian work or teaching/research work abroad. Annual fees vary by region, and there are different schedules of fees for Quebec, Ontario, and then the rest of Canada. The Canadian Medical Protective Association has developed a number of courses, tips, and strategies to help doctors to increase safety and to minimize lawsuits (https://oplfrpd5.cmpa-acpm.ca/documents/10179/25029/com_2011_changing_physician-e.pdf/49455e95-ab1e-4128-bd85-2a078644fa55).

SUMMARY

1. The medical profession can be thought of as an occupation, a process, a power group, or an ideology. There are certain strengths and limitations to each of these descriptions and it is possible for them to overlap.

2. As an occupation, medicine has two basic characteristics: prolonged training in a body of specialized, abstract knowledge and a service orientation. However, the view of profession as occupation accepts the profession at its own valuation and ignores the power of the group, changes over time, and the relationship between the occupation and the rest of society.

3. As a process, doctors are seen as fighting for dominance and professional status over time. Members engage in full-time work, establish a training/education program, belong to an association, gain legal status, and construct a code of ethics. The members of the occupational group must have esoteric knowledge and social distance from the rest of the population and must be more or less homogeneous.

4. As an ideology, the medical profession holds descriptive and prescriptive beliefs that explain and legitimate certain practices and viewpoints. The ideology includes universalism, functional

specificity, affective neutrality, and a collectivist orientation. This ideology has been effective in promoting the dominance and monopoly held by doctors over time.

5. There are three steps to becoming a doctor: an undergraduate education, graduate study leading to the designation MD, and, at minimum, a one-year internship. Medical students generally come from middle- and upper-middle-class family backgrounds. Physicians-in-training become aware of two dominant values: "clinical experience" and "medical responsibility." Medical students learn emotional detachment and the ability to deal with inevitable and constant uncertainty; they also encounter alienation and may develop authoritarian personalities.

6. Power and autonomy of the medical profession have been somewhat curtailed by the emergence of hospital administrators and the involvement of governments, as well as by the provincial Colleges of Physicians and Surgeons and the Canadian Medical Association.

7. Doctors make mistakes. The definition of what constitutes a mistake is variable; doctors use two mechanisms for dealing with undesirable mistakes: neutralization and collective rationalization. There are two kinds of mistakes: technical, which are to be expected and usually are forgiven, and moral, which may indicate that the person who made them is unsuited to be a doctor.

8. Different colleague networks within the medical field develop different sets of beliefs, norms, and practices regarding specific diseases and their appropriate treatment.

9. Medical malpractice and complaints against doctors are diminishing in frequency in Canada.

KEY TERMS

clinical experience	medical responsibility	profession as occupation
exclusion	moral mistakes	profession as process
limitation	practice norms	subordination
medical errors	profession as ideology	technical mistakes

QUESTIONS FOR STUDY AND DISCUSSION

1. Assess the different views of the meaning of profession and the processes of professionalization with respect to allopathic doctors.

2. What are the characteristics of a good doctor? Critically examine the list of responsibilities mentioned in the Canadian Medical Association Code of Ethics. Use your own experience to do so.

3. Explain the reasons for the socio-demographic backgrounds of medical students today. Do you expect that this will change? Why or why not?

4. Compare the alienation of labour described by Shapiro with that of some work in which you have been employed.

5. Explain the distinction between technical and moral mistakes. Is this difference relevant for any other occupation? Discuss.

SUGGESTED READINGS

Broom, Alex. 2005. "Medical Specialists' Accounts of the Impact of the Internet on the Doctor/Patient Relationship." *Health* 9, 3: 319–38. Based on interviews with prostate cancer specialists, this research paper explores some of the complexities involved in the use of the Internet in health consultations between doctors and patients.

King, Sorrel. 2009. *Josie's Story: A Mother's Inspiring Crusade to Make Medical Care Safe*. New York: Atlantic Monthly Press. A personal story of the wrongful death of a child and her mother's subsequent activism to reduce medical errors.

O'Hagan, J., N.J. MacKinnon, D. Persaud, and H. Etchegary. 2009. "Self-reported Medical Error in Seven Countries: Implications for Canada." *Healthcare Quarterly* 12: 55–61. Comparison of self-reported errors in several countries, including Canada—where about one in six people surveyed reported errors over the past two years. Significant variables in medical error included high prescription drug use, lack of patient involvement in care, chronic conditions, and lack of physician time with the patient.

Revah, Giselle, and Chaim Bell. 2007. "Shopping for High-Technology Treatment in Another Province." *Healthcare Policy* 2, 4: 49–55. A discussion of the feasibility and appropriateness of moving patients from province to province for timely health care.

12

Nurses and Midwives: The Stresses and Strains of the Privatizing Medical Care System

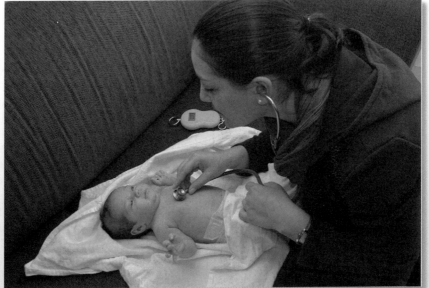

© Lucidwaters | Dreamstime.com

CHAPTER OVERVIEW

▶ Nursing in some form has always existed.

▶ The history of nursing as an occupation is associated with the history of religion and the status and role of women as carers.

▶ Some of the critical issues facing nurses today include sexism, managerial ideology, hospital organization, and financial cutbacks in the context of neo-liberalism.

▶ Florence Nightingale is a central figure in the history and present practice of nursing.

▶ Midwifery has very recently become regulated in a number of provinces in Canada.

▶ Some birthing mothers are assisted by doulas, as well.

▶ Impediments remain to the widespread acceptance and utilization of midwifery for birthing women and their families.

▶ The safety and effectiveness of midwifery are supported by good evidence.

Introduction

Nurses are a fundamental part of the modern medical care system. Hospitals, community clinics, long-term care institutions, home-care organizations, and many doctors' offices could not function without the essential work of nurses. Nurses and nurse practitioners are often responsible for the health of remote communities on a day-to-day basis. Midwives, who have long helped women give birth and continue to do so in most of the world, have been given legal status across many Canadian provinces for maternity care and birth. What are the sociological forces that continue to affect the recruitment, retention, employment venues, and quality of working life of nurses? Who become nurses and midwives—in Canada today and historically? What is the relationship of the work of the allopathic doctor to these other health-care providers? Can the work of the nurse be seen as "separate but equal" to the work of the doctor? Are midwives' rates of mother and infant mortality higher, lower, or the same as those of obstetricians and gynecologists? These are among the questions addressed in this chapter.

Nursing: The Historical Context

Some form of nursing has always been available for sick people, even if it was only unskilled assistance such as help with feeding and being made comfortable. Nursing usually was women's work, an extension of domestic responsibilities. Often, today, nursing is a complex paraprofessional occupation run by rigidly hierarchical bureaucracies segregated "according to sex and race, power and pay, specialty and education" (Armstrong et al., 1993: 11; Zelek and Phillips, 2003; CIHI, 2006), and equipped with complex technology (the vast majority of all Canadian nurses work in hospitals). The duties of the hospital nurse are extremely varied and specialized, and clearly are articulated within a complex division of labour.

Some nursing roles, such as those in the coronary care unit (CCU) or the intensive care unit (ICU), involve highly skilled medical management and quick decision-making in operating sophisticated machinery and other technologies, including multiple drug regimens. Thus, one nurse in an ICU or CCU may spend her/his working hours monitoring and recording the readouts on a series of machines that are keeping a patient alive. Another, working in a psychiatric clinic, may spend her/his days in group and individual therapy, where the tasks involve listening and communicating on an emotional level with patients. But wherever nursing is taking place, it is usually under the jurisdiction of a physician. Interesting exceptions occur, however, such as occupational nursing in which nurses work in industry as on-site caretakers for minor injuries and sickness, including emotional stress caused by such things as work burnout, and develop and administer workplace wellness programs. Nurses are also employed as stand-ins for doctors in remote communities at times. In such cases, they may handle the majority of the day-to-day health complaints of their community members.

The rise of Christianity led to distinctive roles for nurses. Healing and caring for the sick came to be thought of as acts of Christian charity, and nursing became a full-time occupation for the sisters of the Church. They worked with the sick, founded hospitals, and provided bedside care. Commitment to the sick was an acceptable role for devout Christian women because it was an occupation controlled by the Church. Nursing sisters worked for the Church as well as for medical practitioners. This arrangement gave them the autonomy to refuse the orders of doctors, and even to refuse to work for certain types of patients when such work violated their Christian convictions and the values and doctrines of the Church.

Military nursing, too, has a long history. As early as the thirteenth century the Knights of St John of Jerusalem admitted women into their order so they could nurse the wounded. In the seventeenth century, the Knights of Malta maintained a type of nursing service in their hospital at Valetta.

Two knights were assigned to each of the towns surrounding the harbour. Each pair of knights had four nurses "to assist them in their rounds," their duties being to carry supplies to the sick and the poor, to see that the physicians appointed to visit them attended to their duties, and to ensure that patients received the proper care and medicine (Nicholson, 1967: 16).

After the Protestant Reformation of the sixteenth century, nursing disappeared as a respectable service for devout Christian women in countries where the Catholic Church and its organizations were diminished. Those who could afford to pay for services were doctored and nursed at home. Hospitals were built, but they were primarily for the poor and indigent, and were filthy, malodorous, and overcrowded. They usually lacked clean water and adequate drainage. The beds were seldom changed. Patients shared the same dirty sheets. It was not realized that fresh air was healthy and so windows frequently were boarded up. Germs spread and multiplied in such a filthy and airless atmosphere.

Women working in these hospitals were those who had no choice—the poor, infirm, old, and sometimes patients who had recovered but had nowhere else to go. At this time, a stereotype emerged of the nurse as a drunken, poverty-stricken old woman who lived and ate with the sick. Hospitals were considered places to move to die, or when there was no other choice. Frequently, they were infested with rats, had contaminated water supplies, and were inhabited by patients with contagious diseases such as cholera, typhoid, and smallpox: it is no wonder that the mortality rate, even among the nurses, was often as high as 20 or 30 per cent.

Marie Rollet Hébert is thought to have been the first person to provide nursing care in what is now Canada. She and her husband, a surgeon-apothecary, worked together to help the sick from the time of their arrival in Quebec in 1617. Later, nursing sisters, members of various religious orders, emigrated to what are now Quebec City and Montreal, established hospitals, and treated those wounded in the wars. Those nurses were more like doctors than modern nurses; they made

and administered medicines and performed surgery. They headed the hospitals and the missions they founded.

By the eighteenth and nineteenth centuries, epidemics of smallpox, influenza, measles, scarlet fever, typhoid, typhus, and tuberculosis threatened the health of the people. In response, nursing sisters from various orders established hospitals as places where the sick could be segregated and cared for. Still, the hospitals were used especially by the homeless and poor. Over time the hospital system expanded. Today, the hospital has become a place for all classes of people when they are acutely ill and need the specialized, and often high-technology, services offered by doctors, nurses, and others.

Nursing Today: Issues of Sexism, Managerial Ideology, Hospital Organization, and Cutbacks

Nurses comprise about two-thirds of all medical care providers. Altogether there were 365,422 nurses working in Canada in 2012, including 271,807 registered nurses who represented 74 per cent of the health-care provider population; 88,211 licensed practical nurses, representing 24 per cent, and 5,404 registered psychiatric nurses, representing less than 2 per cent of the nurses (http://www.cihi.ca/CIHI-ext-portal/internet/en/document/spending+and+health+workforce/workforce/nurses/release_08oct13). More than 80 per cent of nurses work in health-care institutions—hospitals, community health agencies, and long-term care institutions (Abelson and Strohmenger, 1983: 13; CIHI, 2006: 82). Table 12.1 indicates where nurses in recent years have been employed. Nursing is the most "female" of occupations today—93.6 per cent of all the workers in the field of nursing are female. A minority of registered nurses in Canada are male—6.4 per cent—but their numbers are growing (ibid.). In 1985, about 2 per cent of RNs were male; by 1995 about 4 per cent were male.

TABLE 12.1   Regulated Nursing Workforce, by Sex, Canada, 2011

Jurisdiction	Male	Female	Total
Canada	25,664	334,908	360,572
Newfoundland and Labrador	618	7,912	8,530
Prince Edward Island	99	2,039	2,138
Nova Scotia	591	12,404	12,995
New Brunswick	702	10,421	11,123
Quebec	8,719	79,786	88,505
Ontario	7,157	119,012	126,169
Manitoba	1,263	14,617	15,880
Saskatchewan	789	12,721	13,510
Alberta	2,251	36,908	39,159
British Columbia	3,304	37,629	40,933
Yukon	42	418	460
NWT and Nunavut	129	1,041	1,170

Source: Adapted from *CIHI, Regulated Nurses: Canadian Trends, 2007–2011*, https://secure.cihi.ca/free_products/Regulated_Nurses_EN.pdf.

Males tend to be over-represented in certain fields such as psychiatry, critical care, emergency care, and administration. There tend to be few males in such specialties as maternal/newborn care, pediatrics, and community care. Male nurses, on average, are older than female nurses. This trend may reflect the fact that nursing tends to be a second career for male nurses. Table 12.1 provides a profile of select features (sex and province) of the nursing workforce in Canada in 2008. Table 12.2 provides a

TABLE 12.2   Education Profile of Nurses Working in Canada, 2011

Education Level	Number	Per Cent
Diploma	244,278	67.8
Baccalaureate	105,590	29.3
Master's/Doctorate	10,476	2.9

Source: Adapted from CIHI, Regulated Nurses: Canadian Trends, 2007–2011, https://secure.cihi.ca/free_products/Regulated_Nurses_EN.pdf.

picture of the educational background of the nursing workforce in 2011.

Critical analysis of the work of the contemporary nurse tends to follow one of four lines: (1) the patriarchal/sexist nature of the content of the work and of the position of the nurse in the medical labour force; (2) the impact of the managerial revolution in nursing practice; (3) the impact of the bureaucracy of the hospital on the working life of the nurse and on patient outcomes; and (4) the impact of neo-liberalism through cutbacks on the numbers of nurses and the quality and safety of nursing work. These will be discussed in turn.

Sexism

Sexism is ubiquitous in the medical labour force. Doctors have usually been men and nurses have usually been women (Zelek and Phillips, 2003). The role of the nurse, in fact, the origin of the word, refers to female functions. "Nursing" comes from the Latin *nutrire*, and means to nourish and suckle.

Both historically and today, "nursing" refers both to a mother's action in suckling or breast-feeding her baby and to the act of caring for the sick. Because the earliest nurses were nuns working for the glory of God, nurses have long been called "sisters." The very concepts of caring, nurturing, feeding, and tending to the sick are inextricably tied up with ideas about women (Reverby, 1987; Growe, 1991). The few men who train or are educated to be nurses usually end up moving up the administrative ladder or work where their size and strength are definite assets, such as in psychiatry where sometimes restraint of the patient is required.

Florence Nightingale's views of nurses and their training reinforced a subservient, feminine image of the nurse. It was her view that, while nurses could be trained in some of the detailed duties of bedside care, the most fundamental aspects of the nursing occupation could not be learned. Just as it was impossible to train a person to be a mother, it was impossible to train a woman to nurse. The components of a woman's character—her selfless devotion to others and her obedience to those in authority—could not be learned or taught. Thus, entrance requirements to nursing schools traditionally included an interview in which these nebulous characteristics were evaluated.

Fine-tuning was still necessary, but it could only be managed if the woman was first of all "successful as a woman." One of the first hospitals to train nurses according to the Nightingale model, the New England Hospital for Women and Children in Boston, included among the requirements for admission "that an applicant be between 21 and 31 years old, be well and strong, and have a good reputation as to character and disposition, with a good knowledge of general housework desirable" (Punnett, 1976: 5). The need to "care" is still a preoccupation today, as discussed in the *British Journal of Nursing* (Wood, 2014). There is, however, some recognition that this emotion labour can be costly to the well-being of the nurse (Peate, 2014).

This sexism in ideology is reflected in differences in pay, authority, responsibility, prestige, and

Royal Inland Hospital of Nursing, Kamloops, graduating class of 1948. Can you see some of the gendered (and racialized) assumptions about what makes a "good" nurse reflected in this photo? Look at their disposition, dress, age, and race.

working conditions between men and women in the health-care labour force. Physicians have the advantage over nurses in all of these respects. The nurse has responsibility for carrying out the doctor's orders, but no authority to change them when they are incorrect.

Most nurses in a hospital work shifts, a working arrangement that has been shown to have deleterious effects on health. Their working conditions are problematic in a number of other ways as well: (1) their working hours usually are rigid, except in that they may necessitate unexpected overtime; (2) night and evening shift work is regularly required; (3) they are often restricted in their work to a hospital; (4) they are at risk because of the frequent and often serious occupational health and safety conditions in hospitals (Walters, 1994b; Walters and Haines, 1989; Canadian Nurses Association, at: www.cna-aiic.ca); (5) their workloads are excessively busy and yet demanding of precision and attention to detail, as well as great carefulness and care (Walters and Haines, 1989; Potter et al., 2003; McGillis Hall and Kiesners, 2005); (6) they are, because of underfunding, often forced to do housekeeping and other non-nursing work (Stelling, 1994). Thus, sexism restricts women to an occupational ghetto, and that ghetto provides them with few rewards; much demanding, detailed labour; and little or no authority (Warburton and Carroll, 1988; Cassidy and McIntosh, 2014; https:// www.cna-aiic.ca/en).

Managerial Ideology in Hospitals

The second critical issue today is the managerial ideology in hospital management systems. This ideology is the outcome of a historical trend that reflects the development of the money economy, bureaucracy, capitalism, and rationalization. In particular, this method of financing in the public sector reflects the pressure to keep costs low under neo-liberal governance. **Managerial ideology** assumes that managers are to run organizations as efficiently as possible so as to provide adequate service at minimal cost. In Canada, hospitals are funded chiefly through the public sector; federal and provincial funding provides operating grants; local municipalities also provide funds, as do local fundraising initiatives. They are run under the jurisdiction of provincial government authorities. Hospital managers are accountable to boards and the boards to the provinces. They are faced with limited financial resources and the necessity of setting priorities within the context of extensive cost-cutting by governments. Payments for nursing services must compete with needs for cleaning, equipment upkeep, purchase of new and increasingly expensive technology and pharmaceuticals, as well as payments to the many other hospital personnel, including occupational and physical therapists, social workers, staff physicians, and others. In this context, nurses work on overcrowded and understaffed wards in the midst of patients who are increasingly sick (Urban, 2012).

Several rationalized management systems have been developed for use in hospitals. In many ways these models of nursing care are modelled on the manufacturing sector. They embrace a type of piecework, but in this case, rather than a widget, the piece to be worked on is an organ or a specific set of symptoms related to a particular diagnosis. One management system is case mix groupings (CMGs), introduced in 2007 in Canada according to the Canadian Institute for Health Information. It is a technique for detailing the specific tasks and the time each task takes with reference to the average patient with a particular diagnosis. Productivity and cost-effectiveness are the goals. Nurses must try to work within the specified time limits and still provide adequate nursing care to the patients. CMGs are a set of mutually exclusive categories that can be used for describing patients' clinical attributes. Patients within a particular CMG are believed to require roughly equivalent regimens of care and hence are believed to consume similar amounts of hospital resources (May and Wasserman, 1984: 548; http://www.cihi.ca/CIHI-ext-portal/internet/en/ document/standards+and+data+submission/ standards/case+mix/casemix_cmg).

Case mix grouping assumes that all patients with a particular medical condition will require similar medical treatment (e.g., childbirth by Caesarean section, or chemotherapy with stage-one lung cancer). A cost is then assigned to the nursing care required by the typical patient with that specific diagnosis. Each of the patients in the hospital is accorded a particular time/cost value. Nurses, nursing assistants, orderlies, and other medical care personnel can then be assigned to various wards for specific lengths of time to provide predefined services.

This rationalization, or what Rankin and Campbell call "accounting logic" (2006: 14), seems very reasonable but it has numerous deleterious effects on the working lives of nurses (Campbell, 1988; Rankin and Campbell, 2006). Such a system demeans the authority and autonomy of the nurse and diminishes his/her powers of decision-making. Individual patient needs are not assessed in a holistic way, as a result of experience gained during the practice of the art and science of nursing, but by a predetermined, quantified, and remote system. Nurses know that individual patients always vary from the norm in some way or another. Yet, time for each patient has been allocated by the external— and claimed to be objective—classification system. The nurse, thus, is constrained, by virtue of the time available to his/her, to behave towards all patients, regardless of their individual differences, within certain predefined strictures. Not only is such a requirement destructive to the morale and autonomy of the nurse, but also it may be dangerous or harmful to the patient. Staffing assignments based on the information provided by the CMGs do not allow for the fact that, just as patients differ from the norm, so, too, do nurses. For instance, a small nurse may need help in turning a large patient. Turning may be required hourly. Yet, if the assignment has not considered such characteristics of staff/patient interaction as relative size, it cannot predict costs accurately. In this case the smaller nurse will have to get the assistance of a larger nurse, a nursing assistant, or an orderly. Finding the person to provide such assistance will take additional time; the person who provided the assistance will have to deduct the time taken from his/her total time available for care. A generous allotment of flexible time could enable the nursing staff to manage such situations. However, such flexibility does not exist in the climate of cost containment that typifies the contemporary hospital system. For nurses, the outcomes of such management systems include decreased job satisfaction, burnout, and stress (Conley and Maukasch, 1988; Austin, 2007; Rankin and Campbell, 2006). For patients, the outcomes can include poor quality of care, slower recuperation, and, ultimately, greater long-term susceptibility to recurrent ill health.

Clearly, such newer managerial techniques, combined with restructuring and downsizing in hospitals and in the medical care system more generally, are reducing the autonomy of nurses and making it increasingly difficult to meet the standards of their profession and to care for patients holistically. At the same time, in a new era of awareness of the extensiveness of errors in hospitals initiated by the Institute of Medicine report in 2000, *To Err Is Human* (http://www.nap.edu/openbook.php?record_id=9728), government policies are making it easier for patients to complain about the services provided by individual nurses. Despite the emphasis on errors as problems in systems that resulted from the report, in a highly stratified and unequal system, blame may still be obfuscated by

individualized "accountability" or "responsibilization" and passed down the hospital hierarchy to those nearest the bottom. The new managerialism has also exacerbated differences and has polarized groups such as RNs and RPNs, degree-holding nurses against diploma nurses, and management against staff nurses.

Bureaucratic Hospital Organization

The third area for the critical analysis of the nursing profession today is related to the effect of the hospital's bureaucratic structure on nursing. Opportunity consists of the available career expectations, ambitions, and goals and the probability of reaching these (Kanter, 1977). The structure of opportunity within the organization is determined by rates of promotion, locations for promotion, jobs that lead to promotion, and the like. People who have little opportunity tend to: (1) have lower self-esteem and sense of self-determination, or lack confidence in their ability to change the system; (2) seek satisfaction outside of work; (3) compare themselves with others on the same organizational level rather than with people on a higher level; (4) limit their aspirations; (5) be critical of managers and those in powerful positions; (6) be less likely to expect change; and (7) be more likely to complain (ibid.).

Opportunities for nurses are severely lacking in modern hospital organizations. The structure of promotion in the hospital limits vertical mobility for nurses. The major option open to a nurse with aspirations is to leave nursing and become an administrator. The first step would be to become a head nurse on a ward, with day-to-day responsibility for running the ward and for managing a team of nurses of various types and levels of responsibility. Further movement up the system takes the nurse further and further from the actual practice of nursing.

Power can be defined as the capacity to mobilize resources (ibid.). Power includes the discretionary ability to make decisions that affect the organization, the visibility of the job, the relevance of the job to current organizational problems, and opportunities for promotion. Nurses, by these criteria, have very little organizational power.

HIGHLIGHTED ISSUES

BOX 12.1   The Doctor–Nurse Game

Leonard I. Stein's paper "The Doctor–Nurse Game" (1987) describes one strategy used by doctors and nurses to manage the contradictory position of the doctor, who may have more power and authority, and the nurse, who frequently has more information and knowledge, both about particular patients and their health and well-being on a day-to-day basis while in the hospital, and about hospital routines and common medical practices. This contradiction is especially acute when the doctor in question is a resident, intern, or new graduate. Stein's point is that nurses frequently make suggestions to doctors about how to treat certain situations and cases but that such suggestions must be handled with great subtlety and caution and even disguised. The object of the game is for the nurse to make recommendations to the doctor, all the while pretending to be passive. On the other hand, the doctor must ask for advice without appearing to do so. A typical scene would proceed as follows:

Nurse A: Mr Brown has been complaining of pains in his legs for more than six hours today. He appears to be quite uncomfortable.

Doctor G: Is this a new symptom for Mr Brown or is it recurring?

Nurse A: Mr Brown complained of a similar pain last week when he was admitted. He was given xxxx and it seemed to diminish.

Doctor B: OK. Let's try xxxx. What dosage did he require to get relief?

Nurse A: 3 m/hour.

Doctor G: OK. xxxx, 3 m/hour, nurse, please.

Nurse A: Thank you, doctor.

Stein suggested that the game plan is taught to the nursing students at the same time as they learn the other aspects of nursing care. Doctors usually start to learn once they actually begin to practise in a system with nurses. Holyoake (2011) claims that despite the fact that the game was first observed 40 years ago, it continues to exist today. It is just one way of managing in an unequal bureaucratic system.

The arrest of Susan Nelles on 25 March 1981 for the murder of four infants at the Hospital for Sick Children in Toronto exemplifies powerlessness as responsibility without authority. Even though physicians and others were routinely on the ward and were also frequently involved with patients, it was a nurse who was first suspected and charged in the case of the infant deaths. Furthermore, many nurses (and others) were incensed by the fact that the televised hearing showed that the **Grange Inquiry** treated doctors differently from nurses—dramatically so. Doctors, on the assumption that they were innocent, were questioned with deference and respect. Nurses were questioned under the assumption of guilt and suspicion. "It was as if the police assumed, if it wasn't this nurse who committed the crime, which nurse was it?" (Wilson,

1987: 27). Through this and other incidents, nurses discovered that they were the first to be blamed, but had little respect or authority within the hospital system. The following box provides more detail.

Cutbacks

Today, cutbacks to the health-care system, province by province and by the federal government, represent a grave threat to the public nature of the health-care sector and have had significant effects on hospitals. The overall number of beds in hospitals has already declined but hospitals are actually treating more patients, hospital patients are sicker, and medications and treatments are more frequent and more complex (McGillis Hall and Kiesners, 2005). A new report, *Pushed Out of Hospital, Abandoned at Home: After Twenty Years of Budget*

REMEMBERING OUR HISTORY

BOX 12.2   The Registered Nurses Association of Ontario Responds to the Events at the Hospital for Sick Children and the Grange Inquiry

"The Grange Inquiry was the highest-priced, tax-supported, sexual harassment exercise I've ever encountered," said Alice Baumgart, the Dean of Nursing at Queen's University. The Registered Nurses Association of Ontario agreed, and in a little booklet called *The RNAO Responds* the Association explains why. The following discussion summarizes its arguments.

The arrest of Susan Nelles exemplified sexist bias for a number of reasons.

1. The police and others jumped to the conclusion that the unprecedented number of deaths—36 between 1 July 1980 and 25 March 1981 on wards 4A and 4B at Toronto's Hospital for Sick Children—were the result of murder. They neglected to investigate the possibility that the theory of digoxin overdose was questionable because digoxin is notoriously difficult to measure. It is normal to find some digoxin after death, and there is some evidence that digoxin levels may increase after death. No control groups were used for the baseline data.

2. Once the police and hospital officials decided that the deaths were due to murder, they neglected to examine systematically all the possible sources of digoxin "overdoses." They failed to consider that the drugs might have been tampered with in the hospital pharmacy, or in the manufacturing or distributing branches of the pharmaceutical companies; or that the drugs could have been administered secretly by any of a number of other hospital personnel who had regular access to wards, such as physicians, residents, interns, dieticians, lab technologists, or even a member of the general public who might unobtrusively have entered the hospital on a regular basis. Instead, the focus of suspicion was immediately placed on some of those with less power in the system—the

nurses. Because, according to the first analysis, Susan Nelles appeared to have been the only nurse on duty during a number of suspicious deaths, she was questioned. When she asked to see a lawyer before answering questions, the police assumed that she was guilty and arrested her. The case against her was strengthened because she apparently had not cried when the babies died. Both aspects of her behaviour—asking to see a lawyer, which was, of course, responsible adult behaviour, and her failure to cry—violated sex stereotypes; thus her behaviour was taken as evidence that Nelles must be guilty.

Other sources of bias in the investigation were evident.

3. The focus was on individuals within the bureaucratic system (the hospital) rather than on the malfunctioning of the system itself.

4. The media were accused of biased and sensationalized reporting of unfounded allegations and suspicions. As criminal lawyer Clayton Ruby stated, the media, when reporting on the inquiry, ignored their usual rules of fairness and thus held some responsibility for the damage done to reputations.

5. Justice Grange tended to assume that a nurse was responsible for the murders and to ignore other evidence. He also disregarded the evidence that tended to raise questions about whether or not the "excess" digoxin could have resulted from measurement error or some alternative explanation.

6. The television coverage overemphasized the putative guilt of the nurses. The cameras tended to zoom in on the nurses' faces or hands as they were giving evidence, but rarely seemed to focus on those of the police or the lawyers. Such camera work emphasized the

continued

discomfort of the nurses and encouraged a picture of them as probably guilty.

Among the issues that were raised for nurses by the events at Sick Children's and the Grange Inquiry are the following.

1. Nurses have little status or authority within the hospital, yet they are held responsible or accountable for their work.
2. In contrast to the continuing low status of nurses, their clinical roles have grown for three reasons: (a) the increased number of critical-care patients in hospitals; (b) the increased number of specialists involved with each individual patient; and (c) the increased use of technology, all of which the nurse must co-ordinate.
3. The Associate Administrator: Nursing—the highest level in the nursing echelon—was three administrative levels below that of the senior management of the hospital. Nurses thus had no access to the most senior levels of hospital management.
4. Nurses are expected to be generalists and to move easily from one part of the hospital to another and from one type of care to another. They are expected to perform duties at night that they are not permitted to perform in the day, because during the day only the doctor is thought to have the ability to perform them.
5. The bureaucratic structure, the assumption that nurses are generalists, and the low level in the hierarchy held by top nursing administrators limit the opportunities for nurses' advancement. In addition, nurses suffer from burnout, job stress, low job satisfaction, and the like.
6. The events surrounding the inquiry also reinforced the notion that the "feminine" skills of nurturing and caring are much less important than the "masculine" skills of curing and analysis.
7. It became clear that the image of nursing was infused with negative stereotypes and myths, similar to the negative stereotypes of women in society.

By articulating the issues, promoting their views, lobbying various levels of government, and dealing with the hospital bureaucracy, nurses are beginning to make some changes. Destructive as the events at Sick Children's were, the outcome for the nursing profession in the long run may be hopeful. The Ontario government apparently compensated Nelles for her anguish after her ordeal, which included the arrest and public accusations (www.unb.ca/bruns/0001/issue15/entertainment/book1.html). No one was ever charged for these deaths. Probably the most significant result of the case was the way that the nursing profession rallied around one of their own and in many ways became increasingly empowered. The nursing profession has maintained a very public and political face in subsequent issues faced by the medical profession and the health-care system in Canada, and has often been responsible for broadening the debate beyond a limited medicalized view of health to include a public health and prevention focus.

More recently, when 12 children died after cardiac surgery in Manitoba in 1994, the warnings and ongoing reports given by the nurses of problems with the new cardiac surgeon were repeatedly ignored (Ceci, 2004) until an inquest report was finally published (Sinclair, 2000). The inquest took almost three years, involved testimony from over 80 witnesses, and resulted in more than 60,000 pages of transcripts. In his report, Judge Murray Sinclair made what he considered to be the subordinate position of the nurses in a bureaucratic environment an important part of the explanation for how the deaths were allowed to continue in the face of many attempts by the nurses to bring the serious and life-threatening problems to light.

While the Grange Commission occurred several decades ago the characteristics of nursing work articulated above have not changed substantially. Nurses are still in a very difficult situation in which they have responsibility for their patients but do not have authority. Each one of the points enumerated above continues.

Source: Registered Nurses Association of Ontario (1987).

Cuts Ontario's Health System is Failing Patients, reiterates this (http://www.ochu.on.ca/resources/Events/HOTLINE_REPORT_2014.pdf). The consequence of these budget cuts means that patients may be more likely to be readmitted; there is a decline in referral for various home-care services; there is an increase in hospital-acquired infections; people suffer in emergency wards while waiting to be admitted; and especially elderly and chronically ill patients wait interminably for admittance to long-term care.

Nurses report that they are increasingly overworked, and frequently they have to work overtime, without pay, just to get their necessary work done and the patients and charts ready for the next shift. Jobs are being eliminated or made insecure; nurses are being laid off and those who remain must work harder, under worsening conditions, with decreasing opportunity to provide the care they are trained to provide. A recent research report, *Nurse Fatigue and Patient Safety Report* (http://cna-aiic.ca/~/media/cna/page-content/pdf-en/fatigue_safety_2010_summary_e.pdf), has documented some of the costs of the excesses in nursing work, including long hours and other stresses and strains, in terms of the consequences for patient safety.

Of the nurses working in Canada, significant numbers still work on a casual basis. Twelve per cent were casual and 31 per cent were employed part-time in 2012, and many of those who are considered full-time workers work only on an irregular basis. The lack of a stable and committed workforce makes the job even harder for all concerned. Moreover, benefits often only accrue to those who work on a non-casual basis. Moreover, a substantial percentage, about 12.8 per cent of registered nurses, work for more than one employer to make ends meet (RN Workforce Profiles Year 2010, www.cna-aiic.ca). Although Canada has had a slight decrease in the number of registered nurses from 2008 to 2012, the number of less-trained and less-educated licensed practical nurses has increased substantially (see Figure 12.1).

Major changes in health-care services, such as financial withdrawal of some federal funding

to provinces, aging populations, sicker patients, increasingly advanced technology, and downsizing or restructuring, have affected the world of nurses in recent years. The nursing profession is extremely vulnerable to such changes in the socio-economic and political environment because nurses usually are paid via the government or government-financed institutions. The federal government has withdrawn billions of dollars in transfer payments to the provinces, and with the block funding introduced in 1995 with the Canada Health and Social Transfer, provinces were put in a position—without shared-cost financing with Ottawa—of deciding who would get what in the vast system of health care and social services. This has caused what has been called "the quiet crisis in health care." It is important to note that nursing shortages appear to be associated with an increased rate of infections contracted in hospital (Taunton et al., 1994). The presence of more better-educated nurses (those with baccalaureate or higher nursing education) results in lower surgical mortality (Aiken et al., 2003) and more positive patient outcomes in respect to "functional status, pain and patient perception of nursing care" (McGillis Hall et al., 2003). Both patients and physicians in Ontario feel the staffing is inadequate and adversely affects the health of patients. Several coroners' juries, as a result of unnecessary deaths, have recommended "safe" ratios of trained nurses at various places in the hospital. The Canadian Nurses Association (CNA) has published a report on the supply and demand for nurses in Canada to 2011 indicating a shortage of at least 60,000 registered nurses by 2022 (www.cna.nurses.ca/CNA/issues/hhr/default_e.aspx). This projection took into account the age distribution of registered nurses, the current number of nurses, ages of students in nursing schools, and population growth predictions. With respect to the age distribution the research found that the average age of nurses and of nursing students is increasing.

An optimal number of nurses is crucial to the well-being of all of us, especially hospitalized patients. According to Potter et al. (2003), as hours of nursing for the patient in hospital increase: (1) the level of patient pain decreases; (2) the patient's

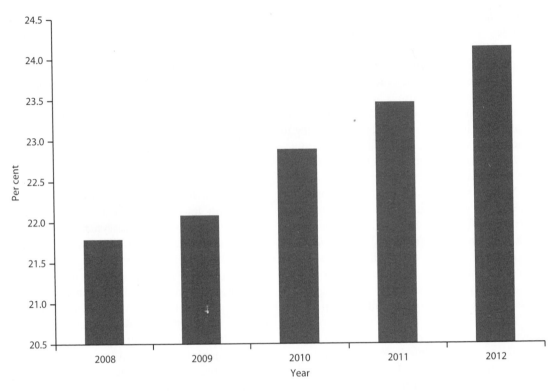

FIGURE 12.1   Cumulative Percentage Growth, Nursing Workforce, 2008–12

Source: Adapted from CIHI, *Regulated Nurses, 2012*, https://secure.cihi.ca/free_products/RegulatedNurses2012Summary_EN.pdf.

perceived health status increases; and (3) the patient's post-discharge satisfaction increases. Furthermore, according to Rogers et al. (2004), the likelihood of making errors increases as (1) the number of hours of work increases (the odds of making an error were three times higher when RNs worked shifts 12.5 hours or longer); (2) when RNs work overtime; and (3) when RNs work more than 40 hours per week.

Nurses often experience a great deal of job strain as a result of many factors, especially overwork, understaffing, and excessive overtime (McGillis Hall and Kiesners, 2005). McGillis Hall and Kiesners have documented how the current workforce patterns are associated with many work–life issues for nurses. In this study, nurses expressed guilt and remorse over their inability to do the job the way they know it needs to be done, because they have too many patients who are too sick, and they simply don't have enough time to provide an adequate level of care (ibid., 2482). They said they felt frustrated, guilty, and stressed by the lack of adequate time and staffing to do a good job at work. Nurses also reported that this work frustration spills over into their family and home life, personal health, and patient outcomes. This richly documented qualitative study of the difficulties of nursing today includes numerous examples of these challenges in the words of the nurses themselves. Nursing unions have done their own research, and a study published in 2011 found that nurses had almost twice the rate of absence due to illness or disability of all other occupations (https://secure.cihi.ca/free_products/RegulatedNurses2012Summary_EN.pdf).

Moreover, to compensate for the mismatch in planned and actual staffing needs, 29 per cent of the work done by nurses was in overtime, and only half of this was in paid overtime while the rest was in unpaid overtime that nurses felt they had to do for the well-being of their patients.

Although violence occurs in all walks of life, nurses are in a particularly vulnerable position as compared to workers in other occupations in general and other occupations within the health-care labour force (http://www.crnns.ca/documents/Resource%20-%20Violence%20in%20the%20Workplace.pdf). According to the International Council of Nurses, as many as 72 per cent of nurses say they do not feel safe from assault at work (www.cna-aiic.ca). Canadian nurses also report a high incidence of emotional abuse (Aiken et al., 2003). Moreover, even compared to prison guards, police officers, bank personnel, and transport workers, health professionals are at the highest risk of assault at work (Kingma, 2001). A survey of 19,000 nurses working in Canada found that 29.6 per cent had been physically abused by a patient over the previous 12 months (Priest, 2008).

Nursing as a Profession

Nurses have been striving in many ways to reach professional status. They have done this through: (1) increasing educational requirements; (2) forming their own "college" to handle questions of practice and the discipline of members; (3) carving out a body of knowledge that is separate from that used by other medical care workers; and (4) emphasizing the special qualities and skills that nurses have and that physicians do not have.

Well over 40 years ago, Freidson (1970: 49) argued that nursing was a paramedical occupation, as were the occupations of laboratory technicians and physical therapists, because of four characteristics they all shared: (1) the technical knowledge used by the paramedical occupations is usually developed and legitimated by physicians; (2) the tasks of paramedics usually are designed to help physicians fulfill their "more important" duties; (3) paramedics

usually work at the request of the physician; and (4) they are accorded less prestige than the medical profession. Despite the efforts of nursing organizations to gain greater autonomy and full professional status for their members, these characteristics have not changed. The medical profession is unique in that no other profession has such a bevy of supportive occupational groups enabling it to do its work. While lawyers use members of other occupational groups regularly, these groups (e.g., accountants, real estate agents, court clerks, bailiffs, and so on) are autonomous and are not considered paralegals.

The modern occupation of nursing has developed out of the context of a historical subservience of women to men and of nurses' subservience to the doctors. Nursing tasks, roles, rights, and duties have arisen to serve the needs of physicians in patient cure and care. From the day that Florence Nightingale and her nurses in the Crimea first waited to nurse until the doctors gave the orders, nurses have waited on doctors. Contemporary nurses, in an effort to enhance their position in the medical labour force and/or to achieve the status of a profession, have taken a number of job-related actions. Krause (1978: 52) lists these:

1. the shift to university training;
2. the taking over of physicians' dirty work;
3. the use of managerial ideology;
4. taking control of technology; and
5. unionizing.

The Shift to University Training

Nurses used to be "trained" while they worked in hospitals for a period of several years. Their days were long in the hospital but they took classes outside of their work as well. For several decades, the most popular program for training registered nurses in Canada was the community college, with some hospital placement. Now, there are programs at community colleges and universities, and joint programs between colleges and universities. There is no question that the Canadian Nurses Association wants all nurses to have a baccalaureate degree in nursing through a university. The Bachelor of

Science in Nursing degree program is designed to increase the credibility of the nurse by providing a theoretical background and greater training in critical thinking as it applies to nursing practice. As of 2010, 57.6 per cent of employed nurses had a diploma, 38.8 per cent had a baccalaureate, 3.3 per cent had a master's, and 0.1 per cent had a doctorate (www.cna-nurses.ca/CNA/documents/). Despite these intentions and hopes, the Canadian government has increasingly invested in less-trained licensed practical nurses. They are given responsibilities that were once restricted to registered nurses but lack the expertise in some cases to provide safe bedside care and health monitoring.

The Canadian Association of University Schools of Nursing is attempting to put a unique focus on nursing education and training. Many different specialty certificates are open to graduate nurses. Nurses with particular types of advanced training can be licensed as nurse practitioners (NPs). The nurse practitioner role has been expanded and includes many responsibilities that were once the sole purview of doctors.

Nurses with a bachelor's degree in nursing and additional training to a level at least parallel with a master's degree have been working as independent practitioners in many Western countries for many decades. For a period, NPs were being trained in Canada as "physician extenders." These courses were terminated for a time in the last part of the twentieth century but have been redeveloped. Originally, nurse practitioners were to work especially in primary care with children. Today, NPs are regulated and covered by legislation in 12 provinces and territories in Canada. In all of these jurisdictions they are able to act autonomously in respect to diagnosis, ordering diagnostic and screening tests, and prescribing medication (CIHI, 2006). In 2010, 2,486 nurse practitioners were working in Canada (Nurse Practitioner Profile—Year 2010). In all jurisdictions NPs can now or will be able to diagnose, order and interpret diagnostic testing, and prescribe medication (www.cihi.ca/cihiweb/dispPage.jsp?cw_page=PG_449_E&cw_topic=449&cw_rel=AR_1263_E).

TABLE 12.3 Nurse Practitioners by Jurisdiction, 2010

Jurisdiction	Number of Nurse Practitioners Employed in Nursing	Ratio of Nurse Practitioners to Population
Canada	2,486	1:13,727
Newfoundland and Labrador	96	1:5,326
Prince Edward Island*	–	–
Nova Scotia	106	1:8,913
New Brunswick	69	1:10,910
Quebec	64	1:123,527
Ontario	1,482	1:8,925
Manitoba*	–	–
Saskatchewan	122	1:8,557
Alberta	263	1:14,148
British Columbia	129	1:35,114
NWT and Nunavut	56	1:1,354

*Prince Edward Island and Manitoba both had fewer than 10 nurse practitioners, and so their numbers were suppressed in order to ensure confidentiality. Yukon has no nurse practitioners.

Source: 2010 Workforce Profile of Nurse Practitioners in Canada. Canadian Nurses Association (2012), p. 3. https://www.cna-aiic.ca/~/media/cna/page-content/pdf-en/2010_np_profiles_e.pdf.

REMEMBERING OUR HISTORY

BOX 12.3   The Story of Florence Nightingale

The story of the transition of hospital nursing from a duty performed out of charity and for the love of God, or by poor women who had no option, to an occupation requiring training must begin with Florence Nightingale. She revolutionized nursing work and laid the foundations for the modern, full-time occupation of nursing. As she described her calling, "On February the 7th, 1837, God spoke to me and called me to his service." Another time she wrote, "I craved for some regular occupation, for something worth doing instead of frittering away my time with useless trifles" (Bull, 1985: 15). This statement has been taken to be a reflection of her motivation to serve the sick despite years of opposition by her wealthy mother and sister and the pleas of several ardent suitors.

Nightingale was born into a wealthy English family in 1820. The upper-class Victorian woman was expected to marry, to provide heirs for her husband, to run his household, and to be a decorative companion at social events. Ideally, her days would have been taken up with organizing the servants and governesses in the household, perhaps engaging in some fancywork, and meeting with other women concerning some charitable cause. As has been said, nursing at that time was for the most part done by the indigent. It most certainly was not a "suitable" occupation for someone of Nightingale's social standing.

Nevertheless, she was committed to making something special of her life in the service of God. Her first experience of the kind of service God might be calling her to occurred one summer when the family was holidaying at their summer place, Lea Hurst, in Derbyshire. Nightingale met and helped a number of poor cottagers, taking them food, medicine, and clothing. Later, she nursed her sick grandmother and an orphaned baby. When she learned of a school for the training of nurses located in Germany, the Kaiserwerth Hospital, she visited it.

Her father, having seen Nightingale refuse suitors, read and study mathematics late into the night, and maintain her fervent commitment to God's call, finally weakened and allowed her to study nursing. When she returned to England, two rich, aristocratic friends, Sidney and Elizabeth Herbert, supported Nightingale and spread the word that she was England's leading expert in matters of health. When a director was required for a nursing home, the Institution for the Care of Sick Gentlewomen in Distressed Circumstances, the Herberts recommended Nightingale. She accepted the position in 1853 and turned the nursing home into a very good and well-run hospital.

Slightly more than one year later, after she had gained invaluable experience in running the hospital, Sidney Herbert, who was then Secretary of War, asked Nightingale to go to Turkey to nurse British soldiers injured in the Crimean War (1853–6). The war, to that point, had been disastrous for the British. They had been unprepared. There were widespread shortages of equipment, food, bedding, and medical supplies. The soldiers were expected to live on mouldy biscuits and salt pork. They slept in the mud in clothes and blankets that were stiff with blood and crawling with lice. In the infirmary, there was no water for washing, and all the drains were blocked. Almost every man had diarrhea, but there were neither diets nor special medicines to relieve it (ibid., 35). There were no hot drinks, because the necessities for lighting a fire were not available.

Nightingale was asked to recruit, organize, and take a group of 40 nurses into this chaotic and squalid situation. She advertised in London and beyond, but was able to find only 38 women, some of whom were religious sisters, with the qualities she required. Nightingale and her staff set out for the Crimea. She laid down strict orders to be followed: all were to be considered equal; all were to obey her. They were to share food and accommodation. All wore uniforms comprised of grey dresses and white caps.

Nightingale and her nurses arrived at the Barroch Hospital in Scutari, in late 1854, ready to

continued

work and armed with financial resources. They were met with hostility by the doctors, who refused to let them see patients and offered all 38 women only six dirty, small rooms (one of which had a corpse in it). They were given no furniture, lighting, or food. Nightingale had experienced much opposition in her life; she was prepared to wait. She told her nurses to make bandages, and offered the doctors milk puddings for the patients. These tasks seemed "suitable" for women, and so the doctors accepted the milk puddings. Less than one week later there was another battle and a huge number of casualties. The doctors, overwhelmed by the enormity of the disaster and the tasks that lay ahead of them, and reassured that the nurses were willing to obey (they had waited) and that they could provide "feminine services" (make milk puddings), asked the nurses to help out.

Nightingale ordered food, cutlery, china, soap, bedpans, and operating tables. Her nurses sewed clean cotton bags for straw mattresses. Men were hired to clean the lavatories and basins. The floors were scrubbed for the first time in anyone's memory. Soldiers' wives were recruited to wash clothes and bedding. Still the mortality rate did not decline significantly. Nightingale, who knew far more than the doctors about the importance of fresh air, cleanliness, and clean water, had the plumbing inspected. The pipes were blocked and the water supply contaminated. Once this was cleaned out, the mortality rate dropped dramatically.

Nightingale was viewed as a heroine both within the hospital and without. Within the hospital she was known as "the lady with the lamp." She offered all kinds of services, even banking and letter-writing, to her patients. At the end of the war, the grateful soldiers dedicated one day's pay to her for the establishment of the Nightingale School of Nursing and the Nightingale Fund. Outside the hospital, and once she returned home to Britain in 1857, she was heralded as the most important woman of her time, except for Queen Victoria. At this time, there were no female judges, MPs, or civil servants. No woman had ever taken charge of an

institution. Florence Nightingale was a heroine to Britain and to the Western world.

Her greatest achievements were in public health reform. Her writing and lobbying in this area continued long after she returned from the Crimea, even though she spent the rest of her long life essentially bedridden. It has been suggested, in fact, that Nightingale's work was the beginning of modern epidemiology. Her work is also thought to have provided the model for the early training of nurses. Eventually, after several unsuccessful attempts, the first nursing school, on the Nightingale model, was established at the General and Marine Hospital in St Catharines, Ontario, in 1874. A few years later, the Toronto General (1881) and Montreal General (1880) hospitals were established. Nursing students often comprised almost the whole staff of these hospitals (Jensen, 1988).

The long-term effects of Nightingale's work on the practice of nursing are often considered to have been equivocal, however (Reverby, 1987). On the one hand, she herself exhibited enormous strength and commitment, and was able to garner extensive personal power as a leader in epidemiological research models, in healthcare policy, in the management of hospitals, in military nursing, and as the most important role model for the secular occupation of nursing in her society. On the other hand, she ensured that the women who worked as nurses for her were taught to be handmaidens to doctors and to be "mother-surrogates" to patients. Even though Nightingale studied hard to become educated and rejected her own assigned gender role, she expected her nurses to be subservient, obedient, and docile in their relationships with medical doctors.

Nursing, under Nightingale, was to be a woman's job. Only women had the necessary character and qualities. While carving out a respectable occupation for women, she also reinforced a ghettoized and subordinated female labour force that is still in place today. This model of nursing supported the traditional stereotype of the physician as father figure and the nurse as mother. Florence Nightingale died in 1910 at the age of 90.

Nurses and NPs are being encouraged through education to engage in critical thinking, independent decision-making, research, and leadership. However, the structures in which they work usually limit their ability to do so. Thus, while there is a definite move towards requiring a university degree in order to practise, there is still no significant change in the hospital authority structure (Armstrong et al., 1993). Even nurses with Ph.D. degrees are not able to claim professional autonomy vis-à-vis the physician. Nevertheless, an increase in the numbers and the authority of nurse practitioners will relieve some of the pressure on medical care costs and on the "shortage" of doctors because the tasks for which NPs are being trained include those that were formerly done only by medical doctors. NPs can work independently outside of hospitals in free-standing clinics as well as in community health centres (www.cna-nurses.ca/CNA/documents/pdf/publications/cnpi/tech-report/section1/01_Integrated_Report.pdf).

Several creative initiatives have been designed to address other critical health shortages. For instance, the Saskatchewan Indian Federation College in Regina (now First Nations University of Canada) started a collaborative program with the University of Saskatchewan to assist Aboriginal students to prepare for nursing. Across Canada other nursing specialties are being developed as well, including parish nursing, school nursing, nursing informatics, forensic nursing, mental health nursing in the schools, and legal nurse consultation (www.allnursingschools.com/faqs/np.php).

Taking Over the Work of the Physician

Nurses have taken over some of the "dirty work" of physicians, including such routine tasks as monitoring blood pressure, setting up intravenous infusions, and giving medications. At the same time, they have passed some of their own "dirty work" down the line to registered nursing assistants, e.g., making beds, bathing, feeding, and other actions for the personal care of patients. Both of these shifts have been attempts to shore up the relative importance of nurses in the medical labour force: they have accepted some of the higher-status tasks of physicians and rejected

some of their own less desirable tasks. Still, the presence of registered nurses (RNs) on the ward makes important differences in the health of patients even after they leave the hospital. A positive relationship has been found between the number of nurses on a ward and a higher level of independence, less pain, better social functioning, and greater satisfaction with care for discharged patients.

Managerial Ideology and Nursing

Managerial ideology applied to nursing has led to a multitude of divisions within the occupational group. These include divisions among nurses by specialty (e.g., intensive-care nurses, pediatric nurses), divisions by type of training (hospital- or university-based training), and divisions by level of responsibility (head nurse, staff nurse). Furthermore, registered nurses have divided the occupations below them in the medical labour force into various classes of subordinates, and have sought to maintain control as the governing body over various types of registered nursing assistants. Below these groups are nursing aides or assistants. The impact of managerial ideology is noticeable both in the increase in the introduction of such efficiency measures as CMGs and other means of speeding up the delivery of nursing care and in the "ideological subordination" of nurses to the interests of the organization or hospital rather than to the patient or the nursing community (Warburton and Carroll, 1988; Rankin and Campbell, 2006).

Rejecting High-Tech Medicine

Many nurses in Canada are seeking advancement for their occupation in part through an anti-technology ideology. Rather than emphasizing their skill and expertise in handling new technologies, nurses are rejecting the value of the medical model and arguing that medical care should be based much more broadly on holistic care, health promotion, and disease prevention. They emphasize the importance of their caring approach versus a curing approach. This argument is particularly persuasive given the current demography of illness, i.e., the increasing rates of chronic illness and the aging population.

Unionization

Unionization has had a positive effect on at least one particular aspect of the status of nursing—income. Paradoxically, however, unionization has also served to proletarianize nurses and to establish their position as members of the skilled working class who work for wages. More research needs to be undertaken on the short- and long-term consequences of the unionization process.

Midwifery

Have you thought about your own experience of birth? Have your parents told you about it? Was your father in the delivery room with your mother? Did your mother have any surgical intervention when she gave birth to you? Do you know anyone who has given birth at home or in an institution other than a hospital? Are you aware of the sorts of services that midwives offer to the mother and father before, during, and after the birth? What is the legal status of the midwife in Canada?

The final section of this chapter describes the history of midwives, their work, and their contemporary situation. The term "midwife" comes from Old English and means "with the women." The French term is *sage-femme*, or "wise-woman." Essentially, the work of the midwife is to assist women as they prepare for and give birth and as they learn to care for their new offspring. Midwives have usually practised their work in the home, where the woman is surrounded by her family and friends. Birth in this environment is seen as a healthy natural event, not an illness or disability.

Thus, midwives have tended not to use artificial or mechanical means to assist with birth because of their assumption that birth is fundamentally a natural event. For instance, a midwife would predict a breech birth (upside down, feet- or buttocks-first presentation) through a manual examination. Massage of the fetus in the uterus would be used to turn the baby for a normal delivery. Manual manipulation rather than forceps would be used to move the baby down the birth canal. Pain would be handled by rubbing the back, shoulders, and neck of the woman in labour, and with encouraging words and assisting women in controlling the pace and depth of their breathing. The woman in labour would be relaxed and comforted by the familiar atmosphere and the presence of a person or persons with experience.

A brief overview of the history of **midwifery** is necessary for understanding its position in Canadian society today. Birthing assistance has almost always and everywhere been the responsibility of women. The practice of midwifery can be traced to ancient history. The Bible includes a number of references. Exodus 1:15–22 is one example: two midwives, Shiprah and Puah, refused to obey the orders of the king of Egypt that all male infants be put to death. The written work of classical Greek and Roman physicians such as Hippocrates and Galen documents the prevalence of midwives. Male physicians were summoned only when special difficulties developed (Litoff, 1978). Until the Middle Ages, women who themselves had given birth were acceptable attendants at other births.

Up to the fourteenth century, midwifery flourished in Europe. Then came the witch hunts in which women healers of all sorts, and particularly midwives, were put to death. Midwives were especially vulnerable because of their close association with the placenta, which was believed to be an essential ingredient in witchcraft. By the end of the fifteenth century, witch-hunting had declined. In Britain, and soon elsewhere in Europe, midwives gained formal legitimacy under the Medical Act of 1512. This Act was to be administered and enforced by local churches. Licensing depended on the good character of the aspiring midwife and required that she be hard-working, faithful, and prepared to provide service to both rich and poor whenever it was needed. She was also forbidden to use witchcraft, charms, or prayers that were not dictated by the Church. Men were not allowed to be present at birth (ibid.). Then, in 1642, the College of Physicians gained authority to license midwives. For the next 300 years the legitimacy, recognition, and power of the male midwives, now obstetricians, grew in England and Europe while those of female midwives declined.

In the last quarter of the nineteenth century, British midwives made numerous attempts to gain legitimacy and recognition as an autonomous professional group. In 1893, a committee of the British House of Commons reported on the significant rate of maternal and infant mortality. These deaths were attributed to poorly trained, unregulated midwives, and the committee report recommended that midwives be registered (Eberts, 1987). Most doctors rejected this suggestion because they argued that midwives did not have the necessary training. The Royal British Nursing Association supported the proposal to create a new occupational category: obstetric midwives or nurses.

Public opinion in favour of midwifery seemed to be growing. By the early part of the twentieth century, midwives in Britain were legitimized through regulation. With the establishment of the National Health Service in 1948, midwives were employed as a form of public health nurse. In 1968, legislation in Britain expanded the role of the midwife.

The earliest mention of midwifery among Euro-Canadian women appears in a deed in the Montreal archives, which reveals that the women of Ville-Marie, in a meeting held on 12 February 1713, elected a community midwife named Catherine Guertin. Also, in the English settlement of Lunenburg, Nova Scotia, Colonel Sutherland, the Commander, wrote to the British government in 1755 asking that two pounds per year be paid to the two practising midwives. Apparently in no other regions in Canada were midwives on government salary (Abbott, 1931).

Until the mid-nineteenth century, most births in Canada took place at home in the presence of midwives (Oppenheimer, 1983), although from this time on home births were attended by physicians. From 1809 until 1895 the legal position of midwives was uncertain and changeable. Whenever midwives did not pose a threat to the work of allopaths they were allowed to practise; but where they did compete with allopaths, primarily in the cities and among the middle and upper classes, there were attempts to restrict them (Wertz and Wertz, 1977; Barrington, 1985; Ehrenreich and English, 1979; Biggs, 1983).

Statistics indicate that in 1899 midwives attended about 3 per cent of all Ontario births and doctors attended 16 per cent (Biggs, 1983). However, as the legal status of the midwife was unclear, the number given for midwife-attended births is probably an underestimate. Over the duration of most of the nineteenth century, apparently, midwives garnered a significant amount of community and media support. The *Globe* newspaper opposed a medical monopoly of childbirth until 1895, when a bill to reinstate licensing of midwives was vehemently defeated in the legislature. At this juncture the *Globe* reversed its position (ibid.).

In the last part of the nineteenth century and into the twentieth century, the importance of the doctor's exclusive right to attend births grew. In Canada, presently, legislation ensures that midwives are qualified to practise in some provinces but not in others. Once legislation comes into effect, the term "midwife" is protected and the practice of midwifery by those who are unlicensed is illegal, just as it is illegal for someone who is unlicensed to practise medicine. Most provinces have consumer advocacy groups working for midwifery legislation. To date, midwives are licensed in most of provinces, and are funded through the provincial/territorial health insurance plans in Ontario, British Columbia, Manitoba, Quebec, Nova Scotia, Alberta, Saskatchewan, the Northwest Territories, and Nunavut (CHSRF, 2006; cmrc-ccosf.ca/node/19). It is estimated that more than 500 midwives are in practice across the country and about 100 are being trained annually (http://www.marketwired.com/press-release/canadian-association-of-midwives-the-world-needs-midwives-now-more-than-ever-1158632.htmwww.cwhn.ca/network-reseau/8-12/8-12pg7.html).

Issues in the History of the Practice of Midwifery

In addition to sexism and patriarchy, other social forces responsible for the contemporary pattern of high-tech, hospital-based, interventionist-oriented, physician-attended births include: (1) bureaucratization and hospitalization, (2) the profit motive, (3) the public health movement,

(4) the emphasis on safety and pain relief in child-birth, and (5) the campaign for ascendancy waged by physicians.

Bureaucratization and Hospitalization

Before 1880 hospital care was almost entirely for the poor and those suffering the wounds of war. The York Hospital, later to become Toronto General Hospital, opened in 1829 as the first real hospital in Ontario. It was established to treat the veterans of the War of 1812 and destitute immi-grants. The first institution for women who needed care during childbirth, the Society for the Relief of Women During Their Confinement, was estab-lished as a charity in 1820. It provided the services of midwife-nurses and doctors, and also cloth-ing and food for the mother and child. In 1848, the Toronto General Dispensary and Lying-In Hospital was established to provide care for des-titute women and a place for training medical midwives. Around the beginning of the twentieth century a concerted effort was made to centralize medical care in the hospital. With this move came the further consolidation of hospital births by male midwives or obstetricians. By 1950, Canadian mid-wifery had all but disappeared.

Concern with modesty spread the belief that decent people did not have their babies at home. Childbirth literature of the time emphasized the complicated, scientifically managed birth event. The new techniques, including the induction of labour, anaesthesia, and the use of mechanical and surgical tools, further entrenched the notions that (1) the hospital was the only place for this potentially complex and dangerous birth proced-ure, and (2) the skilled hands of the equipped and trained obstetrician were the only ones appropri-ate for delivery. This belief was supported further by the fact that the majority of new immigrants who began to populate the cities used midwives. Middle- and upper-class women tried to distance themselves from the poor and immigrant women and from their typical childbirth practices. This, too, reinforced the growing belief in the appro-priateness of the hospital as the place of choice for childbirth for the middle classes.

World War I had an impact on the growth of scientifically managed hospital births. Childbirth came to be described as a dangerous process, and women, with war casualties fresh in their minds, were increasingly concerned to deliver their babies in a safe environment. Many were impressed with the physicians' argument that infant and mater-nal mortality rates could only be substantially decreased when childbirth was recognized as a complicated medical condition (Litoff, 1978). The growth of hospitals provided additional beds. Automobiles and roads reduced the time it took to get to the hospital after labour contractions had started.

Profits for Doctors

Physicians had a lot to lose if midwives were given free rein to practise. According to Biggs (1983), midwives (in about 1873) charged approximately two dollars per birth, whereas male doctors charged five dollars. Biggs states that physicians felt that they should be "protected most stringently against the meddlesome interference on the part of old women," and that the amount of money lost through the competition with midwives would constitute a "decent living for [his] small family" (ibid., 28).

The Public Health Movement

During the last half of the nineteenth century and into the twentieth century, Canada, along with the rest of the Western industrialized world, witnessed a dramatic decrease in mortality rates. The decline in maternal mortality rates corresponded to the gen-eral decrease in mortality and coincided with the increasing prestige of the physician and the growing belief that medicine could cure all ills. This, too, pro-vided ideological support and furthered the move to obstetrician-centred, hospital-based births.

The Emphasis on Safety and Pain Relief in Childbirth

Another element in the move to birth taking place in hospitals was women's search for relief from the pains of childbirth. Among the causes of such pain for nineteenth-century women were the cultural constraints on middle-class women, which demanded a certain delicate beauty. This could best be achieved by wearing boned corsets that constricted their waists, rib cages, and pelvises. Sensitivity to pain was considered feminine, and thus women's pain threshold tended to be low. Women were encouraged to see themselves as fragile, sickly, and weak. For middle-class women at the beginning of the twentieth century, comfort during birth came to mean the obliteration of consciousness through "twilight sleep." Since twilight sleep (a combination of morphine and scopolamine) could be monitored more effectively in the hospital, middle-class women sought to give birth in hospital.

Precautionary measures, including the enema and shave, were developed to preserve hygienic conditions and prevent puerperal fever. Forceps were developed in the nineteenth century; their use became standard because they could speed the birth process if it were slow. A Caesarean section, a potentially life-saving procedure to be used when labour was ineffective or the pelvis was too small, became a frequent and even dangerously overused procedure. By the 1930s there were real safety advantages, including blood transfusions and antibiotics, in treating problematic births at the hospital. Yet, as Barrington (1985) ruefully points out, the necessity for blood transfusions and antibiotics often resulted from hospital-caused infections and doctor-caused hemorrhages.

The Campaign for Ascendancy Waged by the Physician

Doctors described midwives as "dirty, ignorant and dangerous" (Biggs, 1983: 31). Devitt (1977) quotes a midwife's statement, from 1906, that the obstetricians thought of her as the "typical old, gin-fingering, guzzling midwife with her pockets full of forcing drops, her mouth full of snuff, her fingers full of dirt, and her brains full of arrogance and superstition." Biggs (1983) quotes a doctor's view of midwives from the *British American Journal of Medical and Physical Science*:

And when we consider the enormous error which they [midwives] are continually perpetuating and the valuable lives which are frequently sacrificed to their ignorance, the more speedily some legislative interference is taken with respect to them, the better the community at large.

Physicians gained ideological superiority over midwives by portraying their own work as scientific and buttressed by apparently safe and efficient tools such as forceps. Given that physicians were educated men from good families and were coming to have high status, social power, and also often much political influence, it is no wonder that they were successful in advancing the view that their births were the best births.

The Present Status of Midwives

Worldwide, midwives deliver approximately 80 per cent of babies today. The North American situation is different, largely because of the presence and ideological success, as well as the institutional dominance, of allopathic doctors, particularly the specialists in birth, obstetricians. In the past almost half-century the women's and feminist movements have been powerfully critical of the medical profession for denying the autonomy of women in childbirth. Women also have spearheaded a movement for women's rights over childbirth. Romelis (1985) discussed five specific components of this movement, including groups advocating (1) natural childbirth, (2) the Leboyer method, involving gentle birthing and immersion in water, (3) alternative in-hospital births, (4) home births, and (5) non-hospital birth centres. The role of midwifery fits within this view that abhors an unthinking reliance on modern hospital practices, such as "invasive diagnostic procedures, induction and acceleration of labour, reliance on drugs for pain, routine electronic fetal monitoring, dramatically increasing Caesarean-section rates, and separation of mother and baby after the birth" (ibid., 185).

The increasing legitimacy of midwifery reflects both the strategies taken by the state to control health-care costs (e.g., in Ontario midwives are now on salary through the provincial government) and the increasing political influence of women's groups and organized midwives on state policy (Bourgeault et al., 1998). The shift in attitude also reflects the type of service offered by the midwife, who provides more holistic care and a minimum of 44 hours of prenatal and postnatal care, education, and support and emphasizes the importance of the values of the mother-to-be in the choice of birth, allowing births at home, in birth centres, or in hospitals, as well as medical exigencies (www.canadianmidwives.org).

A 1996 Canadian study of 3,470 women attended by midwives noted the following: (1) fewer episiotomies (8 per cent as compared to 50 per cent with physician-attended births); (2) less frequent anaesthesia (5 per cent as compared to 30 per cent with physician-attended births); (3) lower cost (primarily because 40 per cent of midwife-attended births occurred at home); and (4) more frequent breast-feeding (95 per cent of those women who had the assistance of midwives were successfully breast-feeding at six weeks) (www.ucs.mun.ca/pherbert/number8.html). The impact of this shift to midwifery on the medical specialty of obstetrics is yet to be determined, but a number of controversial issues are continuing to be sorted out, including payment inequity between midwives and obstetricians, home birth safety, and malpractice responsibility.

Midwifery has been found to be safe in homes, hospitals, and birthing centres in a wide variety of studies. Moreover, mothers attended by midwives are less likely to use drugs for pain or to have surgical interventions such as episiotomies or Caesarean sections. Midwives are less likely to use forceps, vacuum extraction, or other interventions,

and mothers who choose midwives tend to be very satisfied with their care. In jurisdictions without enabling legislation, midwives risk prosecution if anything goes wrong.

Today, the practice of obstetrics and gynecology has lost some of its attraction for doctors because of its relatively high malpractice insurance costs. Many family doctors, too, for a variety of reasons including insurance costs and time away from general practice, seem to be happy to turn childbirth over to midwives. Still, only a small percentage of Canadian births are attended by midwives, ranging from 6.6 per cent in British Columbia to less than 1 per cent in Alberta (www.asac.ab.ca/updatesMidwiferyCanada.html). However, a growing number of provincial and territorial governments cover the costs of midwives and we can expect this proportion to increase.

In addition to midwives, some women who are giving birth are now also choosing doulas. They are non-medical birth coaches who pay attention to the desires and wishes of the birthing woman. They are not trained to help in the actual physical birth process. Instead, they are trained or simply volunteer to be the emotional voice for women during the process of giving birth. This is particularly important because the role of the midwife has grown in responsibility to encompass the actual safety and efficacy of the birthing process, even in a hospital setting with all of the "high-tech" tools available. Birthing involves physical, intellectual, and spiritual aspects of human experience—the body, the mind, and the spirit. The mind and the spirit are the focus of the support offered by doulas.

SUMMARY

1. Some sort of nursing function has always been associated with illness and treatment. Florence Nightingale was the founder of the contemporary system of nursing care. She led a handpicked team of 38 nurses to serve in the Crimean War. Nightingale pioneered sanitary practices and caused the mortality rate to drop. She also provided many other services for the patients.

2. Although Nightingale established nursing as an important profession in society, she did so by reinforcing a ghettoized and subordinated

female labour force. The view of nursing as a woman's job is still in place today.

3. Critical analysis of the work of the contemporary nurse tends to follow one of three lines: the patriarchal/sexist nature of the content of the work and the low position of nursing in the hierarchy of the medical labour force; the managerial revolution in nursing practice; or the impact of the hospital bureaucracy on the working life of the nurse.

4. Nursing associations have been striving to achieve professional status by increasing educational requirements, forming licensing bodies, attempting to carve a body of knowledge separate from that of physicians, and emphasizing nurses' special qualities and skills. However, some argue that nursing is a paramedical occupation, not a profession, because the technical knowledge that nurses use is created, developed, and legitimated by physicians, the tasks nurses perform are less "important" than those of doctors, and nursing has less prestige than the medical profession.

5. Midwifery is based on the belief that birth is a natural process, and therefore the use of artificial or mechanical means to interfere with birth is avoided. Midwives have almost always been women. Attempts by midwives to gain legitimacy have been met by rejection because doctors argue they do not have the necessary training, and because their presence threatens the work of allopaths.

6. The social conditions that allowed allopathic practitioners to achieve a monopoly of the childbirth process also contributed to the contemporary pattern of high-tech, hospital-based, interventionist-oriented, physician-attended births. These social conditions include patriarchy and sexism, bureaucratization and hospitalization, the profit motive, the association of the medical model with the success of the public health movement, the growth in measures for safety and pain relief, and the campaign for ascendancy waged by the physician.

7. While the legal status of midwives is still ambiguous in some provinces, it is changing. With legal recognition of midwifery in most provinces, salary and workload levels have been established and institutionalized as part of the health-care delivery system.

KEY TERMS

Grange Inquiry   managerial ideology   midwifery

QUESTIONS FOR STUDY AND DISCUSSION

1. Do a media content analysis of the portrayal of nurses in different time periods. Assess if and how the media representation may reflect gender stereotypes.

2. What organizational challenges in hospitals do nurses face today?

3. Are nurses today faced with having responsibility but lacking authority?

4. How do you evaluate the move to increase the status of nursing? In other words, are nurses "professionals" or "paraprofessionals"?

5. Critically evaluate case mix grouping. What are the major drivers of this policy?

6. What is the legal position of midwifery in your province? How does the pay level of midwives compare to nurses and doctors? Discuss.

7. Do you favour the use of a midwife for yourself, your partner, or your surrogate in pregnancy and childbirth? Explain your decision.

SUGGESTED READINGS

Aiken, L.H., S.P. Clarke, R.B. Cheung, D.M. Sloane, and J.H. Silber. 2003. "Education Levels of Hospital Nurses and Surgical Patient Mortality." *Journal of the American Medical Association* 290, 12: 1617–23. An analysis of the outcome benefits of trained nurses on hospital wards.

Austin, Wendy. 2007. "The McDonaldization of Nursing?" *Health: An Interdisciplinary Journal for the Social Study of Health, Illness and Medicine* 11, 2: 265–72. A review article on a book about nursing using an institutional ethnography perspective.

Beardwood, Barbara, and Vivienne Walters. 1999. "Complaints against Nurses: A Reflection of the New Managerialism and Consumerism in Health Care?" *Social Science and Medicine* 48, 3: 363–74. A useful analysis of relationships among work structures, working conditions, and work satisfaction.

Ceci, Christine. 2004. "Nursing, Knowledge and Power: A Case Analysis." *Social Science and Medicine* 59: 1879–89. This paper investigates the deaths of 12 children resulting from heart surgery in Winnipeg and under the supervision of one doctor. It probes the reasons, using a Foucauldian perspective, that the nurses' warnings about this particular surgeon were not acted upon.

Peate, I. 2014. "Compassion Fatigue: The Toll of Emotional Labour." *British Journal of Nursing* 23, 5: 251. A study of the emotion work in nursing.

Urban, Ann-Marie. 2012. "Nurses and Their Work in Hospitals: Ruled by Embedded Ideologies and Moving Discourses." Ph.D. diss., University of Regina. http://ourspace.uregina.ca/bitstream/handle/10294/3553/Urban_Ann-Marie_188003945_PhD_EDUC_Spring2012.pdf?sequence=1. A dissertation about the hospital work of nurses today.

Wood C. 2014. "Choosing the 'Right' People for Nursing: Can We Recruit to Care?" *British Journal of Nursing* 23, 10: 5. An article about whether "caring" can be used as a criterion for recruiting nurses.

13 Complementary and Alternative Medicine

iStock/NatureSmile

CHAPTER OVERVIEW

▶ The acceptability of complementary and alternative medicine (CAM) is growing among Canadians.

▶ The views and practices of allopathic doctors with regard to CAM appear to be changing.

▶ Chiropractic, a major alternative to allopathic medicine, is based on a very different understanding of the nature and cause of disease.

▶ Chiropractors have a unique place in medicare in Canada.

▶ Naturopathy has a different understanding of disease and its causes.

▶ Naturopathic practice is increasingly accepted as legitimate in Canada.

Introduction

Some of you have been to a naturopathic doctor. Others of you routinely use chiropractic services. Some of you meditate or perform regular relaxation training. Some of you may belong to support groups. Some of you exercise regularly. Some of you are vegetarians or follow a macrobiotic diet. Some of you attend church and/or pray regularly and believe that spirituality can be healing. Such actions as these may be examples of complementary and alternative healing practices. Notice the breadth of these options. Note, too, that some involve professional services while others are done without cost and even invisibly. These various health-related actions are the types of issues we will address in this chapter.

Alternative, Complementary, and Allopathic Medicine

As is often the case with a new concept, its definition can be amorphous, expansive, and variable. There are debates about whether the descriptive term ought to be "unconventional," "alternative," "unorthodox," or "complementary" medicine or health care. Each term has its proponents. It is becoming conventional (as unconventional medicine becomes conventional) to use the term **complementary and alternative medicine (CAM)** to describe the methods of treatment used both separately (alternatively) and often preventively, on the one hand, or in association with or complementary to allopathic medicine, on the other. Basically, CAMs are all those health-care practices that differ from allopathic medicine. They have tended not to be taught at allopathic medical schools and most are generally unavailable in North American hospitals (although there are some important exceptions such as therapeutic touch). However, a growing number of variations to that generalization exist, as well as courses offered at post-secondary institutions, including medical schools, across both Canada and the United States.

Today, about 50 medical schools in Canada and the US include CAM in various ways in their conventional medical education (Howell, 2012). Various complementary and alternative treatments have been accepted and are readily available in a number of countries around the world in places where they may be seen as conventional.

Conventional or **allopathic medicine** is the subject matter of most of the second half of this text. It refers to the type of healing based on a theory of opposites, or on the assumption that opposites cure. Health is the biologically natural, not just the preferred state of the body. Disease is an unwanted aberration caused by germs, bacteria, or such things as trauma from outside that attacks the equilibrium of the body. The germ theory of disease provides some of the basic assumptions upon which allopathic medicine has developed. It is the root from which the monumental scientific and biomedical research industry has grown. Insofar as disease is fundamentally an unnatural, abnormal invasion into an otherwise healthy body, treatment involves an attack on the enemy—the disease. Such treatments as surgery, medication, and radiotherapy are the outcomes of this type of thinking.

A variety of criticisms of this medical model have been offered. Advocates of **holistic health care** and CAM criticize the medical model for a reductionist focus on, and limited mechanical and biomedical treatment of, the physical body and, in fact, narrower and narrower components of the human body—e.g., genes. Instead, they advocate treating the whole person—body, mind, and spirit—through a combination of methods best suited to each particular and unique individual. Among the myriad methods included are massage, acupuncture, visualization (imaging a healthy body), herbs, vitamins, hydrotherapy, meditation, prayer, psychic and faith healing, chiropractic, and naturopathy. Sometimes people choose CAM, as really an alternative, when sick and do not go to a conventional medical doctor. Approximately 20 per cent of Americans do not receive conventional medical care in an average year (Nahin et al., 2009).

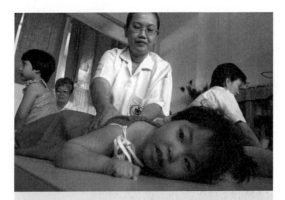

A Thai child with cerebral palsy receives a back massage at a treatment centre in Bangkok, Thailand. A 2003 study revealed that three months of Thai massage therapy techniques helped disabled children by reducing muscle spasms, common in the mobility-disabled, helping them to sleep and talk, and radically improving their health.

They do this for a number of different reasons, including rejecting its theoretical foundation or because it is inaccessible or too expensive.

Theories of the relationship between allopathic medicine and CAM are undergoing radical change. In 1993 and again in 1997, David Eisenberg, a US physician, with a group of colleagues, conducted a national representative survey of the US population to determine the patterns of practice, use, and cost of various unconventional therapies. The team selected the following 16 interventions for their questionnaire: relaxation techniques, chiropractic, massage, imagery, spiritual healing, commercial weight-loss programs, lifestyle diets (e.g., macrobiotics), herbal medicines, megavitamin therapy, self-help groups, energy healing, biofeedback, hypnosis, homeopathy, acupuncture, and folk remedies. Exercise and prayer were included as options, although they were considered to be too various and amorphous for follow-up study of a detailed sort. Approximately one in three of the 1,539 adults who took part in the telephone survey in 1990 had used at least one unconventional therapy in the previous year and a third of these had visited providers of alternative therapy as a part of their own regular health care. Those who did visit alternative providers made an average of 19 visits. Those who used unconventional treatments could be distinguished from others by their greater likelihood of being non-black, between 25 and 49 years of age, and with relatively more education and income. Most people who used unconventional medical care also saw an allopathic physician (83 per cent). However, most people did not disclose to their allopathic doctors that they were using unconventional therapies. The latest available follow-up national survey of 31,044 adults over 18 in the US found that 62 per cent used some type of CAM in the previous 12 months (this includes prayer for health). It also found that CAMs were most often used to treat back pain or back problems, colds, neck pain or neck problems, joint pain or stiffness, and anxiety or depression (Barnes et al., 2004). Of those surveyed, 19.3 per cent did not use any conventional care, and of these about one-quarter used alternative medicine (Nahin et al., 2009).

Eisenberg and colleagues estimated (conservatively) that the out-of-pocket expenses for American people for CAMs were $12.2 billion and the total expenditures (again conservatively) were about $27 billion. Today, the total spent on CAMs, according to the National Center for Complementary and Alternative Health Care in the US, is $33.9 billon. This comprises about 10.2 per cent of the total out-of-pocket expenses on health care (http://nccam.nih.gov/news/camstats/costs/costdatafs.htm). These figures also may suggest that the majority of the money spent on CAMs is funded through health insurance plans. This also underscores the finding that CAM is most likely to be used by the middle and upper classes who either can afford "extra" health care or have insurance to cover such care. This was comparable to the estimated out-of-pocket expenditures for physician services. Clearly, alternative medicine and therapy among basically "well" American people is already substantial and is growing. While this American survey is probably one of the most widely cited of such studies, research in numerous other Western countries currently dominated by allopathic care indicates that unconventional medicine and alternative health practice are mounting elsewhere, as well.

The number of alternative practitioners appears to be growing at a faster rate than that of allopathic physicians, and it is predicted that it will continue to do so. In one instance, Cooper and Stoflet (1996) predicted that the per capita number of alternative medicine clinicians would grow by 88 per cent between 1994 and 2010, while the supply of physicians would grow by only 16 per cent. Whether these predictions are accurate or not is very difficult to know, as there are no complete listings of all of the various CAM practitioners in Canada or the US. Some of the CAM practitioners work "underground" and want to remain invisible to regulatory bodies. Because there is not usually such an investment of years in education, as with allopathic care, and because it is sometimes difficult to make a living, some practitioners may stay in their occupations for only a limited amount of time or work only part-time. Some types of practitioners, such as psychic healers, are fairly widely viewed as "sketchy" and may not be counted in any census of CAM. In any case, the legitimacy of many CAM practitioners is less secure than that of conventional doctors. This is certainly the case historically. At one time, referral by a physician to an alternative health provider was considered such a serious violation of medical practice that it resulted in loss of membership in

medical societies and even the loss of medical licence. Indeed, one physician, in 1878, was reputedly murdered because he consulted with a homeopath (who was also his wife) (Rothouse, 1997).

Many other signs indicate that unconventional medicine is moving into the mainstream. In 1992 the US Congress established an Office of Alternative Medicine at the National Institutes of Health (nccam.nih.gov/health/). The National Library of Medicine in the US has increased access to research and other articles about complementary and alternative medicine. A number of medical schools and hospitals in the US and Canada have developed programs or departments for the study of alternative medicine. Beth Israel Hospital at Harvard University has raised millions of dollars for a Center for Alternative Medicine and numerous medical schools, including such large and important institutions as Georgetown, Columbia, Harvard, Maryland, and Wayne State in the United States and a number of post-secondary schools in Canada, offer courses in alternative medicine. A growing number of scientific and academic journals devoted to alternative medicine and intended for physicians and other health providers are in circulation. In addition, many insurance companies now provide coverage for alternative

---

TABLE 13.1   Selected Alternative Health Programs Offered in Canadian Universities, Colleges, and Complementary Health Institutions

Acupuncture	Music Therapy
Chinese Medicine	Native Addictions Worker Diploma
Chiropractic	Native Community Worker—Healing and Wellness
Complementary Care	Naturopathy
Energy Healing Practitioner	Qigong Instruction
Health Promotion	Reflexology
Holistic Health Practitioner	Reiki Practitioner
Homeopathic Medicine and Sciences Program	Shiatsu Therapy
Massage Therapy	Workplace Wellness and Health Promotion
Midwifery	

Source: © 2002. Canada's Health Care Providers. Used with permission. Published by the Canadian Institute for Health Information, Ottawa, Canada.

health care. At least one, American Western Life, actually offers a "wellness" plan that uses naturopathic rather than conventional physicians as gatekeepers and offers naturopathic remedies as the first stage of treatment. Some insurers reimburse for particular types of CAM only, such as **acupuncture** (see Box 13.1), which is among the most widely accepted of alternatives, especially for pain and substance abuse. Certification as an acupuncturist is often needed for reimbursement. Across Canada, naturopaths, acupuncturists, and Chinese medicine practitioners, among others, are working towards inclusion in health practitioner regulatory legislation. The Vancouver Hospital has established an alternative medicine clinic to perform research on various CAMs. This hospital has also opened a Healing Touch Centre for energy-balancing therapies such as therapeutic touch. **Therapeutic touch** has become a recognized treatment and one found among the skills of many nurses across Canada and the US. Finally, several schools that train CAM practitioners, such as the College of Naturopathic Medicine in Toronto, have expanded or are planning to expand (Imman, 1996:

CANADA IN A GLOBAL CONTEXT

BOX 13.1   Acupuncture

Acupuncture can include use of herbs, tuina (Chinese massage), exercise, and diet, and generally refers to the insertion of fine needles to various parts of body to stimulate the flow of energy (qi). Points are located along 14 main meridian lines or channels through which the body's energy flows. It stimulates the body's natural healing abilities, relieves pain, and restores internal regulation systems. There are two basic approaches. (1) Traditional Chinese medicine includes a holistic system of health care that aims to bring the body, mind, and spirit into balance, and includes such methods as moxibustion, i.e., application of heat, generated by burning dry moxa leaves on or near an acupuncture point; Chinese herbology; tuina, i.e., massage of acupuncture points; nutritional counselling; and therapeutic exercises such as qi gong and Tai Chi. (2) Medical acupuncture or "anatomical acupuncture" stimulates the body's production of endorphins. Electro-acupuncture uses needles with mild electrical impulses; laser may be used in place of needles.

Acupuncture has been widely adopted by a wide variety of health-care providers, including conventional doctors, because of the growing number of studies documenting its effectiveness for various conditions. It is used in childhood cancer to control pain and nausea, and is the most frequently used CAM in the UK, where fully 7 per cent of the adult population has received acupuncture. Providers of acupuncture include allopathic doctors who have taken short courses, Chinese medicine specialists, some of whom have specialized over five years in acupuncture, and physiotherapists.

What is the evidence for its benefits? A review article (Vickers et al., 2002) found studies to support acupuncture for post-operative nausea and vomiting, chemotherapy-related nausea and vomiting, and post-operative dental pain. A meta-analysis of 21 studies done on 1,421 people found that acupuncture improved cognition after a stroke (Liu et al., 2014). Among other things, the studies do not take into account the level of expertise or the amount of experience of the practitioner. The modern and Western use of acupuncture does not reflect the thousands of years of history or the theories of yin and yang and so on under which the Chinese have developed and still use the treatment, and thus to study its effectiveness is complicated. More research is needed.

A3). More and more people are seeking help from CAM specialists for a variety of ailments, especially pain, arthritis, anxiety, insomnia, and headache (Figure 13.1). CAM is often called integrative medicine today to indicate that it is being adopted by and integrated into conventional systems.

Two widely known American allopathic and conventionally trained doctors have been enormously influential in the processes involved in legitimating CAM in the US and Canada. They exemplify the power of the celebrity, or what has been called "celebritization," in influencing health and medical treatments (Beck et al., 2014; Frith et al., 2013; Lernere, 2006; Noar et al., 2014). One is Dr Mehmet Oz, a graduate of Harvard and the University of Pennsylvania School of Medicine as well as of Wharton Business school, who worked as a surgeon at Columbia Medical Center until 2001. Since 2009 Dr Oz has had a daily (Monday to Friday) television show on which he discusses and features both conventional medicine and CAM. That the show won an Emmy in the daytime talk show category speaks to its influence and status. *Time*

magazine listed him as forty-fourth out of the 100 of the most influential Americans in 2008 and *Esquire* magazine listed him in the top 75 most influential people in the twenty-first century. He appears to be extremely open-minded about the various possibilities of healing outside of allopathic care. The other doctor who has achieved a level of fame (he graduated from Harvard Medical School and has been on the *Dr Oz* show, for example) is Andrew Weil. He has published many best-selling books on CAM, or what he calls integrative medicine. He even started a school called Arizona Center for Integrative Medicine (http://integrativemedicine.arizona.edu/) where MDs and medical students, among others, do extra training in integrative medicine.

The recognition of these two conventional doctors in areas of CAM reflects the growing acceptance of various ways to understand healing. It also reflects a growing "healthism" (Crawford, 2006) or focus on health as a symbol of good citizenship and good morality. In this sense, public health campaigns and the emphasis on health in everyday life call on people to pay assiduous attention to their

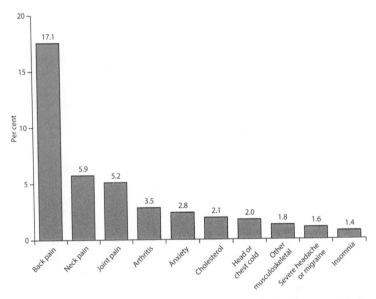

FIGURE 13.1   Diseases/Conditions for which CAM Is Most Frequently Used among Adults, 2007

Source: US National Center for Complementary and Alternative Medicine.

bodies and minds and to ensure that, as good citizens, they make good health a focus of living (Rose, 1999). It is in this context of the uptake of healthism that the expansion of CAMs can best be seen and understood. Indeed, the very idea of a television show dealing with how to be healthy and healthier in an ever-broader way reflects a postmodern sensibility and the biomedicalization of everyday life. The so-called "wellness" focus of CAMs includes body/mind/soul and spirit as relevant for treatment and upkeep, and this emphasis reflects the powerful discourses of healthism and biomedicalization.

At the same time as the broad social trends imbricate discourses of healthism into everyday life as essential to being human, powerful skeptics repudiate the effectiveness of various CAMs because of their lack of research evidence. Thus, another movement involves bringing CAM under the purview of medical science so that it succumbs to the very same research designs and rules of evidence that have captured the practices of major medical research funding bodies in the Western World and in the powerful World Health Organization. In this context, new publications include systematic reviews of the small studies that have been done of various CAMs. One interesting review article in a mainstream medical journal examined the available research literature included in the databases PubMed, Medline, Google Scholar, and Quertile on the topic of CAM use with mood disorders (Qureshi and Al-Bedah, 2013). They justified taking the time to do the review with the comment that between 30 per cent and 40 per cent of patients with major depressive disorders did not respond to conventional anti-depressants but that 30–40 per cent of people with major depressive disorders would respond to CAM. In particular, they found evidence that light therapy, St. John's wort, *Rhodiola rosea*, omega-3 fatty acids, yoga, acupuncture, mindfulness therapies, exercise sleep deprivation, and S-adenosylmethionine are effective in mood disorders. The results for some other interventions were either negative or ambiguous. This review paper is one example of the attempts being made to bring CAM "into the fold" of medical science and evidence-based medicine.

The use of unconventional medicine and healing is clearly increasing. As sociology students, we need to ask a number of questions about this phenomenon. Why are such approaches growing in popularity? To be sure the creeping spread of the concern with healthism is a part of it (Crawford, 2006). However, there is also a move to be more critical of allopathic doctors and allopathic medicine as a part of the expansion of the risk society (Beck, 1992). Because risks are everywhere, expertise in the avoidance or management of risks is not assumed in the same way that it was at one time. People think of themselves as having the ability and indeed as having to take the responsibility for determining what sorts of experts to trust and for what sorts of conditions. In this way, people may be more and more willing to question their allopathic doctors regarding the medical treatments they provide. They need to ask: Are all of the various sorts of treatments effective? Are none of them effective? Is context important to whether they are effective or not? For what sorts of problems are they effective or not? Are there similarities and differences among them?

CAM includes a great deal more than that which is offered by various professional practitioners who provide health services such as massage, acupuncture, homeopathy, and the like. It also includes the services offered by various conventional practitioners. In some areas of medicine there is a history of the inclusion of CAM with regular allopathic treatment. In the case of childhood cancer CAM use has been reported to be as high as 84 per cent (Valji et al., 2013). This includes services offered by professionals such as chiropractors, osteopaths, and acupuncturists as well as over-the-counter vitamins, botanicals, and spiritual healing and yoga, among others (ibid.). Although most patients were taking these treatments along with their regular chemotherapy drugs, most do not tell their regular physicians. The relationships between conventional doctors and CAM practitioners and practices are variable and sometimes fraught, and while some allopathic doctors are supportive of alternatives, others are not (Verhoef and Sutherland, 1995; Kelner et al., 2004). Formal leaders in public health, allopathic medicine, nursing, physiotherapy, and clinical nutrition argue that CAMs lack standards of evidence, standards of education and practice (Kelner et al., 2004: 920), and self-regulation (ibid., 921). In sum, it is difficult to draw conclusions about the relationships of CAM and conventional medicine because of contradictory results from

numerous studies, the use of different concepts and measurements in studies, and various other methodological and theoretical reasons (Hirschkorn and Bourgeault, 2005).

One of the most difficult issues for medical doctors is that they have been trained to trust only research published in good medical journals and using the "best" research designs. This often means the gold standard of designs—the double-blind

HIGHLIGHTED ISSUES

BOX 13.2   Some Alternative Health-Care Methods

Acupressure: Use of finger pressure on acupuncture points on the body to stimulate the flow of energy and promote the body's ability to heal itself. No needles are used. The most widely known form is shiatsu.

Feldenkrais (Russian Method): System of retraining the body to improve its movement and reduce pain from disease or injury; relies on the interaction between the sensory pathways of the central nervous system carrying information to the brain and the motor network carrying messages from the brain to the muscles. It may be particularly useful for accident victims; those with back problems, cerebral palsy, and multiple sclerosis; and musicians, athletes, and others whose careers may benefit from improved body movement.

Herbalism: Plants for healing and preventive medicine. Suggested benefits: skin problems (psoriasis, acne, eczema), digestive disorders, heart and circulation problems, gynecological disorders, allergic responses.

Homeopathy: The use of highly diluted traces of botanical, mineral, and other natural substances to stimulate the body's self-healing abilities; "like is cured by like." A substance that would create symptoms of disease in a healthy person is said to trigger the immune system of the ill person; the homeopathic practitioner's skill lies in matching a person's symptoms and body type correctly with the hundreds of remedies available. It is believed to assist the body's process of healing,

particularly in the case of chronic conditions, such as asthma, cold, and flu, and to alleviate certain emotional disorders and injuries, arthritis, hay fever, PMS, gout, constipation, headache, migraines, children's colic, earache. Homeopathy does not treat structural problems but works with the body's soft tissue, muscle, and ligaments to improve joint movement, back pain, spinal and joint problems, asthma, carpal tunnel syndrome, cramps, migraines, sciatica, respiratory disorders, chronic fatigue syndrome, allergies, digestive disorders, high blood pressure, and cardiac diseases.

Reflexology: Natural healing therapy based on the principle that there are "reflex" points on the feet and hands that correspond to every part of the body. Stimulation of those areas of the extremities causes changes in distant body tissues. It also is used to reduce stress and tension, and is considered an effective relaxation technique.

Rolfing: Manipulates the muscles and connective tissue to shift the body into alignment; pressure applied with the fingers and knuckles, etc. It is thought to be especially beneficial for athletes, dancers, students of yoga, musicians, and people suffering from chronic pain.

Shiatsu: Practitioner applies pressure to points on the body using fingers, palms, knees, or cushioned elbows to relax the body to promote its natural ability to heal.

Source: For further discussion of these and other CAMs, see Harden and Harden (1997).

experimental design in which there is a control group and an experimental group whose reactions to treatment are investigated. What makes this a double-blind study is that no one knows who is in the experimental group and who is in the control group. Most CAM has not been investigated with this model. Much of CAM has not been evaluated for health effects at all. In fact, many CAM providers and theorists argue that such research is impossible because every treatment is individualized and thus calculated for the unique needs of the particular person. On the other hand, allopathic medicine is concerned with smaller and smaller parts of the human body, such as the gene, and the effects of treatments at this level. When treatment systems are not commensurate with the accepted experimental design, financing, policy, and planning become very difficult. Nonetheless, scholars are thinking about this and attempting to devise ways of proving or estimating the varied legitimacy of CAM for health outcomes. As Boon and her colleagues (2007) say, CAM researchers are especially interested in this because of the issues of legitimacy and evidence base raised by insurers, purchasers, providers, regulators, and patients. CAM school students report that they do address

research methods and evidence-based care along with working with conventional medical practitioners (April and Gaboury, 2013).

The many types of CAM can be organized and categorized in various ways. The US Office of Alternative Medicine organizes them into seven categories: diet and nutrition, mind/body techniques, bio-electromagnetics, traditional and folk remedies, pharmacologic and biologic remedies, manual healing, and herbal medicine. Muriel J. Montbriand (1994), a nurse researcher and professor at the University of Saskatchewan, has organized CAM into three categories: spiritual, including prayer and psychic surgery (such as is practised in the Philippines); psychological, including visualization, distraction, and cognitive strategies, e.g., adopting a positive attitude or a one-day-at-a-time philosophy; and physical. Clearly, some of these involve a practitioner but most do not. The following sections describe the philosophies and the occupational status of each of two complementary/alternative practitioners: chiropractors, because they are the largest competing alternative health-care occupation in Canada and in the world; and naturopaths, because of their growing importance in Canadian society.

REMEMBERING OUR HISTORY

BOX 13.3   Christian Science: A Religion and an Alternative Form of Health Care

Religion and medicine are irrevocably intertwined among several major contemporary religious groups. One such group is Christian Science, founded by Mary Baker Eddy in 1866. Born in New Hampshire in 1821 to a Puritan family, Mary Baker Eddy spent the first 45 years of her life poor and in bad health but committed to the self-study of various medical systems, including allopathy, homeopathy, and hydropathy. She met and was influenced by a hypnotist healer named Phineas P. Quimby.

In 1866 Mary Baker Eddy fell on a patch of ice and was said to have been told by doctors that

her life was at an end. Within a week she was well and walking. She claimed that she healed herself with the aid of God and the power of the mind over the body. Overwhelmed by this experience, she told others. She trained students, the first Christian Science practitioners, in a series of 12 lessons for which she charged $100. She wrote *Science and Health with a Key to the Scriptures*, she said, under direct inspiration from God. By 1879 Mary Baker Eddy was able to found a church, the First Church of Christ, Scientist, in Boston. In 1881 she established an educational institution, Mrs Eddy's Massachusetts

continued

Metaphysical College. The church grew quickly and by 1902 there were 24,000 church members and 105 new churches. By 1911, the year Mary Baker Eddy died, there were 1,322 churches in Canada, Great Britain, Europe, Australia, Asia, and Africa.

Today the church is worldwide, and each church around the world follows the same lessons and readings simultaneously while seeking holistic health. While there are no ministers, there are practitioners who must graduate with a Christian Science degree. The basis of the philosophy of Christian Science is that sin and sickness are not real but represent the lack of knowledge of God. According to Mary Baker Eddy:

> Sickness is part of error which truth casts out. Error will not expel error. Christian Science is the law of truth, which heals the sick on the basis of one mind on God. It can heal in no other way, since the human mortal mind so-called is not a healer, but causes the belief in disease. Then comes the question, how do drugs, hygiene and animal magnetism heal?

It may be affirmed that they do not heal but only relieve suffering temporarily, exchanging one disease for another. We classify disease as error, which nothing but truth can heal, and this mind must be divine not human. (Eddy, 1934)

Treatment for sin and sickness involves prayer. Thinking about God and concentrating on God both lead to and constitute healing. Sickness is the result of incorrect, sinful, or ungodly thoughts. Healing, therefore, involves changed thought:

> To remove those objects of sense called sickness and disease, we must appeal to the mind to improve the subjects and objects of thought and give the body those better delineations. (Ibid.)

Christian Science constitutes an archetypal modern example of the tie between religion and medicine. Today it has an estimated 2,300 churches or congregations in 60 countries around the world (http://www.religioustolerance.org/cr_sci.htm).

Chiropractic

Chiropractic has been misunderstood frequently. It is passionately supported by some and passionately repudiated by others. The central tenet of spinal manipulation is an ancient technique legitimated even by Hippocrates: "look well to the spine, for many diseases have their origins in dislocations of the vertebral column" (cited in Caplan, 1984). In the beginning, American allopathic doctors vehemently opposed chiropractic. The American Medical Association (AMA) as late as the mid-1980s claimed that not only was there no scientific evidence for chiropractic but also warned the public against the untold dangers of submitting to such treatment (ibid.). One chiropractor commented that when he first started to practise about 50 years ago, he was refused admittance to service clubs, and people would make a point of stopping him on the street to call him a quack (personal communication). Now chiropractic doctors may receive patients directly as primary-contact practitioners. At times, they routinely refer patients to allopaths or other health-care providers.

The founder of chiropractic, Daniel David Palmer, was born in Port Perry, Ontario, in 1845 and moved to Davenport, Iowa, when he was 20. His work as a healer was based at first on what he thought were magnetic currents through the laying on of hands. His first success in spinal manipulation is said to have occurred in September 1895 when a deaf janitor in Palmer's apartment building dropped by to be examined. After discovering that the man had been deaf for 17 years and that his deafness had begun when he had exerted himself and felt something give way in his back, Palmer manipulated the man's spine. This immediately restored his hearing (Langone, 1982). Encouraged by this remarkable healing, Palmer investigated the impact of vertebral displacements on human disease. He called the newly discovered technique "chiropractic," from a combination of two Greek words, "cheir" and "practikas," meaning "done by hand" (Salmon, 1984).

Palmer campaigned for the legitimation and popularization of this new method of healing. He founded the Palmer School of Chiropractic, whose only admission requirement was a $450 fee. In 1906 Palmer was charged with practising without a licence and put in jail. It was not until 1913 that the first state, Kansas, passed licensing laws to allow the practice of chiropractic.

Palmer's most important pupil was his own son, Bartlett Joshua, or B.J. For 50 years or so, B.J. was able to popularize chiropractic to such an extent that he died a multi-millionaire. He was a gifted salesman who developed mail-order diplomas and advertising strategies that spread chiropractic around the world. B.J. advertised extensively for students, emphasizing the lack of exams or other requirements, lectured on business psychology, and wrote books with titles such as *Radio Salesmanship*. He was fond of making up slogans and having them engraved on the school's walls. One such slogan was, "Early to bed, early to rise; work like hell and advertise" (Weil, 1983: 130). B.J.'s sense of humour was also exhibited in the following question and answer, included in his book, *Questions and Answers About Chiropractic*, published in 1952. "Q. What are the principal functions of the spine? A. (1) to support the head; (2) to support the ribs; (3) to support the chiropractor" (quoted ibid.).

B.J. Palmer believed that vertebral subluxation (misalignment) was the cause of all disease, and thus that chiropractic was a complete system that could cure everything and prevent disease from occurring. His belief that chiropractic was adequate to deal with all problems led to a major schism in 1924, when he introduced an expensive new piece of equipment—the neuro-calometer—and insisted that all chiropractic offices rent one from the Palmer

School at $2,500 per annum. The major dissenter was an Oklahoma City lawyer who had become a chiropractor. In response to the unilateral dictate to buy this equipment, he established his own school of chiropractic. Within a few years he developed the theory that chiropractors should use other methods, such as nutrition and physical therapy, as well as spinal adjustment. Such a combination is called "mix," and this chiropractic philosophy is called "Mixer"; B.J. Palmer's philosophy, in contrast, is called "Straight." The schism continues today. However, Mixers are in the majority.

Chiropractic Theory and the Possible Future of Chiropractic

Two patterns of practice are based on spinal manipulation: osteopathy, founded in 1894 by Andrew Taylor Still, and chiropractic, founded by Daniel David Palmer in 1895. Osteopaths, who now include surgery and chemotherapy among their treatments, have achieved considerable legitimation around the world. Chiropractic has now achieved a good deal of legitimation in Britain, Europe, Australia, and Canada. There are 75,000 chiropractors working in the US, 7,250 in Canada, 4,250 in Australia and 3,000 in the UK, according to a report by the World Chiropractic Association for the World Health Organization (https://www.wfc.org/website/images/wfc/WHO_Submission-Final_Jan2013.pdf). In addition, chiropractors work in more than 100 countries. But as recently as 1971 the AMA established a Committee on Quackery whose purposes included the containment and eventual elimination of chiropractic (Wardell, 1988: 174–84). It had become a significant competitor to allopathic doctors. By the 1960s, 3 million Americans were visiting over 20,000 chiropractors and spending $300 million annually. In spite of the efforts of the AMA, today chiropractic has undisputed if limited legitimacy in many parts of the world for the many people who believe in their treatments. Chiropractors are still included (up to a limit) under Medicaid, veterans' services, and military hospital systems in the US and are covered by various insurance companies and HMOs. Chiropractic education receives federal funds. Chiropractic is now the major healing occupation in competition with allo-pathic medicine throughout the world. The cost-effectiveness of chiropractic for head and neck pain, both of which are enormously prevalent, compare positively with allopathic care (https://www.wfc.org/website/images/wfc/WHO_Submission-Final_Jan2013.pdf).

The theory of chiropractic is based on the idea that vertebral misalignment, by interfering with the patterns of the nervous system, can cause a wide variety of disorders. According to chiropractic, anything that can be said to result from or to develop out of the context of a depressed immune system can be treated or prevented by chiropractic. Chiropractic theory has been distinguished from allopathic theory along three lines (Caplan, 1984). In the first place, allopathic medicine views the symptoms as evidence of the disease and as a result of a simultaneously occurring disease process. The removal of symptoms is tantamount to the removal of disease for the allopath. Chiropractic, on the other hand, theorizes that symptoms are the result of a long-term pathological functioning of the organism via the spinal and the muscle systems. Disease precedes symptoms for a long period of time, perhaps years. The correction of the spinal subluxation by chiropractic allows the body to heal itself.

The second distinction lies in the competing views of the role of pathogens in disease. The allopathic understanding is that pathogens of a specific type and frequency invade the body and begin any of a number of different disease processes. Killing the pathogens thus becomes a goal of treatment and the basis of scientific medicine. All practitioners not subscribing to this view are by definition "unscientific" and have been derogatorily referred to as cultists and quacks (ibid., 84). Chiropractic says that pathogens are a necessary but not a sufficient condition for the initiation of a disease process. Before pathogens can take effect, the body must be vulnerable. While a number of factors can enervate the body, including genetic defects, poor nutrition, and stress, vertebral subluxation is also important.

The third distinction rests in the fact that allopathic doctors, even when they grant chiropractic

some legitimacy, limit it to specific musculoskeletal conditions. Chiropractors, on the other hand, view their work as holistic, preventive care.

There are several alternative future scenarios for chiropractic in Canada. First, chiropractic could remain, as it is now, a marginal occupation in terms of state support, only partially financed through medicare. Second, allopathic physicians could adopt chiropractic techniques to use themselves in addition to the traditional surgical and chemotherapeutic techniques and thus usurp the sovereignty of the increasingly legitimated and regulated occupation. Third, chiropractors could be subjugated, as nurses and pharmacists have been, to work only under the jurisdiction of allopathic doctors. Fourth, chiropractic could increase in status, regulation, and legitimacy and become an equal competitor with allopathic medicine for funding as an alternative to allopathy.

Current Status of Chiropractic in Canada

In Canada, the Canadian Chiropractic Association is an association of Mixers only, as its description of chiropractic indicates:

> Chiropractic is a healing discipline firmly grounded in science. Although its main focus is the relationship between the skeleton (particularly the spine) and the nervous system that runs through it, chiropractic is concerned with the care of the entire body. (www.ccachiro.org/GENQA)

The number of chiropractors has grown from about 100 in 1906 to more than 100,000 around the world in today (https://www.wfc.org/website/images/wfc/WHO_Submission-Final_Jan2013.pdf) as of the end of 2012). Chiropractors constitute the third largest group of primary medical care practitioners in Canada, after physicians and dentists. The number of chiropractors in Canada increased rapidly after World War II when the Canadian Memorial Chiropractic College was established in 1945. The Department of Veterans Affairs gave an early impetus to the development of chiropractic when it funded the education of 250 veterans who desired training in chiropractic. Now the Université du Québec à Trois-Rivières also offers a Doctor of Chiropractic degree.

Still, chiropractic care is unevenly supported by provincial health plans across Canada. Since 2004, chiropractic care has not been covered by the Ontario Health Insurance Plan. Other provinces, such as Manitoba and Quebec, provide partial coverage. However, chiropractic care is covered by many extended health insurance plans across Canada and about 70 per cent of the population has membership in one or another of these privately financed plans. However, only a limited number of visits per year are covered by governments and insurance companies. The relative cost of chiropractic services as a proportion of the total expenditures on health is negligible compared to the proportion of the health-care budget currently expended on allopathic practitioners.

The standards for admission to chiropractic colleges are comparable to those for other health occupations such as dentistry, pharmacy, optometry, and medicine. To enter, a student must have a minimum of three years of university in any discipline, preferably including a full course with labs in organic chemistry and biology, a half-course in introductory psychology, and at least one and a half courses in the humanities or the social sciences (www.ccachiro.org/cdninfo). The chiropractic program is usually four years based on studies of human anatomy and related basic sciences, including X-rays, diagnostic skills, and clinical studies. Graduates see themselves as part of a health-care team and, around the world, chiropractors increasingly work in concert with other health-care providers. Modern chiropractors neither claim nor want to promote the view that their type of health care is the only useful model.

The practice of chiropractic in Canada today is largely limited to musculoskeletal disorders such as headaches, neck and back pain, and soreness in the limbs. Approximately 4 million Canadians use chiropractic services annually (http://www.nbchiropractic.ca/English/facts.php). This is a higher percentage than for those who indicate that they use any other CAMs. Most people report

using chiropractors for lower back pain (Lawrence and Meeker, 2007). In addition, a wide range of functional and internal disorders are believed to be caused fully or in part by spinal dysfunction. Some recent studies have demonstrated but not explained the superiority of chiropractic in treating neck and back injuries. There is some evidence to suggest the efficacy of chiropractic in treating a broader spectrum of disorders, including epilepsy, asthma, and diabetes (Caplan, 1984). Nonetheless, a few critics still claim that chiropractic is not only useless but often dangerous (Benedetti and MacPhail, 2002).

The future prospects for the development and spread of chiropractic, according to the perspectives of leaders in the field, must include a new focus on (1) peer-reviewed research publications; (2) increased monitoring to establish standards of practice; (3) improvement in the quality of chiropractic education and increased intra-group cohesion (Verhoef et al., 2006). Still, many conventional practitioners and their leaders continue to show resistance to the full support and inclusion of chiropractic into the mainstream (Kelner et al., 2004).

Naturopathy

Naturopathy is a form of holistic health care considered by its practitioners to be relevant to all the disabilities and diseases that might bring a patient to a doctor's office. It is "a system of primary care that uses natural methods and substances to support and stimulate the body's inherent self-healing processes" (Verhoef et al., 2006: 409). The term "naturopath" was first adopted in 1901 at a convention of drugless practitioners in the US (Gort, 1986, cited in Boon, 1996: 16). It is based on the assumption that health and illness both are natural components of a total human being—spirit, body, and mind. Just as individuals are unique, this philosophy proposes each individual's sickness is unique to him or her. Healing depends on the activation of the normal healing processes of the human body.

Naturopathy has its philosophic roots in Greek medicine and in the work of Hippocrates, who emphasized the body's own healing powers.

Naturopathic medicine is a distinct system of primary health care that addresses the root causes of illness and promotes health and healing using natural therapies. It supports the body's own healing ability using an integrated approach to disease diagnosis, treatment, and prevention. Naturopathy includes a number of different healing modalities and research streams, including botanical medicine, clinical nutrition, traditional Chinese medicine and acupuncture, hydrotherapy, lifestyle counselling, naturopathic manipulation, and homeopathy (Verhoef et al., 2006; www.cand.ca/index.php?45&L=0). There are six accredited schools of naturopathic medicine in North America. Two are in Canada, one in Toronto (http://www.ccnm.edu/) and the other in British Columbia.

In this text we will look further at only one of these components of naturopathic medicine, homeopathy. Homeopathy was first established by Samuel Hahnemann (1755–1843). A few years after he graduated from medical school in Vienna, because of disillusionment with the therapies available at the time, he left the practice of medicine to be a writer and translator of texts into German. The translation of a text by a Scottish physician, William Cullen, led Hahnemann into developing the theory of homeopathy. What stimulated Hahnemann was Cullen's description of why the bark of the cinchona tree, containing quinine, was able to treat the fever and malaise of malaria. It was already known that quinine was a treatment for malaria. The explanation, however, was unknown. Cullen taught that it was due to its bitterness and astringent qualities. Hahnemann, having translated many other medical treatises, knew that many substances of greater bitterness and astringency were not effective against malaria. Thus began the homeopathic career of Hahnemann, the scientist who used the following method: (1) observation, (2) hypothesis, and (3) experiment. His first experiment was on himself. Knowing that quinine was not toxic in small doses, he ingested some. He developed the symptoms of malaria—chills, malaise, and headaches. He knew he did not have malaria and asked what had happened. Consulting Hippocrates, he found the idea that what causes a condition would also cure it. He rediscovered the old Hippocratic principle—"like cures like." The substances that cause symptoms in a healthy person are able to relieve symptoms in an unwell person. Intuitively, this finding reminds us of the notion of balance—of a natural force. "What homeopathy does is to treat the individual according to his or her own discomforts by pushing the organism in the same direction the vital force is trying to go" (Rothouse, 1997: 224).

Homeopathy, from the Greek words *homoios pathos*, which mean "similar sickness," is based on a number of principles that are in opposition to allopathic medicine. These include the following (Coulter, 1984):

- The key to the cure of illness is embodied in the principle of similars, i.e., minute dosages of a natural substance known to cause similar symptoms to those indicative of the disease are administered as treatment.
- Different people react differently to the same illness because each person is unique.
- The body should receive only one remedy at a time; otherwise the body's healing powers will be divided. The physician looks for the "most similar" remedy, not those that just seem superficially to be similar.
- The physician should administer the minimum dosage required by the patient. This minimum dose will provide the same curative powers as a larger dose.

Sickness is thought of as a message from the body rather than a biological pathology. Sickness provides a crisis through which the person can re-evaluate his or her own life (body, mind, and spirit). Thus, symptoms are not viewed as signs of disease, nor is the goal to eradicate symptoms through heroic measures such as surgical removal or chemical destruction. Rather, symptoms are indications of a healing crisis to be enhanced by the administration of minimum doses of a substance that causes the same symptoms. Naturopathic or homeopathic diagnosis is based on knowledge, not of the disease's normal or standard course,

CRITICAL THINKING

BOX 13.4   Homeopathy

?

The premier medical journal in Great Britain, read throughout the world, *The Lancet*, published a meta-analysis of 119 clinical trials that examined the efficacy of homeopathic medicine. The purpose of the analysis was to investigate the published research reports on homeopathy and its usefulness for particular conditions. In the eternally pessimistic language of the "null hypothesis," the study found that "the results of our meta-analysis are not compatible with the hypothesis that the clinical effects of homeopathy are completely due to placebo" (Linde et al., 1997: 834). In fact, the combined odds ratio for the 89 studies entered into the main meta-analysis was 2.45 (95 per cent, CI 2.05–2.93) in favour of homeopathy. That is, homeopathy was approximately two and a half times as likely to work as not. This finding is contrary to the beliefs of some that the positive results from homeopathy can be explained by the fact that people believe in homeopathy—the placebo effect.

effects, and treatment, but rather of the unique and idiosyncratic characteristics of the interaction of the individual person and the particular patterning of symptoms. Naturopathic medicine, therefore, does not treat diseases but stimulates the individual's vital healing force.

Homeopathy originated at a time when conventional medicine was "primitive and brutal in form, and frequently lethal for the patient" (May and Sirur, 1998: 169). Conventional medical treatments, which might involve the application of purgatives, bloodletting, or cupping, were basically the same as had been used for several centuries. However, because its development paralleled the therapeutic revolution based on the highly visible reactions characteristic of allopathic medicine and often originating in the chemistry lab, many saw homeopathic medicine's longer-term, less obvious results as ineffectual. Because homeopaths, many of whom were trained physicians, continued to focus on the uniqueness of the individual experiences of illness and on relatively benign, virtually invisible treatments and did not develop a theoretical foundation for their therapies that could compete with the "supra-molecular chemistry of the nineteenth century," they were unable to develop legitimacy in the competitive medical marketplace of North America.

Nevertheless, homeopathy is considered a legitimate alternative (and is evidently growing in legitimacy) in many Western countries. In Britain, for example, it had maintained a degree of acceptance among a minority until there was a steep decline from 134,000 to 16,359 prescriptions for homeopathic medications via the National Health Service during the years 2000–10. Four homeopathic hospitals, at Liverpool, London, Glasgow, and Bristol, were incorporated into the National Health Service in Britain at its inception in 1947, although one has since closed and another has been incorporated into the mainstream conventional care. Indeed, some members of the British royal family have always preferred homeopathic medicines. More recently, adopting the blind randomized control trial, homeopathic remedies have been found to be effective in the treatment of respiratory disease (Ferley et al., 1989, cited in May and Sirur, 1998) and pollen allergies (Reilly et al., 1986, cited ibid.). However, in 2010 a House of Commons report in the UK found that homeopathic remedies were no more effective than placebos. At present, it is fairly popular in France. About 10,000 physicians in France practised homeopathy (Rothouse, 1997) almost 20 years ago. Other European countries, too, have a history of greater open access to homeopathic medicine. In France, 25 per cent of pharmacies were homeopathic; in Britain, half of all conventional physicians used or recommended homeopathy. And in India, homeopathy is taught in almost all medical and pharmacy schools (ibid.).

There are numerous and complex methodological difficulties in comparing the efficacy of allopathic and homeopathic remedies, not least of which is that homeopathy is based on designing a unique treatment for each individual whereas evidence-based standards of allopathic practice compare the same treatment over a group of individuals diagnosed with a specific disease. Homeopathy is also based on a holistic model of the person, and a part of the treatment involves spending time with patients and offering psychosocial care whereas conventional medicine looks for one diagnosis at a time. One interesting finding, based on the study of the overall efficacy of homeopathic versus regular hospitals during the nineteenth-century cholera epidemics in America, is that the death rates in regular hospitals were five times greater than in homeopathic hospitals. Similarly, in London, England, in 1854, a Parliament-mandated study found that 59 per cent of those in regular hospitals died, while only 16 per cent died in homeopathic hospitals. Homeopathy treated cholera's symptoms of headache, malaise, diarrhea, anorexia, chills, convulsions, and so on with mild homeopathic remedies—camphora or veratrum album.

Current Status of Naturopathy and Homeopathy

Homeopathy arrived in the United States in 1825. By 1844, some of the most prominent allopathic physicians had adopted its principles and established the American Institute of Homeopathy, the country's first medical association (Coulter, 1984). The allopaths were threatened by this move and in 1846 founded a competing organization, the American Medical Association (AMA). Professional contact between allopaths and homeopaths was prohibited by the AMA's newly established Code of Ethics (ibid.).

The formal system of naturopathic treatment, which incorporated homeopathic medicine, was established by Benedict Lust (1872–1945), who founded the first naturopathic college in 1900 in New York City. Lust's primary method of treatment was hydrotherapy, but this was enhanced by a variety of other techniques, including homeopathy, botanical remedies, nutritional therapy, psychology, massage, and manipulation (Weil, 1983).

Hostility persisted between allopaths and naturopaths until the number of naturopaths began to decline dramatically and they no longer posed a threat. Since then, naturopathy has never constituted a well-organized occupational group, but rather a loose assortment of holistic practitioners providing a variety of healing modalities. Until recently, most naturopaths were also chiropractors.

In Ontario, the Drugless Practitioners Act of 1925 can be seen as the starting point for the formal recognition by the province of naturopathy as a distinct healing occupation. By this Act a Board of Regents, composed of five appointees of the Lieutenant-Governor and made up of allopathic and chiropractic practitioners, was set up to regulate chiropractors and naturopaths. While naturopaths were allowed to practise, they were not formally included under this Act until 1944. In 1948, chiropractors were limited to "hands only, spine only" (Gort, 1986: 87). In the following year, 1949, the Ontario Naturopathic Association was formed by chiropractors who had been deprived of the right to the full range of practice (i.e., including homeopathic medicines) by the 1948 decision. By 1952 each form of drugless therapy was allowed to govern itself because it had become increasingly difficult for one board to regulate practitioners with diverse education, training, and practice modalities.

Naturopathy in Canada

Almost 500 naturopaths were practising and licensed in Canada by 2000 (Verhoef et al., 2006). They are not covered by medicare but operate under provincial jurisdiction. A number of provinces—including British Columbia, Saskatchewan, Manitoba, Ontario, and Alberta—have regulated naturopathic medicine (https://www.cand.ca/). Today, one recognized English-Canadian training institution, the Canadian College of Naturopathic Medicine, is located in Toronto; it began in 1978 as the Ontario College of Naturopathic Medicine. Another is in British Columbia—the Boucher Institute of Naturopathic Medicine (www.cand.ca/index.php?36). At first, the Toronto program offered a post-graduate program to allopaths, chiropractors, and naturopaths to help them upgrade their qualifications. In 1982 the Ontario Ministry of Health appointed a Health Professions Legislative Review Committee to determine which occupations needed regulation for the protection of the public interest. It was decided by this committee that naturopathy should not be regulated by the state but by its own members. The argument was that since (1) naturopathy was not scientific and (2) there was no standardization of practice, it posed a risk of harm to the patients and should not be regulated and thereby given official sanction.

The naturopaths responded in a brief titled *Naturopathic Medicine and Health Care in Ontario*, delivered in July 1983 to Keith Norton, the provincial Minister of Health at the time. The brief justified the value and efficacy of naturopaths as well-educated and trained healers, and made it clear that they believed the allopaths were trying to exclude them from practice. It levied a series of sharp criticisms at the costliness and narrowness of allopathic medicine, its mechanistic fallacy, and its negative social consequences. The final statement highlighted and summarized their critique of allopathic medicine: "We find little cause to applaud allopathy's near monopoly of the medical services of this province" (ONA, 1983: 21).

Among the naturopaths' recommendations were: the establishment of a separate Act to regulate naturopathic medicine; granting of the right to use the title "doctor"; the right to use the terms "naturopathic medicine" and "naturopathic physician"; the elimination of the term "drugless practitioner" in favour of "naturopathic physician"; the right to hospital privileges; the right to refer to various laboratory and X-ray services; and the right to authorize medical exemptions and to sign medical documents. A number of provinces—including British Columbia, Manitoba, Saskatchewan,

Ontario, and Nova Scotia—have moved forward with regulation (www.cand.ca/index.php?36).

In the same year, 1983, the Ontario College of Naturopathic Medicine became the first Canadian institution to offer a complete education in naturopathy, having devoted the five years since its founding in 1978 to fundraising and offering single stand-alone courses. By 1986 the planned deregulation, in spite of the organized opposition of the Ontario Naturopathic Association, was passed by the Ontario government. Despite signs of the resurgence of naturopathy—rising numbers of practitioners and the presence of colleges to provide training—it seems that naturopathy in Ontario is unable to expand because of deregulation.

One of the most difficult issues faced by naturopathic medicine in its struggle for legitimacy lies in the nature of its science. Allopathic medicine claims to be scientific because it is modelled on physics, the prototypical science of the nineteenth century. The goal of this model of research is the establishment of universally true causal laws. Individual differences are ignored in favour of generalizations. Alternatives included in naturopathic medicine such as homeopathy and traditional Chinese medicine, on the other hand, are based on different models of science. These models assume a universally true set of principles that are applied differentially to each individual. By contrast, allopathic scientific doctrine changes considerably over time as the result of new research findings (among other things). With each new discovery some aspect of allopathic medicine is nullified.

In a study of all licensed naturopathic practitioners in Canada, Boon (1998) observed two distinct paradigms of naturopathic practice. One she calls a "scientific world view," the other, "holistic." Those in the first category appear to emphasize physical and structural treatments and to be more practical, concrete, reductionistic, and objective. Those in the second category are more subjective, spiritual, abstract, intuitive, and likely to emphasize treatment at an emotional level.

In Canada, naturopathic doctors are highly trained, including three years of undergraduate work and four years of full-time studies in naturopathic medicine. They have extensive scientific and clinical knowledge of natural remedies, including their use, contraindication, possible adverse reactions, and toxicities (www. naturopathicassoc.ca/dr.html). As the holistic health movement grows, naturopathy may become increasingly accepted as legitimate. Claims of malpractice against chiropractors, massage therapists, and acupuncturists for 1990–6 were compared with those made against conventional doctors (Studdert et al., 1998). CAM practitioners were sued less frequently than conventional doctors and when they were sued the injury at issue was less severe. This might suggest that the safety records of CAM practitioners are better than those of allopathic practitioners. Nevertheless, there are sometimes serious and even fatal results from CAM practice, as there are in allopathic medicine, and more research needs to be done.

According to Verhoef et al. (2006), naturopathic medicine likely faces an uphill battle in efforts to become a fully regulated profession. The reasons for this are several and include: (1) the view that naturopathic medicine does not have a unique body of knowledge; (2) significant overlaps between naturopathic medicine and other healing modalities and practitioners who are also competing for regulation; (3) a lack of cohesion within the naturopathic medical community; and (4) a lack of vacancies (a glut on the market of trained naturopaths in some locations so there is no room for new graduates to open practice). Table 13.2 portrays the wide variety of types of treatment included under naturopathic medicine.

Historically, homeopathic practitioners were self-regulating in Canada. A slight increase in homeopathy in Canada has occurred recently. It is difficult to determine the exact number of homeopaths practising in Canada, although the number appears to be small (Kelner et al., 2006). According to a recent survey, about 2 per cent of Canadians seek the services of homeopaths (Statistics Canada, 2005). As early as 1845, homeopathic doctors began practising in Quebec, and shortly after that homeopaths were at work in Toronto. They became regulated in Canada West (Ontario) in 1859 and in Montreal in 1865. They were represented in the College of Physicians and Surgeons of Ontario from 1869 to 1960. In British Columbia regulation began in 1889. There was a homeopathic hospital in Montreal in 1894; in Toronto, a homeopathic dispensary opened in 1888 and a homeopathic hospital in 1890. Ontario was the first province to regulate homeopathy—as of 1 April 2015—amid a great deal of controversy. For example, the title of an article on this news by Andre Picard, the highly respected health and medicine columnist of the *Globe and Mail*, read: "We're Aiding and Abetting Homeopathic Quackery" (http://www.theglobeandmail.com/globe-debate/were-aiding-and-abetting-homeopathic-quackery/article23701139/).

If the trends in the United States are any indication of the future for naturopathic treatments in Canada, then it looks bright. From its heyday in the nineteenth century, when there were 15,000 practitioners, 14 training schools, dozens of periodicals, and organized groups in every state and large city (Coulter, 1984: 72), naturopathy declined to a low of about 100 practitioners in 1950. In the 1960s, however, this trend was reversed, and today thousands of mainstream practitioners (allopaths, chiropractors, nurses, and clinical psychologists) use at least some homeopathic methods. In Canada about 1,350 naturopathic doctors practise as such (www. cand.ca/index.php?36). As well, a number of firms manufacture and export homeopathic remedies, and a number of governments have adopted licensing laws for the practice of naturopathic medicine.

Therapeutic Touch

One other new and alternative healing modality is quickly being incorporated into the practice of allopathic medicine via the nursing profession. This method is therapeutic touch. According to Michael Lerner in *Choices in Healing*, in which he critically reviews the research literature on the value of a wide variety of complementary and alternative medicines, therapeutic touch is a promising healing modality.

The implications of therapeutic touch for medicine and science are—if the scientific studies of its efficacy are valid—truly awesome.

TABLE 13.2   Types of Modalities Provided by Naturopathic Practitioners

	Provided to More Than 50% of Patients (%)	Provided to Less Than 50% of Patients (%)	Never Provided (%)	Total η
Nutritional supplementation	9.9	89.5	0.7	294
Nutritional counselling (e.g., macrobiotics)	10.2	89.2	0.7	295
Botanical medicine	20.5	78.5	1	293
Homeopathy	28.9	69.5	1.7	298
Laboratory testing	55.1	34.3	10.6	292
Novel assessment methods: VEGA testing, dark field microscopy	23	32.3	43.6	291
Psychological counselling	61.6	31.1	7.3	289
Traditional Chinese medicine	52.4	21.4	26.2	290
Naturopathic manipulation	40.8	15.8	43.4	292
Parenteral therapy, including injections	37.6	14.1	48.3	290
Acupuncture	48.7	13.7	34.2	284
Applied kinesiology	23.3	13.3	61.7	287
Meditation/visualization	64	10.8	25.2	286
Hydrotherapy	65.2	10.8	24	296
Electro-acupuncture	24.4	10.5	65.2	287
Massage	47.8	7	45.3	287
Iridology	23.4	6.5	70.1	291
Acupressure	37.3	5.6	57	268
Fasting	59.8	5.2	35.1	291
Lymphatic drainage	42.5	4.8	52.7	292
Craniosacral therapy	35.3	4.6	60.1	283
Ultrasound	20.5	3.4	76	292
Yoga	32.1	3.1	64.8	287
Colon therapy	14.6	2.8	82.6	281
Reflexology	12.2	1.7	86.1	287
Biofeedback	12.7	1.7	84.9	284
X-ray testing	27.5	1.4	71.1	287
Ayurvedic medicine	24.7	1.4	73.9	283
Natural childbirth	17.4	1.1	81.5	281
Magnetic therapy	22.8	1	76.2	290
Polarity therapy	4.2	0.3	95.5	286
Minor surgery	7.6	0	92.4	290
Hypnosis	7.2	0	92.8	293
Alexander technique	2.3	0	97.5	284

Source: Verhoef, M.J., H.S. Boon, and D.R. Mutasingwa. 2006. 'The Scope of Naturopathic Medicine in Canada: An Emerging Profession', *Social Science and Medicine* 63: 409–17. Reprinted with permission from Elsevier.

Something is happening in these studies, if they are correct, that medicine should attend to and science cannot yet account for. (Lerner, 1994: 362)

Therapeutic touch has become established as a modern and empirically studied practice. It is now widely used in and out of hospitals, usually by nurses, across Canada and the US. It was started by Delores Kreiger, a nursing professor at New York University, and was based on her observations of and her collaboration with a renowned healer,

Dora Kuntz, who believed that healing could be systematized, taught, and studied. Therapeutic touch does not involve touch (at least not primarily) but rather the movement of "energy" along the outside of the body (for about 15–20 minutes) a number of inches from the body in order to balance and restore energy where it is lacking. Research on the efficacy of therapeutic touch has found it to: (a) raise hemoglobin levels, (b) elicit the relaxation response, and (c) heal wounds, among other benefits.

SUMMARY

1. Complementary and alternative medicines are growing in significance, rates of use, and public acceptance at a rapid pace. CAMs are even growing in legitimacy in the minds and referral practices of allopathic practitioners.
2. Daniel David Palmer founded chiropractic in 1895. Attempts to legitimate and popularize this method of healing were stunted by allopathic practitioners. Distinguishing features of chiropractic are: through the corrective manipulation of spinal subluxation the body is able to heal itself; the goal is not to kill germs but to make the body less vulnerable to germs; the work is viewed as holistic, preventive care.

Although chiropractic in Canada today is limited to musculoskeletal disorders, its legitimacy continues to grow.
3. Naturopathy is based on the assumption that health and illness are both natural components of a total but unique human being—spirit, body, and mind. Healing depends on the activation of the normal healing processes of the human body. Initially it was met with opposition by most allopaths. More and more mainstream practitioners use at least some naturopathic methods today.
4. Therapeutic touch is a CAM that is widely accepted and frequently studied.

KEY TERMS

acupuncture
allopathic medicine
chiropractic
complementary and alternative
   medicine (CAM)

herbalism
holistic health care
naturopathy
reflexology
rolfing

shiatsu
therapeutic touch

QUESTIONS FOR STUDY AND DISCUSSION

1. Why is complementary and alternative medicine becoming more acceptable to Canadians?
2. Why are allopathic doctors changing their views regarding chiropractors?
3. Assess the view that naturopathic and chiropractic medicines are non-scientific whereas allopathic medicine is based on scientific evidence.
4. What do you think the medical marketplace will look like in 25 years?
5. Examine a popular magazine or newspaper for its coverage of CAM over a period of time.

SUGGESTED READINGS

April, K.T., and I. Gaboury. 2013. "A Survey of Canadian Regulated Complementary and Alternative Medicine Schools about Research, Evidence Based Health Care and Interprofessional Training, as well as Continuing Education." *BMC Complementary and Alternative Medicine* 13: 374–81. An empirical article on the views of CAM schools regarding medical research and work.

Benedetti, P., and W. MacPhail. 2002. *Spin Doctors: The Chiropractic Industry under Examination.* Toronto: Dundurn. An empirical examination and critique of chiropractic.

Dossey, Larry. 1982. *Space, Time and Medicine.* Boston: New Science Library.

———. 1991. *Meaning and Medicine.* New York: Bantam Books. Popular interpretations of philosophical principles behind some complementary and alternative medicine.

Liu, F., Z.M. Li, Y.J. Jiang, and L.D. Chen. 2014. "A Meta-analysis of Acupuncture Use in the Treatment of Cognitive Impairment after Stroke." *Journal of Alternative and Complementary Medicine* 20, 7: 535–44. A study of the effectiveness of acupuncture.

Qureshi, N.A., and A. Mohammed Al-Bedah. 2013. "Mood Disorders and Complementary and Alternative Medicine: A Literature Review." *Neuropsychiatric Disease and Treatment* 3, 9: 639–65. A literature review of a wide variety of complementary and alternative medicines and their impact on mood disorders.

Weil, A. 2011. *Spontaneous Happiness.* New York: Little Brown & Company. A popular book on how to be happy.

14 The Pharmaceutical Industry and the Medical-Industrial Complex

Thinkstock Images/ Thinkstock.com

CHAPTER OVERVIEW

▶ The medical-industrial complex includes many different organizations, products, and services.

▶ The pharmaceutical industry is one of the largest and most profitable and influential of these.

▶ Pharmaceutical use is affected by the socio-demographic characteristics of users.

▶ Pharmaceutical use is affected by the style of medical practice, the involvement of drug salespersons, and pharmaceutical company initiatives among other things.

▶ Pharmacists' interests also affect patterns of drug purchases and usage.

▶ The pharmaceutical industry retains its position through a number of powerful and effective

marketing, regulating, pricing, and other business strategies.

▶ The cases of DES and thalidomide illustrate two of the historical problems in the regulation of the drug industry in Canada. That unsafe drugs continue to be placed in the Canadian marketplace is evidenced by the cases of HRT, Vioxx, and Diane-35.

▶ Many similar cases of the misuse by the pharmaceutical industry of drug markets in the developing world have been documented.

▶ The Health Protection Branch of the Canadian federal government has an ambiguous record with regard to protecting the health of Canadians from dangerous, ineffective, or questionable drugs.

Introduction

The **medical-industrial complex** is a large and growing network of private and public corporations engaged in the business of providing medical care and medical care products, supplies, and services for a profit. Included in the medical-industrial complex are, among other things, hospitals and nursing homes, home-care services, diagnostic services, including expensive CAT scanners and MRIs, hemodialysis supplies and equipment, pharmaceutical companies, medical tools and technology, and even laundry and food-packaging companies that supply hospitals and other health-care organizations. This complex is global and is a part of a new world order (Usher and Skinner, 2012) under neo-liberalism. The pharmaceutical industry, an important component of the medical-industrial complex, will be discussed in detail in this chapter.

When do you decide to go to the pharmacy for over-the-counter medication? Some of you try to become aware of the side effects of various over-the-counter and other medications. Some of you ask the doctor about long-term effects. Some of you take your prescribed medication exactly as directed—over the length of time suggested and at the prescribed intervals. Most of us assume that all the drugs available in Canada have been adequately tested and are safe. However, this assumption is not true (Canadian Foundation for Health Care Improvement, 2010). Many of you will have heard of thalidomide, Vioxx, Ritalin, Diane-35, or DES. Do you know some of the devastating results of their use? You may have considered the question of the extent to which the pharmaceutical, medical device, and biotechnology companies are reliant on and motivated by making a profit as compared to serving those suffering sickness and pain. Have you ever thought about the effects of pharmaceuticals on the environment? They may be excreted from our bodies (our bodies only absorb a portion of the drugs we routinely administer to ourselves) or flushed as tablets or syrups down a drain when we no longer think they are of use. After a person dies, as the body decomposes, the drugs (or chemicals) leech from the body and are absorbed by the earth. These are among the issues that will be addressed in this chapter.

Drug Use

Any discussion of the pharmaceutical industry and the use of drugs in contemporary Canadian society must be fairly wide-ranging because this topic involves a large number of sociological issues. The drug industry is a major actor in Canadian medical care, and its share of health spending in Canada grew from 9.8 per cent in 1983 to 12.6 per cent in 1990 and to 17.5 per cent in 2005, although there is evidence of the flattening of this trend line according to the projections of the National Health Expenditures database (www.cihi.ca/CIHI-ext-portal/internet/en/document/spending+and+health+workforce/spending/spending+by+geography/spend_nhex). The estimated percentage of health-care expenditures on drugs for 2010 was 16.3 and in 2011 it was actually 16.5 per cent (https://secure.cihi.ca/estore/productFamily.htm?locale=en&pf=PFC2400). The major reasons for the flattening of the drug expenditures is that several "blockbuster" drugs used to treat the high-prevalence conditions of hypertension and high cholesterol have moved off patent (where they are more expensive) and thus are now available in the much less costly generic form (https://secure.cihi.ca/free_products/Drug_Expenditure_2013_EN.pdf). Drugs continue to be the second largest expenditure in the health-care system after that spent on hospitals. Although the proportion spent on physicians has been growing lately, as doctors' salaries and numbers have both grown, it is still only 14.6 per cent as compared to the 16.5 per cent spent on drugs. While the Canada Health Act covers all necessary hospital, physician, surgical-dental, and a portion of long-term care services, it does not include prescription drugs outside of hospital. The vast majority of the overall Canadian drug expenditure, approximately 84 per cent, is for prescribed drugs (CIHI, 2008). The rest is for over-the-counter (OTC) drugs. The costs to consumers who either lack drug insurance altogether or have limitations in respect to drug coverage have grown more quickly than the overall health budget. From 1998 to 2007, the latest year for which figures were available, the costs to consumers grew at a yearly average of 10.1 per cent. This rate of increase reflects the growing reliance on drugs for treatment and for prevention as well as the adoption of new and thus more expensive drugs, according to the National Health Expenditure Trends, 1975–2013 (https://secure.cihi.ca/estore/productFamily.htm?locale=en&pf=PFC2400). This cost increase constitutes another element of mounting privatization in health care in Canada. Just under half of the cost of prescribed drugs, 40.4 per cent, falls to out-of-pocket expenses (ibid.). The rest is covered by various forms of insurance (ibid.).

Most Canadians, approximately 96 per cent, have some form of at least partial coverage for prescription drugs (Kapur and Basu, 2005). Approximately 63.7 per cent of this is from private plans and 36.3 per cent is from public or governmental insurance associated with such considerations as Aboriginal status, age, or military involvement (https://secure.cihi.ca/estore/productFamily.htm?locale=en&pf=PFC2400). A portion of the public coverage comes from public provincial plans for exceptional circumstances, such as catastrophic diseases (Kapur and Basu, 2005). Still, drug coverage varies by socio-economic and socio-demographic groups in Canada. Older people, women, and the working poor are less likely to have coverage (ibid.).

A significant cause of the rapid increase in drug expenditures is the development of "me-too" drugs. These are newer, more expensive drugs marketed and used for the same conditions in the place of older, less expensive pharmaceuticals (Canadian Health Coalition, 2006). These new drugs may or may not be better than the older versions and they may or may not be safe (Canadian Foundation for

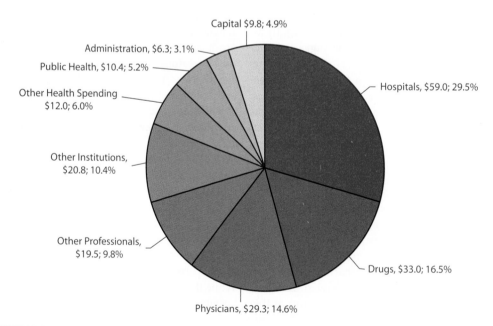

FIGURE 14.1   Total Health Expenditures by Use of Funds, Canada, 2011 (billions of dollars and percentage share)

Source: Total Health Expenditure by Use of Funds, Canada, 2011 (Billions of Dollars and Percentage Share)", in National Health Expenditure Trends, 1975 to 2013, Canadian Institute of Health Information. https://secure.cihi.ca/free_products/3.0_TotalHealthExpenditureFundsEN.pdf.

Health Care Improvement, 2013). The most important of these newer drugs may be the very expensive cancer drugs and immunosuppressive drugs (for transplants primarily), as well as cholesterol-lowering drugs (https://secure.cihi.ca/estore/productFamily.htm?locale=en&pf=PFC2400). The increase in drug expenditures is also due to aggressive advertising both to physicians and to consumers (Canadian Health Coalition, 2006). This advertising is global and highly influential, especially in the presence of the World Wide Web (Usher and Skinner, 2012). Drug "scandals" are frequent. Hormone replacement therapy (HRT) was prescribed to millions of women for a number of years. Then, epidemiological research demonstrated that it caused an increase in strokes, heart attacks, breast cancer, blood clots, and gallstones. It is now to be used only in exceptional circumstances (Canadian Health Coalition, 2006). Another highly popular drug, in possibly the most widely prescribed drug class in Canada, is a cholesterol-lowering statin called Lipitor for which there were many millions of prescriptions per year (ibid.). This drug is intended for basically healthy people to prevent high cholesterol, despite the fact that its value as a preventive is not clear and is hotly debated. In addition, it does have side effects. About 450,000 prescriptions of Diane-35, a drug marketed for acne and sometimes used for birth control, were sold to Canadian women annually (http://www.hc-sc.gc.ca/dhp-mps/medeff/advisories-avis/review-examen/diane-35-eng.php). This drug was responsible for the deaths of 11 young women and over 200 adverse reactions reported to the *Toronto Star* (http://www.thestar.com/news/canada/2013/01/31/diane35_deaths_of_11_canadian_women_linked_to_acne_drug_compared_to_four_in_france.html3). Diane-35 was removed

from sale in France because it was considered unsafe after four girls apparently died as a result of taking it.

It may be helpful to begin our discussion in this chapter with a pictorial representation of the various levels of analysis that will be considered in our explanation and description of pharmaceutical use in Canada (see Figure 14.2).

At the first level the discussion will focus on how the socio-demographic characteristics of patients—age, gender, class—correlate with their legal drug-taking habits. The social characteristics of physicians, too, influence drug prescription—such as the form of medical practice (e.g., solo as compared with group practice), the amount of continuing education, and the size of the practice.

Pharmacists and the pharmaceutical industry are important forces in drug use as well. Cost, availability, advertising, pharmaceutical company websites, perks and benefits offered by pharmaceutical companies, and special pricing arrangements are among the factors known to influence physicians' decisions on what to prescribe and pharmacists' decisions on what to stock. Drug payment schemes—whether government-controlled, those offered by private insurance, or individual payment alternatives—affect drug use. Much of the recent sociological research on drug use in Canada has focused on the pharmaceutical industry, its organization and structure, and especially on the fact that under capitalism and global neoliberalism it must be guided by the profit motive, which at times conflicts with the goal of promoting health. The power of the pharmaceutical industry in negotiating with the Canadian government and in determining how drugs are regulated, brought onto the market, and monitored after they are on

FIGURE 14.2   Factors Affecting Drug Use in Canada

the market must be examined, too. All of these play a role in the safety, efficacy, and side effects related to drug use by Canadians.

Rates of Drug Use and Patient Variables: Age, Gender, and Class

Considerable evidence suggests that drugs are frequently over-prescribed in Canada. For example, it has been estimated that about half of the anti-depressants prescribed do not work except as placebos (Smith, 2012). Today at least 14.3 per cent of children in Canada and 16.7 per cent of children in the US have been diagnosed with one mental illness or another, and if addictions are added then the number jumps to 25.6 per cent in the US (comparative figures for Canada are not available) (Perou et al., 2013). The majority of these children are prescribed medications. Different drugs may be used together, and because many of the drugs prescribed are used "off-label" (not for the condition for which they have been approved) they are tried in the hope that they might work. Some argue that this experimenting essentially violates the human rights of children. This practice and others related to diagnosing and treating children with mental health and developmental issues have been said to contribute to "surplus suffering" (Clarke, 2013). Between 5 per cent and 23 per cent of hospital admissions result from drug-related illnesses. Approximately a third of all emergency room visits among people over 65 are due to adverse drug reactions (Budnitz et al., 2011). Inappropriately prescribing or prescribing a number of medications at one time (polypharmacy) leads to additional expense to Canadians because of hospitalization resulting from drug reactions (Votova et al., 2013). Aside from children, two groups, the elderly and women, are particularly vulnerable to misprescribing and over-prescribing (ibid.; Rachlis and Kushner, 1994). It is very difficult to accurately estimate the effects of misprescribing or over-prescribing because of the lack of systematic community-based follow-up and measurement. Nevertheless, a long history of evidence from a variety of types of studies shows that women are especially likely to be over-prescribed or misprescribed psychotropic drugs or sedatives

(Harding, 1994b; www.bccewh.bc.ca/policy_briefs/Benzo_Brief/benzobriefv3.pdf; Rochon Ford and Saibil, 2010).

Medication errors are relatively common in Canada and can be life-threatening. Approximately 24 per cent of all adverse health events (caused by medical treatment) may be due to medication errors (CIHI, 2007b, citing Baker et al., 2004). Moreover, this figure likely is under-reported (www.cihi.ca/cihiweb/dispPage.jsp?cw_page=PG_376_E&cw_topic=376&cw_rel=AR_43_E; Canadian Foundation for Health Care Improvement, 2010). The most frequent causes of these medication errors include inappropriate prescribing, incorrect use by patients, and the lack of a follow-up monitoring system by regulatory bodies. The proportion of seniors who have been and continue to be incorrectly prescribed drugs has been such a problem that an online list regularly updates prescribed drugs that are internationally recognized to be inappropriate for seniors (the Beers list, named after Mark H. Beers, the geriatrician who first published the criteria for evaluating the safety of pharmaceuticals for aging bodies in 1991). Provincially, of four provinces with available records, the prescription errors among seniors range from 18.8 per cent in New Brunswick to 12.9 per cent in Alberta. Concerted efforts are now being made to reduce these numbers (Butt, 2010) as a part of the new focus on the reduction of all medical errors since the 1999 publication in the US of *To Err Is Human: Building a Safer Health Care System*.

About 9 million people in the US, or 4.3 per cent of the adult population, are using prescription sleeping pills, and most of these people are white, educated women over 50, according to a survey by the Centers for Disease Control and Prevention (http://www.cdc.gov/nchs/data/databriefs/db127.pdf) (see Figure 14.3). Market research has reported a tripling of the use of sleep aids from 1998 to 2007. Some have linked this rising rate of insomnia to the increasing stress of modern life, while others point to the marketing successes of the pharmaceutical industry. This incidence of medication use does not include the many over-the-counter sleep aids

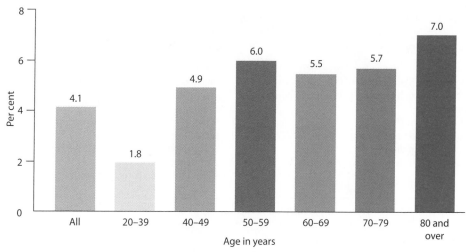

FIGURE 14.3   Age-Adjusted Percentage of Adults Aged 20 and over Who Used Prescription Sleep Aids in the Past 30 Days, by Sex and Ethnicity, United States, 2005–10

Source: Chong, Yinong, Cheryl D. Fryar, and Qiuping Gu, "Prescription Sleep Aid Use Among Adults: United States, 2005–2010." Centers for Disease Control and Prevention, 127 (2013), p. 2. http://www.cdc.gov/nchs/data/databriefs/db127.htm.

or those sold as health products or teas through health food stores. Moreover, because there is a stigma associated with sleeping pill use, these figures are probably underestimates. Sleeping medications may be especially problematic because they are addictive and can cause impaired cognition, memory, and balance. Women also are more likely to be prescribed such sleep aids for longer periods of time and they may be more likely to be prescribed for "problems in living," such as grief and adjusting to new motherhood.

Addiction is especially acute among women over 60. Benzodiazepines are often prescribed for elderly adults with sleep or anxiety problems, for longer periods of time, and at levels that may be unsafe. Benzodiazepines are especially associated with falls and hip fractures, motor vehicle accidents, accidental poisoning, hospitalization for depression, and other psychiatric problems resulting from their chronic use (CIHI, 2010). Moreover, the incidence of multiple drug use, including sleeping pills and other "hypnotics" among women and the elderly (who are more likely female), is well substantiated in the literature. In 2005 a national survey of medication use found that almost all seniors (97 per cent) living

in long-term care institutions had taken prescription medications in the past two days, as had 76 per cent of those living in private households (Ramage-Morin, 2009), as compared to 14 per cent of all Canadians. Further, more than half (53 per cent) of those in institutions and 13.5 per cent in private households reported taking multiple medications.

Multiple drug use increases as Canadians age. One-quarter of all potentially inappropriate drug combinations result from overlapping and similar prescriptions prescribed by two doctors for one patient. There are many potential sources of problems in drug use, especially if a person is at home alone and has been prescribed more than one medication. Table 14.1 outlines inappropriate drug use and inappropriate prescribing. You may be able to add to this list of potential problems with some that you are aware of. I, for example, remember talking with a student a while ago who had received anti-depressants from the health services at the university. She mentioned that she just took them a few at a time when she was depressed. This was despite the fact that they were to be taken daily and that the level necessary for an effective dose level was not usually reached until a person

TABLE 14.1   Inappropriate Drug Use and Inappropriate Prescribing

Inappropriate Drug Use	Inappropriate Prescribing
• Not having a prescription filled or refilled. • Taking too much or too little of the drug prescribed. • Erratic dosing, such as altering time intervals or omitting doses. • Stopping the drug too soon. • Combining prescription drugs with over-the-counter products or illicit drugs. • Combining prescription drugs with alcohol.	• Under-prescribing or not specifying sufficient quantities or correct intervals of dosage. • Over-prescribing or going beyond the maximum therapeutic dosage. • Prolonged use that results in iatrogenic effects and adverse reactions. • Prescribing that is contraindicated by the medical condition. • Contraindicated combinations that produce an undesirable effect.

Source: *The Health of Canadians: The Federal Role—Interim Report* (Kirby Report).

had taken them for about one month. What makes this story all the more telling is that this was a bright, relatively well-educated, and healthy young woman who was taking a potentially dangerous drug casually and on her own whim. Social as well as medical explanations contribute to our understanding of drug use—including the more and the less dangerous of these sleeping pills, tranquilizers, pain medications, heart and blood pressure medications, stomach remedies, and laxatives. Opioid drug use is a particular case in point. It is often prescribed first for pain relief in cases of intractable and serious pain. Often, however, these drugs become addictive and people may move into an addiction that can only be satisfied by the non-medical use of such drugs. The non-medical (street) use opioid analgesics is considered an epidemic in Canada today and has resulted in many deaths, particularly among young people (Shield et al., 2011).

Taking more than one drug at a time can lead to unpredictable problems whether the drug is non-prescription, prescribed, or a vitamin (or other "healthy" drug). Drug interactions can affect the absorption rate, distribution throughout the body, metabolism, and the elimination of a drug, and one drug can diminish or exacerbate the pharmacological effects of another drug. Drug effects are known to be somewhat different among the elderly as well as among people of different weights and overall health, among other things. Pharmaceuticals are routinely tested and prescribed on the assumption that the average user is a male in his thirties. The elderly, on average, differ significantly from the average 30-year-old male. They are more likely to be female, to have slower metabolic rates, to weigh less, and to have some cognitive deficits. For those reasons alone, aside from multiple medication use, the elderly are more likely to experience drug reactions than younger adults.

The use of **over-the-counter drugs** often exacerbates the problems noted above. One study found that as many as 70 per cent of the elderly take over-the-counter medication without discussing this with their physicians. Incidences of medication errors by the elderly have been well documented and many of them are in addition to the standard problems elucidated in Table 14.1. These include: forgetting to take medication, taking a smaller or larger dose than that prescribed, taking medication for the wrong reasons, being unable to read labels, having difficulty opening containers, and having impaired memory (ibid.). Consequences of such drug misuse include falls, dizziness, various illnesses, hospitalization, and even death. If current trends continue, drug use will increase because the rate of drug use for those over 65 is higher than for any other age group, and this part of the population is growing the most quickly.

Females are consistently heavier prescription drug users than males. This pattern of greater use of prescription drugs among females is true of a wide variety of drugs. Those in lower-income groups spend a greater percentage of their incomes on prescription drugs. They also spend a higher percentage of income on food and shelter. In regard to prescription drugs, however, this may be the result of more expensive drugs, as there is some evidence that prices for the same drug can vary considerably, depending on the location where it is sold. It bears mention that pharmacies are essentially competitive businesses and are governed, therefore, by market principles. People in poorer, rural, or isolated neighbourhoods tend to lack the mobility (e.g., automobile transportation) required for comparison shopping and are thus more apt to pay whatever the going rate in the local pharmacy happens to be—or not use the drug.

All provinces have introduced drug programs to subsidize medication purchases by low-income families (Lexchin, 1996; Dewa et al., 2005). However, these programs vary widely from one jurisdiction to another. Thus, for example, about 68 per cent of the people in Newfoundland and Labrador and 75 per cent of those who live in New Brunswick have some coverage, while 100 per cent of those in Quebec are covered (Kapur and Basu, 2005: 185). While these figures are not just for low-income people, they do indicate that efforts are being made. Still, despite the introduction of drug programs for low-income people, per capita spending as a percentage of total family expenditure in the low-income group was almost twice as high as that of the high-income group, both before and after the introduction of drug plans (Lexchin, 1996: 47), and major disparities in drug coverage and expenses by families continue to exist across the country (Kapur and Basu, 2005).

Physicians and Prescribing

There is a high correlation between the number of visits to a physician and the number of prescriptions. In the US, 75.1 per cent of doctor visits

result in a prescription for a medication (http://www.cdc.gov/nchs/fastats/drug-use-therapeutic.htm). The figures in Canada are likely somewhat less because we tend to have a slightly less interventionist/aggressive system. (This may in part reflect the competitive nature of the US medical system as compared to the nationally funded Canadian system, and it may also reflect fundamental philosophical differences.) In Chapter 10 we saw that the number of physicians in a society affects the degree of medicalization. Physicians in general have a tendency towards medical intervention (e.g., to prescribe drugs) when confronted with a patient exhibiting a problem. Various social characteristics and conditions of patients affect the rates at which doctors prescribe drugs just as they affect other aspects of medical care.

Research has documented significant deficiencies in doctors' knowledge about drugs (Tannenbaum and Tsuyiki, 2013). Commercial sources of information, including drug advertising and salespersons, are significant influences on doctors' prescribing habits: the more heavily a drug is promoted the more it is prescribed, despite the fact that doctors themselves believe that "they used scientific sources and shunned commercial ones" (Mintzes, 2010). This may be a growing problem as physicians and patients come to rely more and more on the Internet, where health sites are frequently funded by the pharmaceutical industry even though this link may be invisible or obfuscated in one way or another (Usher and Skinner, 2012). One study, for example, found that more than 70 per cent of physicians made claims about particular drugs that reflected the claims made in drug advertisements even though these claims were diametrically opposite to those in the scientific literature (Mintzes, 2010). Doctors have tended not to be critical of drug advertising. They have tended to trust it and it has been known to be incorporated into medical education through textbooks and guest speakers. Medical schools have just recently begun to develop policies limiting the potential for conflict of interest in medical education among both students and faculty (Glauser, 2013b). Still, numerous studies have found that when patients go to doctors asking for particular drugs they have seen advertised, they are more likely to get them (including the particular brand requested) than not.

Good prescribing by physicians involves maximizing effectiveness, minimizing risks, minimizing costs, and respecting the choices of patients (Barber in Lexchin, 1998: 254). In the context of widespread **direct-to-consumer advertising**, this list now needs to include patient education because patients are often demanding drugs they have seen advertised on television, in magazines, or online, such as anti-depressants that may be of less help and that may be harmful. Even though there are very few studies of appropriate drug prescribing in Canada, those that do exist do not suggest that the values elucidated above are often realized. Drugs may be prescribed when less invasive options such as diet change should be tried first, as is the case in many of the cholesterol-reducing drugs that are so widely prescribed. Even if drugs are prescribed when needed, there may still be problems in drug administration such as dose, rate of absorption, and duration. Studies of elderly people have examined and confirmed "potentially undesirable prescribing." For instance, a study of prescribing in Alberta found that over 2,600 of the elderly population (1.1 per cent) had prescriptions for two or more non-steroid anti-inflammatory drugs (NSAIDs) dispensed on the same day, despite the fact that there is little, if any, rationale for such a practice. In addition, with respect to one of the mood-altering drugs—diazepam—a detailed study found that 14,000 elderly people (3.7 per cent of the province's elderly) received a potentially inappropriate prescription—often from a single physician, i.e., this over-prescription was not entirely or largely the result of seniors visiting more than one doctor at a time for the same problem. According to Joel Lexchin (1998: 256) and based on the available published data, there is a "substantial amount of inappropriate prescribing" (see Table 14.1). This has led to a situation in which adverse drug reaction is one of the top 10 causes of death in

Canada today (Canadian Foundation for Health Care Improvement, 2010). This problem is exacerbated by the uptake of higher-cost newer drugs designed to replace older drugs, which thus increases the profit for pharmaceutical companies. In fact, one in five such new drugs will likely be found to be unsafe or will be withdrawn from the market (ibid.), despite the fact that new drugs have to have regulatory approval after having gone through clinical trials to ensure their safety and effectiveness.

"Safe" is a relative term, as there are virtually always some side effects and some of these may be more or less severe for users. Moreover, clinical trials are not absolutely perfect. As with all research, there are limitations. For example, women have long been excluded because of the possibility of pregnancy and because of the known cyclical and changing nature of their biochemistry through their reproductive cycles. The elderly have often been excluded for convenience or because of the (presumed) possibility that they may be suffering from another disease other than the one whose treatment is being evaluated. Also, while clinical trials may ensure the new drug is being used explicitly and exactly for the problem for which it is designed, off-label use and prescription are endemic. In fact, clinical trials are able, for a variety of reasons, to predict only about half of all serious adverse effects. In addition, all adverse effects are never known because reporting is voluntary and many people either do not know to or know how to report adverse effects (Canadian Foundation for Health Care Improvement, 2010).

Lexchin (1998), a Canadian authority on the pharmaceutical industry, states that the causes of inappropriate prescribing are (1) the lack of knowledge on the part of physicians and (2) the patterns of practice of physicians. The typical Canadian doctor prescribes only a very limited number of the many thousands of drugs presently on the Canadian market: 50 per cent of all prescriptions written by GPs are for about 27 different medications. Between 1991 and 1995, 404 new drugs were patented in Canada and of these only

33 (about 8 per cent) were thought to be either breakthroughs or substantially better than existing drugs. Practising doctors, even though they know that reliable sources of information about prescribing include continuing medical education, peer-reviewed journals (many of which are now easily available online), and association meetings, rely largely on pharmaceutical company sales representatives, who do not "disclose the side effects and contraindications of their products or the prices of their drugs in relation to other drugs, unless asked, and they frequently make incorrect statements about the drugs they are promoting" (ibid., 258).

Research has repeatedly confirmed the following correlations. The more frequently physicians saw drug sales representatives:

- the more likely they were to use drugs even when not using drugs was the best option;
- the more often they sympathized with a "commercial" view of the value of a given drug;
- the more likely they were to prescribe antibiotics inappropriately;
- the less likely they were to prescribe generically;
- the more likely they were to use more expensive medications when equally effective but less costly drugs were available.

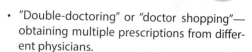

CRITICAL THINKING

BOX 14.1 Prescription Drug Abuse

Prescription drug abuse is a significant problem in Canada today. Although almost any drug can be abused, the pharmaceuticals with psychotropic effects are most often subject to abuse. This includes "opioid-based drugs for pain relief, tranquillizers, stimulants and amphetamines, and sedatives and barbiturates," according to the Canadian Centre on Substance Abuse (www.ccsa.ca/2007%20CCSA%20Documents/ccsa-011519-2007.pdf). Anabolic steroids and asthma inhalers are also used (unsafely) for non-medical purposes at times.

Available evidence regarding legal prescriptions indicates that Canadians are among the highest users of psychotropic drugs in the world. Although it is difficult to get good comprehensive national data on either the prescribed or illegally used psychotropics, a study by the Centre for Addiction and Mental Health found that 11 per cent of their admissions to substance abuse treatment programs were among people with dependencies on these drugs (ibid.).

How and why does prescription drug abuse occur? The Canadian Centre on Substance Abuse suggests the following factors:

- "Double-doctoring" or "doctor shopping"—obtaining multiple prescriptions from different physicians.
- Prescription-pad theft and tampering, resulting in forged or altered prescriptions.
- Physician fraud—fraudulent prescriptions written by doctors in return for money.
- Purchases from friends, relatives, or dealers for whom the drug has been legitimately prescribed.
- Diversion of drugs from substance abuse treatment programs (for example, methadone).
- Diversion from supplies intended for patients in health-care facilities.
- Break-ins and theft from homes, doctors' offices, pharmacies, manufacturers, wholesalers, courier companies, clinics, and hospitals.
- Purchase of drugs on the Internet.

Monitoring any of the above reasons for prescription drug abuse is difficult and ranges into the jurisdiction of the law rather than medicine. What prescription drugs are used illegally on your campus? For what purposes are they used? What are some of the detrimental side effects and long-term effects of their use?

Pharmaceutical firms are a major source of information for doctors and now patients and consumers about to become patients. The pharmaceutical industry works to control information about its products in a variety of ways. This influence is increasingly powerful in the context of globalization, the Internet, and Internet advertising (Usher and Skinner, 2012). Drug companies fund researchers to test their new products (and have been known to contractually prohibit publication of any but positive results from such research [Mather, 2005]. Further, industry-sponsored research has a far greater likelihood of generating positive responses from physicians and the public than non-company-supported research, because the drug companies have the money to advertise their research, and corporate involvement in research leads to a greater likelihood of positive results than non-company-sponsored research. The industry also financially supports medical conferences, clubs in medical schools and hospitals, and continuing education events (ibid.). Numerous gifts are given directly to physicians, including free drug samples, wall charts and posters, three-dimensional models, pen sets, and notepads. Various studies have found that these industry–physician interactions are profitable for industry. They serve to influence doctors to use their drugs. Unfortunately, many sources of information provided by industry to doctors have been found to be in error or misleading (ibid.).

Nonetheless, many doctors learn much of what they know about medicines and their "appropriate" use from drug firms. There is no lack of evidence to document that the drug company representatives who call on physicians regularly with brochures, samples, and gifts are a major source of information about drugs for doctors. If expenditures by drug companies on promotion and advertising are any indication—they spend twice as much on pushing their products as they do on research and development—then these activities have an important impact on prescribing

(Rachlis and Kushner, 1994; Gagnon and Lexchin, 2008). In the United States, pharmaceutical companies spend more on advertising than do either the alcohol or the tobacco companies. Drug advertisements have repeatedly been criticized as misleading and incomplete, and as portraying people in stereotypical ways. For instance, the elderly may be seen engaging in passive activities wearing depressed faces or acting childishly (Foster and Huffman, 1995). Advertisements recommend drugs for such a variety of everyday, "normal" concerns that drugs seem to be suggested as useful to everyone at least some of the time. Drug prescribing, then, is often a symptom of the tendency towards the expanding medicalization of social issues.

Another major source of information for most Canadian doctors is the regularly updated *Compendium of Pharmaceuticals and Specialties* (CPS, http://www.pharmacists.ca/index.cfm/function/store/ProductDetail.cfm?ProdCompanyPassed=cpa&ProdCdPassed=cpa-2014E-1&PriceCategPassed=std&indexstart=1), a Canadian Pharmaceutical Association publication. Although the *Canadian Medical Association Journal* has recommended this as a source of information (Lexchin, 1984), it may be inadequate in a number of ways. It may not be comprehensive, and it is known to have continued recommending certain drugs long after research documenting dangerous side effects had been published in medical journals. The most thorough study of its value, done over 30 years ago, found that 46.3 per cent of the drugs listed by the *Compendium* were "probably useless, obsolete, or irrational mixtures" (Bell and Osterman, 1983). Well-known risks and negative effects were ignored for over 60 per cent of the drugs listed. Scientific errors regarding the biochemical effects of nearly 40 per cent of the entries were evident. Bell and Osterman were led to conclude that the CPS at that time was basically a tool to promote the interests of drug companies. More recent critiques of pharmaceutical regulation suggest ongoing reasons for skepticism and caution in assuming drug safety (e.g., Stelfox et al., 1998;

SPOTLIGHT ON ETHICS

BOX 14.2 Conflict of Interest: Doctors and the Pharmaceutical Industry

There is clear and repeated documentation of conflict of interest in publications in medical journals. This means that at times medical publications are or may be biased because of the personal interests of one of the authors or editors. Financial investment in a particular product is one example. The study in the *New England Journal of Medicine* about publications regarding the safety of calcium blockers in the treatment of cardiovascular disorders is a case in point. The researchers searched the English-language medical literature for articles concerning the safety of calcium-channel antagonists. Articles were categorized as neutral, supportive, or critical of calcium blockers.

The authors of the articles were surveyed about their financial relationships with the manufacturers of the calcium-channel blockers. The findings revealed that authors who supported the use of calcium-channel blockers were significantly more likely than neutral or critical authors to have financial relationships with manufacturers of these products (Stelfox et al., 1998: 102). Conflicts of interest are a continuing problem among Canadian doctors today (Glauser, 2013b). Many schools and medical journals have introduced policies to prevent and to openly acknowledge such conflicts of interest and to eliminate them where possible.

Whitaker, 2010; Lexchin, 2012) and effectiveness even when drugs are used for the purposes officially intended.

What other factors influence doctors' decisions about prescribing drugs? Freidson (1975) distinguishes between client-dependent and colleague-dependent forms of medical practice. His argument is that regulation is more effective in colleague-dependent than in client-dependent practices. When doctors have to account to other doctors for the diagnoses they make and the treatments they choose, they are likely to exhibit higher medical standards than when primarily seeking to satisfy the patient. Following this line of reasoning, it can be predicted that doctors who are involved in medical networks or in some form of group practice are more likely to have appropriate prescribing habits.

Surprisingly, perhaps, especially as it contradicts the common perception, physicians who see fewer patients may spend more time with them but also prescribe more medications.

A Canadian study compared a group of doctors who worked on the basis of fee-for-service with a group of doctors who worked on salary (Lexchin, 1988a). Approximately one-half of the doctors in private clinics, as compared to one-quarter in community health centres, prescribed drugs inappropriately. Doctors in private clinics spent less time per patient. Salaried physicians were more likely to warn patients of side effects and other potential problems. The researchers explained that because salaried physicians had more time per patient, they were able to take the time to prescribe appropriately and to explain when and how to use the drug, as well as potential side effects.

Several studies have shown that both drug advertisements and drug detail men and women (pharmaceutical company representatives who visit doctors with samples and information about drugs) (Lexchin, 1994a) significantly affect the drug-prescribing habits of doctors. Lexchin

(1994b) indicates that much of the over-prescription of antibiotics, stomach ulcer medications, and anti-hypertensives results from drug advertising. The Canadian Medical Association and its journal historically defend the pharmaceutical industry and support its viewpoints (Lexchin, 1994a). Given the amount of money involved, perhaps this is not surprising. The drug industry is also heavily involved in supporting medical education. Apparently almost 56 per cent of the medical residency programs in the US received monies from the pharmaceutical industry (Kondro, 2010a, 2010b). The pharmaceutical industry also is heavily involved in the publication of medical journals (Insel, 2010) and in medical research (ibid.).

Robert Whitaker, who makes the case in *Anatomy of an Epidemic* that the rise of mental illness in the US is the result of pharmaceuticals, cites evidence of the biased trials of psychotropics funded by pharmaceutical companies (Whitaker, 2010: 299–300); of the rescinding of an appointment to the University of Toronto of a researcher for having exposed his findings that suicidal thoughts are caused by SSRIs (ibid., 305–6); of the suppression of the results of research studies (ibid., 307–11); of inappropriate acceptance of money by academic psychiatrists (ibid., 322–5); and of the invention of psychiatric categories of illness to "cover" the conditions created in children by the effects of drugs unnecessarily prescribed (ibid., 325–6). The psychiatric profession routinely emphasizes to schizophrenic patients "the importance of remaining on medications as prescribed"; however, the spectrum of outcomes in schizophrenia patients has been shown at times to be superior when off antipsychotic medications (ibid., 117).

Another powerful influence on the prescribing habits of doctors is direct-to-consumer (DTC) advertising. Although this form of advertising is illegal in Canada, Canadians view television from the US and read newspapers and magazines published in the United States. One study found that 87.4 per cent of Canadian patients reported seeing DTC advertising (Mintzes et al., 2003). Interestingly, physicians were likely to

give patients drugs that the patients, having seen advertisements, had requested (between 72 and 78 per cent of patient requests were filled). These figures compare to a rate of 12.4 per cent of prescriptions given to patients who had not specifically requested them. Direct-to-consumer advertising has been shown to be effective in increasing the sales of particular drugs (Mintzes et al., 2002). According to a cross-sectional survey of primary care physicians in Vancouver and Sacramento, there is a significant likelihood, regardless of the patient's health status, drug payment method, or gender, or of the medical specialty of the physician or number of years in practice, that patients who request a particular drug will be given it. Furthermore, physicians indicated that in at least 40 per cent of the cases in which they prescribed a drug at the request of the patient the physicians were ambivalent about the prescription of the particular drug. Clearly, patients' requests for certain drugs are a powerful factor in the prescribing habits of physicians, despite their possible professional reluctance. There is a direct link between the amount of advertising for a particular drug and the rate of its prescription (Mintzes et al., 2003).

This evident lack of respect for good and systematic knowledge about the efficacy and safety of drugs is exacerbated by the fact that there is no routine, ongoing monitoring of drug effects on an individual or population level in Canada. It is impossible, then, to link specific health outcomes to specific pharmaceutical interventions (Zitner, 2002). It also is impossible to determine whether the use of newer and more expensive drugs results in better outcomes. As Zitner says, "auto repair shops, computer service technicians, and many other industries routinely contact people to learn if service was satisfactory" (ibid., 2). By comparison, he argues, it would seem to be a good thing if our health-care system provided more systematic follow-up. Furthermore, Health Canada apparently has no record of what drugs have been withdrawn (or why) because of safety concerns (Lexchin, 2005). As Lexchin (2009: 3) writes, "Health Canada has explicitly rejected the development of quantitative standards for evaluating its post-marketing pharmaco-surveillance system." The present methods of monitoring the effects of drugs, once they are on the market and used by the public, are very weak. The post-market surveillance system is underfunded and understaffed. As a consequence, there is a significant level of under-reporting of adverse effects both by the public and by health professionals (Fuller, 2010).

Pharmacists

There were approximately 37,490 licensed pharmacists working in Canada in 2014, according to the National Association of Pharmacy Regulatory Authorities (http://napra.ca/pages/Practice_Resources/National_Statistics.aspx?id=2103). This number represents a substantial rate of growth over the past decade or so. Little sociological analysis exists of the role of pharmacists with respect to prescription and non-prescription drugs. Unquestionably, however, they have considerable discretionary influence in making recommendations both to doctors and to individuals who shop for prescribed drugs as well as for over-the-counter drugs for which they offer informed assistance. Consumers frequently ask the pharmacist to recommend "something"—a non-prescription drug—for a cough, sleeplessness, pain, or anxiety. The pharmacist may suggest a particular brand-name drug or a range of suitable products of different brand names. A number of factors will affect the pharmacist's recommendation. Discussion about legally broadening pharmacists' scope of practice beyond these limited tasks has been ongoing for some time. Among the reasons given (www.informedpharmacotherapy.com/Issues8/Editorial/editorial8.htm) for altering their present legal status are the following:

1. The accessibility of pharmacists to the public is greater than that of physicians, and pharmacists already have been advising and monitoring patients in regard to drug therapy for decades.

2. Pharmacists already have a professional relationship with patients that is legislated and that encompasses ethical and professional responsibilities.

3. Usually, the pharmacist is expected to assess prescriptions independently. Frequently, the pharmacist questions the patient to ensure that the need for and the use of the drug are fully understood.

4. Physicians often lack sufficient and appropriate information regarding the drugs they prescribe for patients.

5. Pharmacists already give a significant amount of advice on over-the-counter medications to patients.

Pharmacists do have discretionary power when presented with a drug prescription. Unless the physician has written "no substitution" on it, pharmacists are free to dispense any company's brand of a particular drug. They are also now able to renew prescriptions, refuse to fill prescriptions, initiate drug therapy for a number of self-limiting conditions, and substitute prescriptions (Tannenbaum and Tsuyiki, 2013) (http://www.cmaj.ca/site/press/cmaj.121990.pdf). Depending on the province in which they work, pharmacists can order and interpret the findings of lab tests. Further, there is evidence of the effectiveness of an expanded role for pharmacists in the management of a number of chronic diseases such as diabetes and in avoiding or predicting adverse drug events.

The Pharmaceutical Industry

The Canadian drug industry has always been divided into domestically owned companies, the first one founded by E.B. Shuttleworth in Toronto in 1879, and foreign-owned subsidiaries, the first of which was established in Windsor by Parke, Davis and Company (Lexchin, 1984: 331). The industry grew slowly (the foreign-owned companies stayed in Canada because they could obtain tariff and tax advantages) until the 1940s. The antibiotic revolution and the development of medications to control patients in mental hospitals spurred the rapid growth of the industry. Economies of scale became possible in the manufacture of these drugs, and production was centralized. Centralization, plus the increasing openness of world trade—globalization—meant the small Canadian companies could not compete with the larger foreign-owned companies. After World War II, only one Canadian company of any consequence—Connaught Laboratories—was left. Now again, the domestic drug manufacturing industry is on the decline, decreasing 1.7 per cent per year since 2004 according to Statistics Canada (http://www.ic.gc.ca/eic/site/lsg-pdsv. nsf/eng/h_hn01703.html#sector). Still, the total pharmaceutical sales in Canada are significant, having almost doubled from 2001 to 2013 to $21.6 billion, with 89 per cent sold to retail pharmacies and the rest sold directly to hospitals. Fifty-eight per cent of this expense is covered privately and 42 per cent is paid for by governments.

The pharmaceutical industry is one of the more profitable manufacturing activities in Canada. It still employs about 27,000 people. Canada comprises 2.5 per cent of the world market and is thus the ninth largest world market. The median rate of return for shareholders of large pharmaceutical companies is about twice the median for all manufacturing: 20.1 per cent as compared to 9.8 per cent (Lexchin and Wiktorowicz, 2009). High profitability and the probability of consistent growth due to long-term demographics (e.g., the aging of the population) provide reasons for the likely continuation of these trends. Furthermore, pharmaceuticals appear to be a low-risk industry. What strategies do the drug companies use to maintain their profitability? What is the impact of the great financial success of the multinational drug companies on the health of Canadians and on the health of the people in less-developed countries? In what way do the profit-making strategies of the drug companies affect health negatively? These three questions will be discussed here.

The pharmaceutical industry has been successful in maintaining its position as one of the most profitable industries through a variety of strategies, including: (1) the absence of a link between manufacturing cost and price; (2) patent protection; (3) competition and drug development focused on drugs with widespread potential for use (and thus profit) rather than on drugs for rare conditions; (4) production of brand-name rather than generic products; (5) drug distribution (dumping) in less-developed countries; (6) the change in the availability of many drugs from prescription only to over-the-counter consumer purchase; (7) drug shortages; and (8) advertising and providing select information to physicians and consumers.

One of the major reasons for the high profits in the drug industry is that *the selling price of drugs is not necessarily or only related to drug production costs* (Lexchin, 1984: 41–8). In the absence of price competition with patented drugs, the manufacturer is free to determine prices in the interest of maximizing profits. Thus, variations in the cost to the consumer bear little or no relationship to manufacturing costs. Instead, prices reflect Canada's patent system, the relationship between Health Canada and the industry, the types of research and development undertaken, and advertising costs, among other things (Lexchin and Wiktorowicz, 2009). A study of drugs introduced from 1994 to 2003 showed similar processes resulting in higher drug costs for pharmaceuticals that were of no benefit to consumers (Lexchin, 2006). While high profitability is the case in the pharmaceutical industry worldwide, it appears to be particularly so in Canada. The Canadian Patented Medicine Prices Review Board examined prices for 195 drugs marketed between 1990 and 1992. Of the total, the Canadian price for 111 was above the median price in the international market and in 30 per cent of the cases the Canadian price was the highest in the world (Lexchin, 1991). One reason for this is that the Patented Medicine Prices Review Board allows companies to offer new drugs on the market at a price equivalent to the highest-priced existing treatment (Lexchin and Wiktorowicz,

2009). The wide variation in pricing for drugs from country to country is also reflected in the fact that, in recent years, some US citizens from border states crossed the border into Canada to buy prescription drugs with Canadian dollars in order to save and others have bought online using the relative advantage of today's American dollar. In the recent past, though, when the Canadian dollar was about at par with the US dollar, Canadians could sometimes save by crossing the border (symbolically and actually) and filling prescriptions in the US. Online purchasing of pharmaceuticals is expanding and challenges all of the patenting and safety concerns discussed. Errors and adverse effects will be even less likely to be monitored when purchases are across borders through the Internet and the global pharmaceutical industry. Moreover, the future ability of individual countries to regulate drug costs and availability is threatened today by the accessibility of online pharmaceuticals.

Patent protection is the second technique used to maintain the high level of profits. Patents limit competition. Once the company has invented a new drug, patent protection gives the company an exclusive right to manufacture and distribute the drug for a period of years. Today, Canada offers patent protection for a minimum of seven years but generally 10 years for new drugs before generic drugs are allowed to be developed and marketed (Lexchin and Wiktorowicz, 2009). This period can be extended if the company takes out additional patents on associated drugs. Drug companies claim that patent protection allows them to pay for the research and development involved in the invention of new drugs. However, this argument can be challenged because much of the research done in any drug company is directed towards developing imitative medicines that can compete with products already successfully developed and marketed.

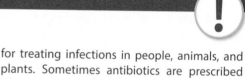

HIGHLIGHTED ISSUES

BOX 14.3   Antibiotic Resistance

In the 1940s antibiotics were introduced. They were viewed as "miracle" drugs. They were able to keep people alive who would have died from pneumonia, tuberculosis, infections in wounds, and sexually transmitted diseases. Now, however, antibiotic resistance (or ineffectiveness) is growing (Branswell, 2002). The US Centers for Disease Control has recently confirmed that one of the most common and difficult of infections is becoming resistant to vancomycin, the strongest antibiotic presently available. The presence and spread of vancomycin-resistant staph aureus (VRSA) may herald a day when there is no antibiotic solution for the many bacterial diseases whose treatments, since the 1940s, we have come to take for granted (ibid.).

The major reasons for the growth of antibiotic resistance appear to be their inappropriate use for treating infections in people, animals, and plants. Sometimes antibiotics are prescribed when they are not necessary because the presence of bacterial rather than viral infection has not been documented. Sometimes people fail to take antibiotics as they have been prescribed. Bacteria are able to constantly adapt to survive. When antibiotics are used inappropriately bacteria have opportunities to change. When antibiotics are used in animals and plants they enter the human food chain and the ecosystem of the water, land, and even air (Batt, 2010). Dumping of excess antibiotics and their excretion via the human body are other processes that increase the growth of antibiotic resistance in populations. The popular use of anti-bacterial soap and alcohol-based hand sanitizer is also associated with the development of resistance (ibid.).

The third strategy is that the *drug compan- ies rarely do research or attempt to develop medi- cines in areas where there is unlikely to be a large market* or with a view to addressing the needs of people with less-than-common diseases or when the materials for the medication are not subject to patent (ibid.). Rather, they tend to develop and produce new drugs based on similar exist- ing drugs, thus maintaining patent protection for large markets that have already been developed. As an example, there are numerous anti-inflamma- tory (anti-arthritis) and benzodiazepine (minor tranquilizer) and anti-depressant drugs currently on the market in Canada (Lexchin, 1988a; Lexchin and Wiktorowicz, 2009). Such a wide choice is of virtually no therapeutic or medical value; indeed, the value of benzodiazepine (Whitaker, 2010: 126–47) and of anti-depressants (ibid., 149–71) is open to question. However, because of the huge market for these two drugs, most every phar- maceutical company has a similar product. The development and introduction of "new" drugs appears to have more to do with profitability than with medical value.

Fourth, *the use of brand-name rather than generic products contributes significantly to the prof- its of the pharmaceutical companies.* (The generic name is the scientific name for a particular drug, while the brand name is the name given to the drug by the pharmaceutical company that produ- ces it.) On average, generics cost considerably less than the most expensive brand-name equivalents. It is clearly to the advantage of the pharmaceut- ical industry to promote brand-name products. Although brand-name products usually are pre- scribed, the pharmacist may substitute a generic if it is available (unless otherwise directed by a physician). Paradoxically, however, that may not always be done because the economic viability of the pharmaceutical industry is important to many people in Canada besides those who directly profit.

Fifth, the history of the pharmaceutical indus- try is replete with stories of drug-related illness and death. The *dumping of out-of-date drugs in the developing countries* is one example. The health- destroying side effects of many drugs, whether they are taken alone or in combination with other drugs, are another problem. The industry some- times markets drugs for a wide variety of symp- toms when they are appropriate for only a limited number of purposes.

Many countries in the developing world face serious problems in relation to pharma- ceuticals. One problem is a lack of drugs, such as antibiotics, that have come to be considered essential in the developed North. Other drugs known to extend or improve the quality of life in a chronic and potentially fatal disease, such as AIDS, are much too expensive for the vast majority of the world's population. For instance, while protease inhibitors could lengthen the life- span of people diagnosed with HIV/AIDS, they are completely out of financial reach for most people in many countries where people cannot even afford a condom. Aside from the costs and the lack of availability, there are other equally serious problems in less-developed countries: at times, drugs are used inappropriately because they lack directions for use or these directions are written in a foreign language, or the con- sumer lacks literacy, or they are to be taken with water that may be unsafe or lacking. Sometimes drugs banned in one country are shipped to and sold in a different country that lacks the regu- latory infrastructure to protect its population (Ollila and Hemminki, 1997: 309).

Sixth, a number of *drugs that were formerly available only by prescription are now available as over-the-counter (OTC) purchases.* This may increase the sales of such medications. Emergency contra- ception (the so-called "morning-after" pill) is one example (http://www.planb.ca/where.php). Now that this emergency contraception can be purchased over the counter it may be more widely used in a situation of fear of pregnancy. This trend to over- the-counter medications may seem a progressive step in that it promotes self-care, but the availability of over the counter medications that formerly had to be gotten by prescription also boosts sales. In addition, this move saves medical insurance com- panies money because they do not pay for any but prescription drugs, and this increases the size of the private health-care system and the out-of-pocket expenses for many Canadians.

It is incorrect to assume that a drug licensed in one country is necessarily appropriate for another group because populations may differ in "metabolism, weight, and nutrition—and these are known to affect the efficacy, safety, occurrence of side effects, and acceptability of a drug" (ibid., 323). For example, the World Health Organization found that schizophrenics had a better outcome in the less-developed world, presumably because they were far less likely to be drugged and because their social policies and cultural values for the mentally ill were more supportive (Whitaker, 2010: x–xi).

Drug licensing is important for ensuring safety and efficacy. The World Health Organization says that national governments are responsible for drug regulation (http://www.who.int/medicines/areas/quality_safety/regulation_legislation/en/). This inevitably means that prescription drug regulation is uneven around the world. Even in the industrialized world conflicts of interest are faced by pharmaceutical companies and their scientists regarding the need for licensing and regulation. Because a patent gives a drug company the exclusive right to manufacture and sell a particular drug for a limited period of time—and because patented drugs are much more profitable to drug companies—it is in their interest to speed a newly patented drug through the approval and regulatory boards in order to have the longest time possible to gain from the patent status (Abraham, 1995). Consequently, even products that have been on the market for a lengthy period of time may be unsafe (Lexchin and Wiktorowicz, 2009).

The Dalkon Shield IUD (an intrauterine device for birth control) is one example of the great health costs of a profit-driven industry (Vavasour and Mennie, 1984). The Dalkon Shield went on the market in 1971 in the United States. By early 1972 there were numerous reports of adverse reactions, such as pelvic inflammatory disease, blood poisoning, and tubal pregnancies. By 1974, 17 people had died from its use. Because the US

market began to look very poor, the manufacturer offered the Dalkon Shield to developing nations at a discounted price of 48 per cent of the original price. The shields were distributed to the developing nations even though they were unsterilized and nine out of 10 lacked the necessary inserter. Furthermore, only one out of 1,000 was distributed with any instructions for insertion (and their insertion is a delicate and potentially dangerous procedure). In 1975, the United States banned the Dalkon Shield, while continuing to sell them to the developing world (Miller, 1996).

A seventh strategy for maximizing pharmaceutical profits is *drug shortages of particular drugs in Canada and around the world*, even though such shortages can potentially be life- and health-threatening (http://www.hc-sc.gc.ca/dhp-mps/prodpharma/shortages-penuries/index-eng.php). A website now lists drug shortages and expected shortages so that patients, druggists, and doctors can be prepared and look for options (http://www.drugshortages.ca/drugshortagehome.asp). Several different policy options to prevent drug shortages are being considered (Gagnon, 2012).

The eighth profit strategy is to *provide select information to doctors and consumers about the efficiency and safety of various drugs*. On average, drug companies in Canada invested about $10,000 per physician in advertising in the early nineties (Williams et al., 1993). But they advertise in such a way as to seem to be educating doctors who say they are so busy that in the absence of adequate knowledge they are likely to "try" something by prescribing drugs to a patient (Williams et al., 1995: 148). Drug industry contacts with physicians are systematic and persistent and often include "perks" such as meals, stationery, conference fees, travel expenses, and computer equipment (physicians who prescribe most are most likely to receive these additional perks) (ibid.). There is also considerable evidence that pharmaceutical companies restrict the information resulting from research studies that could inform doctors and the public, if the research is not supportive of the companies' bottom lines (Olivieri, 2010; Whitaker, 2010).

Fifteen general practitioners in Australia were asked to audiotape three encounters with pharmaceutical representatives (Roughead et al., 1998). Seven of these GPs agreed to take part. They asked 24 pharmaceutical representatives to participate; 16 agreed to do so. They were informed that they were being taped. A total of 64 medicines were described ("detailed") in the recordings. The interpretations averaged 2.75 minutes per drug. However, the information provided by the pharmaceutical company representatives bore very little similarity to the Australian Approved Product Information categories. Thus, there was very little correspondence between the information provided by the drug company representatives and the views and position of the Australian government in respect to indications (for use), pharmacology, pharmacokinetics, side effects, precautions, warnings, interactions, use in special groups, dosage and administration, and availability. Despite the fact that the Australia Pharmaceutical Manufacturers' Code of Conduct is in place to regulate the marketing of drugs and "includes standards for printed promotional material, pharmaceutical representatives' activities, competitions, gifts, samples, trade displays, and symposia" (ibid., 270), the results of this study indicate that pharmaceutical company representatives do not comply with standards outlined in their codes of conduct.

In its policy on "Physicians and the Pharmaceutical Industry," updated in 2007, the Canadian Medical Association has expressed its concern about the conflict of interest that may confront physicians in their dealings with the pharmaceutical industry. The policy contains separate sections on industry-sponsored research, industry-sponsored surveillance studies, continuing medical education and development, electronic continuing development, advisory consultation boards, clinical evaluation packages, gifts, medical students and residents, and other considerations (policybase.cma.ca/dbtw-wpd/Policypdf/PD08-01.pdf). The Pharmaceutical Manufacturers Association of Canada has also developed codes of ethics similar to those of the CMA (www.canadapharma.org/en/about/corporate/OurHistory.aspx). The enforcement of these codes remains somewhat uneven.

In sum, the pharmaceutical industry invests in "educating" doctors because this has proven to be an effective strategy for sales in the developed and developing worlds, particularly as DTC advertising is illegal in most of the world (www.consumersinternational.org/media/311707/drugs,%20doctors%20and%20dinners.pdf). If the industry did not know from experience that marketing to doctors and consumers is effective, it would not have spent billions of dollars annually in recent years on this marketing.

The Case of Thalidomide

Just as the pharmaceutical companies have shown that their marketing strategies in developing countries take health less seriously than profits, so, too, have profits come first in Canada at times, and with deleterious consequences. Probably the incident with the most visibly tragic consequences was the **thalidomide** disaster, which resulted in the birth of over 100 babies in Canada with phocomelia (the absence of limbs and the presence of seal-like flippers instead).

A West German company developed thalidomide in 1954. It was called GRIPPEX, and was initially recommended for the treatment of respiratory infections, colds, coughs, flu, nervousness, and neuralgic and migraine headaches. It was widely available without prescription, quite cheap, and, therefore, very accessible. It was manufactured in West Germany, Canada, Great Britain, Italy, Sweden, and Switzerland under 37 different brand names (Klass, 1975: 92). Later it was marketed in Germany as the "safest" sleeping pill available because it was impossible to take enough at any time to commit suicide. It was advertised in Great Britain (where it was called Distavel) as so safe that the picture accompanying an advertisement was of a little child in front of a medicine chest. The caption read, "This child's life may depend on the safety of Distavel."

CRITICAL THINKING

BOX 14.4   Debate about New Reproductive Technologies

Among the most controversial of medical interventions available today are the new reproductive technologies. Largely unheard of, except in science-fiction literature, before the birth of the first "test-tube baby," Louise Brown, in 1978, these technologies fall roughly into four groups: (1) those concerned with fertility control (conception prevention); (2) labour and delivery "management" (high-tech deliveries in hospital by obstetricians/gynecologists); (3) pre-conception and prenatal screening (and treatment) for abnormalities and sex selection (ultrasound, amniocentesis, genetic screening); and (4) reproductive technologies per se (conception, pregnancy, and birth management via technical, pharmaceutical, and medical intervention) (Eichler, 1988: 211). This discussion will be limited to the last category.

New reproductive technologies have separated gestational, genetic, and social parenthood for both men and women. They have eliminated the need for intercourse between a man and a woman for reproduction. They enable men and women to reproduce without an opposite-sex social parent through surrogate mothering arrangements or sperm banks. With the new reproduction technologies, conception, gestation, and birth can be entirely separated from social parenting.

Approximately 16 per cent of heterosexual Canadian couples experience infertility (http://healthycanadians.gc.ca/health-sante/pregnancy-grossesse/fert-eng.php). Infertility is defined variably by age and sex but basically refers to failure to conceive after regular intercourse for a period of about one year if under 35 and a period of six months if over 35. In the case of infertility the first medical intervention is fertility drugs. If a course of pharmaceutical

treatment is not successful the next options, according to the government of Canada website (ibid.), include surgery, for example, to unblock the fallopian tubes or retrieve eggs or sperm; intrauterine insemination (IUI) whereby a thin catheter delivers sperm directly to the woman's uterus; in-vitro fertilization (IVF), i.e., fertilization of the ovum outside the woman's body; and, finally, an embryo transfer. While cost estimates are difficult to assess, one study suggested that each IVF (in-vitro fertilization) costs about $10,000. The cost of the drugs taken to enhance fertility and the anxiety and recurrent disappointment until fertilization occurs make this a very trying medical intervention for someone who is otherwise healthy. This figure is a significant underestimate of the overall costs because it does not include the other associated costs.

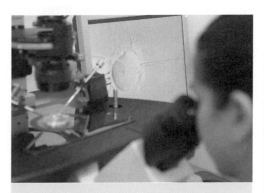

A medical technician performing in-vitro fertilization (IVF) in a laboratory. Procedures such as this one can have serious ramifications for society, but despite this our culture has relatively little social control over innovation. What are some of the concerns that the availability of IVF raises to a health sociologist?

continued

This immensely complex issue has extensive ramifications. Sociologists have long been concerned to understand the relationships between technological innovation and social change. In particular, they have sought to understand the social organization and social control of technological innovation. To simplify, in this case the fundamental questions are: In whose interest are the new reproductive technological developments? Whose interests should they serve? To what extent has the availability of these new technologies reinforced and even exacerbated a pronatalist philosophy? What are the effects of such a philosophy on men and women, particularly those who are infertile? What are the long-range physical, emotional, and social effects on children who have been produced by these technologies?

With respect to just one new intervention, in-vitro fertilization, there may be costs for the mother, father, and the fetus/embryo. For the mother and the fetus/embryo, these costs include significant short- and long-term health effects. The treatments can be very invasive and involve the administration of hormonal drugs at extraordinary levels. In the short run, the mother's body may experience pregnancy/non-pregnancy symptoms in turn, causing numerous minor side effects such as nausea, headaches, cramping, and the like. In the long run, these drugs (like DES, discussed below) may lead to a greater vulnerability to cancers—particularly of the reproductive system. As long-term studies have yet to be completed, the expectations for health or for side effects are now only speculative.

In addition to the biological costs are the social and emotional costs of being preoccupied with bodily functioning, with motherhood, and with the experience of repeated failure to conceive. Estimates suggest a success rate of about one in four cycles of attempts (www.ivf.ca/results). Women have likened the experience of being involved with IVF to a roller coaster of recurrent hope and despair. Even when fertilization is successful, the offspring have higher than average neonatal and perinatal mortality rates; there are much higher incidences of multiple births (about 30 per cent are multiples and with all the attendant risks) (http://healthycanadians.gc.ca/health-sante/pregnancy-grossesse/treatment-traitement-eng.php). The findings are inconclusive about other risks but, according to the Mayo Clinic, they may include ovarian cancer in the mother and birth defects in the offspring (http://www.mayoclinic.org/tests-procedures/in-vitro-fertilization/basics/risks/prc-20018905).

Given these side effects and the ethical issues, it is no wonder that new reproductive technologies have been the subject of widespread and ongoing debate about the various options and about whether or not they should be privately funded or covered by medicare. What do you think?

By the summer of 1959 a number of reports in Germany, Australia, and Britain had noted serious side effects. These indicated that the drug caused nerve damage, affected balance, and caused tingling in the hands and feet. This should have been a warning about the potency of the drug and its effects on the central nervous system (Winsor, 1973). But the manufacturer continued to market the drug in Germany and licensed another company to produce and market the drug in Canada and the US. The drug was tested briefly in the US and then samples were distributed. It was manufactured, beginning 1 April 1961, under the name KEVADON in Canada. A warning was included in the package about peripheral neuritis. It was distributed in Canada under a number of different names.

By 1 December 1961 two representatives of the German companies reported to Ottawa that a number of babies with congenital deformities had been born in Germany and that the mothers of these babies had taken thalidomide. Rather than contacting the research centres in Germany, England, and Australia directly, the Canadian government relied on the ambiguous and evasive reports presented by the pharmaceutical companies involved. It was not until three months later, on 2 March 1962, that the Food and Drug Directorate of National Health and Welfare decided to withdraw the drug, claiming that, until then, the evidence for its removal was "only statistical" (ibid.). Removing the drug was complicated. Unlike France, Belgium, the US, and Britain, Canada did not require the drug manufacturers to label the drug with its international name—thalidomide—under which its side effects were being publicized (*Kitchener-Waterloo Record*, 27 Sept. 1972). As a result, a number of pharmacists were not aware that their shelves contained the drug in question. By the time it was removed the damage had been done.

Approximately 125 babies were born in Canada with phocomelia (Peritz, 2010). Other external defects included small ears, eye defects, depressed noses, and facial tumours. Internal problems were found in the cardiovascular system and the intestinal tract. There were several cases of missing organs, such as gall bladder or liver. These physical anomalies meant emotional traumas for those born with health and body-function problems, as well as for the mothers, fathers, siblings, other family members, and anyone who was involved with the "thalidomide babies." In some communities the birth of the deformed children made local newspaper headlines, and townspeople "flocked" to the hospital to see for themselves. Some people blamed the mothers for having taken the drug. Whole families were stigmatized. There were approximately 3,000 disabled babies in West Germany and 500 in Great Britain. When Belgium, Sweden, Portugal, and other affected countries are included, the number of babies reached more than 10,000 (Dove, 2011).

Very few cases ever occurred in the US. Dr Frances Kelsey, the medical officer who reviewed safety data for the Food and Drug Administration, was skeptical and critical of the drug. She had, by chance, read a letter to the editor in a medical journal, which presented negative information about the drug (*Kitchener-Waterloo Record*, 17 Aug. 1972). She was dissatisfied with the available information on the safety of the product and did not allow it to be marketed. In particular, she was concerned that the drug could cross the placenta of the mother. In the US, only the few samples of the drug given to doctors were ever used. Apparently, Dr Kelsey resisted extraordinary pressure from the drug company, which made "no less than 50 approaches of submissions to the FDA" (Winsor, 1973). (Kelsey, who was a Canadian doctor, died in August 2015 at the age of 101.)

The drug companies had used a number of tactics to increase the sales of thalidomide. One involved planting an article in the June 1961 issue of the *American Journal of Obstetrics and Gynecology*, allegedly written by Dr Ray Neilson of Cincinnati. The article said that the drug was safe for pregnant women (ibid.). Later, Dr Neilson admitted that the article had been written by the medical research director for the manufacturer and was based on incomplete evidence, i.e., on evidence only that the drug was harmless when taken in the last few months of pregnancy, when, of course, the limbs had already developed. Nevertheless, it was advertised as safe for pregnant women when it was clearly known to be unsafe if ingested in the early months. Canadians were reminded of this tragedy, and of the outcome for the people who suffered physical anomalies and emotional and social scars as a result, when the Canadian Broadcasting Company aired a documentary, *Broken Promises*, on the events and their aftermath. This documentary revealed the culpability of the Canadian government in failing to keep the drug out of Canada. The *Globe and Mail* (15 February 1989) reported on the program as follows: "the most striking impression left by 'Broken Promises' is that a number of pharmaceutical companies, druggists, doctors and prosthesis manufacturers have callously exploited the victims of thalidomide with the crudest and most obvious motive—profit." In addition, the Canadian government was criticized for failing to provide compensation. It has subsequently compensated those who were directly affected by thalidomide. However, financial compensation cannot ever be a completely satisfactory conclusion to such a life-changing mishap.

The *Globe and Mail* reported in February 2010 that many of those affected by thalidomide at birth have numerous health problems and have aged prematurely. Only 96 people of the estimated 125 born with phocomelia are still alive. Some were shunned by their parents throughout their lives. Some now live alone and in poverty. According to the spokesperson for the survivors, "Today, some of Canada's 'thalidomiders,' as they call themselves, live fulfilling lives, with jobs, spouses and children. Most, however, are struggling" (Peritz, 2010).

The Cases of DES and HRT

From the 1940s through the 1960s, many physicians prescribed the synthetic estrogen hormone **diethylstilbestrol** (DES), also called simply stilbestrol, to pregnant women who had histories of miscarriage, diabetes, or toxemia during pregnancy. More than 4 million women worldwide took DES over this period. In the US, approximately 2 million male and 2 million female children of these women were exposed to DES in utero; there are approximately 400,000 children of "DES mothers" in Canada. The girl children have developed a number of health difficulties, including a rare vaginal cancer, adenocarcinoma, and a variety of apparently benign structural changes of the uterus, cervix, and vagina. As many as 97 per cent of the DES daughters have cervical abnormalities. Adenosis, the most common problem, is estimated to occur in 43 to 95 per cent of the women. About one-half of DES daughters have had or may have problems with pregnancy, including primary infertility (difficulty in becoming pregnant), premature births, stillbirths, and ectopic pregnancies (gestation outside the uterus). Ectopic pregnancies, which may be dangerous to the mother as well as the fetus, appear to occur in five times as many DES daughters as in other women. Problems have

been seen in DES sons as well. About 30 per cent have genital tract and semen abnormalities, including cysts and extremely small and undescended testicles. The impact of DES has become evident only over the past three decades or so. There may be links between DES exposure in mothers and testicular and prostate cancers in sons (www.cancer.gov/cancertopics/sons-exposed-to-des). However, all of the long-term effects may not yet be known. Studies are currently being undertaken on the health of the grandchildren of women who used DES (ibid.; 72.14.205.104/search?q=cache:197c0ZJTP68J:reports.eea.europa.eu/environmental_issue_report_2001_22/en/issue-22-part-08.pdf+des+update+long+term+consequences&hl=en&ct=clnk&cd=1&gl=ca).

DES is one of a series of hormone-based drug interventions developed in the last century for women. For more than a decade women had been advised to take hormone replacement therapy (HRT) to prevent the "symptoms" of menopause such as hot flashes and night sweats. Millions of women responded and began to take various admixtures of HRT despite the ongoing questioning of the severity of the side effects by the women's health movement (O'Grady, 2003). Hormone replacement therapies were widely prescribed before research by the National Heart, Lung, and Blood Institute of the National Institutes of Health in the US, with large and significant collaboration of the Women's Health Initiative, was complete. In the middle of the research on the effects and safety of hormone replacement therapy—three years before all the data were collected—the study was abandoned because HRT was found to be associated with an increased risk of breast cancer, stroke, and blood clots (ibid.). After the publication of these results in 2002, the prescription of HRT decreased and, at the same time, the prescription of anti-depressants increased (McIntyre et al., 2005). It appears that anti-depressants are sometimes being prescribed for the same symptom presentation as HRT (ibid.).

REMEMBERING OUR HISTORY

BOX 14.5 The Discovery of the DES Problem in Canada

In 1982, Harriet Simard was a healthy, 21-year-old philosophy student at McGill University in Montreal. Suddenly, after what was supposed to be a routine medical examination, Harriet was diagnosed with a rare cancer: clear cell adenocarcinoma of the cervix and vagina. She had to have a hysterectomy. She was given an 85 per cent chance of survival after five years. Later she discovered that the cancer was linked to DES, a "wonder" drug marketed between 1941 and 1971 to prevent miscarriage. Harriet's mother had tried unsuccessfully to carry a baby to term eight years before becoming pregnant with Harriet. To prevent another miscarriage, the doctors prescribed DES.

At the time DES was prescribed for a variety of "female conditions," including irregular bleeding and spotting and menopause, and as a "morning-after pill" to prevent successful implantation after conception. In fact, it was prescribed as a "morning-after pill" to numerous college and university students who had engaged in unprotected sexual intercourse and did not want to get pregnant.

Approximately one out of every thousand daughters of women prescribed DES will develop cancer. DES daughters also have an increased risk of contracting a precancerous condition called cervical dysplasia, of giving birth prematurely, of miscarriage during the second trimester, of ectopic pregnancy, of genital organ malformations, and perhaps of breast cancer. DES sons have an increased risk of undescended testicles, a condition sometimes related to testicular cancer. They may also have low sperm counts and abnormal sperm formation.

When Harriet Simard learned that she had this rare form of cancer, she began to read up on the subject and to ask questions. She discovered that American medical journals had already published a number of papers on some of the results of DES. Harriet was shocked to discover that the Canadian government was not taking action to inform people of the potential long-term intergenerational effects of DES, even though early screening is known to have beneficial effects on the outcome of the disease. Partly because of the lobbying efforts of women's groups in the US, the American federal government had sponsored screening clinics for DES daughters and sons, as well as a widespread information campaign. Doctors were encouraged to inform the government of patients who had ever been prescribed DES.

None of this had happened in Canada. Yet Harriet and her mother Shirley, working together, found DES-related cancers in Quebec and in Ontario, and discovered that approximately 100,000 people had been exposed to the drug.

In response, the Simards founded DES Action Canada. They set up an office and initially received a $50,000 annual grant from the federal government. Numerous newspaper and magazine stories have publicized their concerns. Many doctors have volunteered to help in screening DES daughters and in contacting patients who had taken the drug. The National Film Board has produced a film on the subject. DES Action Canada hosted an international conference. Nine chapters of the organization have been established across the country.

DES Action Canada is one example of a highly successful grassroots movement. Harriet and Shirley Simard have shown what people can do to increase awareness and effect change. (For further information on the contemporary situation, see: www.desaction.org).

The Withdrawal of Vioxx

Rofecoxib is a non-steroidal anti-inflammatory drug (NSAID) that was approved in 1999 by the Food and Drug Administration in the US and in Canada and many other countries, It was marketed under the name of Vioxx (as well as Ceoxx and Ceeoxx) and sold to over 80 million people around the world suffering from pain. By the time this drug had to be withdrawn from the market because it was linked to an increased risk of heart attacks and stroke, it was one of the most widely used drugs ever to be withdrawn. According to Bombardier et al. (2000), there was a fourfold increase in risk of heart attack over a period of 12 months. Merck, the drug manufacturer, voluntarily withdrew the drug from the worldwide market on 30 September 2004. *The Lancet* published a meta-analysis of all of the studies published on the safety of rofecoxib and concluded that the drug should have been taken off the market seven years earlier, when there was already sufficient information about adverse cardiac events (Juni et al., 2004). This recent high-profile case has raised questions in the minds of many people about the ongoing independence of the drug approval process from the pharmaceutical industry (Eggertson, 2005). It has led to renewed questions about the potential conflict of interest that is a part of the drug approval process in Canada and the US (ibid.; see below).

Other Negative Effects of the Pharmaceutical Industry

Finally, the pharmaceutical industry must also be challenged for being part of a larger set of industries causing ill health in another way (thecanadianencyclopedia.com/index.cfm?PgNm=TCE&Params=A1SEC818119). Harding (1987), for example, suggests that "the pharmaceutical industry is an outgrowth of the interlocking petrochemical industry, which also produces pesticides, herbicides and fertilizers." Toxins from the petrochemical industry have been responsible for environmental health calamities. Sharon Batt (2010) has documented the difficulties we face because of how the drugs we use and those that we throw out unused become a part of

our natural world and pollute it in untold ways. For example, there are already trace amounts of pharmaceuticals to be found in the streams, rivers, lakes, and tap water that Canadians rely on. Remember, as you think about this, that pharmaceutical manufacturing is a relatively new phenomenon and thus the effects of long-term and increasing "dumping" of drugs into the environment are not yet known. Chemicals from food and personal products, such as those for cleaning, hygiene, shampooing, and food additives, and new genetic and biological chemicals have all been found in the ecosystem. Just as the methods for detecting such chemicals are improving, so is the growing inventory of the pollutants being uncovered. Although the short-term and the long-term consequences of this pollution are not known, a few cases for concern are already evident. The deleterious consequences for birds and fish of the excess of estrogen products in the water are beginning to be documented. For example, fish living downstream from sewage treatment plants have been found to be feminized and to have lost interest in spawning. Trace amounts of antibiotics, painkillers, anti-inflammatory drugs, hormones, tranquilizers, chemotherapy drugs, and drugs for cholesterol and epilepsy have been observed. Without knowing much about the specific effects of such pollutants, it is easy to imagine possibilities. Drinking water, too, has been found to carry personal care and pharmaceutical products. Some of these chemicals are persistent and do not dissolve or breakdown. The precautionary principle declares that we should not act until we know the consequences of the action. Clearly, the evidence is in that we are already causing harm to the ecosystem by the use of medical, cosmetic, and cleaning and health products. The public health dangers of these industries are potentially widespread and serious.

Issues in Drug Regulation

Governments can have an important role in the regulation of the drug industry and ultimately in the drug-related health of their citizens. However, most government regulations are inadequate. As a result: (1) half the drugs now on the Canadian market have never passed modern tests regarding safety or effectiveness; (2) even where regulations are in place in the industrialized world, substandard drugs are being marketed and distributed overseas; (3) drug companies seem to have a monopoly on the information available to doctors as well as on the side effects of various drugs. One reason that the safety and effectiveness of drugs in Canada may even be declining is that responsibility for testing new drugs is increasingly being given over to the industry that manufactures and sells drugs for profit (Armstrong and Armstrong, 2003; Silversides, 2010). The balance of power between the Health Products and Foods Branch and the industry has been moving towards the industry as Canadian government policies have generally moved to the ideological right, with an emphasis on relying on market principles and globalization. The budget for the department of the government responsible for ensuring safety has declined and independent government laboratories for testing drugs have been closed (Armstrong and Armstrong, 2003). In practical terms, this means that the pharmaceutical industry "is now providing a substantial fraction of the money needed to run the drug regulatory system" (Lexchin, 2012: 285). Since 1994, pharmaceutical companies have been charged a fee every time they submit a new drug for approval. In return, they have asked for a speedier approval process for new drugs (ibid.). "Greater public scrutiny of the drug approval process is essential" (Silversides, 2010: 138).

A study of drug withdrawals from the Canadian market between 1963 and 2004 because of safety concerns is instructive in regard to the historical safety of the drugs introduced (Lexchin, 2005). Lexchin undertook a systematic study of drugs that had been removed from the market over a period of more than 20 years. He found that it was very difficult to get the information because Health Canada "does not maintain a comprehensive list of drugs that have been removed from Canada because of safety concerns" (ibid., 765). In addition, he notes that even asking the question about withdrawals led to further questions and concerns, such as the fact that drugs tend to be tested for a short period of time on a highly select group of patients, including

"those with clear evidence of disease, who are not taking other products and who do not have other conditions that might interfere with an analysis of the efficacy of the product being tested" (ibid.). By contrast, many patients have multiple conditions and unknown conditions, and many use the drugs over a long period of time. In conclusion, Lexchin, who has been studying issues related to the pharmaceutical industry for many years, states that "the current safety system is inadequate" (ibid., 767).

However stringent the laws, the government cannot guarantee that any drug is safe for all the uses to which it may be put. It is not difficult to imagine a situation in which a drug is prescribed for one use or for one person, and is then used again by the same person on another occasion when the symptoms seem to be similar or is passed on to a friend or a family member who seems to have the same problem. People often regulate their drug use, ignoring the specific directions given by the physician and/or the pharmacist. In addition, people have been known to develop drug allergies very suddenly and unpredictably.

While the government can insist that patients be told about drug interactions, it cannot regulate the actual mixture of drugs taken by any one individual. Some drugs react negatively when taken in conjunction with alcohol. One characteristic of many alcoholics or even people who now and then have a glass or two of wine or a bottle or two of beer is that they may try to keep their drinking habit secret—even from their doctor. Untold problems result from drug–alcohol interactions. In addition, a number of drug-related problems or side effects are only discovered after long-term use. For these and other reasons, the drug regulations established by the government can only be considered as partial protection.

The Canadian government is also in a weak position because of the Canadian branch-plant economy in the pharmaceutical industry. Most drugs are developed and tested elsewhere. The Canadian government frequently relies on tests done abroad by other governmental bodies or by the drug firms' research departments. This raises complex problems of biased information from pharmaceutical companies and political problems of intergovernmental relations. Moreover, as Lexchin documents, in spite of the fact that Canadian drug laws are among the strictest in the world, there are still major gaps that may jeopardize people's health.

Medical Devices and Bioengineering

Medical devices range from contact lenses to CAT scanners, MRI machines, knee and hip replacement parts, and beyond. Companies that produce and sell various medical devices, such as artificial heart valves, artificial limbs, kidney dialysis machines, anaesthesiology equipment, surgical equipment, and heart pacemakers, are all medical device companies and belong among one of the largest growth industries in the world. The regulations controlling the industry are uneven, especially under globalization and in the context of free trade. Health Canada has a continuous list of advisories, warnings, and recalls for all sorts of health-related products that are often used by people before they are found to cause death, disability, or disease (www.hc-sc.gc.ca/dhp-mps/medeff/advisories-avis/prof/2004/index_e.html).

SPOTLIGHT ON ETHICS

BOX 14.6   Patenting Genetic Material: What Are the Ethical Issues?

The patenting of genetic material has been accepted in the US since 1980, when the US Supreme Court decided, in a 5–4 split, that it was legal to patent bacteria that had been modified to break down oil spills. Since the mapping of the human genome this decision has become very controversial. One of the debates concerns the recently "discovered" genes for breast cancer, the BRCA1 and BRCA2. They were discovered by a private laboratory, Myriad Genetics Laboratories, in the early 1990s. Myriad then claimed a patent on future testing of the presence of these genes.

Tests for the presence of the BRCA1 or BRCA2 are sometimes advised for or requested by women with a high risk of breast cancer because of family history. The presence or absence of one of the genes can help women decide what sorts of prophylactic action they might take. Because of the costs to Canada's health-care system of the testing of patented genes, there have been many debates about whether should be covered by medicare or should have to pay out of their own pockets for such a test. Regardless of who was to pay, Myriad declared in 2001 that hospitals in several provinces were violating its patent on the genetic susceptibility to breast cancer because they were testing for the genes but not paying Myriad. Myriad demanded that all tests were to be done in their US labs. This would cost about five times the current costs in Canada.

One province, Ontario, decided to challenge Myriad with respect to its right to control and to profit from diagnostic and medical tests using its patent. What do you think? Should human genes be able to be patented for the profit of the individual or company who discovers the gene? What are the possible consequences of this decision? For further discussion, see the commentary in the 6 August 2002 *Canadian Medical Association Journal* and its references (www.cmaj.ca/cgi/content/full/167/3/259).

In 2013, many years after Myriad Genetics Laboratories "patented" the newly discovered BRCA1 and BRCA2 genes, the Supreme Court in the US struck done its right to patent, claiming that genes were a "product of nature" and could not therefore be patented (McVeigh, 2013) (http://www.theguardian.com/law/2013/jun/13/supreme-court-genes-patent-dna).

Source: Willison and MacLeod (2002).

Among the responsibilities of biomedical engineers are the evaluation and testing of equipment, the investigation and explanation of the causes of accidents, and the supervision of the repair of biomedical equipment. There is, however, a shortage of such personnel in Canada, owing in part to the lack of training programs as well as the lack of adequate government investment in monitoring and surveillance. From what limited information is available, it is clear that the whole issue of medical devices and **bioengineering** needs a great deal of research and more thorough and systematic regulation. At present, the Health Products and Foods Branch of Health Canada does not generally require adequate evidence concerning the potential for harm or benefit, or assurance of the safety of the various devices. The exceptions are for tampons, condoms, contact lenses, and devices implanted in the body for more than 30 days (see the website of the Health Protection Branch of the federal government: www.hc-sc.gc.ca/ahc-asc/branch-dirgen/hpfb-dgpsa/index-eng.php). These are accepted for marketing only after the government has examined the evidence—provided by the manufacturing firm itself—as to the safety of the device.

SUMMARY

1. There is a correlation between people's sociodemographic characteristics and their drug-taking habits.

2. Psychoactive drugs are among the most heavily prescribed and often misprescribed drugs in Canada. Females, the elderly, and the unemployed are high users. Frequently, chronically ill patients are prescribed two or more psychoactive drugs simultaneously. Often, these mood-modifying drugs are given for social and personal reasons and not for medical problems.

3. Large differences exist in rates of prescription from doctor to doctor and even from one geographic area to another. Doctors receive much of their "information" about drugs from pharmaceutical companies. Other factors in the rate at which doctors prescribe drugs include education, type of practice, and method of remuneration.

4. Pharmacists may tend to recommend drugs that will maximize their profit. Pharmacists may often choose between a brand-name (more expensive) and a generic drug for a customer when filling a prescription. Pharmaceutical companies offer incentives to ensure that the pharmacist will choose their brand.

5. Multinationals control the vast majority of the Canadian prescription drug market. Pharmaceutical manufacturing is one of the more profitable manufacturing activities in Canada. Some of the reasons for this are: the absence of a link between manufacturing cost and price, the presence of patent protection, price-fixing, discount pricing, advertising, and drug distribution (dumping) in the less-developed countries.

6. In several Canadian instances, drug company profits have come before health. One is the case of thalidomide, which resulted in the birth of an estimated 125 babies in Canada with phocomelia. DES is another drug that was used by pregnant women with disastrous consequences. It is now known that it has caused cancer and many other many abnormalities in the reproductive systems of the offspring of these mothers.

7. The government has not adequately regulated the use of pharmaceuticals in Canada. After-market surveillance continues to be weak. Drug companies control much of the information available to doctors regarding various drugs, including the side effects.

8. The medical devices industry is a profitable and growing industry. Government regulation and monitoring of this industry needs improvement.

KEY TERMS

bioengineering
diethylstilbestrol (DES)

direct-to-consumer advertising
medical-industrial complex

over-the-counter drugs
thalidomide

QUESTIONS FOR STUDY AND DISCUSSION

1. Explain antibiotic resistance.
2. Discuss the reasons for and the consequences of multiple drug use among seniors in Canada.
3. What factors influence the prescribing patterns of doctors?
4. What are some of the reasons for the high profitability of the pharmaceutical industry?
5. Name and discuss three continuing problems in regard to drug promotion in the developing world.
6. Could a drug with the devastating effects of DES be marketed in Canada today?
7. Explain the challenges to adequate post-market surveillance of pharmaceuticals.

SUGGESTED READINGS

Abraham, J. 2010. "Pharmaceuticalization of Society in Context: Theoretical, Empirical and Health Dimensions." *Sociology* 44, 4: 603–22. An examination of health and pharmaceuticals in the context of an increasing reliance on medication.

Barker, K. 2011. "Pharmaceutical Determinism." *Social Science and Medicine* 73: 833–42. An argument that the existence of a drug aids in legitimating a contested disorder.

Metzl, J.M., and J. Angel. 2004. "Assessing the Impact of SSRI Antidepressants on Popular Notions of Women's Depressive Illness." *Social Science and Medicine* 58: 577–84. An analysis of the gendered portrayal of anti-depressant medications.

Murray, E., B. Lo, L. Pollack, K. Donelan, and K. Lee. 2003. "Direct-to-Consumer Advertising: Physicians' Views of Its Effects on Quality of Care and the Doctor–Patient Relationship." *Journal of the American Board of Family Practice* 16, 6: 513–24. A study of what doctors say about how prescribing is altered by advertising.

Whitaker, Robert. 2010. *Anatomy of an Epidemic: Magic Bullets, Psychiatric Drugs, and the Astonishing Rise of Mental Illness in America*. New York: Crown. A thorough and highly readable critique by an investigative journalist of how psychoactive drugs—a pharmaceutical "bestseller"—have negatively affected individuals and populations.

15 Globalization and Health-Care Systems

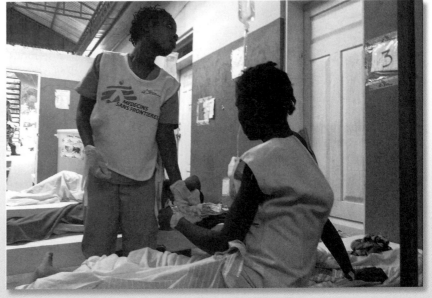

CHAPTER OVERVIEW

▶ Health care and changes in health care around the world must be considered in the context of globalization.

▶ Globalization presents challenges and benefits to health care.

▶ Globalization has meant the spread of conventional allopathic medicine throughout the world. This has been accompanied by both increased equality and inequality.

▶ The changes in health in South Africa since democratization are a case in point.

▶ The first significant policy initiative regarding standardizing worldwide health using the conventional medical model occurred at Alma-Alta, Kazakhstan, and resulted in an accord in 1978 that essentially declared "Health for All by 2000."

▶ Arguably, the most important policy development of the accord was widespread propagation of primary health care (PHC), which involves a modern epidemiological approach to health along with medicalization.

▶ PHC involves such facets as prevention, social determinants of health, maternal and infant care, and direct clinical care offered by a various providers.

▶ The World Health Organization (WHO) monitors, encourages, funds, and supports PHC and other specific initiatives with the help of 194 member nations.

▶ Traditional medicine is still prevalent worldwide although it is threatened in various places.

▶ In the US, health care is largely composed of a wide variety of competing, for-profit, expensive, high-tech services. After the introduction of President Barack Obama's Affordable Care Act the number of uninsured Americans had apparently decreased to 11.4 per cent by 2015 (although this is likely an underestimate).

▶ In the UK, health-care coverage is comprehensive and universal, with a small parallel private sector. Concerns are expressed about waiting times, the lack of coverage for some procedures, and deterioration in some of the state-supported infrastructure such as hospitals.

▶ In Brazil, a universal system, begun with the constitution of 1988, has not yet been fully implemented. There is a thriving parallel private system and large inequities in service provision based on race, income, and region.

Introduction

We discussed disease and death around the world in Chapter 2. We noted that the people in the developing world experience some different diseases than those living in the developed world, and to a considerable extent they do not live long enough to experience the "diseases of civilization." The rates of under-five mortality are very high in the developing world, often from preventable diseases. In this chapter we are going to look briefly at some of the diverse health-care organizations for providing medical care around the world.

Interest in global health has expanded in the past few decades and has been reflected in the powerful and dramatic pictures broadcast around the world about such events as the widely reported famines in Ethiopia, Somalia, and Sudan; the devastating civil wars in Bosnia and Rwanda; natural disasters such as the 2010 earthquake in Haiti and the 2004 tsunami in Asia; and the Ebola epidemic of 2014–15 in sub-Saharan Africa that threatened to become a global pandemic. The nuclear "accident" in Japan is continuing to affect the rest of the world, including Canada. In fact, Canadians' concern for those affected by such crises sometimes has been so strong that the Red Cross had to refuse donations because they had received more money than they could use.

It is hard to think of these global issues without thinking of the celebrities who are attached to the various organizations. Our culture is a celebrity-watching one and such celebritization is spreading around the globe, often supposedly in the interests of health and development or humanitarian aid.

For example, among the many goodwill ambassadors used to raise funds and awareness for the health and well-being of people around the globe for UNICEF are Katy Perry, Lang Lang, Orlando Bloom, Susan Sarandon, Mia Farrow, and Whoopi Goldberg. OXFAM has Meryl Streep, Colin Firth, and "Lady Mary" from the popular television series *Downton Abbey*. Many of you are also familiar with pop musicians such as Bob Geldof and his Band Aid concert of 1984, which was then a revolutionary way to raise money for the famine in Ethiopia. His co-written song "Do They Know It's Christmas?" is one of the best-selling of all time. Band Aid was followed by other concerts to raise funds for international aid such as Live Aid and Live 8, and in the United States, Farm Aid, organized and led by Willie Nelson, John Mellencamp, and Neil Young, which held its first concert to assist family farmers threatened with mortgage foreclosures in 1985 and continues today to hold large outdoor concerts to aid farmers. Bono, of the stadium rock band U2, is perhaps the most widely renowned global music star to dedicate concerts to global humanitarian efforts. This celebritization points to the increasing prominence of global health concerns and to the increased funds raised for various issues under the constraints and possibilities of neo-liberalism. It also may be driven, at times, by neo-liberalism and privatization. Kapoor (2012) argues that this celebritization of international aid is often self-serving, promoting the brand of a particular celebrity, advancing consumerism, and depoliticizing the underlying causes of inequity and injustice throughout the world.

The neo-liberal project that we have already discussed in relation to Canada is a global one. Major institutions have promoted global economic amalgamation since just after World War II. Called the Bretton Woods system, this institutional integration included the International Monetary Fund, the World Bank, and the General Agreement on Tariff and Trade (GATT), which evolved into the more institutionalized World Trade Organization in 1995 (De Vogli, 2011). The interlocking system was primarily intended to provide a regulatory framework for the maintenance of peace and economic stability following the disruptions of the two world wars of the twentieth century. It was designed to provide global stability and to prefer some state intervention in several areas such as exchange rates, capital control, and welfare and employment policies. However, in the early 1970s the Bretton Woods system began to change dramatically when, with the so-called "Nixon Shock" of August 1971, the US went away from the gold standard, whereby American dollars had been guaranteed to be backed by gold held by the US Treasury so that foreign holders of American dollars could convert their holdings to gold at the fixed price of $35 an ounce. This meant stability in the international monetary system with fixed exchange rates. After August 1971, however, national currencies were free-floating and fluctuated, and the focus shifted away from state intervention in the economy in favour of neo-liberalism and market independence or market fundamentalism. This essentially meant that markets were to be independent of state interference except for the role of the state in property rights and ensuring the freedom of capital. These changes in international economic policy occurred shortly before the conservative governments of Margaret Thatcher in the UK and Ronald Reagan in the US came to power. Their policies of privatization, the reduction in state responsibilities, trade expansion, and the deregulation of markets were hallmarks of neo-liberalism. Through these processes markets and transnational companies began to hold sway even over national governments, all the while spreading the view that such policies would develop wealth that would then trickle down from the rich to the poor. Theoretically, then, global economic inequality would diminish along with health inequalities.

Unfortunately, just as trickle-down economics never really worked in national economies or globally, so the expected trends in health and life expectancy have not materialized despite the many pockets of improvements in health and well-being. If we look at the trends in life expectancy across regions of the world over the last 50 years or so we see that there have been health improvements in East and South Asia. However, the effects of these policies have been disastrous in sub-Saharan Africa. The poorest continent in the world has experienced a decrease in life expectancy and increasing poverty along with economic stagnation. Although HIV/AIDS has certainly been a significant factor in the economic and health problems confronted by Africa, that the spread of HIV/AIDS is linked to poverty cannot be overlooked. In many countries in sub-Saharan Africa the under-five mortality rate has also grown, especially in the decade of the 1990s. Not only is there increasing inequality in some areas of the globe but there is also increasing inequality within many countries as a result of neo-liberalism. One dramatic and memorable example of the effects of global neo-liberalism can be found in the fact that the average CEO in the US made about 40 times that of the average worker in 1980 but by 2001 the average CEO made about 350 times that of the average worker (Frydman and Saks, 2005, cited in De Vogli, 2011).

Many interventions made by international organizations, however, are of obvious assistance to the beneficiaries, at least in the short run. One small but important example addresses the seemingly simple fact that about one in 10 girls in Africa has to miss school during menstruation or drop out completely once menses begins because they do not have sanitary pads or tampons available. Instead of hygienic sanitary products women use leaves, paper, old clothes, and rags and are vulnerable to infections and to leakage. This can also challenge their self-confidence about being in public. Although menstrual pads are available in the cities in some places, they are often very expensive.

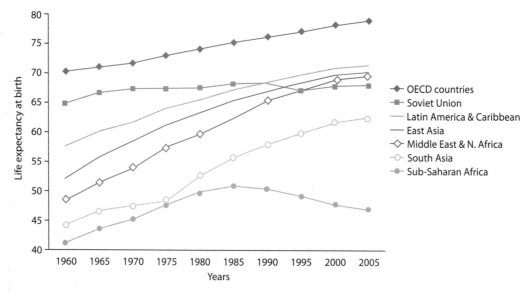

FIGURE 15.1   Regional Trends in Life Expectancy at Birth

Source: Reprinted by permission from Macmillan Publishers Ltd: *Social Theory & Health* Volume 9, Number 4, 'Neoliberal Globalisation and Health in a Time of Economic Crisis' by Roberto De Vogli. Copyright 2011, published by Palgrave Macmillan.

One young Canadian woman who was in Uganda to do volunteer work struggled to find pads to buy for herself and realized that her problem was an ongoing problem for most of the women of the country. She and her partner decided to make pads for sale at an affordable cost. They hired a tailor, rented a small room and two sewing machines, and started Afripads as a pilot project. It has now been running for four years and its value has spread to include hiring local workers, conducting reproductive health classes, and in general offering numerous additional positive results. "Every day we are demonstrating the power of a simple innovation to transform lives. We've reached over 150,000 women and girls so far," says the founder (Fallon, 2013: 162). Global celebrities became involved when the couple won a social entrepreneurship award. The award was supported by names such as Stella McCarthy, Yves Saint Laurent, and Gucci.

Canadians have also watched the changes in South Africa with great hope and enthusiasm. Nelson Mandela became an honorary citizen of Canada in 2001. Under Mandela's presidency, South Africa became a democracy some 20 years ago and moved to try to eradicate inequality in

health. The striking contrasts in health care offered to whites in South Africa as compared to the vast majority of black and coloured people continue today in spite of the goals originally set by Mandela's government. Unfortunately, the hope that accompanied the democratization of South Africa under the leadership of Nelson Mandela and the African National Congress (ANC) has been stalled by political and economic realities at both the global and national levels. In sum, the health inequalities in South Africa are quickly worsening. In 1994, under Mandela, a number of policies were put in place supporting equity across the races and across the geographic areas. Health care became enshrined in the Constitution, and over the next few years the government constructed health-care facilities, provided free maternal and child care, and developed programs to make clean water available, improve nutrition for the poor, and provide welfare. These policies should have improved the social and health situations of the people of South Africa. However, these plans for state intervention in welfare came at a time when the major economic institutions of the world were embracing neo-liberalism and decrying state intervention.

Until the late 1980s apartheid, whereby different racial groups were legally treated differently and unequally, held sway and extreme racial discrimination and segregation were legalized and normalized. Severe racial inequalities in all areas of life resulted. Thus, among blacks the mortality and morbidity rates were excessively high, while white rates tended to mirror those of the West. Indeed, white South Africa was known for its highly successful medical care system around the world (Sanders and Chopra, 2006). Dr Christiaan Barnard pioneered the first heart transplant in 1967 while the world looked on in awe. South African researchers also contributed critical insights into understanding such important public health issues as child malnutrition. They were also known for health system innovation, particularly a model of community-oriented primary care (ibid.). These signs of wealth and scientific expertise belonged to the white population, and their health continued to be well served.

Despite the promise of the end of apartheid and the beginning of democracy hoped for when Mandela became President, the health status of the country has not improved and in the context of the spread of HIV/AIDS is, in many ways, substantially worse. From 1995 to 2002 life expectancy declined by about 16.3 per cent, from 61.4 years to 51.4 years. It is now about 56 years but still has not reached the average of the mid-1990s (http://data.worldbank.org/country/south-africa).

However, these overall life expectancy figures obfuscate the reality that great disparities based on race remain. The infant mortality rate in the black population is four times that among whites. Even in 2001 the life expectancy of black people was 18 years less than that of whites. Furthermore, the average infant mortality rate of 59 per 1,000 observed in 2007 is similar to that in the late 1990s. This, too, supports the argument that the health benefits of the end of apartheid have not been realized (http://www.ncbi.nlm.nih.gov/pmc/articles/PMC3250938/#B10). These rates are also extremely varied across the country: people living in the formerly segregated Transkei Homeland of the Eastern Cape have an infant mortality rate of 99 per 1,000 live births as compared to urban blacks, whose infant mortality rate is about 28 per 1,000

live births. Diseases among the white population are similar to those in Canada and the US, but the diseases experienced by black South Africans reflect the diseases of development discussed in Chapter 2. Violence and traffic accidents are also rampant in the black population. The murder rate in the poorer districts of Capetown, a city that is one of the premier tourist destinations in the world, is among the highest in the world at 100 per 100,000 people.

Post-apartheid South Africa demonstrates many of the difficulties facing the world and the World Health Organization's goal of health for all. Table 15.1 provides a comparative picture from early in the twenty-first century of significant measures of health such as average life expectancy, infant mortality, and height of children under five years old for South Africa and five other so-called developing countries. All of these poor outcomes resulted from ongoing extreme inequalities in South Africa. Despite the formal intentions and the policies designed to equalize opportunity and health outcomes, there have been many barriers. Chief among them is perhaps what is called the "absorptive" capacity. This essentially means that investment in primary, secondary, and tertiary health care depends on the available infrastructure. Thus, the already rich and mostly private health-care sector was poised to receive investment because it already had trained personnel, roads, clinics, hospitals, and the like upon which to build (McIntyre and Gilson, 2000). Regions with the greatest capacity to spend funds, extend their services, and create more infrastructure received more funding than those without such capacity. This has created an "infrastructure inequality trap" characterized by the greatest distribution of funds going to those with the greatest "absorptive capacity." This "trap" perpetuates and even exacerbates the inequalities already in existence (Stuckler et al., 2011).

Globalization, Medicalization, and Health Care

Health-care systems around the world must be seen in the context of the powerful effects of political and economic globalization, which alters and eliminates the boundaries that separate societies and

TABLE 15.1   Selected Health Indicators for South Africa and Five Other Developing Countries

	Cuba	Malaysia	Brazil	Thailand	China	South Africa
2002 GDP per capita, purchasing power parity, US$	5,259	9,120	7,770	7,010	4,580	10,070
2002 public health expenditure, % of GDP	6.2	2.1	3.2	2.1	2	3.6
Children fully immunized against measles at one year of age in 2002, %	98	92	93	94	79	78
Physicians per 100,000 population, 1990–2003	596	68	206	30	164	25
Children younger than five years below average height, 1995–2002, %	5	n.a.	11	16	16	25
Life expectancy at birth in 2000, years	76.7	73	68.1	71	71	47.7
Infant mortality rate per 1,000 live births, 2002	7	8	30	31	31	52

Source: Sanders, David and Mickey Chopra, "Key Challenges to Achieving Health for All in an Inequitable Society: The Case of South Africa." *American Journal of Public Health* January 2006 96(1): p. 74.

people from one another. The consequences of the neo-liberal philosophy that undergirds economic globalization are complex and contradictory, with effects that are both detrimental and beneficial to health and health care for people around the world. Globalization is changing the relative importance of the sovereignty of nation-states and their geographic and governing structures as compared to huge multinational corporations. The imperatives of profit-making supersede the state-level regulations regarding equity, an adequate standard of living, health, and safety for workers. The environmental sustainability of communities and countries is challenged. Globalization is also linked to the spread of various diseases such as SARS and the various strains of influenza, as well as the appearance of Ebola in Europe and North America in 2014 (see Garrett, 1995). Global development has already been associated with climate change and the spread of diseases such as malaria, encephalitis, and dengue fever. This rapid transmission of new infectious diseases represents one of the many potential negative consequences of the global movement of people and capital.

Simultaneously, globalization supports the extension of particular types of mainly Western knowledge and new technologies of health, prevention, medical care, and epidemiology through powerful global organizations such as the **World Health Organization** (WHO), travel and tourism, academic and medical research, and so on. Personal and instant communication via the Internet and social media plays a significant role in the transmission of health-care information and cultures. The processes of global change are homogenizing medical cultures, values, knowledge, technologies, and beliefs; in other words, they have assisted in expanding medicalization and diffusing the Western biomedical model. They have also led to increases in life expectancy and decreases in infant mortality around the globe, as well as, at times, the reverse.

The World Health Organization has assessed the state of health care globally based on extensive research about global health. The WHO's *World Health Report* of 2008 listed the most important failures of biomedical care systems around the world (www.globalissues.org/article/774/health-care-around-the-world):

- **Inverse care** whereby the richest consume the greatest amount of the health care available around the world.
- **Impoverishing care** whereby millions of people around the world are still completely impoverished as the result of trying to pay for medical care resulting from a catastrophic health-care crisis.

- **Fragmented and fragmenting care** whereby the excessive specialization of providers and services threatens the routine care of the whole person and marginalizes some of the sick and suffering.
- **Unsafe care** whereby the provision of health care can be unsafe and unsanitary, leading to medical error and hospital-acquired infections.
- **Misdirected care** whereby the emphasis on secondary and tertiary care obscures the potentially greater benefits of primary care.

There are significant barriers to achieving health for all both in an unequal world and in unequal societies.

A Brief History of the Worldwide Concern for Health

The concerted effort to improve the health of people around the world predates the intensive globalization of the past two plus decades or so. One beginning marker of this effort was the international forum on health held at Alma-Alta (now called Almaty), Kazakhstan, in 1978, which included 134 governments and 67 international organizations. The Alma-Alta Accord, a unanimous resolution calling for "Health for All by 2000" (Seear, 2007), was to be based on the worldwide expansion of primary health care (PHC) as defined by the ethical principles of equity, community participation, intersectoral co-ordination, and the use of appropriate technology. The aims and goals encompassed medical care, essential drug provision, immunization, maternal and child care, disease control, local epidemiological research, and prevention efforts through improved education, sanitation, and nutrition (ibid.). In addition, Alma-Alta reinvigorated the efforts to prevent and treat such prevalent diseases as malaria and tuberculosis through specific disease-related initiatives (ibid.). Although it has been uneven in its operation, PHC has been linked to significant declines in maternal and infant mortality as well as to increases in life expectancy evident today in some parts of the developing world.

Health-Care System Differences around the Globe

The most useful way to understand the globalization of health and medical care is to use data and analysis from the WHO (www.who.int/en). We discussed core, periphery, and semi-periphery countries in Chapter 2. These terms reflect the theoretical perspective of dependency theory (Wermuth, 2003) and are important to bear in mind in the context of this discussion. The World Health Organization distinguishes among countries for comparative and statistical purposes based on related ideas: region and level of income. The regions, representing the 194 WHO member states, are Africa, the Americas, Southeast Asia, Europe, Eastern Mediterranean, and Western Pacific. Countries are also divided into income categories: low income, lower-middle income, upper-middle income, and high income. The six major regions, classified according to what WHO calls its Global Burden of Disease regional system, are roughly equivalent to the world's geographical regions or continents. They are comprised of 14 sub-regions differentiated by income, health outcomes and resources, and epidemiological factors. Thus, for example, countries in North Africa are classified as Eastern Mediterranean, as are some countries in the Horn of Africa, while other Horn of Africa countries are classified in the African region. Likewise, former Soviet republics in Central Asia are classified as part of Europe, and while South Korea falls in the WHO's Western Pacific region, North Korea is considered part of the Southeast Asia region, though clearly, in geographical terms, the Democratic People's Republic of Korea is not situated geographically in what we generally consider to be Southeast Asia.

The WHO has documented the direct link between the spread of Western biomedicine and income level of the countries in a region. Thus, on average, there are 2.8 physicians per 10,000 people in low-income countries, 10.1 per 10,000 in lower-middle-income countries, 22.4 per 10,000 in upper-middle-income countries, and 28.6 per 10,000 in high-income countries. Table 15.2 portrays the availability/density of physicians, nurses/

TABLE 15.2   Global Health Workforce as Ratio of Population, by Region and Income Group

	Physicians*	Nursing and Midwifery Personnel*	Dentistry Personnel*	Pharmaceutical Personnel*	Environment and Public Health Workers*	Community Health Workers*	Hospital Beds*	Radio-therapy Units**
	2000–10	2000–10	2000–10	2000–10	2000–10	2000–10	2000–9	2010
WHO Region								
Africa	2.3	10.9	0.3	0.8	0.4	–	9	0.1
Americas	22.5	61.5	12	6.9	–	–	24	5.2
Southeast Asia	5.4	13.3	0.7	3.8	–	0.9	11	0.3
Europe	33.3	74.7	4.9	5.4	–	–	62	3.9
Eastern Mediterranean	11	15.4	2	4	0.7	1.3	12	0.4
Western Pacific	14.5	20.3	1.4	3.9	–	8.1	47	1.5
Income Group								
Low income	2.8	6.7	0.3	0.5	0.4	2.9	13	0.1
Lower-middle income	10.1	16.8	0.9	3.5	–	4.2	22	0.6
Upper-middle income	22.4	44.5	6.5	3.7	4.7	–	36	1.4
High income	28.6	78.6	9.1	8.9	–	–	59	7.3
Global	14	29.7	3	4.1	–	4	29	1.8

*Per 10,000 population.

**Per 1,000,000 population.

Source: WHO World Health Statistics, 2011, pp. 124–5, at: www.who.int/whosis/whostat/EN_WHS2011_Full.pdf.

midwives, dentists, pharmaceutical personnel, hospital beds, and radiotherapy units across regions and income groups. The findings are consistent: the richer the country, the more entrenched is allopathic or conventional Western medicine. These figures are paralleled by infant mortality rates, for the most part, and male and female life expectancy, i.e., the poorest health outcomes are in the poorest countries. Among them are Swaziland, Angola, Botswana, and most of the rest of the continent of Africa (Figures 15.2, 15.3, and 15.4).

Traditional Medicines in Global Context

The discussion so far has been focused on allopathic or conventional Western biomedicine. However, a parallel type of medicine sometimes called traditional medicine (TM) or folk healing (Helman, 2007) is widespread throughout the world. In the developed world it is known as complementary and alternative medicine (CAM). TM is not really a

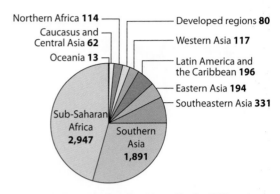

FIGURE 15.2   Under-Five Mortality by Millennium Development Goal Region, 2015 (thousands)

Source: Levels and Trends in Child Mortality, Report 2015, Estimates Developed by the UN Inter-agency Group for Child Mortality Estimation; UNICEF, WHO, The World Bank, United Nations DESA/Population Division. http://childmortality.org/files_v20/download/IGME%20report%202015%20child%20mortality%20final.pdf.

system but refers to a group of disparate methods of healing and health care incorporating herbal medicines, spiritual practices, use of animal parts, manual treatments, acupuncture, and indigenous medicines, among other things (WHO, 2002, 2008;

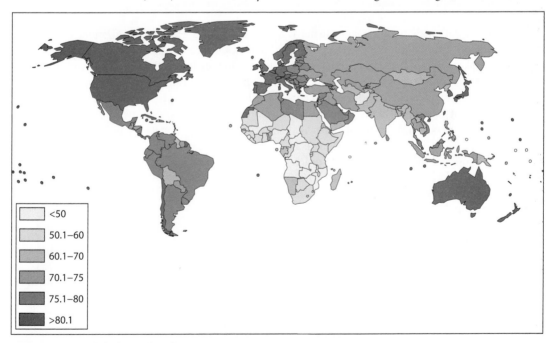

FIGURE 15.3   Global Female Life Expectancy

Source: Based on data from: United Nations Development Programme, Human Development Reports 2009, and The World Bank.

FIGURE 15.4   Global Male Life Expectancy

Source: Based on data from: United Nations Development Programme, Human Development Reports 2009, and The World Bank.

Helman, 2007). Although traditional medicine is widespread, valid information is not yet available about the extent to which it is practised or its effectiveness across cultures or even in many particular situations. However, researchers and governments estimate that about 80 per cent of the population in Africa and India rely on TM, as do about 40 per cent of the population in China (WHO, 2008: 12). In Uganda it is projected that the ratio of TM practitioners to the population is in the range of 1 to 200 or 1 to 400. By comparison, the ratio of allopathic doctors to the population is about 1 to 20,000 or less (ibid.). Some traditional medicines may very well be dangerous, some innocuous, and some others may be beneficial to healing and health. Little is known using modern science about the benefits and costs of various treatments (see, for instance, the following published report by the World Health Organization: http://www.who.int/intellectualproperty/studies/traditional_medicine/en/). Figure 15.5 provides a snapshot of the extent of the use of TM in just a few countries for which data are available.

The World Health Organization, its member countries, and other interested groups are working to develop an international strategy for evaluating and monitoring TM. To this end, a series of objectives has been developed for integrating TM/CAM into allopathic care. These objectives set goals in relation to overseeing the impacts of policy, safety, efficacy,

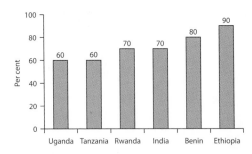

FIGURE 15.5   Use of TM for Primary Health Care, Selected Developing Countries

Source: WHO, Traditional Medicine Strategy 2002–2005, (2002), p. 9. http://www.wpro.who.int/health_technology/book_who_traditional_medicine_strategy_2002_2005.pdf.

Spotlight on Ethics

BOX 15.1   Medical Tourism

"Medical tourism" is a relatively new term that reflects an industry that is growing rapidly as a result of globalization. It involves travelling away from one's home country to seek conventional Western medical treatment. The travel goes both to and from the developed and the developing parts of the world. Among the most popular places for North Americans to seek health care internationally are Mexico, India, Singapore, Thailand, Malaysia, and the Philippines. The rich in poorer countries also travel to the US and Canada and to other developed nations to acquire modern allopathic care when they are ill or just want discretionary medical treatment.

People from the US often travel because they are uninsured or underinsured (the particular medical interventions they seek are not covered by their insurer or they lack money for the co-payment). At times, US insurance companies and even state governments encourage their clients to go abroad for cheaper care. They may offer rewards such as five-star hotel rooms, flat-screen televisions, and holidays to tourist destinations because such care may be relatively inexpensive (Turner, 2007). Health insurance companies in the US and Canada and other Western nations benefit from this, too, as it boosts their profits or lowers their expenses. Patients from the developing world travel to the US because of the prestige and the perceived safety and effectiveness of gaining treatment in world-renowned and branded institutions such as the Mayo Clinic, Johns Hopkins, and the Cleveland Clinic. Canadians travel, at times, because of the wait times they may face for particular discretionary surgeries or other treatments and sometimes because the treatment they want is not available or not covered in Canada. Some provincial governments have institutionalized and thus supported this process with websites clearly indicating the process through which hopeful medical tourists must

go to seamlessly enter the health-care system back in Canada for follow-up care. This becomes especially important in cases where there are problematic side effects of the offshore treatment (medicaltourism.ca/medical-tourism-canada.html). Some Canadian hospitals are also working to attract wealthy patients from around the world. Media accounts document plans to market British Columbia and Ontario medical care much like Canadian education is marketed for foreign students (www.cbc.ca/news/canada/british-columbia/story/2010/03/09/bc-health-tourism-falcon-dix.html; www.cbc.ca/whitecoat/blog/2011/02/07/reverse-medical-tourism/).

Table 15.3, from the website of an organization that arranges medical treatments, travel, and accommodations for US patients seeking less expensive hospital procedures abroad, demonstrates the advertising and the relative costs of popular treatments. As you can see there is a significant difference in the cost of surgical procedures between the US and India and Costa Rica.

For the lower-income countries medical tourism is a source of income. Reliance on medical tourists by poorer countries, however, may be detrimental to citizens seeking care in their own countries. If doctors and hospitals are busy with tourists, they may not have the time and resources to care for their own citizens. As a result, the "best" care, reflecting the Western biomedical model, is often only available to the richest within these developing countries. Nevertheless, this global industry is flourishing and is considered an important source of revenue by governments in developing countries.

One example is the Bumrungrad International Hospital in Bangkok, Thailand. It is one of the top destinations for medical tourism in the world today (Finch, 2014a). The hospital can be compared to an upscale shopping plaza or a five-star hotel. It includes 21 VIP suites. The commercial

continued

TABLE 15.3   Costs of Particular Medical Treatments in the United States, India, and Costa Rica, 2014

Type of Procedure	US Retail Price Range	India: Average Overall Package Price	Costa Rica: Average Overall Package Price
Laparoscopic gastric bypass	$35,000–$45,000	$17,800	$20,700
Laparoscopic sleeve gastrectomy	$30,000–$40,000	$15,500	$18,700
Hip replacement, unilateral	$40,000–$55,000	$17,000	$22,300
Hip replacement, bilateral	$80,000–$100,000	$25,000	$35,500
Knee replacement, unilateral	$35,000–$50,000	$16,000	$20,600
Knee replacement, bilateral	$70,000–$95,000	$23,000	$33,400
Knee arthroscopy*	$9,000–$16,000	$8,900	$9,300
ACL repair	$25,000–$35,000	$11,500	$11,800
Shoulder replacement	$35,000–$45,000	$17,500	$19,400
Shoulder arthroscopy*	$10,000–$18,000	$9,000	$10,400
Rotator cuff repair	$19,000–$28,000	$15,000	$14,400
Hysterectomy	$16,000–$27,000	$14,700	$16,500
Hernia repair*	$10,000–$20,000	$10,200	$12,400
Spinal fusion (1-level)	$90,000–$120,000	$19,500	–
Spinal fusion (2-level)	$120,000–$160,000	$24,500	–
Spinal fusion (3-level)	$150,000–$200,000	$29,500	–
Spinal disc replacement (1-level)	$160,000–$380,000	$20,500	–
Spinal disc replacement (2-level)	–	$25,500	–
CABG (heart bypass)	$120,000–$170,000	$17,500	–
Single heart valve replacement	$150,000–$200,000	$21,000	–
Double heart valve replacement	$170,000–$240,000	$23,000	–

*Package costs shown for these outpatient procedures do not include the companion travel benefit due to the relatively low levels of cost savings.

Note: The combined package pricing for India and Costa Rica includes all customary costs associated with the hospital stay, operating room/ICU/recovery charges, doctors' fees, anesthesiologist fees, pre/post-surgical consultations and diagnostics, medications, nursing care, physical therapy and rehabilitation services, as well as all costs associated with case management, expedited passport processing fees, applicable visas and permits, air travel, travel insurance, local transportation, consultations, communications, and hotel stay and meals for the patient and an accompanying companion.

Source: Adapted from IndUShealth, http://www.indushealth.com/pricing/.

floors host both Starbucks and McDonald's restaurants. Thailand's Ministry of Public Health estimates that Thailand hosts about 2.5 million people for medical tourism. Others say this is an overestimate. Regardless, it is a highly sought-after destination because it is affordable and offers advanced high-quality medical care. Singapore and India are next in line in popularity.

Unfortunately, medical tourism may be initiating and exacerbating health-care disparity among the citizens of the country (Finch, 2014b). It may be adding to the brain drain of doctors to other countries and the shortage of physicians as well as the increased costs for Thai and other citizens of developing countries.

Sources: Herrick (2007); Turner (2007); Finch(2014a, 2014b).

quality, accessibility, and consistent and rational use of TM. They are being monitored and studied.

Research on some types of TM is extremely difficult. TM practices range from the highly secretive, mystical, and subjective procedures that may be linked to the particular abilities, skills, and beliefs of individual practitioners, to more standardized systems. TM often has a spiritual and/or non-visible component. Standardized indigenous traditional methods such as Chinese medicine, which includes acupuncture, moxibustion, and herbs, and Indian Ayurvedic medicine are well-developed and entrenched systems and much easier to assess. They are taught in many medical schools in China and India, respectively (Helman, 2007). The most widely accepted aspect of TM is the **traditional birth attendant** (TBA). TBAs attend the majority of the births worldwide and have played a significant role in the decreases in infant and maternal mortality.

Many traditional medical practices are not standardized but based on local cultural beliefs, actions, and sometimes charismatic healers such as John of God, the internationally popular Brazilian healer. Frequently, such healers are trained through apprenticeship and/or chosen at birth, through inheritance, or revelation. They may incorporate families and communities into a combination of spiritual, relationship, community,

and bodily care. Some traditional healers are working to organize and professionalize to become included in state-sponsored medical care. The law, in most countries of the world, upholds allopathic medicine. Successful parallel systems of TM and Western medicine are practised in some countries. In China, for example, traditional Chinese and Western medical schools, hospitals, and practitioners coexist, showing that co-operation is possible. People tend to prioritize one or the other healing mode depending on their medical problems. However, the medicine with the most cachet in the developing world is usually Western or allopathic medicine. It also tends to be the medicine to which the rich around the world turn when ill. It is the medical model most likely to be supported through international development dollars.

Although traditional medicines and medical practices tend to be less expensive than allopathic medicine and treatment, they can be very costly. It is thought that herbal medicines alone are generating many billions of dollars annually. In Europe, yearly revenues averaged about $5 billion by 2003–4 (www.who.int/mediacentre/factsheets/fs134/en/). In China, sales of products reached $14 billion in 2005, and in Brazil, herbal medicines alone generated $160 million in 2006 (ibid.). The revenues from herbs and botanicals apparently constituted $33 billion around the world in

---

HIGHLIGHTED ISSUES

BOX 15.2   Research on TM Is Growing

There is not very much research on traditional medicine. One study in Peru looked at the health experiences of 339 patients, of whom 170 were being treated with various CAMs and the other 169 with conventional allopathic medicine. This year-long study evaluated CAM in respect to efficacy, user satisfaction, and reduction of future risk. The groups were matched in regard to their health problems, which included, among others, moderate osteoarthritis, back pain, anxiety, light or

intermittent asthma, tension migraine headache, and exogenous obesity. The conclusions were that:

- CAM was less expensive.
- CAM was more effective.
- Patients were more satisfied.
- Patients learned more about the role of health care in their lives.
- There were fewer side effects.

Source: WHO (2002).

SPOTLIGHT ON ETHICS

BOX 15.3   Health as a Human Right

The World Health Organization advocates the idea that health is a human right. Thus, we owe it to one another as members of the species to ensure that at least the following conditions, which would allow for the possibility of health for all, are universally fulfilled. These conditions include:

• safe drinking water and sanitation;
• safe food and adequate nutrition;
• adequate housing;
• safe working and living conditions;

• health-related education and knowledge;
• gender equality;
• timely access to such medical services as are available;
• free health care;
• prevention, treatment, and control of disease;
• essential medicines;
• child and maternal care.

Do you think health care and the other precursors to the possibility of a healthy life should be international human rights?

2010, and the sector is growing rapidly (http://www.nutraceuticalsworld.com/issues/2012-07/view_features/2012-international-herb-botanical-trends/). By 2015, revenues were expected to grow to $93 billion, according to industry analysts. Various traditional medicines, above and beyond herbs and botanicals, are often more accessible, particularly in the developing world where allopathic medicine may be largely unavailable to rural residents and those lacking in income. Western medicine may be culturally unacceptable, at times, because of such widespread beliefs as that illness is the result.

Health Care in the United States

We turn now to look at medical care in three countries—the US, the UK, and Brazil. Many studies of medical care in the US have found that although it is the most expensive medical care system in the world it consistently underperforms in terms of five key indicators of health system performance: quality, access, efficiency, equity, and healthy lives (Davis et al., 2010). Table 15.4 tells this story in data from the highly respected Commonwealth Fund. The US (as earlier in the 2004, 2006, and 2007

studies) ranks poorest overall among seven leading developed nations even though it spends considerably more per person (and, notably, Canada is next to last, although our per capita expenditures are only slightly higher than the other countries surveyed except for the US, where per capita expenses are about double the average of the other six countries).

The US not only underperforms other developed countries, according to WHO data, but also spends the highest proportion of its **gross domestic product (GDP)**—15.3 per cent—on health care. However, it only ranks thirty-seventh out of 191 countries in performance (www.npr.org/templates/story/story.php?storyId=110997469). According to the World Bank data, expenditures per capita for health care in the US have continued to climb, from $8,299 in 2010 to $9,146 in 2013.

How can the discrepancy between cost and value be explained? Whereas elsewhere in the world health is considered a human right, in the US it is treated as a commodity to be traded in the marketplace. One of the first and most notable features of American health care is that no universal, federal system exists, but rather a patchwork of competitive systems and corporations, although with the Affordable Care Act President Barack Obama has

TABLE 15.4 Overall Ranking for Health Care, Selected Developed Countries, 2010

	Australia	Canada	Germany	Netherlands	NZ	UK	US
Overall ranking	3	6	4	1	5	2	7
Quality care	4	7	5	2	1	3	6
Effective care	2	7	6	3	5	1	4
Safe care	6	5	3	1	4	2	7
Co-ordinated care	4	5	7	2	1	3	6
Patient-centred care	2	5	3	6	1	7	4
Access	6.5	5	3	1	4	2	6.5
Cost-related problems	6	3.5	3.5	2	5	1	7
Timeliness of care	6	7	2	1	3	4	5
Efficiency	2	6	5	3	4	1	7
Equity	4	5	3	1	6	2	7
Long, healthy, productive lives	1	2	3	4	5	6	7
Health expenditures per capita, 2007	$3,357	$3,895	$3,588	$3,837*	$2,454	$2,992	$7,290

*Estimate.

Note: Expenditures shown in $US PPP (purchasing power parity).

Source: Adapted from Davis/Schoen/Stremikis, Mirror, Mirror on the Wall: An International Update on the Comparative Performance of American Health Care. Commonwealth (2010).

moved towards a national health system. This Act is far from secure, however, as the opposition to it remains strong among Republicans, and they continue to threaten to dismantle it. Besides "Obamacare," there are a few specialized government and tax-based programs, such as Medicaid and Medicare for the elderly, military families, the disabled, and the very poor, but these are piecemeal. The Children's Health Insurance Program (CHIP) created in 1997 is government supported, but is still unevenly available, and about 15 per cent of children remain uninsured (Weiss and Lonnquist, 2012). Millions of people in the US—about 11.4 per cent of the population—remain uninsured and at risk of being unable to pay for routine medical care, early detection technologies, or treatment for catastrophic illnesses (http://obamacarefacts.com/uninsured-rates/). Many others are underinsured and have insurance for only some medical procedures. In addition, it is essential to remember that many of the people without health-care coverage are those who are not counted in various censuses because they are homeless or insecurely housed, are illegal immigrants, or in a number of other ways are among the invisible, powerless, and poor. Thus, this is likely an underestimate of the percentage of people not covered under the new Act. It is also important to remember that statistics are not necessarily objective and can be influenced by politics.

Historically, health care in the US has been provided by a conglomeration of fee-for-service physicians, mostly private (for-profit) hospitals, and insurance companies. Most Americans who have insurance obtained it as a benefit of their employment. But only certain larger organizations include health insurance for their employees. Other people have to pay individually and privately. Many others lack the means to buy insurance. Currently, approximately 1,300 private insurance companies offer medical care insurance and compete against one another for subscribers to their plans. In this context of competition, insurance companies have turned to **managed care**. Health maintenance organizations (HMOs) are one type of insured managed care, which involves a group of physicians and hospitals who agree to provide services in return for premium payments from enrollees. However, as the majority of managed-care organizations are for-profit companies, they are motivated to provide fewer services and services that are less expensive to maximize profits. This "system," led by the insurance industry and HMOs, results in disparities in health-care services and outcomes across social classes. It takes place among a myriad of diagnostic, early detection, and prevention technologies. The result is substantial inequity between the poorer, underinsured, uninsured, and insured members of society—and the rich.

Another notable feature of medical care in the US is that it supports and develops extensive innovative medical research, leading-edge technologies, experimental drug and other trials, along with expensive and sophisticated medical devices such as CT scanners and magnetic resonance imaging machines (MRIs). These advances are often picked up by health-care systems elsewhere. In a sense, then, the US investment in original research and technologies subsidizes their use in the rest of the world, although there is no doubt that the US also profits from this investment. Many would argue that the US system is overly developed in high-technology and tertiary care procedures and capabilities at the expense of primary care. Comparisons with regard to just two relatively new and very expensive technologies, CAT scanners and MRIs, are illustrative of this point. Canada, according to the latest figures available, had 11.3 CAT scanners per million people, whereas the US had 32.2 scanners per million. The disparity was even greater with respect to MRIs, with 5.5 per million Canadians versus 26.6

per million Americans (www.healthimaginghub. com/news/digital-radiography/3203-ct-and-mri-utilization-varies-according-to-differences-in-access.html).

Despite the great successes in innovation and development, hospital-acquired infections and medical mistakes are a leading cause of illness, disability, and death in the US. According to a 2005 report by the Commonwealth Fund, the US led the other five nations surveyed in respect to medical errors (Figure 15.6). Medical error may very well be the third leading cause of death in the US, according to a 2013 report (http://www.scientificamerican.com/article/how-many-die-from-medical-mistakes-in-us-hospitals/).

US health care is very expensive for a number of reasons. The *first* and most important is the tremendous power and prevalence of the profit-making corporations such as the managed-care organizations, the pharmaceutical and medical device industries, most hospitals, and a variety of other health services. *Second* is the reliance on tertiary care, high-technology solutions, and medical testing rather than on primary care. *Third* is the aging of the population combined with the medicalization of aging (Weiss and Lonnquist, 2012). Most people in the US die in hospital in old age, often after being subjected to heroic and very expensive medical interventions that may extend their lives for only a few days, weeks, or months. *Fourth*, the administrative costs of managing the

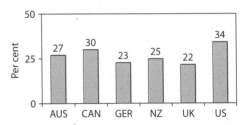

FIGURE 15.6 Percentage of Patients Reporting Any Medical Mistake, Medication Error, or Lab/Diagnostic Test Error in Past Two Years

Source: Commonwealth Fund Press Release, November 2005, at: http://www.commonwealthfund.org/publications/press-releases/2005/nov/international-survey--u-s--leads-in-medical-errors.

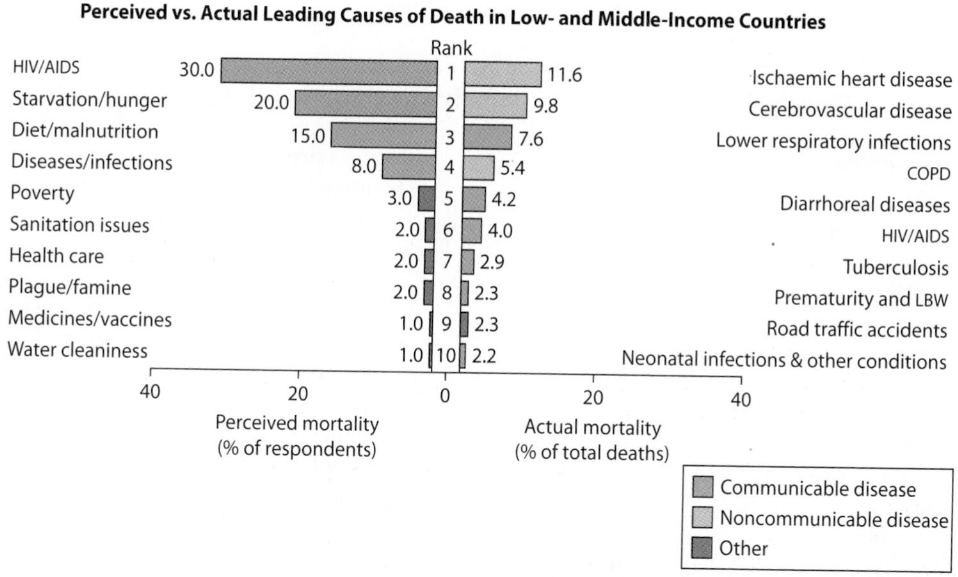

Perceived vs. Actual Leading Causes of Death in Low- and Middle-Income Countries

	Perceived mortality	Rank	Actual mortality	
HIV/AIDS	30.0	1	11.6	Ischaemic heart disease
Starvation/hunger	20.0	2	9.8	Cerebrovascular disease
Diet/malnutrition	15.0	3	7.6	Lower respiratory infections
Diseases/infections	8.0	4	5.4	COPD
Poverty	3.0	5	4.2	Diarrhoeal diseases
Sanitation issues	2.0	6	4.0	HIV/AIDS
Health care	2.0	7	2.9	Tuberculosis
Plague/famine	2.0	8	2.3	Prematurity and LBW
Medicines/vaccines	1.0	9	2.3	Road traffic accidents
Water cleaniness	1.0	10	2.2	Neonatal infections & other conditions

Perceived mortality
(% of respondents)

Actual mortality
(% of total deaths)

Communicable disease
Noncommunicable disease
Other

FIGURE 15.7   Misalignment between Americans' Perceptions and Actual Burden of Disease Worldwide

Source: Siegel, Karen R. Andrea B. Feigl, Sandeep P. Kishore, and David Stuckler. "Misalignment between Perceptions and Actual Burden of Disease: Evidence from the US Population", *Global Health Action* 4 (9 May) (2011).

mélange of insurance and managed care and the numerous other medical institutions are significant—about 20–30 per cent of the total (ibid.). *Fifth* is physician self-referral (ibid.), when physicians prescribe drugs, tests, and other services for which they may have partial ownership; i.e., a conflict of interest exists. *Sixth*, some corporations such as pharmaceutical companies are among the highest profit-making businesses in the US. As an illustration, some top executives of pharmaceutical, medical testing, and medical device companies make millions of dollars in annual salary or compensation (e.g., at Pfizer, $8 million; at Abbott Laboratories, $22 million). *Seventh*, Weiss and Lonnquist note that medical fraud is a substantial problem—medical fraud is estimated to add about $470 billion annually to the US health-care costs. Finally, *eighth*, doctors' salaries in the US are relatively higher than elsewhere and the reliance on specialty medicine pushes doctors' total income even higher.

Most Americans are unhappy with their health care. Costs are rising more quickly than inflation.

Almost half of personal bankruptcies result from the inability to pay medical bills. Increasing costs are unsustainable, particularly in the face of the lack of effectiveness and the recent financial crisis. Although the US has emphasized allopathic or conventional medicine, of late there has been a substantial increase in the use of CAM (Nahin et al., 2009). Such care, as we saw in Chapter 13, tends to be less expensive than Western, allopathic medical care.

Health-care reform and the development of a universal system have been a priority for Democratic Party governments for many years. President Obama managed to shepherd the passage of the Patient Protection and Affordable Care Act (PPACA), dubbed "Obamacare," in 2010, which will allow some reform and extension of insurance across the country. The Act that was passed was a watered-down version of the bill that the Democrats had been proposing, and, as noted above, it may be vulnerable with an election coming in 2016 and the Republicans poised to eradicate the legislation as soon as they possibly can.

CANADA IN A GLOBAL CONTEXT

BOX 15.4   Selected Facts Regarding Globalization and Health Today

The Good News

1. Life expectancy around the world has improved more in the last 40 years than in the previous 4,000 years.
2. Smallpox, once a major cause of mortality, has been (almost) eradicated.
3. Child and maternal mortality has declined significantly around the world and by more than 90 per cent in some places.
4. Widespread use of oral rehydration therapy and improvements in sanitation have contributed to a substantial decline in deaths from diarrhea.
5. Disease surveillance is more widely available and helped prevent the spread of SARS in 2003.
6. The spread of gender rights and equality has improved numerous health outcomes.
7. Information for health promotion and prevention is diffusing.

More to Be Done

1. Tobacco use is spreading and with it the diseases it causes. By 2020 it is expected to be the largest health problem in the world and responsible for 8.5 million deaths annually.
2. HIV/AIDS continues to cause death, disability, and suffering around the world, particularly in sub-Saharan Africa.
3. More than 10 million children die every year from preventable diseases. Most of these deaths occur in low-income countries.
4. Malaria continues to cost lives and health despite the availability of preventative measures and treatment.
5. The gap in income between the high-income and the low-income countries and between people within these countries continues to widen.
6. Environmental destruction of the earth, air, and water, and climate change are spreading rapidly along with development.
7. Obesity, and with it diabetes, is spreading.
8. The overuse of natural resources threatens the viability of the planet.

Sources: Canadian Society for International Health, "Facts and Figures: Global Health," www.csih.org; Adapted from WHO, www.who.int/en.

Health Care in the United Kingdom

The United Kingdom is comprised of England, Scotland, Wales, and Northern Ireland. The total population is approximately 63 million and is 90 per cent urban. Founded in 1948, the health-care system is called the **National Health Service (NHS)**. It is a nationalized, tax-supported, and government-run system that provides universal coverage, although the health system of each part of the country differs in some ways and thus there may be some discrepancies from area to area. Formally, the government covers necessary services for all people ordinarily resident in the UK. General practitioners (GPs) usually have the right to add an individual or family to their roster simply by filling out a form. In this way, refugees and immigrants frequently are included in health-care provision. Emergency service is provided to anyone needing it. All other necessary health-care services, such as tests, physician visits, and hospitalization costs are covered. Certain procedures such as cosmetic surgery or highly expensive or experimental medical interventions may not be covered in the public system. There is a small out-of-pocket co-payment for some services or products. This revenue amounts to about 4 per cent of the NHS budget and includes such things as out-of-hospital drugs, eyeglasses, dentures, and pharmaceuticals. Particular groups of people, such as the elderly, pregnant women, children, and people with certain medical conditions, may be exempt from the user fees. Doctors are paid a base salary plus capitation (per patient on a fixed patient load); they are also paid for additional services rendered, such as vaccinations. Patients have a choice of their primary care provider or GP. Physicians receive a supplement for caring for some categories of people, such as the poor and the elderly. The majority of the budget is paid to primary care physicians. Referral is necessary from GPs to specialists or consultants. Specialists are paid for through hospital budgets. Hospitals bill the government for their costs.

Since 2002, Primary Care Trusts (PCTs) have been ceded decision-making powers in the interests of decentralization. They now manage about 75 per cent of the NHS budget with an eye to improving health care in their respective areas. Regional Strategic Health Authorities oversee the PCTs and develop policy and engage in local planning. There has been a move to allow competition among hospitals and other health-care facilities in order to improve service, decrease wait times, and lower costs.

As in other European countries, there is a parallel private system into which people can choose to pay and from which they can then seek services. Generally, the private system offers shorter waiting time, private hospital room provision, and some superior hospital services such as better food. About 12 per cent of the British population pays for private insurance to improve their guaranteed coverage. Nevertheless, the NHS is one of the world's largest employers, with 1.7 million employees. Only Walmart, India Railways, and the Chinese People's Liberation Army directly employ more individuals (www.nhs.uk/NHSEngland/thenhs/about/Pages/nhsstructure.aspx).

A wide variety of CAM or TM is practised in the UK. Herbalism, reflexology, massage, aromatherapy, and acupuncture are among the most popular services. Homeopathy is unevenly and less often covered by the NHS. However, despite recent research critical of the effectiveness of homeopathy, the attachment of members of the influential royal family to this mode of treatment may still have some influence. A 2010 report of the effectiveness of homeopathy concluded that it performed "No better than placebos" (http://www.publications.parliament.uk/pa/cm200910/cmselect/cmsctech/45/4502.htm). That this finding contrasts that described in Box 13.4 is interesting and difficult to understand without recognizing that homeopathic treatments are individualized

---

HIGHLIGHTED ISSUES

BOX 15.5   Global Clinical Trials Industry

Before new drugs and other medical interventions are introduced into the marketplace they must be tested for such things as safety, efficacy, side effects, acceptability, and other criteria. Most often, the testing begins in the lab and on animals. When sufficient success has been proven on animals, they are tested on humans. People are enrolled in a clinical trial in which they may be randomized either to test the new treatment or to receive the standard treatment. This process goes on around the world and has become an enormous industry. In 2007 alone in the US, clinical trial expenditures reached 40 per cent of the research and development budget of pharmaceutical companies, or about $18 billion.

Due to the size of the pharmaceutical industry and the concomitant need for huge samples of people to test new drugs, clinical trials have become globalized. A large part of the expansion of this industry, because of the less stringent regulations regarding patient safety and the cheaper costs, has been in lower-income countries in Asia, Latin America, and Eastern Europe. This strategy sometimes leads to death, side effects, long-term problems, and permanent residual effects for the people who enrol in clinical trials to earn money.

Source: Petryna (2009).

rather than generalized and thus very difficult to study or to compare with other treatments. Further, the impact of the political economy of research and the role of the pharmaceutical companies in supporting both certain research and certain findings (Whitaker, 2010) cannot be overlooked as we try to understand such dramatic differences in findings. The UK's hybrid system works fairly well. People have a lot of choice as to health-care providers and are allowed to supplement their tax-supported service level. This system ranks very well on the Commonwealth Fund indicators (Table 15.4) for quality, access, efficiency, and equity. It is relatively inexpensive. Some users and commentators are critical of wait times as well as the restrictions with regard to what services are considered necessary. Some citizens and health-care policy writers argue that this system is underfunded and has not maintained its physical infrastructure (e.g., many hospitals are deteriorating). According to the Commonwealth Fund, the NHS does relatively poorly in terms of supporting long, healthy, and productive lives, ranking sixth and just ahead of the US (Table 15.4). Part of this poor showing in life expectancy relates to inequality in the various social determinants of health. On the other hand, the rate of medication error was the lowest of the surveyed countries (Figure 15.6).

Health Care in Brazil

The acronym **BRIC**, coined in 2001, refers to four developing countries: Brazil, Russia, India, and China. Some analysts have believed the BRIC countries are about to capture the balance of economic power thought to have been lost by the OECD countries in the wake of globalization and exacerbated by the financial crisis of 2008 (O'Neill et al., 2005). BRIC populations are huge and growing, as are their domestic economies and international trade. Investors around the world are paying close attention to these economies and many suspect that they are critical to future financial growth and world prosperity. For the purposes of this chapter, we will confine this discussion to Brazil, although many of the lessons

evident there are also true elsewhere in the developing world.

Brazil, the fifth most populous nation in the world, has improved its health services and outcomes through a combination of social, political, and medical reforms. Throughout the world, the most important improvements in the health of populations have arisen as the result of changes in the social and ecological systems. Brazil provides the example, with a significant increase in sanitation and infrastructure. In 1970, only approximately one-third of the population had water piped to their houses; by 2010, slightly more than 93 per cent did. In 1970, about 17 per cent of the households had access to sewage systems to dispose of household waste; in 2010 about 60 per cent of houses were connected to municipal sewerage systems. No households had garbage collection in 1980 but by 2010 almost 90 per cent did (Table 15.5). These improvements must be seen as the bedrock of the changes in health outcomes. In addition, there has been a rapid increase in vaccinations, with no record of vaccinations until after the country's **Sistema Único de Saúde (SUS)**, or Unified Health System, was established in 1988. For example, in 1990 less than 9 per cent of the population had received immunization for hepatitis B, but 98 per cent had by 2010. Similarly, prior to the formation of SUS, only the wealthy few who could afford health care sought it privately, whereas now well over half of population are served by community health workers (60.4 per cent) and family health teams (49.5 per cent), and more than 45 per cent are cared for, as well, by oral (i.e., dental) health teams.

The Brazilian health system is relatively new. Thus, one of the reasons that coverage is not wider is that about 20 per cent of the population live in remote rural areas and it will take time for access to health services to permeate the countryside. Public health and medical coverage is much greater in the cities than in the rural areas, the mountains, and the rain forest. Nevertheless, as Table 15.6 shows, the infant mortality rate has declined dramatically, from 113 per 1,000 in 1975 to 19 per 1,000 in 2007, and life expectancy has climbed from 52.3 to 72.8 years over the past four decades.

TABLE 15.5   Sanitation and Utility Infrastructure, Brazil, 1970–2010

	1970	1980	1990	2000	2010
Households with piped water	32.8%	79.6%	90.7%	91.6%	93.1%
		(1981)		(2001)	(2007)
Households with sewerage	17.5%	39.8%	48.0%	52.8%	59.5%
		(1981)	(1992)		
Households with refuse collection	n.a.	n.a.	64.5%	83.2%	88.4%
Households with electricity	48.6%	67.4%	88.8%	96.0%	98.5%
			(1992)		
Households consuming firewood (10³ thermoelectric power units)	19,070	14,974	7,960	6,325	5,713

n.a. = not available

Source: Reprinted from *The Lancet* 377, Paim, Jairnilson, Claudia Travassos, Celia Almeida, Ligia Bahia, James Macinko, "The Brazilian Health System: History, Advances, and Challenges", 1778–97, Copyright 2011, with permission from Elsevier."

The poverty rate has declined from 67.9 to 30.7 per cent. Education, literacy, and employment have increased dramatically over this period, and significant increases in prevention efforts have been realized. Table 15.6 indicates that improvements in health and life expectancy outcomes are associated with the dramatic changes in the provision of health care from 1970 to 2010.

Brazil's health-care system, the SUS, was initiated with the passage of the constitution in 1988, which proclaims health as the right of all citizens and the duty of the state to protect and maintain. Other health- and equity-related changes in Brazil have been particularly dramatic since the defeat of the military dictatorship. In fact, universal health care for the people had been one of the most important rallying cries of the protest movements organized to topple the dictatorship. Today the SUS is a federally sponsored system enshrined in the constitution but decentralized into the 26 states and 5,563 municipalities and dedicated to, among other things, improving the health of the 190 million Brazilians (www.globalhealthequity.ca/electronic%20library/Brazil%20Abstract%20English.pdf; www.who.int/bulletin/volumes/86/4/08-030408/en/index.html). SUS care is divided into regional groups for administration, and a primary health-care model and services are offered through about 32,000 family health teams and 240,000 community health workers who focus on the poor and, as much as possible, those living in rural and remote areas.

Despite the vast improvements in coverage, the number and spread of public health interventions, and improved health outcomes, problems remain (Paim et al., 2011). One is the disproportionate concentration on the provision of care in urban areas. Another is underfunding of the public sector. Care provision is inequitable so that the poorer and racialized people (Brazil is about half brown- or black-skinned, and this group suffers stigma and discrimination) receive less care and inferior care. A parallel private and for-profit health sector, into which individuals can pay and for which they can also buy insurance as individuals, groups, or through their workplace, thrives. This sector is growing rapidly, and both international and national investments are quickly being made in the large and growing pharmaceutical, medical testing, and medical devices industries. About 26 per cent of the population has private insurance and is able to buy the best care available. The public sector supports the private sector in that it sometimes purchases care from private hospitals and clinics. Secondary and tertiary care is disproportionately provided through the private sector and is more available to the wealthiest. The public sector

TABLE 15.6   Demographic, Social, and Macroeconomic Indicators, Brazil, 1970–2010

	1970	1980	1990	2000	2010
Population	95,993,400	121,611,375	147,593,859	170,143,121	190,732,694
	(1971)				
Urban population	55.9%	67.5%	75.5%	81.2%	83.8%
Infant mortality (per 1,000 live births)	113.9	69.1	45.2	27.4	19
	(1975)				(2007)
Life expectancy (years)	52.3	62.6	66.6	70.4	72.8
					(2008)
Men	n.a.	59.7	63.1	66.71	68.7
Women	n.a.	65.7	70.9	74.35	76.4
Female-headed households (% of families)	13.0%	15.4%	22.7%	27.3%	33.0%
		(1977)	(1993)	(2001)	(2007)
Functional illiteracy*	n.a.	n.a.	36.9%	27.3%	20.3%
			(1992)	(2001)	(2009)
Health spending per capita (purchasing power parity, $US)	n.a.	n.a.	$473	$572	$771.56
			(1995)		(2008)
Proportion of GDP spent on health	n.a.	n.a.	6.7%	7.2%	8.4%
					(2007)
Proportion of health spending in the private sector	n.a.	n.a.	56.9%	60.6%	57.1%
	n.a.	n.a.			(2007)

n.a. = not available

*Individuals aged 15 or older with less than four years of formal education.

Source: Reprinted from *The Lancet* 377, Paim, Jairnilson, Claudia Travassos, Celia Almeida, Ligia Bahia, James Macinko, "The Brazilian Health System: History, Advances, and Challenges", 1778–97, Copyright 2011, with permission from Elsevier."

struggles with long waiting lists and crowded hospitals and clinics. Furthermore, the public infrastructure is deteriorating and the disjointed public/private system is in crisis (ibid.). Traditional medicine plays an important role in Brazil, among both the rich and others. Its origins are both African and Portuguese, and it is the predominant means of health care along the northeast coast, including the Amazon River and rain forest.

Brazil is one of the most popular medical tourism destinations in the world and provides such popular services as cosmetic surgery at competitive prices. Most of the hospitals are in the private sector as is most of the sophisticated technology. For example, only about 24 per cent of the CAT scanners and 13 per cent of the MRIs are available in the public system; the rest are available only privately. In addition, with the rapid growth of the private sector (Couttolenc and Alexandre, 2007), private medical practitioners, specialists, and diagnostic clinics tend to offer more select and speedier service. Brazil's health system stands on the brink of becoming more

TABLE 15.7 Comparative Health Expenditures, Health Workforce, and Demographic Characteristics: US, UK, and Brazil

Indicator	Year(s)	Brazil	United Kingdom	United States
Programs, funding, and financing				
Health expenditure per capita	2008	$875	$3,222	$7,164
Government health expenditure as per cent of total public and private health costs	2008	44.0%	82.6%	47.8%
Private expenditure on health	2008	56.0%	17.4%	52.2%
Out-of-pocket expenditure on health	2008	57.1%	63.7%	24.4%
Health workforce and capacity				
Physicians per 10,000	2000–10	17	27	27
Births attended by skilled health personnel	2000–10	98%	n.a.	99%
Hospital beds per 10,000	2000–9	24	39	31
Demography				
Infant mortality rate per 1,000 live births	2011	21.8	4.6	6.1
Maternal mortality rate per 100,000	2008	58	12	24
Life expectancy, female (years)	2009	77	82	81
Life expectancy, male (years)	2009	70	78	76

Source: WHO, at: www.who.int/medicines/areas/policy/world_medicines_situation/WMS_ch18_wTraditionalMed.pdf.

like that of either the US or the UK. The forces of global development and investment will play a significant role in its future.

Indicators of health-care effectiveness and costs in Brazil compare favourably relative to the UK and the US. As shown in Table 15.7, although infant and maternal mortality rates are still significantly higher than in the more developed countries, the overall life expectancy, particularly for females, has become quite similar at 77 years, as compared to 81 in the US and 82 in the UK. The health expenditures per person in the public sector are decidedly smaller in Brazil, at about $875. Brazilian government spending on health as a percentage of total public and private health expenditures is slightly lower than in the US, at 44 per cent as compared to 47.8 per cent, but substantially lower than in the UK. Proportionally, Brazil has fewer doctors and hospital beds, but the country now offers almost complete coverage by birth attendants.

SUMMARY

1. The process of globalization is advancing rapidly around the world.
2. There are health benefits and costs to globalization.
3. The mortality rates of low-income and high-income countries differ substantially.
4. South Africa provides an excellent example of health disparities within a country.
5. The World Health Organization monitors global mortality and morbidity by maintaining up-to-date statistical profiles of the health and health-care systems of nations and by working to improve health around the globe.
6. Both Western and traditional medicine are used worldwide. Many more studies document

the effects of Western medicine than of traditional medicine.

7. Health care in the US is a patchwork of mostly for-profit medicine that is relatively expensive and frequently unavailable to a significant minority of people.

8. Health care in the UK is a universal and comprehensive system that is relatively inexpensive and effective.

9. Health care in Brazil is in a transitional state; it encompasses a mixture of the universally provided UK system and the American free-enterprise system. The public infrastructure is deteriorating and the disjointed public/private system is in crisis; its future will depend on investment.

KEY TERMS

BRIC
fragmented/fragmenting care
gross domestic product (GDP)
inverse care
impoverishing care

managed care
misdirected care
National Health Service (NHS)
Sistema Único de Saúde (SUS)
traditional birth attendant

unsafe care
World Health Organization
(WHO)

QUESTIONS FOR STUDY AND DISCUSSION

1. Information about health care and health-care outcomes around the world is uneven and sometimes difficult to obtain. Can you explain why reliable and valid information and statistics are not always available?

2. Global development has produced a tension between improvements in living standards and consequent health, on the one hand, and the potential to spread illness and illness-causing behaviours, such as cigarette smoking, on the other. Discuss.

3. The US health-care "non-system" is a patchwork that does not provide free health care to all of its citizens and results in some very poor health outcomes, particularly for those Americans who are at the bottom of the social hierarchy. Discuss.

4. Investigate what simple things could be done to eradicate malaria and tuberculosis, two of the most challenging diseases worldwide.

5. Tobacco smoking has increased in parts of the developing world, such as China, even while it has decreased in the developed world. Explain.

SUGGESTED READINGS

Davies, Sara E. 2010. *Global Politics of Health*. Cambridge: Polity Press. An overview of a political and economic understanding of global health.

De Vogli, R. 2011. "Neoliberal Globalisation and Health in a Time of Economic Crisis." *Social Theory & Health* 9: 311–25. A paper about the growth of inequality under globalization.

Finch, S. 2014. "Medical Tourism Driving Health Care Disparity in Thailand." *Canadian Medical Association Journal* 186, 1: 11. A discussion of some of the negative effects of health-care tourism on Thailand.

Kapoor, Ilan. 2012. *Celebrity Humanitarianism: The Ideology of Global Charity*. Oxford: Routledge. A critical look at the impact of celebrity fundraising for global development.

Appendix

Websites for Sociological Research on Health and Medicine

www.anu.edu.au/polsci/marx/marx.html
This site includes the Communist Manifesto as well as other classic Marxist texts and contemporary examples of Marxist materials.

www.cihi.ca
The Canadian Institute for Health Information site is full of useful information for understanding health and medicine in Canada.

www.statcan.gc.ca/start-debut-eng.htm
The Statistics Canada website includes daily news, census materials, Canadian statistics, and so on.

www.igc.org
The goal of this site of the Institutions of Global Communications is "connecting the people who are changing the world." It provides international communication links for activists around the world.

www.networklobby.org
The Catholic Social Justice Lobby promotes economic and social justice, including welfare reform, anti-poverty efforts, and health-care reform.

www.worldbank.org/publications
The World Bank site includes ordering details for various publications related to international development, such as *World Development Indicators, World Bank Atlas,* and *Global Development Finance*, and complete text for such sources as the *World Bank Annual Report*.

www.who.org
The World Health Organization offers the biggest collection of current news stories about global health issues. The site includes information on diseases, the environment and lifestyle, family and reproductive health, health policies, statistics, and systems.

www.csih.org
The Canadian Society for International Health is the leading Canadian health and development organization.

www.paho.org
The Pan-American Health Organization's bilingual English/Spanish site contains lots of publications and links to useful documents.

www.idrc.ca
The International Development Resource Centre is a Canadian government-based organization dedicated to helping communities in the developing world find solutions to social, political, economic, environmental, and health problems.

www.iwh.on.ca
The Institute for Work and Health is an independent, not-for-profit organization that conducts and disseminates research related to the underlying factors that contribute to workplace health and disability.

www.ccohs.ca
The Canadian Centre for Occupational Health and Safety offers information and research related to the promotion of safe and healthy working environments.

www.eohsi.rutgers.edu
The Environmental and Occupational Health Sciences Institute at Rutgers University sponsors research, education, and service programs related to environmental health, toxicology, occupational

health, exposure assessment, public policy, and health assessment.

www.iglhrc.org
The International Gay and Lesbian Human Rights Commission seeks to protect and advance the human rights of all people and communities who experience discrimination and abuse on the basis of sexual orientation, gender identity, or HIV/AIDS status.

www.wilpf.org
The Women's International League for Peace and Freedom, founded in 1915, works on issues including but not limited to women's rights, disarmament, ending US overseas intervention, and racial justice.

www.cwhn.ca/en
The Canadian Women's Health Network includes databases on women's health and links to other sources of information.

www.priory.com/med.htm
The *International Journal of Medicine* is a widely read online journal of current medical research results and opinions.

www.feminist.com/resources/links/links_health.html
This website focuses on women and health. It includes links to international sites of relevance.

www.cwp-csp.ca
The National Anti-Poverty Organization site includes news, information about research, and activist advocacy.

www.ccsd.ca/facts.html
The Canadian Council on Social Development site includes information about poverty and child poverty in Canada, welfare, and income.

www.hc-sc.gc.ca
Health Canada provides a wide variety of information on topics such as Aboriginal health, alcohol and drug use, HIV/AIDS, diabetes, the Great Lakes environment, family violence, and other related health issues.

www.cmaj.ca
The Canadian Medical Association provides information about many current issues facing the medical profession in Canada, as well as the *Canadian Medical Association Journal*. It includes its own internal search engine.

www.ama-assn.org
The American Medical Association site includes journal articles, links, and many timely, international medicine-related concerns. *JAMA*, one of the most influential medical journals, is available online via this site.

www.cna-nurses.ca
The website of the Canadian Nurses Association offers a wealth of data on numerous topics related to nursing, as well as news and current events, links to other sites, and access to CNA publications.

nccam.nih.gov
The National Centre for Complementary and Alternative Medicine is associated with the National Institutes of Health in the US.

www.drweil.com
The website of one of America's best-known natural health advocates, Dr Andrew Weil, includes an interactive component, updated daily, in which the user can ask Dr Weil questions.

www.ccachiro.org
The Canadian Chiropractic Association site includes health tips and information on chiropractic.

www.chiro.org
This site is organized and maintained by volunteer chiropractors. It includes numerous links regarding a wide variety of chiropractic practice from history to journals to listings of new doctors of chiropractic medicine.

www.naturopathicassoc.ca
The Canadian Naturopathic Association site includes links to related Canadian and international resources.

www.homeopathyhome.com
This UK-based homeopathy site includes a chat room, links, a directory, references to books and articles, and related issues.

www.infobase.phac-aspc.gc.ca
This database has numerous indicators related to chronic disease in Canada. It is useful for creating tables and figures to represent various chronic disease indicators.

www.phac-aspc.gc.ca/index-eng.php
At the website of the Public Health Agency of Canada you can find up-to-date information about chronic disease, public health emergencies, influenza outbreaks, vaccines, and various topics constantly under surveillance by this agency.

www.oecd.org
The website for the Organisation for Economic Co-operation and Development publishes comparative health and social indicators for a number of countries.

www.fnhc.ca
The website of the First Nations Health Council of Canada includes discussions of health concerns and their potential solutions.

www.seniorsinfo.ca
This Ontario government site provides examples of and links to statistics and research related to seniors and their health needs in Canada.

Glossary

absolute homelessness The condition of those who have no home and spend their nights either in homeless shelters or on the streets.

accessibility One of the five principles of medicare: that health care is accessible to all Canadians, regardless of where they live.

acupuncture Such practices as the insertion of fine needles into particular places on the body, moxibustion (burning of leaves on the skin), and other techniques based on Chinese medicine, designed to stimulate the flow of chi (energy) through the body to maximize the ability of the body to heal.

administration One of the five principles of medicare: that it is administered on a not-for-profit basis.

allopathic doctors Doctors practising within the Western paradigm of medicine who use the conventional methods of their training to oppose disease. Typical methods of opposing the disease process include removing it surgically, burning it through radiation, and killing, diminishing, or controlling it through pharmaceuticals.

allopathic medicine Medical practice based on the assumption of a division between the body and the mind, and an approach to the treatment of disease by opposing it through surgery, drugs, and radiation.

anti-racist theory A theoretical approach, that views racialization and racism as a cause of much social inequality.

aspirational health The use of medicine to change one's identity and improve or enhance the self.

attachment process The process whereby more and more of social life becomes medicalized as medicine expands its jurisdiction in four different ways related to technology, living the good life, and the sovereignty of the individual body.

barber-surgeons Early surgeons who were also barbers and limited their cutting to external parts of the body and to limbs.

BBC chain Biography, body, and self-conception: an approach to understanding how people cope with chronic illness affecting the body by modifying or "rewriting" their personal biographies and their conceptions of self.

bioengineering Applying the techniques of engineering to biological processes, in areas ranging from organ transplants, joint replacements, and prosthetics to in-vitro fertilization.

biomedicalization The intensification of medicalization over the past 20–30 years through such technoscientific processes as computer programming, genomization, molecular biology, developments in transplant medicine, and new, expensive diagnostic technology.

birth rate The number of babies born in a given place over a given period of time expressed as a function of the total population.

BRIC Brazil, Russia, India, and China: four countries believed to be on the verge of becoming economic superpowers.

capitation A method of physician payment through which the doctor receives a set fee for managing a particular number of patients annually.

chiropractic Health care concerned primarily with the well-being of the spine, based on the idea that disease results from partial spinal dislocation or subluxation.

climate change Changes in temperature and weather patterns resulting from the emission of greenhouse gases into the atmosphere. Consequences include rising sea levels, alterations in regional precipitation, heat waves, flooding, thawing of the tundra, and other extreme events.

clinical experience A dominant value in the profession of medicine that much of medical practice is an art of joining accumulated knowledge to the interpersonal relationship with the patient, the nature of the disease, and appropriate treatment.

commodification A view of health and the provision of health care as a commodity to which cost–benefit analyses can be applied, as espoused by many health administrators and by those in the for-profit health services sector.

complementary and alternative medicine (CAM) A broad range of health and medical care that falls outside of the practice of conventional or allopathic medicine, including acupuncture, traditional Chinese medicine, homeopathy, and chiropractic; often conceptualized as preventative, holistic, and focusing on health rather than on disease.

comprehensive coverage One of the five principles of medicare: that coverage should be for an extensive range of conditions.

conflict theory A foundational sociological theory based on Marxian belief that the social classes are in fundamental conflict with one another. The social world is understood in terms of opposing/conflictual forces.

core, periphery, and semi-periphery countries A schema that differentiates nation-states on the basis of their stages of economic development and governance stability.

cumulative advantage theory A theory that points to the importance of early life experiences of advantage (generally, of socio-economic advantage).

cumulative effects The accumulation of advantage or disadvantage over a lifetime and how this affects the subsequent probability of health or illness as the person ages.

dependent variables The presumed effect of other, independent variables that must precede the dependent variables in a study of human social behaviour, i.e., the observed results of independent variables. For example, in seeking a cause of diabetes, a diet high (or low) in sugars and starches would be an independent variable, while the rate of diabetes within a population would be the dependent variable.

DES (diethylstilbestrol) Also called stilbestrol, a synthetic estrogen hormone given to pregnant women from the 1940s through the 1960s that led to assorted medical complaints. Its use by pregnant mothers in Canada led to numerous cancers in their sons and daughters as they matured and may have affected the third generation as well.

diarrheal disease A leading cause of infant death in the developing world; caused by polluted water, poor hygiene, and inadequate sanitation.

direct-to-consumer advertising Advertising for various sorts of drugs to the public through the mass media.

discourse Ways of conceiving and talking about issues, such as medicine, so that reality is defined in particular terms by the power of language.

disease A medical diagnosis pertaining to ill health.

disease-mongering The idea that corporations such as pharmaceutical companies sometimes market a new disease after they have developed a new and relevant treatment.

diseases of civilization Diseases that result from lifestyle behaviours and social determinants of health rather than from the lack of clean water, ample food, and the like. They tend to occur later in life.

doctrine of specific etiology The idea that each disease is the result of a particular pathogen or organ malfunction.

downstream model Interventions to cure the illness that occur after disease has started.

drapetomania A "disease" prevalent in the nineteenth century, which was said to cause slaves to run away from their masters.

dysaethesia aethiopis A "disease" discovered among slaves in the nineteenth century, which referred to poor work habits.

environmental illness A painful and sickening sensitivity to the environment; also called "twentieth-century disease."

epidemiology The field of study that focuses on patterns of disease and disease outbreak.

essentialized The assumption made that there is an essential or basic biologically driven gender, race, sexuality, and so on. This notion ignores the powerful effects of the social on these categories.

ethnicity Characteristics of a group of people because of a shared cultural background, including such factors as religion, family patterns, and language.

evidence-based medicine A relatively new development in medical practice that aims to provide clinicians with information based on the best and the latest scientific research for their decision-making.

e-waste All of the waste that results from the rapid obsolescence of electronic equipment such as computers, cell phones, and associated products.

exclusion A process used by an occupational group to deny the legitimacy of its practice by a different occupational group.

fee-for-service A method of paying physicians based on a set fee for a particular diagnosis and intervention.

female circumcision Surgical procedures (performed without anaesthetic by folk practitioners) such as circumcision, where the hood of the clitoris is cut; excision, where the clitoris and all or part of the labia minora are cut out; and infibulation, which includes cutting the clitoris, labia minora, and at least part of the labia majora and suturing the two sides of the vulva, leaving only a minuscule opening.

feminist theory A theoretical approach that views patriarchal structures in society, including in the family, the workplace, and other social institutions, as the cause of a lack of gender equality and, consequently, of numerous social problems.

Flexner Report An evaluation of medical schools across North America in the early part of the last century, which led to radical reforms in medical education and an emphasis on science as the basis for medicine.

food security A situation, either chronic or acute, in which people do not have access to enough safe, nutritious, and culturally acceptable food.

fragmented and fragmenting care Excessively specialized care that mitigates the provision of basic primary care for all.

fundamental cause The first or fundamental cause of illness.

global ecosystem The ecosphere, where environmental policies and actions in one region or country can affect aspects of the environment in other parts of the world.

Grange Inquiry An Ontario commission chaired by Justice Grange that examined the actions surrounding suspicious infant deaths at the Hospital for Sick Children in 1980 and 1981.

greenhouse gases (GHGs) Gases emitted on earth—mostly due to the burning of fossil fuels and the methane resulting from intensive or "factory" farming of animals—that absorb and reflect radiation, trapping heat in the atmosphere to cause global warming.

gross domestic product (GDP) The value of the goods and services produced within a particular country during a specified period of time.

health in all policies (HiAP) The assertion that all social policies have consequences for the health of a population.

health indicators Rates of occurrence of activities or conditions used by governments to assess the levels of health of the population or of subpopulations, including such factors as smoking, obesity, alcohol consumption, clean water supply, diabetes, influenza, and infant mortality rates.

healthism A focus on health as a source of life's meaning.

healthy immigrant effect The tendency of immigrants upon arrival in the receiving country and for some period of time afterwards to be healthier than non-immigrants of the same ages.

herbalism The use of plants for healing and in preventive medicine.

holistic health care Health care that attempts to consider the body/mind and spirit as integrated and, thus, in need of integrated treatment.

home health-care work Work in the home, most often done by women, that involves providing healthy conditions, nursing the sick, teaching about health, and mediating with those in the medical care system on behalf of family members with health problems.

homeopathy A type of health care based on the principle of "similars" or the idea that "like treats like." Rather than opposing disease, as in allopathic medicine, highly diluted traces of botanical, mineral, and other natural substances are used to stimulate the body's self-healing abilities and to build the body's defences to promote health.

hyperkinesis Disability, especially among young boys, "discovered" and diagnosed in the past century and now called attention deficit disorder (ADD), attention deficit hyperactivity disorder (ADHD), or dyslexic syndrome, and characterized by such traits as reversals of letters in words and words in sentences, difficulty ordering objects and activities, mood swings, hyperactivity, intermittent attention span, restlessness, and poor co-ordination (clumsiness).

iatrogenesis Illness or disability that results from a medical intervention.

illness The experience of feeling not well.

illness candidate Someone in remission from a life-threatening condition.

illness iceberg The notion that, just as most of an iceberg is under water and unseen, much of illness, individually or within society as a whole, is undetected or not acknowledged.

impoverishing care The circumstance in which people become impoverished because of their need for and the high cost of medical care.

incidence The rate or number of new cases of disease (either diagnoses or deaths) in a population in a given period of time.

independent variables The presumed causes of a change that must precede the changes observed in a study of human social behaviour.

infant mortality rates Measurements of the number of deaths of infants (usually infants of less than one year) in a given year as a function of the total number in the cohort, usually presented as deaths per 1,000 live births.

intersectionality A theoretical understanding that individuals and groups of people cannot be defined and understood by only one characteristic of their identity, such as gender, "race," or income status, but that various identities are dynamically entwined.

inverse care Where the richest consume the greatest proportion of the medical care.

Kyoto Protocol A 1997 agreement among most countries, using 1990 emissions as a baseline, to cut greenhouse gas emissions in order to control climate change. Although Canada ratified the agreement in 2002, pledging by 2008–12 to lower emissions by 6 per cent from 1990 levels, Canadian emissions soon thereafter exceeded the target by more than 20 per cent, and in late 2011 the Conservative government officially reneged on the Canadian commitment to Kyoto.

latency effects The long-term health impacts on individuals of early developmental characteristics, such as premature birth or being underweight or overweight at birth.

life course approach The perspective on the social determinants of health that focuses on the additive or cumulative effects of inequity or equity on the life chances and health of individuals.

life course transitions Changes in status over a lifetime such as beginning and ending different levels and types of schooling, getting married or divorced, being widowed, and so on.

life expectancy The average age to which people born in a given year in a particular country or region of a country can expect to live.

limitation A process used by a dominant professional group whereby it limits the areas of work allowed to members of another occupational group.

machine metaphor The notion that the body is like a machine in that it has discrete parts operating together in order to function.

managed care Medical care provided through a health maintenance organization (HMO) in the US, whereby a person who enrols with an HMO and pays a premium to that organization has access to the physicians and hospitals who are participants within the plan of the HMO.

managerial ideology A viewpoint that organizes work into bureaucratic order and numerous specialty divisions.

materialist approach An approach to the social determinants of health that focuses on how health is impacted by the extent to which people can access such material things as adequate and nutritious food and good housing.

mediated Experiences of life often mediated or transformed through their presentation in the mass media.

medical errors The harmful results of the actions of doctors that do not fit within the norms worked out in practice and agreed on within the profession.

medical-industrial complex A large and growing network of private and public corporations engaged in the business of providing medical care and medical care products, supplies, and services for a profit, such as the pharmaceutical and medical device industries.

medicalization The tendency for more and more of people's lives to be encompassed by medical definitions of reality, for example, the drawing of birthing and dying into the purview of medical definitions of appropriate behaviour and care.

medical responsibility The sometimes onerous moral weight attached to making decisions that impinge on the life and death of the patient.

microaggressions Casual and seemingly minor slurs, slights, and interpersonal assumptions directed towards racialized people.

midwifery The long tradition of women trained and experienced in childbirth accompanying and assisting women during the birthing process.

mind–body dualism A philosophical assumption fundamental to the development of allopathic medicine that posits the separation of the mind or soul and the body; known as the Cartesian duality, after Descartes.

minority status A numerical under-representation of an identifiably different group within a population.

misdirected care An emphasis on secondary or tertiary care that limits the availability of primary care.

moral entrepreneur Someone who, through his/her position, intentionally or unwittingly imposes a personal moral paradigm on others, as when the work of the doctor involves moral decision-making and the patient can be coerced or unduly influenced into the doctor's way of thinking.

moral mistakes Mistakes, usually interpersonal, that call into question the physician's attitude, reliability, or responsibility to the patient, which is considered moral failure and, therefore, more egregious than a technical mistake.

morbidity Being or feeling sick to the point of being unable to do and accomplish all that one normally would on a daily or weekly basis.

mortality rate The number of people who die in a given year as a function of the total population of a designated region, usually calculated as the number of deaths per 1,000 people.

National Health Service (NHS) The nationalized, tax-supported, and government-run health-care system in the UK that provides universal coverage.

naturopathy The practice of a number of different, alternative methods, including homeopathy, acupuncture, and hydrotherapy, that employ natural methods and substances to support and stimulate the body's inherent healing processes.

neo-liberalism Political ideology that focuses on the primacy of the market and free enterprise in economic development and on social and political values that give priority to individual freedom rather than to group rights.

neo-materialist approach A view of inequality and health that considers the importance of adequate material resources but then acknowledges the importance of the relative distribution of material and social goods within a society as a critical factor in subsequent health outcomes.

non-disease The "non-existent" category in medical practice, because doctors diagnose disease, and their focus usually is not on health per se but on returning the patient to that condition where disease is not present.

occupational stress Work-related stress that can lead to a number of health problems, caused by such factors as unreasonable deadlines, interpersonal conflicts, lack of feedback, unclear job requirements, and lack of influence.

over-the-counter drugs Drugs available for purchase without a prescription from a doctor.

pathologized Conceptualized as problematic and/or needing medical treatment.

pathway effects Early experiences of equity or inequity that set a person on a course towards better or poorer health.

patient-in-waiting Someone living with the statistically or genetically predicted expectation of disease.

pharmacare Publicly funded prescription drug program for all of society or some segment of society.

pharmaceuticalization The increasing emphasis and reliance on drugs within the medical profession, and within society, to address issues of health and illness.

pharmaceuticals and personal care products (PPCPs) Cosmetics and over-the-counter medicines that can have a negative impact on the health of consumers and that are harmful to the environment in their production and/or disposal.

phenomenological Analytical and descriptive, focusing on direct personal experience and consciousness.

physical reductionism The notion that the smallest unit of observation and analysis is a microcosm of the whole.

political economy perspective A perspective on world development that considers the place of nations in respect to their economic and political condition, and that examines how national and international politics and economies feed off one another.

population pyramid A type of graph portraying a population by age and gender, with the younger ages at the bottom and, conventionally, males on the left half and females on the right half.

portability One of the five principles of medicare: that Canadian residents can take their coverage from province to province if they move or travel.

positivism A philosophy of science that holds valid such values as objectivity, observation, replication, experimental design, and numerical analysis. It has often been used in concert with structural-functional theory.

post-structuralism Theoretical stance emphasizing contingency and the shifting meanings and values of words, concepts, and identities, which rejects the validity of binary thinking and analysis, e.g., male or female, well or ill, sane or insane.

post-traumatic stress disorder (PTSD) A psychiatric term referring to anxiety, as well to psychological and physical suffering, that results from the experience of trauma.

practice norms Generally accepted beliefs and practices regarding the diagnosis and treatment of specific diseases and medical problems within a particular identifiable area, whether a hospital, a province or state, or a country.

precautionary principle The need for caution in regard to the introduction and acceptance of new technologies; "first, do no harm."

prevalence The extent to which a disease (diagnoses or deaths) occurs in a population at a particular time interval.

primary health care The essential and basic medical care that people and societies receive or should receive, including necessary drug provision, immunization, maternal and child care, disease control, local epidemiological research, and prevention efforts through improved education, sanitation, and nutrition.

principles of medicare Values that include universality, portability, comprehensive coverage, administration, and accessibility.

privatization A shift from the public sector to the private sector in the provision of health services, often with the assumption that the individual rather than the state must pay for these services.

profession as ideology The status of a profession based on its success in perpetuating a particular set of beliefs and values, such as, in the case of allopathic medicine, unemotional neutrality in dealing with patients, altruism, and placing the needs of others above one's own welfare.

profession as occupation The trait approach to defining occupation as an accumulation of more or less unique traits acquired through training and experience.

profession as process The acquisition by an occupational group of professional status over a period of time through fulfilling certain prerequisites, such as establishing its own criteria and institutions for education, licensing, practice, administration, ethics, and self-censure.

provisionally accommodated Those who live in a car, "couch surfers" who live with friends or family, and those in long-term institutions.

psychoneuroimmunology The theory in modern biological science that focuses on the body's immune response to psychological states.

psychosomatic Illnesses and diseases caused by psychological, mental, or emotional conditions.

"race" A social construction based on external physical characteristics, such as skin colour.

racialization The process whereby social distinctions are constructed by and about groups of people on the basis of skin colour and other perceived differences.

racism A process of evaluating and acting prejudicially and negatively towards people of a different social group and skin colour.

reflexology Natural healing therapy based on the principle that there are "reflex" points on the feet, hands, and ears that correspond to every part of the body. Stimulation of those areas is believed by practitioners and adherents to cause changes in related body tissues at a distance from the reflex points.

regimen and control The idea that the body is to be managed and controlled through eating, exercising, and so on.

remission society The social situation caused by the increase in people who are alive after a serious diagnosis, such as cancer, yet are continually on the lookout for the disease to return.

resilience Ability to respond to challenges, such as loss of a loved one or a serious accident or diagnosis, in ways that are helpful to one's well-being.

risk society Postmodern society characterized by ubiquitous risks, many of which are created in the process of manufacturing our supposed quality of life, ranging from the cars we drive to the medicines we take and various risky but pleasurable behaviours.

rolfing Deep manipulation of the muscles and connective tissue to shift the body into alignment; pressure is applied with the fingers and knuckles, etc.

secondary gains The "additional" benefits of feigning sickness.

secondary health care Health care directed towards disease treatment in hospital and community via various (usually Western-style) medical practitioners.

sense of coherence A belief that the world makes sense and that the individual knows how to achieve desired goals and cope with life's vicissitudes because of the confidence that, in the long run, things will work out well.

sequential model of medicalization The idea that medicalization is a process that increases over time through sequential stages including the definition of a behaviour as deviant, prospecting, claims-making, legitimation, and institutionalization.

sex-mortality differential The difference between male and female mortality rates expressed as a percentage, proportion, or fraction of the population.

shiatsu A type of massage therapy in which the practitioner applies pressure to points on the body using fingers, palms, knees, or cushioned elbows to relax the body to promote its natural ability to heal.

sickness The behaviours engaged in by the person who feels ill, such as staying in bed or going to the doctor.

sick role A concept from structural functionalism that holds that sickness is a social role characterized by two rights and two duties.

Sistema Único de Saúde (SUS) Brazil's national health system, established in 1988.

social capital The power and well-being—economic, relational, emotional, and spiritual—gained by individuals as members of social networks.

social cohesion The relational "glue" of interactions and shared activities that bind, integrate, and foster mutual interdependence of people into social life.

social determinants of health The social conditions of inequity based on such factors as income, gender, age, education, housing, and neighbourhood that lead to differences in health outcomes.

social inclusion Characteristics of communities, such as civic engagement, voter turnout, and the representation of people of diverse backgrounds in positions of power in local governments and community organizations, that allow people of different backgrounds and incomes to feel part of and to participate in the larger community.

Social Readjustment Rating Scale A scale that measures the amount of social change an individual has undergone in a given period of time. The results are said to predict the likelihood of subsequent illness.

social support Practical help, sympathetic understanding, and/or integration into social life offered to an individual.

stigma The "othering" or blaming of a person or group as a result of a particular characteristic, such as mental illness or ethnicity.

stress Adverse physiological and/or psychological manifestations that result from demands in the individual's environment—natural, work, family, interpersonal, financial, etc.—that are greater than one usually experiences or is able to cope with over an extended period of time.

structural functionalism A foundational sociological theory that views the social world as a system of interlocking parts working together to fulfill functions geared to the sustainability of the social order.

subordination A process used by a dominant occupational group to restrict the work of another group under its jurisdiction.

survivor Someone who has not succumbed to a deadly disease or accident and has been given a qualified or tentative "clean bill of health."

symbolic interactionist/interpretive/social constructionist theory An approach to understanding society that focuses on meaning-making and discourses of social life.

technical mistakes Medical mistakes that harm the patient, caused by error in using technology; considered not as important as moral mistakes.

technological imperative The concept that technological development precedes social change.

technologies of self Governing the self in the interests of the prevailing medical power/knowledges.

tertiary care Health care that occurs in a teaching hospital attached to a university, with a side emphasis on health promotion.

thalidomide A medication developed in Germany for the treatment of respiratory infections, colds, coughs, flu, nervousness, and neuralgic and migraine headaches that was given to some pregnant women in Canada in 1961–2 before it was withdrawn because it caused serious birth defects, including phocomelia (absence of limbs).

therapeutic touch A type of treatment based on the idea that that the body is surrounded by energy fields that are affected by disease and that can be manipulated. Treatment, in this perspective, can include the therapist's "smoothing" and otherwise working with the energy fields by moving the hands above the surface of the body.

traditional birth attendant Health-care provider specializing in reproduction issues.

twentieth-century disease Hypersensitivity to toxic chemicals in the environment; also known as "total allergy syndrome" and "environmental illness."

uncertainty Not knowing what the outcome of a diagnosis will be.

universality One of the five principles of medicare: its availability to the whole population.

unsafe care Health care causing illness or death.

upstream model Interventions that occur prior to disease occurrence, intended to prevent illness.

verstehen A term used by German sociologist Max Weber meaning "empathetic understanding," the desired approach to research.

World Health Organization (WHO) A United Nations organization comprised of 193 countries that administers and reports on global and regional health issues and concerns.

Bibliography

Abbott, Maude. 1931. *The History of Medicine in the Province of Quebec*. Montreal: McGill University Press.

Abelson, J. Paddon, and C. Strohmenger. 1983. *Perspectives on Health*. Ottawa: Statistics Canada.

Abraham, John. 1995. *Science, Politics, and the Pharmaceutical Industry*. New York: St Martin's Press.

———. 2010. "Pharmaceuticalization of Society in Context: Theoretical, Empirical and Health Dimensions." *Sociology* 44, 4: 603–22.

Abrams, D., and A. Weil. 2009. *Integrative Oncology*. Oxford: Oxford University Press.

Academic American Encyclopedia. 1980. Princeton, NJ: Arete Publishing.

Access Alliance Multicultural Community Health Centre. 2005. "A Literature Review Exploring Poverty, Housing, Race-based Discrimination and Access to Health Care as Determinants of Health for Racialised Groups." In *Racialised Groups and Health Status*, 1–16. Toronto: AAMCHC.

Achilles, Rona. 1990. *Desperately Seeking Babies: New Technologies of Hope and Despair*. London: Routledge.

Achterberg, Jeanne. 1985. *Imagery in Healing*. Boston: Shambhala.

Ackerman-Ross, F.S., and N. Sochat. 1980. "Close Encounters of the Medical Kind: Attitudes toward Male and Female Physicians." *Social Science and Medicine* 14A: 61–4.

Aday, L.A., ed. 2005. *Reinventing Public Health: Policies and Practices for a Healthy Nation*. San Francisco: Jossey-Bass.

Addison, Brian. 2006. "Directory of Canadian Nursing Associations, 2007." www.canadianrn.com/directory/assoc.htm.

Adelson, Naomi. 2005. "The Embodiment of Inequity: Health Disparities in Aboriginal Canada." *Canadian Journal of Public Health* 96 (suppl. 2): S45–S61. http://journal.cpha.ca/index.php/cjph/article/viewFile/1490/1679.

Adler, Nancy, and Karen Mathews. 1994. "Health Psychology: Why Do Some People Get Sick and Some Stay Well?" *American Review of Psychology* 45: 229–59.

Agius, Raymond. 2007. "Airborne Environmental Pollutants and Asthma." www.agius.com/hew/resource/asthma.htm.

Aiken, L.H., S.P. Clarke, R.B. Cheung, D.M. Sloane, and J.H. Silber. 2003. "Baccalaureate or Higher Nurse Education Related to Fewer Surgical Patient Deaths." *Journal of the American Medical Association* (hereafter *JAMA*) 290, 12: 1617–23.

Alberta Agriculture, Food and Rural Development. 2004. "Consumer Food Trends."

Albin, M., et al. 2002. "Incidence of Asthma in Swedish Hairdressers." *Occupational and Environmental Medicine* 59, 2: 119–23.

Albrekt Larsen, C. 2013. *The Rise and Fall of Social Cohesion: The Construction and De-construction of Social Trust in the US, UK, Sweden and Denmark*. Oxford: Oxford University Press.

Album, D., and S. Westin. 2008. "Do Diseases Have a Prestige Hierarchy? A Survey among Physicians and Medical Students." *Social Science and Medicine* 66, 1: 182–8.

Allentuck, Andrew. 1978. *Who Speaks for the Patient?* Toronto: Burns & MacEachern.

All Nursing Schools. 2007. "Common Q&A—Nursing Careers." www.allnursingschools.com/faqs/careers.php.

Altman, D. 1986. *AIDS in the Mind of America*. New York: Anchor Press/Doubleday.

Al-Yagon, M. 2007. "Socioemotional and Behavioral Adjustment among School-Age Children with Learning Disabilities." *Journal of Special Education* 40, 4: 205–17.

Anderson, A. 1994. "The Health of Aboriginal People in Saskatchewan: Recent Trends and Policy Implications." In Bolaria and Bolaria (1994a: 311–22).

Anderson, G.F., and P. Markovich. 2010. "Multinational Comparisons of Health Systems Data, 2008." Commonwealth Fund, Apr. www.commonwealthfund.org/Content/Publications/Chartbooks/2010/Apr/Multinational-Comparisonsof-Health-Systems-Data-2008.aspx.

Anderson, J. 2003. "Aboriginal Children in Poverty in Urban Communities: Social Exclusion and the Growing Racialization of Poverty in Canada." www.ccsd.ca/pr/2003/aboriginal.htm.

Anstey, Kaarin J., Gary Andrews, and Mary A. Luszcz. 2001. "Psychosocial Factors, Gender and Late-life Mortality." *Aging International* 27, 2: 73–89.

Antonovsky, A. 1967. "Social Class, Life Expectancy and Overall Mortality." *Milbank Memorial Fund Quarterly* 45: 31–73.

———. 1979. *Health, Stress and Coping*. San Francisco: Jossey-Bass.

———. 1993. "The Structure and Properties of the Sense of Coherence Scale." *Social Science and Medicine* 36, 6: 725–33.

April, K.T., and I. Gaboury. 2013. "A Survey of Canadian Regulated Complementary and Alternative Medicine Schools about Research, Evidence-Based Health Care and Interprofessional Training, as well as Continuing Education." *BMC Complementary and Alternative Medicine* 13: 374–81.

Armstrong, Pat, and Hugh Armstrong.1996, 2003. *Wasting Away: The Undermining of Canadian Health Care.* Toronto: Oxford University Press.

———, Jacqueline Choiniere, and Elaine Day. 1993. *Vital Signs: Nursing in Transition.* Toronto: Garamond Press.

Ashford, Nicholas A., and Claudia S. Miller. 1991. *Chemical Exposures.* New York: Van Nostrand Reinhold.

Aslund, C., B. Starrin, and K. Nilsson. 2010. "Social Capital in Relation to Depression, Musculoskeletal Pain, and Psychosomatic Symptoms: A Cross-Sectional Study of a Large Population-based Cohort of Swedish Adolescents." *BMC Public Health* 10: 715.

Association of American Medical Colleges. 1984. *Physicians for the Twenty-first Century: Report of the Panel on the General Professional Education of the Physician and College Preparation for Medicine.* Washington: Anthon.

Association of Canadian Medical Colleges. 1998. *Canadian Medical Education Statistics 1998.* Ottawa: ACMA.

Association for Safe Alternatives in Childbirth. 2001. "Midwifery across Canada." www.asac.ab.ca/updates MidwiferyCanada.html.

Austin, W. 2007. "The McDonaldization of Nursing?" *Health: An Interdisciplinary Journal for the Social Study of Health, Illness and Medicine* 11, 2: 265–72.

Avert.org. 2007. "AIDS and HIV Statistics for Canada by Year and Age." www.avert.org/canstatr.htm.

Ayo, N. 2012. "Understanding Health Promotion in a Neoliberal Climate and the Making of Health Conscious Citizens." *Critical Public Health* 22, 1: 99–105.

Baetz, M., and J. Toews. 2009. "Clinical Implications of Research on Religion, Spirituality, and Mental Health." *Canadian Review of Psychiatry* 54, 5: 292–301.

Bakwin, H. 1945. "Pseudoxia Pediatricia." *New England Journal of Medicine* 232: 691–7.

Balshem, Martha. 1991. "Cancer, Control and Causality: Talking about Cancer in a Working Class Community." *American Ethnologist* 18: 152–72.

Barer, M.L., R.G. Evans, and G.L. Stoddart. 1979. "Controlling Health Care Costs by Direct Charges to Patients: Snare or Delusion?" Occasional Paper No. 10. Toronto: Ontario Economic Council.

——— and G.L. Stoddart. 1999. *Improving Access to Needed Medical Services in Rural and Remote Canadian Communities: Recruitment and Retention Revisited.* Ottawa: Federal, Provincial, and Territorial Committee on Health Human Resources.

Barker, K. 2002. "Self-Help Literature and the Making of an Illness Identity: The Case of Fibromyalgia Syndrome (FMS)." *Social Problems* 49, 3: 279–300.

———. 2005. *The Fibromyalgia Story: Medical Authority and Women's Worlds of Pain.* Philadelphia: Temple University Press.

———. 2011. "Pharmaceutical Determinism." *Social Science and Medicine* 73: 833–42.

Barker-Benfield, G.L. 1976. *The Horrors of the Half-Known Life.* New York: Harper Colophon Books.

Barnes, P.M., E. Powell-Griner, K. McFann, and R.L. Nahin. 2004. "Complementary and Alternative Medicine Use among Adults: United States, 2002." *Seminars in Integrative Medicine* 2, 2: 54–71.

Barrett, S. 2006. "An Analysis of the National Environmental Justice Advisory Council Enforcement Subcommittee's Resolution #21 on Multiple Chemical Sensitivity." www.quackwatch.org/01QuackeryRelatedTopics/nejac.html.

Barrington, E. 1985. *Midwifery Is Catching.* Toronto: NC Press.

Barsh, Russel L. 1994. "Canada's Aboriginal Peoples: Social Integration or Disintegration?" *Canadian Journal of Native Studies* 14, 1: 1–46.

Barton, S.S., H.V. Thommasen, B. Tallio, W. Zhang, and A.C. Michalos. 2005. "Health and Quality of Life of Aboriginal Residential School Survivors." *Social Indications Research* 73, 2: 295–312.

Batt, Sharon. 1994. *Patient No More: The Politics of Breast Cancer.* Charlottetown, PEI: Gynergy Books.

———. 2004. "Pharmaceuticals in Our Water: A New Threat to Public Health?" Facts to Act on from Women and Health Protection. www.whp-apsf.ca/en/documetns/phrmWater.html.

———. 2010. "Full Circle: Drugs, the Environment, and Our Health." In Rochon Ford and Saibil (2010: 185–206).

Battershell, Charles. 1994. "Social Dimensions in the Production and Practice of Canadian Health Care Professionals." In Bolaria and Dickinson (1994: 135–57).

Baum, A., J.P. Garofalo, and A.M. Yali. 1999. "Socioeconomic Status and Chronic Stress: Does Stress Account for SES Effects on Health?" *Annals, New York Academy of Sciences* 896: 131–44.

Beardwood, Barbara, and Vivienne Walters. 1999. "Complaints against Nurses: A Reflection of the New Managerialism and Consumerism in Health Care?" *Social Science and Medicine* 48, 3: 363–74.

Beck, Christina S., Stellina M. Aubuchon, Timothy P. McKenna, Stephanie Ruhl, and Nathaniel Simmons. 2014. "Blurring Personal Health and Public Priorities: An Analysis of Celebrity Health Narratives in the Public Space." *Health Communication* 29: 244–56.

Beck, U. 1992. *Risk Society: Towards a New Modernity.* Trans. M. Ritter. London: Sage.

———. 1994. *Ecological Politics in an Age of Risk.* London: Polity Press.

Becker, Howard S. 1963. *Outsiders: Studies in the Sociology of Deviance.* New York: Free Press.

——— et al. 1961. *Boys in White: Student Culture in Medical School.* Chicago: University of Chicago Press.

——— et al. 1982. "Union Activity in Hospitals: Past, Present, and Future." *Health Care Financing Review* 3: 1–110.

Beckfield, J. 2004. "Does Income Inequality Harm Health? New Cross-National Evidence." *Journal of Health and Social Behavior* 45, 3: 231–48.

Beckman, L.F. 1977. "Social Networks, Host Resistance and Mortality: A Follow-Up Study of Alameda County

Residents." Ph.D. dissertation, University of California, Berkeley.

Been, V. 1994. "Unpopular Neighbours: Are Dumps and Landfills Sited Equitably?" *Resources* 115: 16–19.

Begley, S. 2014. "WHO Urged to Regulate E-cigarettes." *Globe and Mail*, 18 June, L5.

Beiser, M. 2005. "The Health of Immigrants and Refugees in Canada." *Canadian Journal of Public Health* 96: S30–S44.

Belkin, Lisa. 1990. "Seekers of Urban Living Head for Texas Hills." *New York Times*, 2 Dec., A1, A32.

Bell, N., and M. Hayes. 2012. "The Vancouver Area Neighbourhood Deprivation Index Vandix: A Census-Based Tool for Assessing Small-Area Variations in Health Status." *Canadian Journal of Public Health* 103 (suppl. 2): 528–32.

Bell, R.W., and J. Osterman. 1983. "The Compendium of Pharmaceuticals and Specialties: A Critical Analysis." *International Journal of Health Services* 13: 107–18.

Belliveau, Jo-Anne, and Leslie Gaudette. 1995. "Changes in Cancer Incidence." *Canadian Social Trends* (Winter): 2–7.

Benedetti, P., and W. MacPhail. 2002. *Spin Doctors: The Chiropractic Industry under Examination.* Toronto: Dundurn.

Bennett, M.P., and C. Lengacher. 2008. "Humour and Laughter May Influence Health: III. Laughter and Health Outcomes." *Evidence-Based Complementary and Alternative Medicine* 5, 1: 37–40.

Benoit, C., L. Shumka, K. Vallance, H. Hallgrimsdottir, R. Phillips, K. Kobayashi, O. Hankivsky, C. Reid, and E. Brief. 2009. "Explaining the Health Gap Experienced by Girls and Women in Canada: A Social Determinants of Health Perspective." *Sociological Research Online* 14, 5. www.socresonline.org.uk/14/5/9.html.

Benson, J.E. 2014. "Re-evaluating the 'Subjective Weathering Hypothesis': Subjective Aging, Coping Resources, and the Stress Process." *Journal of Health and Social Behavior* 55, 1: 73–90.

Bérard, Guy. 1993. *Hearing Equals Behavior.* New Canaan, Conn.: Keats Publishing.

Berger, Peter L., and Thomas Luckmann. 1966. *The Social Construction of Reality.* Garden City, NY: Doubleday.

Bergob, Michael. 1994. "Drug Use among Senior Canadians." *Canadian Social Trends* (Summer): 25–9.

Berwick, Donald. 2002. "We All Have AIDS: The Case for Reducing the Cost of HIV Drugs to Zero." *British Medical Journal* 324: 214–18.

Beyond Adjustment: Responding to the Health Crisis in Africa. 1993. Toronto: Inter-Church Coalition on Africa.

Bhopal, Raj. 2005. "Hitler on Race and Health in Mein Kampf: A Stimulus to Anti-Racism in the Health Professions." *Diversity in Health and Social Care* 2, 2: 119–26.

Bieliauskas, Linas A. 1982. *Stress and Its Relationship to Health and Illness.* Boulder, Colo.: Westview Press.

Biggs, C. Lesley. 1983. "The Case of the Missing Midwives: A History of Midwifery in Ontario from 1795–1900." *Ontario History* 75: 21–35.

———. 1988. "The Professionalization of Chiropractic in Canada: Its Current Status and Future Prospects." In Bolaria and Dickinson (1988: 328–45).

Billette, J.M., and T. Janz. 2011. "Injuries in Canada: Insights from the Community Health Survey." Statistics Canada. http://www.statcan.gc.ca/pub/82-624x/2011001/article/11506-eng.htm.

Bilson, Geoffrey. 1980. *A Darkened House: Cholera in Nineteenth-Century Canada.* Toronto: University of Toronto Press.

Black Report—DHSS Inequalities in Health: Report of Research Writing Group. 1982. London: Department of Health and Social Security.

Blaxter, Mildred. 1978. "Diagnosis as Category and Process: The Case of Alcoholism." *Social Science and Medicine* 12: 9–77.

Blishen, Bernard R. 1969. *Doctors and Doctrines: The Ideology of Medical Care in Canada.* Toronto: University of Toronto Press.

———. 1991. *Doctors in Canada.* Toronto: University of Toronto Press.

Bliss, Michael. 1982. *The Discovery of Insulin.* Toronto: McClelland & Stewart.

———. 1984. *Banting: A Biography.* Toronto: McClelland & Stewart.

Block, W.D., and D. Muradali. 2013. "Breast Cancer in Men." *Canadian Medical Association Journal* (hereafter *CMAJ*) 185, 14: 1247.

Bloom, Joan, and Larry Kessler. 1994. "Emotional Support Following Cancer: A Test of the Stigma and Social Activity Hypothesis." *Journal of Health and Social Behavior* 35 (June): 118–33.

Bluebond-Langer, Myra. 1978. *The Private Worlds of Dying Children.* Princeton, NJ: Princeton University Press.

Bodecker, G., C.K. Ong, C. Grundy, G. Burford, and K. Shein. 2005. WHO *Global Atlas of Traditional, Complementary and Alternative Medicine*, 2 vols. Kobe, Japan: WHO Centre for Health Development.

Bolaria, B. Singh, and Rosemary Bolaria, eds. 1994a. *Racial Minorities: Medicine and Health.* Halifax: Fernwood.

——— and ———, eds. 1994b. *Women, Medicine and Health.* Halifax: Fernwood.

——— and Harley D. Dickinson, eds. 1988. *Sociology of Health Care in Canada.* Toronto: Harcourt Brace Jovanovich.

——— and ———, eds. 1994. *Health, Illness, and Health Care in Canada,* 2nd edn. Toronto: Harcourt Brace & Company.

——— and ———. 2009. *Health, Illness, and Health Care in Canada,* 4th edn. Toronto: Nelson.

Bombardier, C., et al. 2000. "Comparison of Upper-Gastrointestinal Toxicity of Rofecoxib and Naproxen in Patients with Rheumatoid Arthritis." *New England Journal of Medicine* 21: 1520–8.

Bone, Robert M. 2016. *The Canadian North: Issues and Challenges,* 5th edn. Toronto: Oxford University Press.

Bonnett, A. 2006. "The Americanization of Anti-Racism? Global Power and Hegemony in Ethnic Equity." *Journal of Ethnic and Migration Studies* 32, 7: 1083–1103.

Boon, Heather. 1995. "The Making of a Naturopathic Practitioner: The Education of 'Alternative' Practitioners in Canada." *Health and Canadian Society* 3, 1–2: 15–41.

———. 1996. "Canadian Naturopathic Practitioners: Holistic and Scientific World Views." *Social Science and Medicine* 46, 9: 1213–25.

———, H. MacPherson, S. Fleishman, S. Grimsgaard, M. Koithan, A.J. Norheim, and H. Walach. 2007. "Evaluating Complex Health Care Systems: A Critique of Four Approaches." eCAM 4, 3: 279–85.

———, S. Welsh, M.K. Kelner, and B. Wellman. 2005. "CAM Practitioners and the Health Care System: The Role of the State in Creating the Necessary Vacancies." *Journal of Complementary and Integrative Medicine* 2, 1: 12 (abstract).

Boseley, S. 2008. "Mbeki's AIDS Denial 'Caused 300,000 Deaths.'" *The Guardian*, 26 Nov. http://www.theguardian.com/world/2008/nov/26/aids-south-africa.

Bosk, Charles. 1979. *Forgive and Remember: Managing Medical Failure*. Chicago: University of Chicago Press.

Boston Women's Health Collective. 2011. *Our Bodies, Our Selves*, 25th anniversary edn. New York: Simon & Schuster.

Boulos, D., and M.A. Zamorski. 2013. "Deployment-related Mental Disorders among Canadian Forces Personnel Deployed in Support of the Mission in Afghanistan 2001–2008." *CMAJ* 185, 11: 545–52.

Bourdieu, Pierre. 1984. *Distinction: A Social Critique of the Judgment of Taste*. Cambridge, Mass.: Harvard University Press.

Bourgeault, Ivy Lynn, Jan Angus, and Mary Fynes. 1998. "Gender, Medicine Dominance and the State: Nurse Practitioners and Midwives in Ontario." Paper presented at International Sociological Association meeting.

———and K. Hirschkorn. 2005. "What Really Accounts for Mainstream Provider's Views of CAM: A Comparative Examination of Medical, Nursing and Midwifery Educators and Practitioners in B.C. and Ontario." *Journal of Complementary and Integrative Medicine* 2, 1: 13 (abstract).

Boushel, M. 2000. "What Kind of People Are We? 'Race', Anti-Racism and Social Welfare Research." *British Journal of Social Work* 30: 71–89.

Boushey, H.A., and D. Sheppard. 1988. "Air Pollution." In J.F. Murray and J.A. Nadel, eds, *Textbook of Respiratory Medicine*. Toronto: Saunders.

Braden, Charles Samuel. 1958. *Christian Science Today: Power, Policy, Practice*. Dallas: Southern Methodist University Press.

Bransen, Els. 1992. "Has Menstruation Been Medicalized or Will It Never Happen?" *Sociology of Health and Illness* 14, 1: 98–110.

Branswell, Helen. 2002. "Superbug Genie Is out of the Bottle." *National Post*, 8 July, A4.

Brauer, M., C. Reynolds, and P. Hystad. 2013. "Traffic-related Air Pollution and Health in Canada." *CMAJ* 185, 18: 1557–8.

Breggin, P.R. 2014. "The Rights of Children and Parents in Regard to Children Receiving Psychiatric Diagnoses and Drugs." *Children & Society* 28: 231–41.

Breslin, J.M., S.K. MacRae, J. Bell, P.A. Singer, and the University of Toronto Joint Centre for Bioethics Clinical Ethics Group. 2005. "Top 10 Health Care Challenges Facing the Public: Views of Toronto Bioethicists." *BMC Medical Ethics* 6, 5. http://www.biomedcentral.com/1472-6939/6/5.

Bricker, Jon. 2002. "Four Killings Bring Horrors of War Home." *National Post*, 27 July, A3.

Brook, R.H., C.J. Kanberg, A. Mayer Oakes, et al. 1989. *Appropriateness of Acute Medical Care for the Elderly*. Santa Monica, Calif.: Rand Corporation.

Broom, A. 2005. "Medical Specialists' Accounts of the Impact of the Internet on the Doctor/Patient Relationship." *Health* 9, 3: 319–38.

Broom, Dorothy H., and Roslyn V. Woodward. 1996. "Medicalization Reconsidered: Toward a Collaborative Approach to Care." *Sociology of Health and Illness* 18, 3: 357–78.

Brown, C.G. 2012. *Testing Prayer: Science and Healing*. Cambridge, Mass.: Harvard University Press.

Brown, K.L. 2013. "I Can't Believe I Had a Heart Attack." *Chatelaine* (Oct.): 146–50.

Brown, Phil. 1992. "Popular Epidemiology and Toxic Waste Contamination: Lay and Professional Ways of Knowing." *Journal of Health and Social Behavior* 33 (Sept.): 267–8.

Brown, Richard E. 1979. *Rockefeller Medical Men: Medicine and Capitalism in America*. Berkeley: University of California Press.

Browne, A., J. Fiske, and G. Thomas. 2000. *First Nations Women's Encounters with Mainstream Health Care Services and Systems*. Vancouver: Centre for Excellence for Women's Health.

Browning, C.R., and K.A. Cagney. 2003. "Moving beyond Poverty: Neighborhood Structure, Social Processes, and Health." *Journal of Health and Social Behavior* 44, 1: 552–71.

Brym, R.J., and B.J. Fox. 1989. *From Culture to Power: The Sociology of English Canada*. Toronto: Oxford University Press.

Buckley, Richard E., and Peter H. Harasym. 1999. "Level Symptoms and Causes of Surgical Residents' Stress." *Annals, Royal College of Physicians and Surgeons of Canada* 324 (June): 216–21.

Budnitz, D.S., M.C. Lovegrove, N. Shehab, and C.L. Richards. 2011. "Emergency Hospitalizations for Adverse Drug Reactions in Older Americans." *New England Journal of Medicine* 365: 2002–12.

Bull, Angela. 1985. *Florence Nightingale*. London: Hamish Hamilton.

Bullough, Bonnie, and Vern Bullough. 1972. "A Brief History of Medical Practice." In Judith Lorber and Eliot Freidson, eds, *Medical Men and Their Work: A Sociological Reader*. New York: Aldone Atherton, 86–101.

Bulow, P.H., and L. Hyden. 2003. "Patient School as a Way of Creating Meaning in a Contested Illness: The Case of CFS." *Health: An Interdisciplinary Journal for the Social Study of Health, Illness, and Medicine* 7, 2: 227–49.

Bunker, John. 1970. "Surgical Manpower: A Comparison of Operations and Surgeons in the United States and in England and Wales." *New England Journal of Medicine* 282, 3: 135–44.

———, V.C. Donahue, P. Cole, and M.P. Knotman. 1976. "Public Health Rounds at the Harvard School of Public Health. Elective Hysterectomy: Pro and Con." *New England Journal of Medicine* 295, 5: 264–8.

——— 1985. "When Doctors Disagree." *New York Times Review of Books*, 25 Apr., 7–12.

Burke, Mary Ann, Joan Lindsay, Ian McDowell, and Gerry Hill. 1997. "Dementia among Seniors." *Canadian Social Trends* (Summer): 24–7.

Burke, Mike, and H. Michael Stevenson. 1993. "Fiscal Crises and Restructuring in Medicine: The Politics and Political Science of Health in Canada." *Health and Canadian Society* 1, 1: 51–80.

Burnett, Richard T., Sabit Cakmak, and Jeffrey R. Brook. 1998. "The Effect of the Urban Ambient Air Pollution Mix on Daily Mortality Rates in 11 Canadian Cities." *Canadian Journal of Public Health* 89, 3: 152–5.

Burnfield, A. 1977. "Multiple Sclerosis: A Doctor's Personal Experience." *British Medical Journal* 6058 (12 Feb.): 435–6.

Burstyn, Verna. 1992. "Making Babies." *Canadian Forum* (Mar.): 12–17.

Burtch, Brian E. 1994. "Promoting Midwifery, Prosecuting Midwives: The State and the Midwifery Movement in Canada." In Bolaria and Dickinson (1994: 504–23).

Bury, M.R. 1986. "Social Constructionism and the Development of Medical Sociology." *Sociology of Health and Illness* 2: 137–69.

Business Week. 1979. "A Boycott over Infant Formula," 12 Apr., 137–40.

Buske, Lynda. 1999a. "Our Incredible Shrinking Medical Schools." *CMAJ* 160: 772.

———. 1999b. "MDs Second on Honesty Scale, Lawyers and Politicians Lag." *CMAJ* 160: 1547.

Butler, A., T. Elliot, and N. Stopard. 2003. "Living up to the Standards We Set: A Critical Account of the Development of Anti-Racist Standards." *Social Work Education* 22, 3: 271–82.

Butler, Irene. 1993. "Premature Adoptions and Routinization of Medical Technology: Illustrations from Childbirth Technology." *Journal of Social Issues* 49, 2: 11–34.

Butt, A.R. 2010. "Medical Error in Canada: Issues Relating to Reporting of Medical Error and Methods to Increase Reporting." *McMaster University Medical Journal* 7, 1: 15–18.

Calnan, Michael, and Simon Williams. 1992. "Images of Scientific Medicine." *Sociology of Health and Illness* 14, 2: 233–54.

Campaign 2000. 2009. *2009 Report Card on Child and Family Poverty in Canada*. www.campaign2000.ca/reportCards/national/2009EnglishC2000NationalReportCard.pdf.

Campbell, Marie. 1988. "The Structure of Stress in Nurses' Work." In Bolaria and Dickinson (1988: 393–406).

Canada's Green Plan. 1994. Ottawa: Minister of Supply and Services.

Canada Year Book. Various years. Ottawa: Statistics Canada.

Canadian Advisory Council on the Status of Women (CACSW). 1987. *Recommendations*. Ottawa.

———. 1995. *What Women Prescribe: Report and Recommendations*. National Symposium on Women in Partnership: Working Towards Inclusive, Gender-Sensitive Health Policies. Ottawa, May.

Canadian Association of Food Banks (CAFB). 2006. *Hunger Count 2006*. www.feednovascotia.ca.

Canadian Association of Physicians for the Environment. 2000. "Pesticides." www.cape.ca/toxics/pesticides.html.

Canadian Association of Social Workers. 2005. *Income of Black Women in Canada*. www.casw-acts.ca/advocacy/blackwomen_e.pdf.

Canadian Cancer Research Alliance. 2009. "Investment in Research in Childhood and Adolescent Cancers (2005–2007)." www.ccra-acrc.ca/aboutus_mediareleases_oct09_en.htm.

———. 2010. *Investment in Cancer Risk and Prevention Research, 2005–2007*. www.ccra-acrc.ca/PDF%20Files/Prev_2005-07_EN.pdf.

———. 2015. *Cancer Research Investment in Canada, 2008–2012*. Toronto: CCRA. http://www.ccra-acrc.ca/index.php/publications-en/investment-reports-annual.

Canadian Foundation for Health Care Improvement (CFHI). 2010. "Myth: If a Drug Makes It to Market, It's Safe for Everyone." 1 Oct. http://www.cfhi-fcass.ca/searchresultsnews/2010/10/01/f1ca3fcf-f9aa-4dcb-a64c-a95f2bbadd8d.aspx.

———. 2011. "Myth: The Aging Population Is to Blame for Uncontrollable Health Costs." *Mythbusters* (Feb.).

———. 2013. "Myth: When It Comes to Drugs and Devices, Newer Is Always Better." 13 Mar. http://www.cfhi-fcass.ca/SearchResultsNews/13-03-13/7081e550-fed8-4c8c-84c6-bfd360e48f19.aspx.

Canadian Health Coalition. 2006. *More for Less: A National Pharmacare Strategy*. www.nursesunions.ca/cms/updir/moreforless-6.pdf.

Canadian Health Services Research Foundation (CHSRF). 2001. *Mythbusters* (pamphlet). www.chsrf.ca.

———. 2001. "Myth: The Aging Population Will Overwhelm the Healthcare System." *Mythbusters*. Ottawa: CHSRF.

———. 2004. "Myth: Direct-to-Consumer Advertising Is Educational for Patients." *Mythbusters*. Ottawa: CHSRF.

———. 2004. "Myth: We Can Eliminate Errors in Healthcare by Getting Rid of the 'Bad Apples.'" *Mythbusters*. Ottawa: CHSRF.

———. 2006. "Allow Midwives to Participate as Full Members of the Healthcare Team." *Evidence Boost*. Ottawa: CHSRF.

Canadian Institute for Health Information (CIHI). 2002. "Health Care in Canada." www.cihi.ca.

———. 2004. "Slight Rise in Canada's Physician Supply, More Specialists and Fewer Family Physicians, Reports CIHI." secure.cihi.ca/cihiweb/dispPage.jsp?cw_page=media_09aug2001_e.

———. 2005a. *Geographic Distribution of Physicians in Canada: Beyond How Many Where.* secure.cihi.ca/cihiweb/products/Geographic_Distribution_of_Physicians_FINAL_e.pdf.

———. 2005b. *The Regulation and Supply of Nurse Practitioners in Canada: Technical Appendix.* Ottawa: CIHI.

———. 2006a. *Highlights from the Regulated Nursing Workforce in Canada, 2005.* Ottawa: CIHI.

———. 2006b. *The Regulation and Supply of Nurse Practitioners in Canada: 2006 Update.* secure.cihi.ca/cihiweb/products/The_Nurse_Practitioner_Workforce_in_Canada_2006_Update_final.pdf.

———. 2007a. *Health Care in Canada.* secure.cihi.ca/cihiweb/dispPage.jsp?cw_page=home_e.

———. 2007b. *Quality of Healthcare in Canada: A Chartbook.* Ottawa: CIHI.

———. 2008. *Health Care in Canada 2008.* Ottawa: CIHI.

———. 2009. *Health Care in Canada 2009: A Decade in Review.* Ottawa: CIHI.

———. 2010. *Healthcare in Canada: A Chartbook.* Ottawa: CIHI.

———. 2011. *Health Indicators 2011.* secure.cihi.ca/cihiweb/products/health_indicators_2011_en.pdf.

———. 2013. Health Indicators 2013. https://secure.cihi.ca/free_products/HI2013_EN.pdf.

Canadian Medical Association. 2004. *Code of Ethics.*

Canadian Nurses Association. 2000. "The Bigger Picture." *Nursing Now: Issues and Trends in Canadian Nursing* 8 (May): 2007.

Canadian Pharmacists Association. 2007. "About Pharmacy in Canada." www.pharmacists.ca/content/about_cpha/about_pharmacy_in_can/index.cfm.

Canadian Press. 2009. "Teens Buying More Black Market Cigarettes: Study." 14 Oct.

Canadian Social Trends. Various years and issue numbers. Ottawa: Statistics Canada, Catalogue no. 11–008E.

Cannon, William B. 1932. *The Wisdom of the Body.* New York: W.W. Norton.

CanWest News Service. 2008. "Morning-After Pill Approved for Over-the-Counter Sales." Canada.com/*Ottawa Citizen,* 16 May. www.canada.com/ottawacitizen/news/story.html?id=eb9a322c-0b86-414c-8a28-a21d22c8c6a3.

Caplan, Ronald Lee. 1984. "Chiropractic." In *Alternative Medicines: Popular and Policy Perspectives,* 80–113. New York: Tavistock.

Carlson, Rick. 1975. *The End of Medicine.* Toronto: Wiley.

Carpiano, R.M. 2006. "Toward a Neighborhood Resource-based Theory of Social Capital for Health: Can Bourdieu and Sociology Help?" *Social Science and Medicine* 62: 165–75.

Carrim, N. 2000. "Critical Anti-Racism and Problems in Self-Articulated Forms of Identities." *Race, Ethnicity and Education* 3, 1: 25–44.

Cascade, E., A.H. Kalali, J.A. Kwentus, and M. Bharmal. 2009. "Trends in CNS Prescribing Following the Economic Slowdown." *Psychiatry* 6, 1: 15–77.

Cassidy, A., and B. McIntosh. 2014. "The Return of Autonomy in Nursing: The Way Forward." *British Journal of Nursing* 23, 11: 562–3.

Cassileth, Barrie R. 1986. "Unorthodox Cancer Medicine." *Cancer Investigation* 4: 591–8.

———, E.J. Lusk, D. Guerry, A.D. Blake, W. P. Walsh, L. Kascius, and D.J. Schultz. 1991. "Survival and Quality of Life among Patients Receiving Unproven as Compared with Conventional Cancer Therapy." *New England Journal of Medicine* 324, 17: 1180–5.

———, ———, T.B. Strouse, and B.J. Bodenheimer. 1984. "Contemporary Unorthodox Treatments in Cancer Medicine: A Study of Patients, Treatments, and Practitioners." *Annals of International Medicine* 101: 105–12.

Castiglioni, Arturo. 1941. *A History of Medicine.* New York: Knopf.

Cavaliere, Courtney. 2006. "WHO Atlas Provides Global Perspective on Traditional and CAM Trends." *Herbal Gram: Journal of the American Botanical Council* no. 70: 26–7. content.herbalgram.org/iherb/herbalgram/articleview.asp?a=2960.

CBC News. 2006. "CBC News: Year in Review." www.cbc.ca/news/background/yearinreview2006/2006.

———. 2006. "Health Care." www.cbc.ca/news/background/healthcare/.

Ceci, C. 2004. "Nursing, Knowledge and Power: A Case Analysis." *Social Science and Medicine* 59: 1879–89.

Centers for Disease Control and Prevention, Department of Health and Human Services. 2004. "The Impact of Malaria, a Leading Cause of Death Worldwide." www.cdc.gov/malaria/impact/index.htm.

Centres of Excellence for Women's Health. 2006. *Research Bulletin* 5, 2.

Chan, Angelina O.M., and C.Y. Huak. 2004. "Psychological Impact of the 2003 Severe Acute Respiratory Syndrome Outbreak on Health Care Workers in a Medium Size Regional General Hospital in Singapore." *Occupational Medicine* 54: 190–6.

Chang, V.W., and D.S. Lauderdale. 2009. "Fundamental Cause Theory, Technological Innovation, and Health Disparities: The Case of Cholesterol in the Era of Statins." *Journal of Health and Social Behavior* 50, 3: 245–60.

Charles, Catherine A. 1976. "The Medical Profession and Health Insurance: An Ottawa Case Study." *Social Science and Medicine* 10: 33–8.

Charmaz, Kathy. 1987. "Struggling for a Self: Identity Levels of the Chronically Ill." *Research in the Sociology of Health Care* 6: 283–321.

Charney, W. "Do No Harm? The Epidemic of Fatal medial Errors in the US and Canada." *Canadian Dimension*. 63,3. http://canadiandimension.com/articles/4671/.

Chen, Benjamin T.B. 2002. "From Perceived Surplus to Perceived Shortage: What Happened to Canada's Physician Work Force in the 1990's?" Canadian Institute for Health Information.

Cheng, S., and A. Chan. 2006. "Social Support and Self-rated Health Revisited: Is There a Gender Difference in Later Life?" *Social Science and Medicine* 63: 117–22.

Chenier, H. 2013. "Older Canadians at Risk of Undernourishment." *CMAJ* 185, 10: 473.

Cherrington, J., and M. Breheny. 2005. "Politicizing Dominant Discursive Constructions about Teenage Pregnancy: Re-locating the Subject as Social." *Health: An Interdisciplinary Journal for the Social Study of Health, Illness, and Medicine* 9, 1: 89–111.

Chirayath, H.T. 2006. "Who Serves the Underserved? Predictors of Physician Care to Medically Indigent Patients." *Health: An Interdisciplinary Journal for the Social Study of Health, Illness, and Medicine* 10, 3: 259–82.

Chivian, Eric, Michael McCally, Howard Hu, and Andrew Haines. 1993. *Critical Condition: Human Health and Environment*. Cambridge, Mass.: MIT Press.

Chopra, A.K., and J.A. Doody. 2007. "Schizophrenia, an Illness and a Metaphor: Analysis of the Use of the Term 'Schizophrenia' in U.K. National Newspapers." *Journal of the Royal Society of Medicine* 100, 9: 423–6.

Chopra, Deepak. 1987. *Creating Health*. Boston: Houghton Mifflin.

———. 1989. *Quantum Healing: Exploring the Frontiers of Body Medicine*. New York: Bantam Books.

Chow, Sue. 1998. "Specialty Group Differences over Tonsillectomy: Pediatricians versus Otolaryngologists." *Qualitative Health Research* 8, 1: 61–75.

Chu, P. L., W. McFarland, S. Gibson, D. Weide, J. Henne, P. Miller, T. Partridge, and S. Schwarcz. 2003. "Viagra Use in a Community-Recruited Sample of Men Who Have Sex with Men, San Francisco." *JAIDS: Journal of Acquired Immune Deficiency Syndromes* 33, 2: 191–3.

Claeson, M., and R.J. Waldman. 2000. "The Evolution of Child Health Programmes in Developing Countries: From Targeting Diseases to Targeting People." *Bulletin of the World Health Organization* 78, 10: 1234–45.

Clark, Jack A., and Elliot G. Mishler. 1992. "Attending to Patients' Stories: Reframing the Clinical Task." *Sociology of Health and Illness* 14, 3: 344–72.

———, Deborah A. Potter, and John B. McKinlay. 1991. "Bringing Social Structure Back Into Clinical Decision Making." *Social Science and Medicine* 32, 8: 853–63.

Clark, Warren. 1996. "Youth Smoking." *Canadian Social Trends* (Winter): 2–7.

———. 1998. "Exposure to Second Hand Smoke." *Canadian Social Trends* (Summer): 41.

———. 2002. "Time Alone." *Canadian Social Trends* (Autumn): 2–6.

Clarke, Adele E., Laura Mamo, Jennifer R. Fishman, Janet K. Shim, and Jennifer Ruth Fosket. 2003. "Biomedicalization: The Technoscientific Transformations of Health, Illness, and U.S. Biomedicine." *American Sociological Review* 68, 2: 161–94.

Clarke, Juanne N. 1980. "Medicalization in the Past Century in the Province of Ontario: The Physician as Moral Entrepreneur." Ph.D. dissertation, University of Waterloo.

———. 1985. *It's Cancer: The Personal Experiences of Women Who Have Received a Cancer Diagnosis*. Toronto: IPI Publishing.

———. 1992. "Cancer, Heart Disease, and AIDS: What Do the Media Tell Us about These Diseases?" *Health Communication* 4, 2: 105–20.

———. 1995. "Breast Cancer in Mothers: Impact on Adolescent Daughters." *Family Perspectives* 29, 3: 243–57.

———. 1999a. "Prostate Cancer's Hegemonic Masculinity, in Select Print Mass Media Depictions (1974–1995)." *Health Communication* 11, 1: 59–74.

———. 1999b. "Breast Cancer in Mass Circulating Magazines in the USA and Canada (1974–1995)." *Women and Health* 28: 113–30.

———. 2006. "Homophobia out of the Closet in the Media Portrayal of HIV/AIDS 1991, 1996, 2001: Celebrity, Heterosexism and the Silent Victims." *Critical Public Health* 6, 4: 317–30.

———. 2010. "The Paradoxical Portrayal of Sexually Transmitted Infections and Sexuality in US Magazines 'Glamour' and 'Cosmopolitan', 2000–2007." *Health, Risk and Society* 12, 6: 561–75.

———. 2013. "Surplus Suffering: The Search for Help When a Child Has Mental Health Issues." *Child and Family Social Work* 18, 2: 217–25.

——— and J. Binns. 2006. "The Portrayal of Heart Disease in Mass Print Magazines, 1991–2001." *Health Communication* 19, 1: 39–48.

———. 2010. "Heart Disease and Gender in Mass Print Media." *Maturitas* 65(3): 215–218.

———, with Lauren N. Clarke. 1999. *Finding Strength: A Mother and Daughter's Story of Childhood Cancer*. Toronto: Oxford University Press.

——— and M. Everest. 2006. "Cancer in the Mass Print Media: Fear, Uncertainty and the Medical Model." *Social Science and Medicine* 62, 10: 2591–600.

——— and A. Gawley. 2009. "The Triumph of Pharmaceuticals: The Portrayal of Depression 1980–2006." *Administration and Policy in Mental Health* 36: 91–101.

——— and S. James. 2003. "The Radicalized Self: The Impact on the Self of the Contested Nature of the Diagnosis of Chronic Fatigue Syndrome." *Social Science and Medicine* 57, 8: 1387–95.

——, L. McClellan, and L. Hoffman-Goetz. 2006. "The Portrayal of HIV/AIDS in Two Popular African American Magazines." *Journal of Health Communication: International Perspectives* 11, 5: 495–507.

—— and J. Robinson. 1999. "Testicular Cancer: Medicine and Machismo in the Media (1980–1994)." *Health* 3, 3: 263–82.

Clements, F.E. 1932. "Primitive Concepts of Disease." *Publications—American Archeology and Ethnology* 32, 2: 182–252.

Clendening, Logan, ed. 1960. *Source Book of Medical History*. New York: Dover.

"Clioquinol: Time to Act." 1977. *Lancet* 1, 8022 (28 May): 1139.

Closson, Tom R., and Margaret Catt. 1996. "Funding System Initiatives and the Restructuring of Health Care." *Canadian Journal of Public Health* 87, 2: 86–9.

Cobb, Sidney. 1976. "Social Support as a Moderator of Life Stress." *Psychosomatic Medicine* 38: 301–14.

Coburn, D. 2003. "Income Inequality, Social Cohesion, and the Health Status of Populations: The Role of Neo-liberalism." In Hofrichter (2003: 335–41).

—— and C. Lesley Biggs. 1986. "Limits to Medical Dominance: The Case of Chiropractic." *Social Science and Medicine* 22, 10: 1035–46.

—— and ——. 1987. "Chiropractic: Legitimation or Medicalization?" In Coburn et al. (1987: 336–84).

——, Carl D'Arcy, and George Torrance, eds. 1998. *Health and Canadian Society: Sociological Perspectives*, 3rd edn. Toronto: University of Toronto Press.

——, ——, ——, and Peter New. 1987. *Health and Canadian Society: Sociological Perspectives*, 2nd edn. Markham, Ont.: Fitzhenry & Whiteside.

—— and J. Eakin. 1993. "The Sociology of Health in Canada: First Impressions." *Health and Canadian Society* 1, 1: 83–112.

—— and ——. 1998. "The Sociology of Health in Canada." In Coburn et al. (1998: 619–34).

——, Susan Rappolt, and Ivy Bourgeault. 1997. "Decline vs. Retention of Medical Power through Rest Ratification: An Examination of the Ontario Case." *Sociology of Health and Illness* 19, 1: 1–22.

——, G.M. Torrance, and J.M. Kaufert. 1983. "Medical Dominance in Canada in Historical Perspective: The Rise and Fall of Medicine." *International Journal of Health Services* 13, 3: 407–32.

Cockerham, W.C., B.P. Hinote, and P. Abbott. 2006. "Psychological Distress, Gender, and Health Lifestyles in Belarus, Kazakhstan, Russia, and Ukraine." *Social Science and Medicine* 63: 2381–94.

——, ——, G.B. Cockerham, and P. Abbott. 2006. "Healthy Lifestyles and Political Ideology in Belarus, Russia, and Ukraine." *Social Science and Medicine* 62: 1799–1809.

Cohen, Donna. 2002. "Ageism Can Be Lethal: Undetected Homicides in Older People." *British Medical Journal* 325 (27 July): 181.

Cohen, P., et al. 2006. "Current Affairs and the Public Psyche: American Anxiety in the Post 9/11 World." *Social Psychiatry* 41: 251–60.

Cole, Stephen, and Robert Lejeune. 1972. "Illness and the Legitimation of Failure." *American Sociological Review* 37: 347–56.

Cole, T.R., and N. Carlin. 2009. "The Suffering of Physicians." *Lancet* 374, 9699: 1414–15.

College of Family Physicians Singapore. 2003. "Severe Acute Respiratory Syndrome (SARS): Self-Declaration of Symptoms." www.cfps.org.sg.

Colliers Encyclopedia. 1973. New York: Crowell-Collier.

Colour of Justice Network. 2007. "Colour of Poverty: Fact Sheets." cop.openconcept.ca/.

Colquitt, W., and C. Killian. 1991. "Students Who Consider Medicine but Decide Against It." *Academic Medicine* 66, 5: 273–8.

Commissioner of the Environment and Sustainable Development. 2011. *2011 Report of the Commissioner of the Environment and Sustainable Development*. Ottawa: Office of the Auditor General, 4 Oct.

Commission on the Future of Health Care in Canada (Roy Romanow, chairman). 2002. *Final Report*. Ottawa. www.hc-sc.gc.ca/english/care/romanow/index1.html.

Conley, M.C., and H.O. Maukasch. 1988. "Registered Nurses, Gender and Commitment." In A. Statham, E.M. Miller, and H.O. Maukasch, eds, *The Worth of Women's Work: A Qualitative Synthesis*. Albany: State University of New York Press.

Connell, E., and A. Hunt. 2010. "The HPV Vaccination Campaign: A Project of Moral Regulation in an Era of Biopolitics." *Canadian Journal of Sociology* 35, 1: 63–82.

Conrad, Peter. 1975. "The Discovery of Hyperkinesis: Notes on the Medicalization of Deviant Behaviour." *Social Problems* 23 (Oct.): 12–21.

——. 1987. "The Experience of Illness: Recent and New Directions." In J. Roth and P. Conrad, eds, *Research in the Sociology of Health Care*, vol. 6, 1–31. Greenwich, Conn.: JAI Press.

——. 1998. "Learning to Doctor: Reflections on Recent Accounts of the Medical School Years." In William C. Cockerham, Michael Glassen, and Linda S. Huess, eds, *Readings in Medical Sociology*. Upper Saddle River, NJ: Prentice-Hall, 335–45.

——. 2005. "The Shifting Engines of Medicalization." *Journal of Health and Social Behavior*. 46(1): 3–14.

—— and Rochelle Kern, eds. 1990. *The Sociology of Health and Illness*, 3rd edn. New York: St Martin's Press.

—— and Joseph W. Schneider. 1980. *Deviance and Medicalization: From Badness to Sickness*. St Louis: Mosby.

Coombes, Rebecca. 2005. "Developing World Is Robbing African Countries of Health Staff." *British Medical Journal* 230 (23 Apr.): 923.

Cooper, R.A., and S.J. Stoflet. 1996. "Trends in the Education and Practice of Alternative Medicine Clinicians." *Health Affairs* 15, 3: 226–38.

Cooperstock, Ruth, and Henry L. Lennard. 1987. "Role Strains and Tranquilizer Use." In Coburn et al. (1987: 314–32).

Coovadia, H.M., and J. Hadingham. 2005. "HIV/AIDS: Global Trends, Global Funds and Delivery Bottlenecks." *Globalization and Health* 1: 1–13.

Corbin, Juliet, and Anselm Strauss. 1987. "Accompaniments of Chronic Illness: Changes in Body, Self, Biography and Biographical Time." *Research in the Sociology of Health Care* 6: 249–81.

Cornwell, E.Y., and L.J. Waite. 2012. "Social Network Resources and Management of Hypertension." *Journal of Health and Social Behavior* 53, 2: 215–31.

Cornwell, Jocelyn. 1984. *Hard-Earned Lives: Accounts of Health and Illness from East London.* London: Tavistock.

Cortis, J., and I.G. Law. 2005. "Anti-racist Innovation and Nurse Education." *Nurse Education Today* 25: 204–13.

Coulter, Harris L. 1984. "Homeopathy." In *Alternative Medicines: Popular and Policy Perspectives*, 57–9. New York: Tavistock.

Cousins, Norman. 1979. *Anatomy of an Illness as Perceived by the Patient.* Toronto: Bantam Books.

———. 1983. *The Healing Heart.* New York: Norton.

Couttolenc, B., and N. Alexandre. 2007. "Private Health Insurance in Brazil: Features and Impact on Access and Utilization." Paper presented at IHEA 6th World Congress: Explorations in Health Economics, 15 Jan. ssrn.com/abstract=992821.

Crandall, Christian, and Dallie Moriarty. 1995. "Physical Illness Stigma and Social Rejection." *British Journal of Social Psychology* 34: 67–83.

Crane, Diana. 1975. *The Sanctity of Social Life: Physicians' Treatment of Critically Ill Patients.* New York: Russell Sage Foundation.

Crawford, R. 2006. "Healthism and the Medicalization of Everyday Life." *Health* 10: 401–20.

Crichton, A., A. Robertson, C. Gordon, and W. Farrant. 1997. *Health Care: A Community Concern? Developments in the Organization of Canadian Health Services.* Calgary: University of Calgary Press.

Crowe, Kelly. 2014. "Grassy Narrows: Why Is Japan Still Studying the Mercury Poisoning When Canada Isn't?" CBC News, 2 Sept.

CTV News. 2004. "Canada's Caesarean Section Rate Highest Ever." www.ctv.ca/servlet/ArticleNews/story/CTVNews/1082553935798_40.

———. 2005. "Fontaine Calls for Immediate Action on Water Crisis." www.ctv.ca/servlet/ArticleNews/story/CTVNews/20051027/kashechewanwater.

Culane, Dara Speck. 1987. *An Error in Judgement: The Politics of Medical Care in an Indian/White Community.* Vancouver: Talon Books.

Culos-Reed, N.S., L.E. Carlson, L.M. Daroux, and S. Hately-Aldous. 2006. "A Pilot Study of Yoga for Breast Cancer Survivors: Physical and Psychological Benefits." *Psycho-Oncology* 15: 891–7.

Cunningham, Alastair J. 1992. *The Healing Journey.* Toronto: Key Porter Books.

Cunningham, J.A., G. Faulkner, P. Selby, and J. Cordingley. 2006. "Motivating Smoking Reductions by Framing Health Information as Safer Smoking Tips." *Addictive Behaviours* 31, 8: 1465–8.

Cunningham, M.M., and C. Jillings. 2006. "Individuals' Descriptions of Living with Fibromyalgia." *Clinical Nursing Research* 15, 4: 258–73.

Cunningham, Rob. 1996. *Smoke and Mirrors: The Canadian Tobacco War.* Ottawa: International Development Research Centre.

Currie, Dawn. 1988a. "Starvation amidst Abundance: Female Adolescence and Anorexia." In Bolaria and Dickinson (1988: 198–216).

———. 1988b. "Re-thinking What We Do and How We Do It: A Study of Reproductive Decisions." *Canadian Review of Sociology and Anthropology* 25, 2: 231–53.

——— and Valerie Raoul, eds. 1992. *Anatomy of Gender: Women's Struggle for the Body.* Ottawa: Carleton University Press.

Currie, J. 2003. "The Overprescription of Benzo-diazepines and Sleeping Pills to Women in Canada." www.benzo.org.uk/amisc/benzobrief.pdf.

Daniels, Arlene Kaplan. 1975. "Advisory and Coercive Functions in Psychiatry." *Sociology of Work and Occupations* 2, 1: 55–78.

D'Arcy, Carl. 1998. "Health Status of Canadians." In Coburn et al. (1998: 43–68).

Davidhizar, R. 1994. "The Pursuit of Illness for Secondary Gain." *Health Care Supervisor* 13, 1: 10–15.

Davidson, R., J. Kitzinger, and K. Hunt. 2006. "The Wealthy Get Healthy, the Poor Get Poorly? Lay Perceptions of Health Inequalities." *Social Science and Medicine* 62: 2171–82.

Davis, Devra. 2007. *The Secret History of the War on Cancer.* Philadelphia: Basic Books.

Davis, Karen, Cathy Schoen, and Kristof Stremikis. 2010. *Mirror, Mirror on the Wall: An International Update on the Comparative Performance of American Health Care.* Commonwealth Fund. www.commonwealthfund.org/~/media/Files/Publications/Fund%20Report/2010/Jun/1400_Davis_Mirror_Mirror_on_the_wall_2010.pdf.

de Kok, I.M., F.J. van Lenthe, M. Avendano, M. Louwman, J.W. Coebergh, and J.P. Mackenbach. 2008. "Childhood Class and Cancer Incidence: Results of the Globe Study." *Social Science and Medicine* 66, 5: 1131–9.

Demas, D. 1993. "Triple Jeopardy: Native Women with Disabilities." *Canadian Women's Studies* 113, 4: 53–5.

Demont, John. 2002. "Growing Up Large." *Maclean's*, 5 Aug., 20–6.

Denscombe, Martyn. 2001. "Uncertain Identities and Health-Risking Behaviour: The Case of Young People and Smoking in Late Modernity." *British Journal of Sociology* 52, 1: 157–77.

Desai, N., E.J. Dole, S.T. Yeaton, and W.G. Troutman. 1997. "Evaluation of Drug Information in an Internet Newsgroup." *Journal of the American Pharmaceutical Association* 37, 4: 391–4.

Development Outreach. 2001. "Engendering Development through Gender Equality." www1.worldbank.org/devoutreach//spring01/textonly.

Devita, V.T., Jr, S. Hellman, and S.A. Rosenberg. 1985. *AIDS: Etiology, Diagnosis, Treatment, and Prevention.* Philadelphia: J.B. Lippincott.

Devitt, Neil. 1977. "The Transition from Home to Hospital Birth in the U.S. 1930–1960." *Birth and Family Journal* (Summer): 45–58.

De Vogli, Roberto. 2011. "Neoliberal Globalisation and Health in a Time of Economic Crisis." *Social Theory & Health* 9, 4: 311–25.

Dewa, C.S., J.S. Hoch, and L. Steele. 2005. "Prescription Drug Benefits and Canada's Uninsured." *International Journal of Law and Psychiatry* 28, 5: 496–513.

Dickason, Olive Patricia. 2002. *Canada's First Nations: A History of Founding Peoples from Earliest Times*, 3rd edn. Toronto: Oxford University Press.

Dickin McGinnis, Janice P. 1977. "The Impact of Epidemic Influenza: Canada 1918–1919." Canadian Historical Association, *Historical Papers*.

Dickinson, Harley D., and Mark Stobbe. 1988. "Occupational Health and Safety in Canada." In Bolaria and Dickinson (1988: 426–38).

Dickson, Geri L. 1990. "A Feminist Poststructural Analysis of the Knowledge of Menopause." *Advances in Nursing Science* (Apr.): 15–31.

Dimich-Ward, Helen, et al. 1988. "Occupational Mortality among Bartenders and Waiters." *Canadian Journal of Public Health* 79 (May–June): 194–7.

Dispatch Magazine. 2007. "An Overview of Bill 171: Proposed Changes to the Regulated Health Professions Act." 7–8.

Doidge, Norman. 2007. *The Brain That Changes Itself: Stories of Personal Triumph from the Frontiers of Brain Science.* New York: Penguin.

———. 2015. *The Brain's Way of Healing: Remarkable Discoveries and Recoveries from the Frontiers of Neuroplasticity.* New York: Viking.

Donaldson, C., G. Currie, and C. Mitton. 2002. "Cost-Effectiveness Analysis in Health Care: Contraindications." *British Medical Journal* 325: 891–4.

Doran, Chris. 1988. "Canadian Workers' Compensation: Political, Medical and Health Issues." In Bolaria and Dickinson (1988: 460–72).

Dossey, Larry. 1982. *Space, Time and Medicine.* Boston: New Science Library.

———. 1991. *Meaning and Medicine.* New York: Bantam Books.

Dove, Frederick. 2011. "What's Happened to Thalidomide Babies?" BBC News Online, 2 Nov. www.bbc.co.uk/news/magazine-15536544.

Dowbiggin, I. 2009. "High Anxieties: The Social Construction of Anxiety Disorders." *Canadian Journal of Psychiatry* 54, 7: 429–36.

Downy, L., and M. van Willigen. 2005. "Environmental Stressors: The Mental Health Impacts of Living near Industrial Activity." *Journal of Health and Social Behavior* 46, 3: 289–305.

Doyal, Lesley. 1979. *The Political Economy of Health.* London: Pluto Press.

———. 1995. *What Makes Women Sick: Gender and the Political Economy of Health.* New Brunswick, NJ: Rutgers University Press.

———. 2000. "Gender Equity in Health: Debates and Dilemmas." *Social Science and Medicine* 51: 931–9.

———. 2003. "Sex and Gender: The Challenges for Epidemiologists." *International Journal of Health Services.* 33(3):569–579

Drentea, P., O.J. Clay, D.L. Roth, and M.S. Mittelman. 2006. "Predictors of Improvement in Social Support: Five-Year Effects of a Structured Intervention for Caregivers of Spouses with Alzheimer's Disease." *Social Science and Medicine* 63: 957–67.

Drew, S. 2003. "Self-reconstruction and Biographical Revisioning: Survival Following Cancer in Childhood or Adolescence." *Health: An Interdisciplinary Journal for the Social Study of Health, Illness, and Medicine* 7, 2: 181–99.

Druzin, Paul, Ian Shrier, Mayer Yacowar, and Michael Rossignol. 1998. "Discrimination against Gay, Lesbian and Bisexual Family Physicians by Patients." *CMAJ* 158: 593–7.

Dubos, Rene. 1959. *The Mirage of Health.* Garden City, NY: Doubleday.

Duhaime's Canadian Family Law Centre. 2004. "Abortion Law in Canada." www.duhaime.org/family/ca-abor.aspx.

Dumit, J. 2006. "Illnesses You Have to Fight to Get: Facts as Forces in Uncertain, Emergent Illnesses." *Social Science and Medicine* 62, 3: 577–90.

Dunkel-Schetter, C., and C. Wortman. 1982. "Interpersonal Dynamics of Cancer: Problems in Social Relationships and Their Impact on the Patient." In Howard S.F. Friedman and M. Robin DeMatteo, eds, *Interpersonal Issues in Health Care, 69–117.* New York: Academic Press.

Dunn, J.R., and I. Dyck. 2000. "Social Determinants of Health in Canada's Immigrant Population: Results from the National Population Health Survey." *Social Science and Medicine* 51: 1573–93.

Durkheim, Émile. 1947 [1915]. *Elementary Forms of Religious Life.* Trans. Joseph Ward Swain. New York: Free Press.

———. 1951 [1897]. *Suicide.* Glencoe, Ill.: Free Press.

Dyer, Owen. 2002. "Black Twins Are Born to White Parents after Infertility Treatment." *British Medical Journal* 325 (6 July): 64.

Eberts, Mary. 1987. *Report of the Task Force on the Implementation of Midwifery in Ontario*. Toronto: Ontario Ministry of Health.

Ebley, E.M., D.B. Hogan, and T.S. Fung. 1996. "Correlates of Self-Rated Health in Persons Aged 85 and Over: Results from the Canadian Study of Health and Aging." *Canadian Journal of Public Health* 87, 1: 28–31.

Eddy, Mary Baker. 1934. *Science and Health with a Key to the Scriptures*. Boston: Published by the Trustees under the Will of Mary Baker Eddy.

Eggertson, L. 2005. "Drug Approval System Questioned in US and Canada." *CMAJ* 172, 3: 317–18.

———. 2013. "Hospitalizations for Self-Harm Higher in Poorer Neighbourhoods." *CMAJ* 185, 10: 449–50.

Ehrenreich, Barbara. 2001. *Nickel and Dimed: On (Not) Getting By in America*. New York: Metropolitan Books.

———. 2009. *Bright-Sided: How the Relentless Promotion of Positive Thinking Has Undermined America*. New York: Henry Holt.

——— and Deirdre English. 1973a. *Witches, Midwives and Nurses: A History of Women Healers*. Old Westbury, NY: Feminist Press.

——— and ———. 1973b. *Complaints and Disorders: The Sexual Politics of Sickness*. Old Westbury, NY: Feminist Press.

——— and ———. 1979. *For Her Own Good: 150 Years of the Experts' Advice to Women*. New York: Anchor Press/ Doubleday.

Eichler, Margrit. 1988. *Families in Canada Today*. Toronto: Gage.

Eisenberg, D.M., R.C. Kessler, C. Foster, F.E. Norlock, D.R. Calkins, T.L. Delbanco, et al. 1993. "Unconventional Medicine in the United States: Prevalence, Costs and Patterns of Use." *New England Journal of Medicine* 328: 246–52.

———, R.B. Davis, S.L. Appel, S. Wilkey, M. Van Rompay, and R.C. Kessler. 1998. "Trends in Alternative Medicine Use in the United States, 1990–1997: Results of a Follow-up National Survey." *JAMA* 280, 18: 1569–75.

Elliott, C. 2003. *Better Than Well: American Medicine Meets the American Dream*. New York: Norton.

———. 2004. *Better Than Well: American Medicine Meets the American Dream*. New York, New York. W. W. Norton & Company.

Elliott, C.D., R. Carruthers, D. Hood, and M.J. Conlon. 2013. "Food Branding and Young Children's Taste Preferences: A Reassessment." *Canadian Review of Public Health* 104, 5: 364–8.

Ellison, Christopher. 1991. "Religious Involvement and Subjective Well-Being." *Journal of Health and Social Behavior* 32 (Mar.): 80–99.

Encyclopedia Britannica. 1976. Chicago: William Benton.

Engel, George L. 1971. "Sudden and Rapid Death during Psychological Stress: Folklore or Folk Wisdom?" *Annals of Internal Medicine* 74: 771–82.

Engels, Friedrich. 1985 [1845]. *The Condition of the Working Class in England*. Stanford, Calif.: Stanford University Press.

Environment Canada. 2002. "Acid Rain and the Facts." www.ec.gc.ca/acidrain/acidfact.html.

———. 2006. "Greenhouse Gas Sources and Sinks." www.ec.gc/ pdb/ghg/about/FAQ_e.cfm.

———. 2011. "National Greenhouse Gas Emissions." www.ec.gc.ca/indicateurs-indicators/default. asp?lang=en&n=FBF8455E-1#ghg1.

Epp, Jake. 1986. *Achieving Health for All: A Framework for Health Promotion*. Ottawa: Minister of National Health and Welfare.

Epstein, Samuel S. 1979. *The Politics of Cancer*, rev. edn. New York: Doubleday.

———. 1993. "Evaluation of the National Cancer Program and Proposed Responses." *International Journal of Health Services* 23, 1: 15–44.

———. 1998. *The Politics of Cancer Revisited*. Fremont Centre, NY: East Ridge Press.

Eriksson, M., and B. Lindstrom. 2006. "Antonovsky's Sense of Coherence Scale and the Relation with Health: A Systematic Review." *Journal of Epidemiology and Community Health* 60: 376–81.

Esmail, Nadeem. 2005. "Canada's Physician Shortage: Problem Solved, or Disaster in the Making?" *Fraser Forum* (May): 15–19. www.fraserinstitute.org/researchandpublications/ publications/newsletters/fraserforum.htm.

Eyer, Joe. 1984. "Capitalism, Health and Illness." In John B. McKinley, ed., *Issues in the Political Economy of Health Care*, 23–59 New York: Tavistock.

Fallon, A. 2013. "Rags to Riches." *Chatelaine* (Oct.): 161–2.

Fancourt, D., A. Ockelford, and A. Belai. 2014. "The Psychoneurological Effects of Music: A Systematic Review and New Model." *Brain, Behavior, and Immunity* 36: 15–26.

Fantus, D., B.R. Shah, F. Qui, J. Hux, and P. Rochon. 2009. "Injury in First Nations Communities in Ontario." *Canadian Journal of Public Health* 100, 4: 258–63.

Faw, C., et al. 1977. "Unproven Cancer Remedies." *JAMA* 238: 1536–8.

Feldman, L., C. McMullan, and T. Abernathy. 2004. "Angina and Socio-economic Status in Ontario." *Canadian Journal of Public Health* 95, 3: 228–32.

Ferguson, J.A. 1990. "Patient Age as a Factor in Drug Prescribing Practices." *Canadian Journal of Aging* 9: 278–95.

Ferley, J. P., D. Zmirou, D. D'Adhemar, and F. Balducci. 1989. "A Controlled Evaluation of a Homoeopathic Preparation in the Treatment of Influenza-Like Syndromes." *British Journal of Clinical Pharmacology* 27, 3: 329–35.

Ferragina, E. 2012. *Social Capital in Europe: A Comparative Regional Analysis*. Cheltenham, UK: Edward Elgar.

Fife, Betsy. 1994. "The Conceptualization of Meaning in Illness." *Social Science and Medicine* 38, 2: 309–16.

Finch, S. 2014a. "Thailand Top Destination for Medical Tourists." *CMAJ* 186, 1: 1–2.

——. 2014b. "Medical Tourism Driving Health Care Disparity in Thailand." *CMAJ* 186, 1: 11.

Findlay, Deborah. 1993. "The Good, the Normal and the Healthy: The Social Construction of Medical Knowledge about Women." *Canadian Journal of Sociology* 18, 2: 115–33.

Firth, Matthew, James Brophy, and Margaret Keith. 1997. *Workplace Roulette: Gambling with Cancer*. Toronto: Between the Lines.

Fisher, P.A., B.I. Fagot, and C.S. Leve. 1998. "Assessment of Family Stress across Low-, Medium-, and High-Risk Samples Using the Family Events Checklist." *Family Relations* 47, 3: 215–19.

Fisher, Peter, and Adam Ward. 1994. "Complementary Medicine in Europe." *British Medical Journal* (July): 309–10.

Fisher, Sue. 1986. *In the Patient's Best Interest: Women and the Politics of Medical Decisions*. New Brunswick, NJ: Rutgers University Press.

—— and Alexandra Dundas Todd, eds. 1963. *The Social Organization of the Doctor–Patient Communication*. Washington: Center for Applied Linguistics.

Flegel, K. 2013. "Big Alcohol Catches Up with Adolescent Girls." *CMAJ* 185, 10: 859.

Flexner, Abraham. 1910. *Medical Education in the United States and Canada. A Report to the Carnegie Foundation for the Advancement of Teaching*. Bulletin No. 4. New York: Carnegie Foundation.

Food and Agriculture Organization of the United Nations (FAO). 2004. *Report from Task Force on Hunger: Helping to Build a World without Hunger*. www.fao.org.

Food Banks Canada. 2011. *Hunger Count 2011: A Comprehensive Report on Hunger and Food Bank Use in Canada, and Recommendations for Change*. foodbankscanada.ca/getmedia/dc2aa860-4c33-4929-ac36-fb5d40f0b7e7/HungerCount-2011.pdf.aspx?ext=.pdf.

Fortune, M.K., C. Mustard, and J.J.C. Etches. 2013. "Work-Attributed Illness Arising from Excess Heat Exposure in Ontario, 2004–2010." *Canadian Review of Public Health* 104, 5: 420–6.

Foster, Michelle, and Elizabeth Huffman. 1995. "The Portrayal of the Elderly in Medical Journals." Paper written for Qualitative Methods sociology course at Wilfrid Laurier University.

Foucault, Michel. 1964. *Madness and Civilization: A History of Insanity in the Age of Reason*. New York: Vintage Books.

——. 1973. *The Birth of Illness*. Trans. A.M. Sheridan Smith. New York: Pantheon Books.

Foucault, M. (1991). "Governmentality," trans. Rosi Braidotti and revised by Colin Gordon, in Graham Burchell, Colin Gordon and Peter Miller (eds) The Foucault Effect: Studies in Governmentality. Chicago, IL: University of Chicago Press. 87–104.

——. 1994 [1975]. *The Birth of the Clinic: An Archeology of Medical Perception*. Trans. A.M. Sheridan Smith. New York: Vintage Books.

——. 2006. *History of Madness*. Ed. and trans. J. Khalfa; trans., J. Murphy. Abingdon, Oxford, UK: Routledge.

Fox, Nicholas J. 1993. "Discourse, Organization and the Surgical Ward Round." *Sociology of Health and Illness* 15, 1.

——. 1994a. "Anaesthetists, the Discourse on Patient Fitness and the Organization of Surgery." *Sociology of Health and Illness* 16, 1: 1–18.

——. 1994b. *Postmodernism, Sociology and Health*. Toronto: University of Toronto Press.

Fox, Renee C. 1957. "Training for Uncertainty." In Merton, Reader, and Kendall (1957: 207–18, 228–41).

——. 1977. "The Medicalization and Demedicalization of American Society." In John H. Knowles, ed., *Doing Better and Feeling Worse: Health in the United States*, 9–22. New York: Norton.

Frank, Arthur. 1991. *At the Will of the Body*. Boston: Houghton Mifflin.

——. 1993. "The Rhetoric of Self-change: Illness Experience as Narrative." *Sociological Quarterly* 32, 1: 39–52.

——. 1997. *The Wounded Storyteller: Body, Illness and Ethics*. Chicago: University of Chicago Press.

Frank, Jeffrey. 1996. "15 Years of AIDS in Canada." *Canadian Social Trends* (Summer): 4–7.

Frankel, Gail B., Mark Speechley, and Terence Wade. 1996. *Sociology of Health and Health Care: A Canadian Perspective*. Toronto: Copp Clark.

Frankl, V. 1965. *Man's Search for Meaning*. Trans. I. Lasch. Boston: Beacon Press.

Freedman, L.P., R.J. Waldman, H. de Pinho, and M.E. Wirth. 2005. *Who's Got the Power? Transforming Health Systems for Women and Children*. New York: United Nations Development Programme.

Freidson, Eliot. 1970. *Professional Dominance: The Social Structure of Medical Care*. New York: Atherton Press.

——. 1975. *The Profession of Medicine: Study in the Sociology of Applied Knowledge*. New York: Dodd Mead.

Freund, Peter, and Meredith B. McGuire. 1991. *Health, Illness and the Social Body*. Englewood Cliffs, NJ: Prentice-Hall.

——, ——, and Linda S. Podhurst. 2003. *Health, Illness and the Social Body: A Critical Sociology*, 4th edn. Upper Saddle River, NJ: Prentice-Hall.

Frideres, James S. 1994. "Health Promotion and Indian Communities: Social Support or Social Disorganization." In Bolaria and Bolaria (1994a: 269–96).

——. 2011. *First Nations in the Twenty-First Century*. Toronto: Oxford University Press.

Friendly, Martha. 2009. "Early Childhood Education and Care As a Social Determinant of Health." In Dennis Raphael, ed., *Social Determinants of Health: Canadian Perspectives*, 128–42. Toronto: Canadian Scholar's Press.

Fries, J.F. 1980. "Aging, Natural Death and Compression of Morbidity." *New England Journal of Medicine* 303: 130–5.

Frith, H., J. Raisborough, and O. Klein. 2013. "Making Death 'Good': Instructional Tales for Dying in Newspaper Accounts of Jade Goody's Death." *Sociology of Health and Illness* 35, 3: 419–33.

Frydman, C., and S. Saks. 2005. "Historical Trends in Executive Compensation, 1936–2003." Working paper. Cited in De Vogli (2011).

Fuchs, M. 1974. "Health Care Patterns of Urbanized Native Americans." Ph.D. dissertation, University of Michigan.

Fuller, Colleen. 1998. *Caring for Profit: How Corporations Are Taking Over Canada's Health Care System.* Vancouver: New Star Books.

———. 2010. "Reporting Adverse Drug Reactions: What Happens in the Real World?" in Rochon Ford and Saibil (2010: 139–60).

Furnham, Adrian, and Julie Forey. 1994. "The Attitudes, Behaviours and Beliefs of Patients of Conventional vs. Complementary (Alternative) Medicine." *Journal of Clinical Psychology* 50, 3: 458–69.

——— and Chris Smith. 1988. "Choosing Alternative Medicine: A Comparison of the Beliefs of Patients Visiting a General Practitioner and a Homeopath." *Social Science and Medicine* 26, 7: 685–9.

Gabe, J., and M. Calnan. 1989. "The Limits of Medicine: Women's Perception of Medical Technology." *Social Science and Medicine* 28: 223–31.

Gagnon, Louise. 2002. "Montreal Physicians Protest Poverty." *CMAJ* 167, 1 (9 July).

———. 2004. "Medical Error Affects Nearly 25% of Canadians." *CMAJ* 171, 2: 123.

Gagnon, M.A. 2012. "Drug Shortages: Searching for a Cure." *Health Care Policy* 7, 4: 10–17.

——— and Joel Lexchin. 2008. "The Cost of Pushing Pills: New Estimate of the Cost of Pharmaceutical Promotion Expenditures in the United States." *PLOS Medicine* 5, 1. doi:10.1371/journal.pmed.0050001.

Galabuzi, G.E. 2001."Canada's Creeping Economic Apartheid." CSJ Foundation for Research and Education. www.socialjustice.org.

———. 2004. "Social Exclusion." in Raphael (2004: 235–52).

Gallagher, Eugene B., and C. Maureen Searle. 1989. "Content and Context in Health Professional Education." In Howard E. Freeman and Sol Levine, eds, *Handbook of Medical Sociology,* 4th edn, 437–55. Englewood Cliffs, NJ: Prentice-Hall.

Galloway, G. 2014. "Government Mum on Asbestos Policy." *Globe and Mail,* 18 June.

Gansler, T., C. Kaw, C. Crammer, and T. Smith. 2008. "A Population-Based Study of Prevalence of Complementary Methods Use by Cancer Survivors: A Report from the American Cancer Society's Studies of Cancer Survivors." *Cancer* 113, 5: 1048–57.

Garrett, L. 1995. *The Coming Plague: Newly Emerging Diseases in a World Out of Balance.* New York: Penguin Group.

Geise, R. 2013. "The Mainstreaming of Mental Health." *The Walrus* (Mar.): 30–9.

"Gender Equality and the Millennium Development Goals." n.d. www.mdgender.net.

Genova, Lisa. 2009. *Still Alice.* New York: Pocket Books.

Geran, L. 1992. "Occupational Stress." *Canadian Social Trends* (Autumn): 14–17.

Gerber, L.A. 1983. *Married to Their Careers: Career and Family Dilemmas in Doctors' Lives.* New York: Tavistock.

Ghosh, Sabitri. 2002. "HIV/AIDS: One Generation's Story." *Voices* 9: 10.

Giacomini, M., P. Rozee-Koker, and F. Pepitone-Arreola-Rockwell. 1986. "Gender Bias in Human Anatomy Textbook Illustrations." *Psychology of Women Quarterly* 10: 413–20.

Gibson, R.G., S.L.M. Gibson, A.D. MacNeill, W. Watson, and W. Buchanan. 1980. "Homeopathic Therapy in Rheumatoid Arthritis: Evaluation of Double-Blind Clinical Therapeutic Trial." *British Journal of Clinical Pharmacology* 9: 453–9.

Giddens, A. 1999. "Risk and Responsibility." *Modern Law Review* 62: 1–10.

Gidney, R.D., and W.P.S. Millar. 1984. "Origins of Organized Medicine, Ontario, 1850–1869." In Charles G. Roland, ed., *Health, Disease and Medicine: Essays in Canadian History,* 72–95. Toronto: Hannah Institute for the History of Medicine.

Giger, J., R.E. Davidhizar, L. Purell, J.T. Harden, J. Phillips, and O. Strickland. 2007. "American Academy of Nursing Expert Panel Report: Developing Cultural Competence to Eliminate Health Disparities in Ethnic Minorities and Other Vulnerable Populations." *Journal of Transcultural Nursing* 18, 2: 95–102.

Gilbert, M., M. Dawer, and R. Armour. 2006. "Fire-related Deaths among Aboriginal People in British Columbia, 1991–2001." *Canadian Journal of Public Health* 97, 4: 300–4.

Gillborn, D. 2006. "Critical Race Theory and Education: Racism and Anti-Racism in Educational Theory and Praxis." *Discourse: Studies in the Cultural Politics of Education* 27, 1: 11–32.

Gilman, Charlotte Perkins. 1973 [1899]. *The Yellow Wallpaper.* Old Westbury, NY: Feminist Press.

Glauser, W. 2013a. "Delhi's Dumps Are 'Public Health Time Bombs'." *CMAJ* 185, 8: 319–20.

———. 2013b. "Pharma Influence Widespread at Medical Schools: Study." *CMAJ* 185, 13: 1121–2.

Globalis. 2007. "Canada: Population Aged 65 and Above." globalis.gvu.unu.edu/indicator_detail.cfm?IndicatorID=32&Country=CA.

Globe and Mail. 12 June 1970; 5, 14 Feb. 1989.

———. 2006. "Refugees with HIV." 29 Sept, A18.

Godderis, Rebecca. 2010. "Precarious Beginnings: Gendered Risk Discourses in Psychiatric Research Literature about Postpartum Depression." *Health* 14, 5: 451–66.

Goffman, Erving. 1959. "The Moral Career of the Mental Patient." *Psychiatry* 22: 123–35.

———. 1961. *Asylums: Essays on the Situation of Mental Patients and Other Inmates*. New York: Anchor Press/Doubleday.

———. 1963. *Stigma: Notes on the Management of Spoiled Identity*. Englewood Cliffs, NJ: Prentice-Hall.

Goldscheider, C. 1971. *Population, Modernization and Social Structure*. Boston: Little, Brown.

Goodall, Alan. 1992. "Motor Vehicles and Air Pollution." *Canadian Social Trends* (Spring): 21–6.

Goode, William J. 1956. "Community within a Community: The Professions." *American Sociological Review* 22 (Apr.): 194–200.

———. 1960. "Encroachment, Charlatanism and the Emerging Profession: Psychology." *Sociology Review* 25, 6: 902–14.

Goodwin, R.M., C. Gould, M. Blanko, and M. Olfson. 2001. "Prescription of Psychotropic Medications to Youths in Office-based Practice." *Psychiatric Services* 52: 1081–7.

Gordon, Sidney, and Ted Allan. 1952. *The Scalpel, the Sword*. Toronto: McClelland & Stewart.

Gorey, K.M. 2009. "Breast Cancer Survival in Canada and the US: Meta-Analytic Evidence of Canadian Survival Advantage in Low-Income Areas." *International Journal of Epidemiology* 38, 6: 1543–51.

Gorman, B.K., and J.G. Read. 2006. "Gender Disparities in Adult Health: An Examination of Three Measures of Morbidity." *Journal of Health and Social Behavior* 47, 2: 95–110.

Gort, Elaine. 1986. "A Social History of Naturopathy in Ontario: The Formation of an Occupation." MA thesis, University of Toronto.

Gourvish, S. 1995. "Learning about 'Race' and Anti-Racism: The Experience of Students on a Diploma in Social Work Programme." *Social Work Education* 14, 1: 24–43.

Graham, Hilary. 1984. *Women, Health and the Family*. Brighton, Sussex: Wheatsheaf Books.

Graham, Wendy. 1994. "Sexual Harassment of Physicians." *Women's Health Office Newsletter*, 14 Apr.

Gray, Charlotte. 1998. "The Private Sector Invades Medical's Home-Town." *CMAJ* 15, 9: 165–7.

Gray, Ross. 1998. "Four Perspectives on Unconventional Therapies." *Health* 2, 1: 55–74.

Gregoire, H., and M. Roufail. 2005. *Racialised Groups and Health Status: A Literature Review Exploring Poverty, Housing, Race-based Discrimination and Access to Health Care as Determinants of Health for Racialised Groups*. Toronto: Access Alliance Multicultural Community Health Centre.

Growe, S.J. 1991. "The Nature and Type of Doctors' Cultural Assumptions about Patients as Men." *Sociological Focus* 24, 3: 211–23.

Grymonpre, R.E., P.A. Metenko, et al. 1988. "Drug Associated Hospital Admission in Older Medical Patients." *Journal of American Geriatric Society* 36: 1092–8.

Guglielmi, R.S., and K. Tatrow. 1998. "Occupational Stress, Burnout and Health in Teachers: A Methodological and Theoretical Analysis." *Review of Educational Research* 68, 1: 61–9.

Haas, S.A. 2006. "Health Selection and the Process of Social Stratification: The Effect of Childhood Health on Socioeconomic Attainment." *Journal of Health and Social Behavior* 47: 339–54.

Hadler, N.M. 2011. *Rethinking Aging: Growing Old and Living Well in an Overtreated Society*. Chapel Hill: University of North Carolina Press.

Haines, A. 1990. "The Implications for Health." In S. Leggett, ed., *Global Warming: The Greenpeace Report*. New York: Oxford University Press.

Hall, Emmett M. 1980. *Canadian National–Provincial Health Program for the 1980s: A Commitment for Renewal*. Ottawa: National Health and Welfare.

Hall, Oswald. 1946. "Some Organizational Considerations in the Professional-Organizational Relationship." *Administrative Science Quarterly* 12, 3: 461–78.

———. 1948. "The Stages of a Medical Career." *American Journal of Sociology* 53 (Mar.): 328–36.

Hamilton, J.T. 1995. "Testing for Environmental Racism: Prejudice, Profits, Political Power?" *Journal of Policy Analysis and Management* 14: 104–32.

Hamilton, Vivian, and Barton Hamilton. 1993. "Does Universal Health Insurance Equalize Access to Care? A Canadian–U.S. Comparison." Paper presented at Northwestern University Fourth Annual Health Economics Workshop, Aug.

Hamowy, Ronald. 1984. *Canadian Medicine: A Study in Restricted Entry*. Vancouver: Fraser Institute.

Hanauer, Nick. 2014. "The Pitchforks Are Coming . . . For Us Plutocrats." *Politico* (July–Aug.). http://www.politico.com/magazine/story/2014/06/the-pitchforks-are-coming-for-us-plutocrats-108014.html#.VViJQ1LFtT4.

Hankivsky, Olena, with S. de Leeuw, J. Lee, B. Vissandjee, and N. Khanlou. 2011. *Health Inequities in Canada: Intersectional Frameworks and Practices*. Vancouver: University of British Columbia Press.

Harden, Bonnie L., and Craig R. Harden. 1997. *Alternative Health Care: The Canadian Directory*. Toronto: Noble Ages Publishing.

Harding, Jim. 1987. "The Pharmaceutical Industry as a Public Health Hazard and an Institution of Social Control." In Coburn et al. (1987: 314–32).

———. 1994a. "Environmental Degradation and Rising Cancer Rates: Exploring the Links in Cancer." In Bolaria and Dickinson (1994: 649–67).

———. 1994b. "Social Basis of the Over Prescribing of Mood-Modifying Pharmaceuticals to Women." In Bolaria and Bolaria (1994b: 157–81).

Harman, J., H. Graham, B. Francis, and H. Inskip. 2006. "Socioeconomic Gradients in Smoking among Young Women: A British Survey." *Social Science and Medicine* 63: 2791–800.

Harris, R., M. Tobias, M. Jeffreys, K. Waldegrave, S. Karlsen, and J. Nazroo. 2006. "Racism and

Health: The Relationship between Experience of Racial Discrimination and Health in New Zealand." *Social Science and Medicine* 63: 1428–41.

Harrison, Michelle. 1982. *A Woman in Residence*. New York: Random House.

Hart, K., and T.L. Wilson. 2006. "A Psychosocial Resilience Model to Account for Medical Well-Being in Relation to Sense of Coherence." *Journal of Health Psychology* 11, 6: 857–62.

Hart, N., N. Grand, and K. Riley. 2006. "Making the Grade: The Gender Gap, ADHD, and the Medicalization of Boyhood." In Rosenfeld and Faircloth (2006: 132–64).

Hawkley, L.C., and J.T. Cacioppo. 2010. "Loneliness Matters: A Theoretical and Empirical Review of Consequences and Mechanisms." *Annals of Behavioral Medicine* 40, 2: 218–27.

Hawthorne, G. 2006. "Measuring Social Isolation in Older Adults: Development and Initial Validation of the Friendship Scale." *Social Indications Research* 77: 521–48.

Haythornthwaite, C., and L. Kendall. 2010. "Internet and Community." *American Behavioral Scientist* 53: 1083–94.

Heagerty, John J. 1928. *Four Centuries of Medical History in Canada*, 2 vols. Toronto: Macmillan.

Health and the Status of Women. 1980. Geneva: World Health Organization.

Health and Welfare Canada.1982, 1984. *National Health Expenditures in Canada 1970–1982*. Ottawa.

———. 1986. *Issues for Health Promotion in Family and Child Health: A Sourcebook*. Ottawa: Medical Service Branch, Indian and Inuit Services.

———, Mental Health Division. 1984. *Alzheimer's Disease: A Family Information Handbook*. Ottawa: Published in co-operation with the Alzheimer Society.

——— and Statistics Canada. 1981. *The Health of Canadians: Report of the Canada Health Survey*. Catalogue no. 82–538E. Ottawa: Minister of Supply and Services and the Ministry of National Health and Welfare.

Health Canada. 2003. "Smog and Your Health." www.hc.sc. gc.ca/iyh-vsv/environ/smog_e.html.

———. 2004. *Air Pollution: Information Needs and the Knowledge, Attitudes and Behaviour of Canadians—Final Report*. www.hc-sc.gc.ca/ewh-semt/pubs/air/pollution/determinants_e.html.

———. 2006a. "Diseases and Conditions: Heart and Stroke." www.hc.gc.ca/dc-ma/heart-coeur/index_e.html.

———. 2006b. *Healthy Canadians: A Federal Report on Comparable Health Indicators 2006*. www.hc-sc.gc.ca/hcs-sss/pubs/care-soins/2006-fed-comp-indicat/index_e.html.

———. 2006c. "Health Effects of Air Pollution." www.hc-sc. gc.ca/ewh-semt/air/out-ext/effe/health_effects-effects_sante_e.html.

———. 2009. *A Statistical Profile on the Health of First Nations in Canada: Self-Rated Health and Selected Conditions, 2002 to 2005*. Ottawa: Health Canada, Dec. www.hc-sc.gc.ca/fniah-spnia/pubs/aborig-autoch/2009-stats-profil-vol3/index-eng.php.

Health Council of Canada. 2013. *Canada's Most Vulnerable: Improving Health Care for First Nations, Inuit, and Métis Seniors*. Toronto: Health Council of Canada. http://www.metisnation.org/media/422632/senior_ab_report_2013_en_final.pdf.

Health On the Net Foundation. 2000. "HON's Fourth Survey on the Use of the Internet for Medical and Health Purposes." www.hon.ch/Survey/ResumeApr99.html.

Helman, C.G. 2007. *Culture, Health and Illness*, 5th edn. London: Hodder Arnold.

Herrick, D.M. 2007. *Medical Tourism: Global Competition in Health Care*. NCPA Policy Report No. 304, Nov.

Hesse, B.W., et al. 2005. "Trust and Sources of Health Information: The Impact of the Internet and Its Implications for Health Care Providers: Findings from the First Health Information National Trends Survey." *Archives of Internal Medicine* 165, 22: 2618–24.

Hilfiker, David. 1985. *Healing the Wounds: A Physician Looks at His Work*. New York: Pantheon Books.

Hirschkorn, K.A., and I.L. Bourgeault. 2005. "Conceptualizing Mainstream Healthcare Providers' Behaviours in Relation to Complementary and Alternative Medicine." *Social Science and Medicine* 61: 157–70.

Hochschild, A. 2012 [1983]. *The Managed Heart: The Commercialization of Human Feeling*. Berkeley: University of California Press.

Hoffman-Goetz, Laurie, and Juanne N. Clarke. 2000. "Quality of Breast Cancer Sites on the World Wide Web." *Canadian Journal of Public Health* 91: 281–4.

Hofrichter, Richard, ed. 2003. *Health and Social Justice: Politics, Ideology and Inequity in the Distribution of Disease*. San Francisco: Jossey-Bass.

Holland, Jimmie C., and Julia H. Rowland, eds. 1989. *Handbook of Psychooncology: Psychological Care of the Patent with Cancer*. New York: Oxford University Press.

Hollander, Ilyssa. 2006. "Viagra's Rise above Women's Health Issues: An Analysis of the Social and Political Influences on Drug Approval in the United States and Japan." *Social Science and Medicine* 62: 683-93.

Holling, S.A. 1981. "Primitive Medicine among the Indians of Ontario." In Holling et al., eds, *Medicine for Heroes*. Mississauga, Ont.: Mississauga Historical Society.

Holmes, T.H., and R.H. Rahe. 1967. "The Social Readjustment Rating Scale." *Journal of Psychosomatic Research* 11, 2: 213–18.

Holyoake, D.D. 2011. "Is the Doctor–Nurse Game Still Being Played?" *Nursing Times* 107: 43.

Hopkins, Janne Janice. 2002. "High Level of Resources for Neonatal Intensive Care Do Not Give Better Outcome." *British Medical Journal* 324: 1353.

Horowitz, Lawrence C. 1988. *Taking Charge of Your Medical Fate*. New York: Random House.

Horwitz, A.V. 2013. *Anxiety: A Short History of Anxiety*. Baltimore: Johns Hopkins University Press.

—— and J.C. Wakefield. 2012. *All We Have to Fear: Psychiatry's Transformation of Natural Anxieties into Mental Disorders.* New York: Oxford University Press.

Hour, F., and J. Myles. 2005. "Neighbourhood Inequality, Neighbourhood Affluence and Population Health." *Social Science and Medicine* 60, 7: 1557–69.

Howell, W.L.J. 2012. "More Medical Schools Offer Instruction in Complementary and Alternative Therapies." *AAMC Reporter* (Feb.). https://www.aamc.org/newsroom/reporter/feb2012/273812/therapies.html.

Howson, Alexandra. 1998. "Surveillance, Knowledge and Risk: The Embodied Experience of Cervical Screening." *Health* 2, 2: 195–215.

Hua, W., and B. Wellman. 2010. "Social Connectivity in America: Changes in Adult Friendship Network Size from 2002 to 2007." *American Behavioral Scientist* 53, 8: 1148–69.

Hughes, C.C. 1967. "Ethnomedicine." In David Gills, ed., *International Encyclopedia of Social Sciences*, vol. 10, 87–92. New York: Macmillan and Free Press.

Hughner, R.S., and S.S. Kleine. 2004. "Views of Health in the Lay Sector: A Compilation and Review of How Individuals Think about Health." *Health: An Interdisciplinary Journal for the Social Study of Health, Illness, and Medicine* 8, 4: 395–422.

Huiting, H. 2002. "Family Planning Law and China's Birth Control Situation." www.china.org.en/english/2002/Oct/46138.htm.

Hunt, Charles W. 1989. "Migrant Labour and Sexually Transmitted Disease: AIDS in Africa." *Journal of Health and Social Behavior* 30: 353–73.

Hunt, L., B. Jordan, S. Irwin, and C.H. Browner. 1989. "Compliance and the Patient's Perspective: Controlling Symptoms in Everyday Life." *Culture, Medicine and Psychiatry* 13: 315–34.

Hurley, J., and M. Grignon. 2006. "Income and Equity of Access to Physician Services." *CMAJ* 174, 2: 187–8.

Hurtig, Mel. 2000. *Pay the Rent or Feed the Kids: The Tragedy and Disgrace of Poverty in Canada.* Toronto: McClelland & Stewart.

Hutten-Czapski, Peter. 2000. "Primary Care Reform: A Rural Perspective Discussion Paper." Society of Rural Physicians of Canada. www.srpc.ca/PDF/primary-care-reform.pdf.

Huynen, M., P. Martens, and H. Hilderink. 2005. "The Health Impacts of Globalization: A Conceptual Framework." *Globalization and Health* 1, 14: 1–12.

Hystad, P., M. Brauer, P.A. Demers, K.C. Johnson, E. Setton, A. Cervantes-Larios, K. Poplawski, A. McFarlane, A. Whitehead, and A.M. Nichol. 2014. "Geographic Variation in Radon and Associated Lung Cancer Risk in Canada." *Canadian Journal of Public Health* 105, 1: 4–10.

Ideas. 1983. "We Know Best: Experts' Advice to Women." Toronto: Canadian Broadcasting Corporation, 2–23 Jan., broadcast transcript.

Iedema, R., A. Flabouris, S. Grant, and C. Jorm. 2006. "Narrativizing Errors of Care: Critical Incident Reporting in Clinical Practice." *Social Science and Medicine* 62: 134–44.

Illich, Ivan. 1976. *Limits to Medicine.* Toronto: McClelland & Stewart.

Imman, Wallace. 1996. "Alternate Treatments Gaining Ground." *Globe and Mail*, 28 Dec., A3.

Impicciatore, P., C. Pandolfini, N. Casella, and M. Bonati. 1994. "Reliability of Health Information for the Public on the World Wide Web: Systematic Survey of Advice on Managing Fever in Children at Home." *British Medical Journal* 314: 1875–81.

Inaba, A., P.A. Thoits, K. Ueno, W.R. Gove, R.J. Evenson, and M. Sloan. 2005. "Depression in the United States and Japan: Gender, Marital Status, and SES Patterns." *Social Science and Medicine* 61: 2280–92.

Insel, T.R. 2010. "Psychiatrists' Relationships with Pharmaceutical Companies." *JAMA* 303, 12: 1192.

Institute for Clinical Evaluative Sciences. 2006. "Oh Canada! Too Many Children in Poverty for Too Long: 2006 Report Card on Child and Family Poverty in Canada." *Informed: Using Research in Your Practice.* www.campaign2000.ca/rc/.

——. 2006. "That's Not Baby Fat: Weighing the Risks of Obesity in Children." *Informed: Using Research in Your Practice* 12, 1: 1–8.

International Joint Commission. n.d. *Status of Restoration Activities in Great Lake Areas of Concern: Progress toward Restoration.* www.ijc/php/publications/html/aoc_rep/english/report/chapter3/contaminated_sediment.html.

Intraspec.ca. 2011. "Homeless in Canada Resources." intraspec.ca/homelesssCanada.php.

Izadnegahdar, M., J. Singer, M.K. Lee, M. Gao, C.R. Thompson, J. Kopec, and K.H. Humphries. 2014. "Do Younger Women Fare Worse? Sex Differences in Acute Myocardial Infarction Hospitalization and Early Mortality Rates over Ten Years." *Journal of Women's Health* 23, 1: 10–17.

Jackson, Andrew. 2009. "The Unhealthy Canadian Workplace." In Dennis Raphael, ed., *Social Determinants of Health: Canadian Perspectives*, 99–113. Toronto: Canadian Scholar's Press.

Jackson, M. 2003. *Pain: The Science and Culture of Why We Hurt.* Toronto: Vintage Canada.

James, W.J., and S. Lieberman. 1975. "What the American Public Knows about Cancer and Cancer Tests." In Patricia Hubbs, ed., *Public Education about Cancer.* Geneva: International Union Against Cancer.

Jeffcoate, Thomas N.A. 1957. *Principles of Gynecology.* London: Butterworth.

Jefferies, Barbara J.M.H., Chris Power, and Clyde Hertzman. 2002. "Birth Weight, Childhood Socio-economic Environment, and Cognitive Development in the 1958 British Cohort Study." *British Medical Journal* 325 (10 Aug.): 305.

Jennett, P.A., M. Cooper, S. Edworthy, et al. 1991. "Consumer Use of Official Health Care: Facts and Implications." Proceedings of the 5th ACMC Conference on Physician Manpower, Association of Canadian Medical Colleges, Ottawa, 28 Apr.

Jensen, Phyllis Marie. 1988. "Nursing." In *The Canadian Encyclopedia*, vol. 3, 1546. Edmonton: Hurtig.

Johnson, C. 2010. "Pesticides Linked to ADHD in Children." *Globe and Mail*, 18 May, L3.

Johnson, Hillary. 1996. *Osler's Web: Inside the Labyrinth of the Chronic Fatigue Syndrome Epidemic*. New York: Crown.

Johnson, Terence. 1972. *The Professions and Power*. London: Macmillan.

——. 1977. "Industrial Society: Class, Change and Control." In R. Scase, ed., *The Professions in the Class Structure*, 93–110. London: Allen and Unwin.

——. 1982. "Social Class and the Division of Labour." In A. Giddens and G. Mackenzie, eds, *The State and the Professions: Peculiarities of the British*, 182–208. Cambridge: Cambridge University Press.

Jones, W.H.S. 1943. *Hippocrates*, vol. 2. London: Heinemann.

Judd, Charles M., Eliot R. Smith, and Louise H. Kidder. 1991. *Research Methods in Social Relations*, 6th edn. Fort Worth, Texas: Holt, Rinehart and Winston.

Juni, P., L. Nartey, S. Reichenbach, R. Sterchi, P.A. Dieppe, and M. Egger. 2004. "Risk of Cardiovascular Events and Rofecoxib: Cumulative Meta-analysis." *Lancet* 364, 9450: 2012–19.

Kafetsios, K., F. Anagnostopuolos, E. Lempesis, and A. Valindra. 2014. "Doctors' Emotion Regulation and Patient Satisfaction: A Social Functional Perspective." *Health Communication* 29: 205–14.

Kanter, Rosabeth Moss. 1977. *Men and Women of the Corporation*. New York: Basic Books.

Kaplan, Howard B. 1991. "Social Psychology and the Immune System: A Conceptual Framework and Review of the Literature." *Social Science and Medicine*: 909–23.

Kapoor, Ilan. 2012. *Celebrity Humanitarianism: The Ideology of Global Charity*. Abingdon, Oxford: Routledge.

Kapur, V., and K. Basu. 2005. "Drug Coverage in Canada: Who Is at Risk?" *Health Policy* 71, 2: 181–93.

Karp, D. 1996. *Speaking of Sadness, Depression, Disconnection and the Meanings of Illness*. New York: Oxford University Press.

Kasman, N.M., and E.M. Badley. 2004. "Beyond Access: Who Reports That Health Care Is Not Being Received When Needed in a Publicly-funded Health Care System?" *Canadian Journal of Public Health* 95, 4: 304–8.

Kasner, E.J., et al. 2012. "Gender Differences in Acute Pesticide: Related Illnesses and Injuries among Farm Workers in the United States, 1998–2007." *American Journal of Industrial Medicine* 55, 7: 551–83.

Kasperski, Janet M. 2001. *Where Have All the Doctors Gone? Responses to the George Panel on Health Professional Human Resources Report*. Toronto: Ontario College of Family Physicians.

Kassulke, Desley, Karen Stenner-Day, Michael Coory, and Ian Ring. 1993. "Information-seeking Behaviour and Sources of Health Information: Associations with Risk Factor Status in an Analysis of Three Queensland Electorates." *Australian Journal of Public Health* 17, 1.

Katzmarzyk, Peter T. 2002. "The Canadian Obesity Epidemic, 1985–1998." *CMAJ* 166 (16 Apr.): 8.

Kaufert, Patricia. 1988. "Through Women's Eyes: The Case for Feminist Epidemiology." *Healthsharing*: 10–13.

—— and P. Gilbert. 1987. "Medicalization and the Menopause." In Coburn et al. (1987).

Kawachi, I., B.P. Kennedy, V. Gupta, and D. Prothrow-Stith. 1999. "Women's Status and the Health of Women and Men: A View from the States." *Social Science and Medicine* 48: 21–32.

Kelly, Orville E., and W. Cotter Murray. 1975. *Make Today Count*. New York: Delacorte Press.

Kelner, Merrijoy, Oswald Hall, and Jan Coultner. 1980. *Chiropractors: Do They Help?* Toronto: Fitzhenry & Whiteside.

——, B. Wellman, H. Boon, and S. Welsh. 2004. "Responses of Established Healthcare to the Professionalization of Complementary and Alternative Medicine in Ontario." *Social Science and Medicine* 59: 915–30.

——, ——, S. Welsh, and H. Boon. 2006. "How Far Can Complementary and Alternative Medicine Go? The Case of Chiropractic and Homeopathy." *Social Science and Medicine* 63: 2617–27.

Kemeny, M.E. 2007. "Psychoneuroimmunology." In H. Friedman and R.C. Silver, eds, *Foundations of Health Psychology*, 92–116. New York: Oxford University Press.

Kemery, Anna. 2002. "Driven to Excel: A Portrait of Canada's Workaholics." *Canadian Social Trends* (Spring): 2–6.

Kendall, P.P., and G.G. Reader. 1988. "Innovations in Medical Education of the 1950's Contrasted with Those of the Early 1970's and 1980's." *Journal of Health and Social Behavior* 29, 4: 279–93.

Kiec-Swierczynska, M., D. Chomiczewska-Skora, D. Swierczyriska-Machura, and B. Krecisz. 2013. "Manicurists and Pedicurists—Occupation Group at High Risk of Dermatoses." *Medycyna Pracy* 64, 4: 579–91.

Kim, D., S.V. Subramanian, S.L. Gormaker, and I. Kawachi. 2006. "US State- and Country-level Social Capital in Relation to Obesity and Physical Inactivity: A Multilevel, Multivariable Analysis." *Social Science and Medicine* 63: 1045–59.

Kim, Kwang-Kee, and Phillip M. Moody. 1992. "More Resources, Better Health? A Cross-National Perspective." *Social Science and Medicine* 34, 8: 837–42.

Kim, P. "Vioxx (rofecoxib)." www.vioxx.com.

King, Samantha. 2006. *Pink Ribbons, Inc.: Breast Cancer and the Politics of Philanthropy*. Minneapolis: University of Minnesota Press.

King, Sorrel. 2009. *Josie's Story: A Mother's Inspiring Crusade to Make Medical Care Safe*. New York: Atlantic Monthly Press.

Kingma, M. 2001. "Workplace Violence in the Health Sector: A Problem of Epidemic Proportion." *International Nursing Review* 48, 3: 129–30.

Kirk, Jo-Ann. 1994. "A Feminist Analysis of Women in Medical School." In Bolaria and Dickinson (1994: 158–83).

Klass, Alan. 1975. *There's Gold in Them Thar Pills*. London: Penguin Books.

Klauer, S.G., Feng Guo, B.G. Simons-Morton, M.C. Ouimet, S.E. Lee, and T.A. Dingus. 2014. "Distracted Driving and Risk of Road Crashes among Novice and Experienced Drivers." *New England Journal of Medicine* 370, 1: 54–9.

Klawiter, Maren. 1999. "Racing for the Cure, Walking Women, and Toxic Touring: Mapping Cultures of Action within the Bay Area Terrain of Breast Cancer." *Social Problems* 46, 1: 104–26.

———. 2004. "Breast Cancer in Two Regimes: The Impact of Social Movements on Illness Experience." *Sociology of Health and Illness* 26, 6: 845–74.

Kleinman, Arthur. 1988. *The Illness Narratives: Suffering, Healing and the Human Condition*. New York: Basic Books.

Koenen, K.C., A. Lincoln, and A. Appleton. 2006. "Women's Status and Child Well-Being: A State-level Analysis." *Social Science and Medicine* 63: 2999–3012.

Koenig, H.G. 2009. "Research on Religion, Spirituality, and Mental Health: A Review." *Canadian Journal of Psychiatry* 54, 5: 283–91.

———, M. McCullough, and D.B. Larson. 2001. *Handbook of Religion and Health: A Century of Research Reviewed*. New York: Oxford University Press.

Kondro, W. 2010a. "Drug Industry Cash." *CMAJ* 182, 6: E266.

———. 2010b. "Pfizer Handouts." *CMAJ* 182, 8: E345.

Kornstein, S.G., and A.F. Schatzberg. 2000. "Gender Differences in Treatment Response to Sentraline versus Imipimine in Chronic Depression." *American Journal of Psychiatry* 157: 1445–52.

Koss, Mary P., Lori Heise, and Nancy F. Russo. 1994. "The Global Health Burden of Rape." *Psychology of Women Quarterly* 18: 509–37.

Kowser, Omer Hashi, and Joan Silver. 1994. "No Words Can Express: Two Voices on Female Genital Mutilation." *Canadian Women's Studies* 14, 3: 62–5.

Kramer, Peter D. 1993. *Listening to Prozac*. New York: Penguin Books.

Krause, Elliot A. 1978. *Power and Illness: The Political Sociology of Health and Medical Care*. New York: Elsevier.

Kreiger, N. 2011. *Epidemiology and the People's Health*. New York: Oxford University Press.

Kristin, B. 2011. "Listening to Lyrica: Contested Diagnoses and Pharmaceutical Determinism." *Social Science and Medicine* 73: 833–42.

Kronenfeld, Jennie Jacobs, Mark Reiser, Deborah C. Glik, Carlos Alatorre, and Kirby Jackson. 1997. "Safety Behaviours of Mothers of Young Children: Impact of Cognitive, Stress and Background Factors." *Health* 1, 2: 205–25.

Krucoff, M.W., et al. 2005. "Music, Imagery, Touch, and Prayer as Adjuncts to Interventional Cardiac Care: The Monitoring and Actualisation of Noetic Trainings (MANTRA) II Randomised Study." *Lancet* 366: 211–17.

Kudlow, P. 2013. "The Perils of Diagnostic Inflation." *CMAJ* 185, 1: 25–6.

Kuhn, Thomas. 1962. *The Structure of Scientific Revolutions*. Chicago: University of Chicago Press.

Labonte, R. 2003. *Dying for Trade: Why Globalization Can Be Bad for Our Health*. Toronto: CSJ Foundation for Research and Education.

Laing, R.D., and A. Esterson. 1970 [1964]. *Sanity, Madness and the Family*. New York: Penguin.

Lakoff, Andrew. 2004. "The Anxieties of Globalization: Antidepressant Sales and Economic Crisis in Argentina." *Social Studies of Science* 34, 2: 247–69.

Lalonde, Marc. 1974. *A New Perspective on the Health of Canadians*. Ottawa: Information Canada.

Lambert, T., and K. Benzies. 2004. "Child Health and the Environment." *Canadian Journal of Public Health* 95, 6: 423.

Landro, L. 2003. "Personal Health (a Special Report)—Net Benefits: Where To Find Reliable Sources on Alternative Medicine." *Wall Street Journal*, 21 Oct.

Langlois, Stéphanie, and Peter Morrison. 2002. "Suicide Deaths and Attempts." *Canadian Social Trends* (Autumn): 20–5.

Langone, John. 1982. *Chiropractors*. New York: Addison-Wesley.

Lantz, P.M., J.S. House, R.P. Mero, and D.R. Williams. 2005. "Stress, Life Events, and Socioeconomic Disparity: Results from the Americans' Changing Lives Study." *Journal of Health and Social Behavior* 46: 274–88.

Last, J. 1963. "The Iceberg: Completing the Clinical Picture in General Practice." *Lancet* 2, 729: 28–31.

Latkin, C.A., and A.D. Curry. 2003. "Stressful Neighborhoods and Depression: A Prospective Study of the Impact of Neighborhood Disorders." *Journal of Health and Social Behavior* 44: 34–44.

LaVeist, Thomas A. 1992. "The Political Empowerment and Health Status of African-Americans: Mapping a New Territory." *American Journal of Sociology* 97, 4: 1080–95.

LaVigne, Michele, and Gregory J. Van Rybroek. 2011. "Breakdown in the Language Zone: The Prevalence of Language Impairments among Juvenile and Adult Offenders and Why It Matters." *UC Davis Journal of Juvenile Law and Policy* 15, 1: 37–123. http://ssrn.com/abstract=1663805.

Lawrence, D.J., and W.C. Meeker. 2007. "Chiropractic and CAM Utilization: A Descriptive Review." *Chiropractic and Osteopathy* 15, 2: 1–27. www.chiroandosteo.com/content/pdf/1746-1340-15-2.pdf.

Lawton, R., and D. Parker. 2002. "Barriers to Incident Reporting in a Healthcare System." *Quality and Safety in Health Care* 11: 15–18.

Lazarus, Ellen S. 1997. "Politicizing Abortion: Personal Morality and Professional Responsibility of Residents Training in the United States." *Social Science and Medicine* 44, 9: 1417–25.

Lazarus, R.S., and A. Delongis. 1983. "Psychological Stress and Coping in Aging." *American Psychologist* 38: 245–54.

Lee, Charles. 1987. *Toxic Waste and Race in the U.S.* New York Commission for Racial Justice, United Church of Christ.

Leece, P.N., S. Hopkins, C. Marshall, A. Orkin, M.A. Gassanov, and R.M. Shabin. 2013. "Development and Implementation of an Opioid Overdose Prevention and Response Program in Toronto, Ontario." *Canadian Review of Public Health* 104, 3: 200–4.

Lemmens, Trudo, and L. Peter Singer. 1998. "Bioethics for Clinicians: Conflict of Interest in Research, Education, and Patient Care." *CMAJ* 159: 960–5.

Lerner, Michael. 1994. *Choices in Healing.* Cambridge, Mass.: MIT Press.

Lernere, B.H. 2006. *When Illness Goes Public: Celebrity Patients and How We Look at Medicine.* Baltimore: Johns Hopkins University Press.

Lesage, J. 1991. "Polypharmacy in Geriatric Patients." *Nursing Clinics of North America* 26: 273–90.

LeShan, Larry. 1978. *You Can Fight for Your Life.* New York: M. Evans.

Lett, D. 2010. "Police Launch Criminal Investigation into Actions of Emergency Department." *CMAJ* 182, 18: 817.

Levin, J.S. 1993. "Esoteric vs. Exoteric Explanations for Findings Linking Spirituality and Health." *Advances* 9, 4: 54–6.

——— and P.L. Schiller. 1987. "Is There a Religious Factor in Health?" *Journal of Religion and Health* 26, 1: 9–36.

——— and H.Y. Vanderpool. 1989. "Is Religion Therapeutically Significant for Hypertension?" *Social Science and Medicine* 29, 1: 69–78.

Levine, Mitchell A.H., and Ashish Pradhan. 1999. "Can the Health Care System Buy Better Antibiotic Prescribing Behaviour?" *CMAJ* 160: 1023–4.

Lewinsohn, Rachel. 1998. "Medical Theories, Science and the Practice of Medicine." *Social Science and Medicine* 46, 10: 1261–70.

Lexchin, Joel. 1984. *The Real Pushers: A Critical Analysis of the Canadian Drug Industry.* Vancouver: New Star Books.

———. 1988a. "Profits First: The Pharmaceutical Industry in Canada." In Bolaria and Dickinson (1988: 497–513).

———. 1988b. "Pushing Pills: Who's to Blame for So Much Poor Prescribing?" *Globe and Mail*, 13 Dec., A7.

———. 1988c. "Pharmaceutical Industry." In *The Canadian Encyclopedia*, vol. 3, 1653–4. Edmonton: Hurtig.

———. 1990. "Drug Makers and Drug Regulators: Too Close for Comfort: A Study of the Canadian Situation." *Social Science and Medicine* 31, 11: 1257–63.

———. 1991. "Adverse Drug Reaction: Review of the Canadian Literature." *Canadian Family Physician* 37: 109–18.

———. 1994a. "Profits First: The Pharmaceutical Industry in Canada." In Bolaria and Dickinson (1994: 700–20).

———. 1994b. "Canadian Marketing Codes: How Well Are They Controlling Pharmaceutical Promotion." *International Journal of Health Services* 24, 1: 91–104.

———. 1996. "Cost-Effective Pharmaceutical Care for the Elderly and the Formulation of Pharmaceutical Policy in Canada." *Health and Canadian Society* 3, 1–2: 119–33.

———. 1998. "Improving the Appropriateness of Physician Prescribing." *International Journal of Health Services* 28, 2: 253–67.

———. 2004. "New Directions in Drug Approval." *CMAJ* 171, 3: 229–30.

———. 2005. "Drug Withdrawals from the Canadian Market for Safety Reasons, 1963–2004." *CMAJ* 172, 6: 765–7.

———. 2006. "Do Manufacturers of Brand Name Drugs Engage in Price Competition? An Analysis of Introductory Pricing." *CMAJ* 174, 8: 1120–1.

———. 2009. "Drug Safety and Health Canada: Going, Going . . . Gone?" Canadian Centre for Policy Alternatives. http://www.policyalternatives.ca/sites/default/files/uploads/publications/National_Office_Pubs/2009/Drug_Safety_and_Health_Canada.pdf.

———. 2012. "The Pharmaceutical Industry and Health Canada: Values in Conflict." In John Germov and Jennie Hornosty, eds, *Second Opinion: An Introduction to Health Sociology*, Canadian edn, 277–95. Toronto: Oxford University Press.

——— and M.E. Wiktorowicz. 2009. "Profits First: The Pharmaceutical Industry in Canada." In Bolaria and Dickinson (2009: 437–57).

Li, S., and A. Arber. 2006. "The Construction of Troubled and Credible Patients: A Study of Emotion Talk in Palliative Care Setting." *Qualitative Health Research* 16, 1: 27–46.

Liang, B.A. 2002. "A System of Medical Error Disclosure." *Quality and Safety in Health Care* 11: 64–8.

Liebenberg, L., M. Ungar, and J.C. LeBlanc. 2013. "The CYRM-12: A Brief Measure of Resilience." *Canadian Journal of Public Health* 104, 2: 131–5.

Linch, S.M. 2006. "Explaining Life Course and Cohort Variation in the Relationship between Education and Health: The Role of Income." *Journal of Health and Social Behavior* 47, 4: 324–38.

Lincoln, A. 2006. "Psychiatric Emergency Room Decision-Making, Social Control and the 'Undeserving Sick.'" *Sociology of Health and Illness* 28, 1: 54–75.

Linde, Klaus, Nicola Clasius, Gilbert Ramirez, Dieter Melchart, Florian Eitel, Larry V. Hedges, and Wayne B. Toras. 1997. "Are the Clinical Effects of Homeopathy Placebo Effects? A Meta-analysis of Placebo-controlled Trials." *Lancet* 350 (20 Sept.): 834–41.

Lippman, Abby, Ryan Melnychuk, Carolyn Shimmin, and Madeline Boscoe. 2007. "Human Papillomavirus, Vaccines and Women's Health: Questions and Cautions." *CMAJ* 177, 5. doi: 10.1503/cmaj.0709.

Litoff, J. 1978. *American Midwives: 1860 to the Present.* Westport, Conn.: Greenwood Press.

Liu, F., Z.M. Li, Y.J. Jiang, and L.D. Chen. 2014. "A Meta-analysis of Acupuncture Use in the Treatment of Cognitive Impairment after Stroke." *Journal of Alternative and Complementary Medicine* 20, 7: 535–44.

Locke, Michael, and Joel G. Ray. 1999. "Higher Neonatal Morbidity after Routine Early Hospital Discharge: Are We Sending Newborns Home Too Early?" *CMAJ* 161: 249–53.

Lockwood, N.L., and S.M. Yoshimura. 2014. "The Heart of the Matter: The Effects of Humor on Well-being during Recovery from Cardiovascular Disease." *Health Communication* 29: 410–20.

Loe, M. 2006. "The Viagra Blues: Embracing or Resisting the Viagra Body." In Rosenfeld and Faircloth (2006: 21–44).

Lopez, A.D. 2005. "The Evolution of the Global Burden of Disease Framework for Disease, Injury and Risk Factor Quantification: Developing the Evidence Base for National, Regional and Global Public Health Action." *Globalization and Health* 1, 5: 1–5.

Lundqvist, G., C.G. Svedin, K. Hansson, and I. Broman. 2006. "Group Therapy for Women Sexually Abused as Children: Mental Health before and after Group Therapy." *Journal of Interpersonal Violence* 21, 12: 1665–77.

Lupton, Deborah. 1993. "Risk as Moral Danger: The Social Political Functions of Risk Discourse in Public Health." *International Journal of Health Services* 23, 3: 425–35.

———. 2012. "M-health and Health Promotion: The Digital Cyborg and Surveillance Society." *Social Theory & Health* 10, 3: 229–34.

Lynch, James L. 1977. *The Broken Heart: The Medical Consequences of Loneliness*. New York: Basic Books.

Mabry, B.J., and J.K. Klecolt. 2005. "Anger in Black and White: Race, Alienation, and Anger." *Journal of Health and Social Behavior* 46, 1: 85–101.

McAndrew, Brian. 1999. "Innu Suicide Rate Highest in World." *Toronto Star*, 8 Nov., A1, A14.

McCallum, Jack. 2008. "Steroids in America: The Real Dope." *Sports Illustrated*, 11 Mar. sportsillustrated.cnn.com/2008/magazine/03/11/steroids1/index.html.

McCauley, L.A., W.K. Anger, M. Keifer, R. Langley, M.G. Robson, and D. Rohiman. 2006. "Studying Health Outcomes in Farmworker Populations Exposed to Pesticides." *Environmental Health Perspectives* 114, 6: 953–60.

McCormick, Rod, Richard Nedan, Paul McNicoll, and Judith Lynam. 1997. "Taking Back the Wisdom: Moving Forward to Recovery and Action." *Canadian Journal of Community Mental Health* 16, 2: 5–8.

McCrea, F.B. 1983. "The Politics of Menopause: The Discovery of a Deficiency Disease." *Social Problems* 31, 1: 111–23.

Macdonald, David, and Daniel Wilson. 2013. *Poverty or Prosperity: Indigenous Children in Canada*. Ottawa: Canadian Centre for Policy Alternatives. https://www.policyalternatives.ca/sites/default/files/uploads/publications/National%20Office/2013/06/Poverty_or_Prosperity_Indigenous_Children.pdf.

MacDonald, S., G. Watt, and U. MacLeod. 2013. "In Search of the Cancer Candidate: Can Lay Epidemiology Help?" *Sociology of Health and Illness* 35, 4: 575–91.

McGibbon, E.A., and J.B. Etowa. 2009. *Anti-Racist Health Care Practice*. Toronto: Canadian Scholars' Press.

McGillis Hall, L., D. Doran, G.R. Baker, G.H. Pink, S. Sidani, L. O'Brien-Pallas, and G.J. Donner. 2003. "Nurse Staffing Models as Predictors of Patient Outcomes." *Medical Care* 41, 9: 1096–1109.

——— and D. Kiesners. 2005. "A Narrative Approach to Understanding the Nursing Work Environment in Canada." *Social Science and Medicine* 61: 2482–91.

McInerney, F. 2006. "Heroic Frames: Discursive Constructions around the Requested Death Movement in Australia in the Late 1990s." *Social Science and Medicine* 62(3): 654–667.

McInturff, K. 2013. *The Gap in the Gender Gap: Violence against Women in Canada*. Canadian Centre for Policy Alternatives Report. www.policyalternatives.com.

McIntyre, D., and L. Gilson. 2000. "Redressing Disadvantage: Promoting Vertical Equity within South Africa." *Health Care Analysis* 8, 3: 235–58.

McIntyre, R.S., J.Z. Konarshi, S. Grigoriadis, N.C. Fan, D.A. Mancini, K.A. Fulton, D.E. Stewart, and S.H. Kennedy. 2005. "Hormone Replacement Therapy and Antidepressant Prescription Patterns: A Reciprocal Relationship." *CMAJ* 172, 1: 57.

MacIntyre, S., and D. Oldman. 1984. "Coping with Migraine." In N. Black et al., eds, *Health and Disease: A Reader*, 271–5. Milton Keynes: Open University Press.

McKenzie, H., and M. Crouch. 2004. "Discordant Feelings in the Lifeworld of Cancer Survivors." *Health: An Interdisciplinary Journal for the Social Study of Health, Illness, and Medicine* 8, 2: 139–57.

McKenzie, Kwame. 2003. "Racism and Health." *British Medical Journal* 326, 7380: 65–6.

McKeown, T. 1976. *The Role of Medicine: Dream, Mirage or Nemesis*. London: Neufeld Provincial Hospitals Trust.

——— and R.G. Record. 1975. "An Interpretation of the Decline of Mortality in England and Wales during the Twentieth Century." *Population Studies* 29: 391–422.

McKinlay, John B. 1982. "Toward the Proletarianization of Physicians." In C. Derber, ed., *Professionals as Workers*, 37–62. Boston: Hall.

———. 1996. "Some Contribution from the Social System to Gender Inequality in Heart Disease." *Journal of Health and Social Behavior* 37, 1: 1–26.

——— and Sonja M. McKinlay. 1977. "The Questionable Contribution of Medical Measures to the Decline of Mortality in the United States in the Twentieth Century." *Milbank Memorial Fund Quarterly* (Summer): 405–28.

——— and ———. 1981. "From Promising Report to Standard Procedure: Seven Stages in the Career of a Medical Innovation." *Milbank Memorial Fund Quarterly* 59: 374–411.

——— and ———. 1987. "Medical Measures and the Decline of Mortality." In Howard D. Schwartz, ed., *Dominant Issues in Medical Sociology*, 2nd edn. New York: Random House.

MacKinnon, Melanie. 2005. "A First Nations Voice in the Present Creates Healing in the Future." *Canadian Journal of Public Health* 96 (suppl. 1): S13–S16.

McLeod, C.B., J.N. Lavis, C.A. Mustard, and G.L. Stoddart. 2003. "Income Inequality, Household Income, and Health Status in Canada: A Prospective Cohort Study." *American Journal of Public Health* 93, 8: 1287–93.

McLeod, Thomas H., and Ina McLeod. 1987. *Tommy Douglas: The Road to Jerusalem*. Edmonton: Hurtig.

McPherson, K., S. Kerr, E. McGee, F. Cheater, and A. Morgan. 2013. *The Role and Impact of Social Capital on the Health and Well-being of Children and Adolescents: A Systematic Review*. Glasgow, Scotland: Glasgow Centre for Population Health.

McVeigh, K. 2013. "US Supreme Court Rules Human Genes Cannot Be Patented." *The Guardian*, 13 June.

Maggie, H. 1993. *Impact of Residential Schools and Other Root Causes of Poor Mental Health*. Edmonton: Nechi Institute.

Major, Ralph H. 1954. *A History of Medicine*, 2 vols. Springfield, Ill.: Thomas.

Makdessian, Frances. 1987. *Occupational Health and Safety Management Book*. Don Mills, Ont.: Corpus Information Services.

Malacrida, Claudia. 2003. *Cold Comfort: Mothers, Professionals and Attention Deficit (Hyperactivity) Disorder*. Toronto: University of Toronto Press.

Manning, Peter K., and Horatio Fabrega. 1973. "The Experience of Self and Body: Health and Illness in the Chipas Highlands." In George Psathas, ed., *Phenomenological Sociology*. New York: John Wiley and Sons.

Mariotto, A.B., J.H. Rowland, K.R. Yabroff, S. Scoppa, M. Hachey, L. Ries, and E.J. Feuer. 2009. "Long-term Survivors of Childhood Cancers in the United States." *Cancer Epidemiology Biomarkers Prevention* 18: 1033.

Markowitz, Fred E. 1998. "The Effects of Stigma on the Psychological Well-Being and Life Satisfaction of Persons with Mental Illness." *Journal of Health and Social Behavior* 39, 4: 335–47.

Marks, Geoffrey, and William K. Beatty. 1976. *Epidemics*. New York: Charles Scribner's.

Marsh, S.C., S.S. Clinkinbeard, R.M. Thomas, and W.P. Evans. 2007. "Risk and Protective Factors Predictive of Sense of Coherence during Adolescence." *Journal of Health Psychology* 12, 2: 281–4.

Marshall, V.W. 1980. *Last Chapters: A Sociology of Aging and Dying*. Monterey Calif.: Brooks/Cole Publishing.

Martin, Emily. 1987. *The Woman in the Body: A Cultural Analysis of Reproduction*. Boston: Beacon Press.

Martin, G. 2005. "Globalization and Health." *Globalization and Health* 1, 1: 1–2.

Martin, M.C., E. Seanna, N.D. Willows, I. Colman, asnd A. Ohinma. 2013. "Diet Quality and Feelings of Worry, Sadness or Unhappiness in Canadian Children." *Canadian Journal of Public Health* 104, 4: 322–6.

Martindale, Don. 1960. *The Nature and Types of Sociological Theory*. Boston: Houghton Mifflin.

Marx, Karl. 1964. *The Economic and Philosophic Manuscripts of 1844*. Trans. M. Milligan. New York: International Publishers.

Maselko, J., and L.D. Kubzansky. 2005. "Gender Differences in Religious Practices, Spiritual Experiences and Health: Results from the US General Social Survey." *Social Science and Medicine* 62, 11: 2848–60.

Mather, C. 2005. "The Pipeline and the Porcupine: Alternate Metaphors of the Physician–Industry Relationship." *Social Science and Medicine* 60: 1323–34.

May, Carl, and Deepak Sirur. 1998. "Art, Science and Placebo: Incorporating Homeopathy in General Practice." *Sociology of Health and Illness* 20, 2: 168–90.

May, J., and J. Wasserman. 1984. "Selected Results from an Evaluation of the New Jersey Diagnosis-related Group System." *Health Services Research* 19, 5 (Dec.): 548.

Meador, Clifton. 1965. "The Art and Science of Non-Disease." *New England Journal of Medicine* 235: 424–45.

Mechanic, David. 1978. *Medical Sociology: A Comprehensive Text*. New York: Free Press.

———. 1993. "Sociological Research in Health and the American Socio-political Context." *Social Science and Medicine* 36, 2: 95–102.

Mecredy, G.C., L.M. Diemert, R.C. Callaghan, and J.E. Cohen. 2013. "Association between Use of Contraband Tobacco and Smoking Cessation Outcomes: A Population-based Cohort Study." *CMAJ* 185, 7: 287–94.

Meel, B.L. 2003. "The Myth of Child Rape as a Cure for HIV/AIDS in Transkei." *Medicine, Science & the Law* 43, 1: 85–8.

Mehta, Paul, Vinicius Antao, Wendy Kaye, Marchelle Sanchez, David Williamson, Leah Bryan, Oleg Muravov, and Kevin Horton. 2014. "Prevalence of Amyotrophic Lateral Sclerosis in the United States, 2010–2011." *Morbidity and Mortality Weekly Report*, 25 July, 1–14.

Merton, Robert K., George Reader, and Patricia Kendall, eds. 1957. *The Student Physician: Introductory Studies in the Sociology of Medical Education*. Cambridge, Mass.: Harvard University Press.

Messing, Karen. 1998. *One-Eyed Science: Occupational Health and Women Workers*. Philadelphia: Temple University Press.

Metraux, S., L.X. Clegg, J.D. Daigh, D.P. Culhane, and V. Kane. 2013. "Risk Factors for Becoming Homeless among a Cohort of Veterans Who Served in the Era of the Iraq and Afghanistan Conflicts." *American Journal of Public Health* 103 (suppl. 2): 255–61.

Metzl, J. 2010. *The Protest Psychosis: How Schizophrenia Became a Black Disease*. Beacon Press. Beacon Hill Press. Boston, MA.

Metzl, J.M., and J. Angel. 2004. "Assessing the Impact of SSRI Antidepressants on Popular Notions of Women's Depressive Illness." *Social Science and Medicine* 58: 577–84.

Mikkonen, Juha, and Dennis Raphael. 2010. *Social Determinants of Health: The Canadian Facts*. Toronto: York University School of Health Policy and Management.

Milgram, Stanley. 1974. *Obedience to Authority*. New York: Harper & Row.

Millar, Wayne, Jill Strachan, and Surinder Wadhera. 1993. "Trends in Low Birthweight." *Canadian Social Trends* 28 (Spring): 26–9.

Miller, Adam. 2013. "Incorporating Theology into Medical Education." *CMAJ* 185, 1: 35–7.

Miller, Anthony B. 1992. "Planning Cancer Control Strategies." *Chronic Diseases in Canada*. Ottawa: Health Canada.

——, C. Wall, P. Sun, C.J. Baines, T. To, and S.A. Narod. 2014. "Twenty-five Year Follow-up for Breast Cancer Incidence and Mortality of the Canadian National Breast Cancer Screening Study: Randomized Screening Trial." *British Medical Journal*: 348.

Miller, James A. 1996. "Money for Mischief: USAID and Pathfinder Tag-team Women in the Developing World." *Population Reserve Institute* 6, 5. http://www.pop.org/content/money-for-mischief-usaid-and-pathfinder-1694.

Miller, L.E. 2014. "Uncertainty Management and Information Seeking in Cancer Survivorship." *Health Communication* 29: 233–43.

Millman, Marcia. 1977. *The Unkindest Cut*. New York: William Morrow.

Mills, C. Wright. 1959. *The Sociological Imagination*. New York: Oxford University Press.

Min, S.T. and D.A. Redelmeier. 1998. "Car Phones and Car Crashes: An Ecologic Analysis." *Canadian Journal of Public Health* 89, 3: 157–61.

Mintzes, Barbara. 2010. "'Ask Your Doctor': Women and Direct-to-Consumer Advertising." In Rochon Ford and Saibil (2010: 17–46).

——, Morris L. Barer, Richard L. Kravitz, et al. 2002. "Influence of Direct-to-Consumer Pharmaceutical Advertising and Patients' Requests on Prescribing Decisions: Two-Site Cross-Sectional Survey." *British Medical Journal* 324: 278–9.

——, ——, ——, et al. 2003. "How Does Direct-to-Consumer Advertising (DTCA) Affect Prescribing? A Survey in Primary Care Environments with and without Legal DTCA." *CMAJ* 169, 5: 405.

Mishler, Elliot. 1984. *The Discourse of Medicine: Dialectics of Medical Interviews*. Norwood, NJ: Ablex.

Mitchinson, Wendy. 1987. "Medical Perceptions of Healthy Women: The Case of Nineteenth Century Canada." *Canadian Women's Studies* 8, 4: 42–3.

Monaghan, L.F., R. Colls, and B. Evans. 2013. "Editorial: Obesity Discourse and Fat Politics: Research, Critique and Intervention." *Critical Public Health* 23, 3: 249–62.

Montbriand, Muriel J. 1994. "An Overview of Alternate Therapies Chosen by Patients with Cancer." *Oncology Nursing Forum* 21, 9: 1547–54.

——. 1995. "Decision Tree Model Describing Alternative Health Care Choices Made by Oncology Patients." *Cancer Nursing* 18, 4: 104–17.

Montini, Theresa, and Kathleen Slobin. 1991. "Tensions between Good Science and Good Practice: Lagging Behind and Leapfrogging Ahead Along the Cancer Care Continuum." *Research in the Sociology of Health Care* 9: 127–40.

Moore, S., A.C. Teixeira, and A. Shiell. 2006. "The Health of Nations in a Global Context: Trade, Global Stratification, and Infant Mortality Rates." *Social Science and Medicine* 63: 165–78.

Moreira-Almeida, A., and H.G. Koenig. 2006. "Retaining the Meaning of the Words and Spirituality: A Commentary on the WHOQOLSRPB Group's 'A Cross-cultural Study of Spirituality, Religion, and Personal Beliefs as Components of Quality of Life.'" *Social Science and Medicine* 63: 843–5.

Mosby, I. 2013. "Administering Colonial Science: Nutrition Research and Human Biomedical Experimentation in Aboriginal Communities and Residential Schools, 1942–1952." *Histoire sociale/Social History* 46, 91: 145–72.

Moss, Nancy E. 2002. "Gender Equity and Socio-economic Inequality: A Framework for the Patterning of Women's Health." *Social Science and Medicine* 54: 649–61.

Moyer, Anne, Susan Grenner, John Beavis, and Peter Salovey. 1994. "Accuracy of Health Research Reported in the Popular Press: Breast Cancer and Mammography." *Health Communication* 7, 1: 147–61.

Moynihan, Ray. 2003. "The Making of a Disease: Female Sexual Dysfunction." *British Medical Journal* 326, 7379: 45–7.

——. 2006. "Scientists Find New Disease: Motivational Deficiency Disorder." *British Medical Journal* 332: 745.

——, Iona Heath, and David Henry. 2002. "Selling Sickness: The Pharmaceutical Industry and Disease Mongering." *British Medical Journal* 324: 886–91.

Mulé, N.J., L.E. Ross, B. Deeprose, B.E. Jackson, A. Daley, A. Travers, and D. Moore. 2009. "Promoting LGBT Health and Wellbeing through Inclusive Policy Development." *International Journal for Equity in Health* 8: 18.

Muller, M. 1982. *The Health of Nations*. London: Faber and Faber.

Mumford, Emily. 1983. *Medical Sociology: Patients, Providers and Policies*. New York: Random House.

Murray, E., et al. 2003a. "The Impact of Health Information on the Internet on Health Care and the Physician–Patient Relationship: National US Survey among 1,050 US Physicians. " *Journal of Medical Internet Research* 5, 3. www.ncbi.nlm.nih.gov/entrez/query.fcgi?itool+abstractplus&db=pubmed&cmd=Re.

—— et al. 2003b. "Direct-to-Consumer Advertising: Physicians' Views of Its Effects on Quality of Care and the Doctor–Patient Relationship." *Journal of the American Board of Family Practice* 16, 6: 513–24.

Musick, M.A., J.S. House, and D.R. Williams. 2004. "Attendance at Religious Services and Mortality in a National Sample." *Journal of Health and Social Behavior* 45, 2: 198–213.

Mustard, Fraser. 1987. "Health in a Post-Industrial Society." In J. Clarke et al., eds, *Health Care in Canada: Looking Ahead.* Ottawa: Canadian Public Health Association.

Muzzin, Linda J., Gregory P. Brown, and Roy W. Hornosty.1993. "Professional Ideology in Canadian Pharmacy." *Health and Canadian Society* 1, 2: 319–46.

Myers, David G. 2000. *A Quiet World: Living with Hearing Loss.* New Haven: Yale University Press.

Nahin, R.L., P.M. Barnes, B.J. Stussman, and B. Bloom. 2009. "Costs of Complementary and Alternative Medicine (CAM) and Frequency of Visits to CAM Practitioners: United States, 2007." *National Health Statistics Report* 18 (30 July): 1–14.

——, J.M. Dahlhamer, and B.J. Stussman. 2010. "Health Need and the Use of Alternative Medicine among Adults Who Do Not Use Conventional Medicine." *BMC Health Services Research*, 10: 220.

Nathanson, C.A. 1977. "Sex, Illness and Medical Care: A Review of Data, Theory and Method." *Social Science and Medicine* 11: 13–25.

National Center for Complementary and Alternative Medicine (NCCAM). 2006. *The Use of Complementary and Alternative Medicine in the United States.* nccam.nih.gov/news/camsurvey_fs1.htm.

National Council of Welfare. 2002. "National Council of Welfare Reports." *Poverty Profile* (Summer). Ottawa: National Council of Welfare.

Nault, Francois. 1997. "Narrowing Mortality Gaps 1978 to 1995." *Health Reports* 9, 1 (Summer): 35–41.

Nausheen, B., Y. Gidron, R. Peveler, and R. Moss-Morris. 2009. "Social Support and Cancer Progression: A Systematic Review." *Journal of Psychosomatic Research* 67, 5: 403–15.

Navarro, Vincente. 1975a. "The Industrialization of Fetishism or the Fetishism of Industrialization: A Critique of Ivan Illich." *Social Science and Medicine* 9, 7: 351–63.

——. 1975b. "Women in Health Care." *New England Journal of Medicine* 202: 398–402.

——. 1976. "Social Class, Political Power and the State and Their Implications for Medicine." *Social Science and Medicine* 10: 437–57.

——. 1992. "Has Socialism Failed? An Analysis of Health Indicators under Socialism." *International Journal of Health Services* 22, 4: 585–601.

—— and C. Borrell. 2004. *The Political and Social Contexts of Health.* Amityville, NY: Baywood Publishing.

—— and V. Shi. 2003. "The Political Context of Social Inequalities and Health." In Hofrichter (2003: 195–216).

Naylor, C.D. 1982. "In Defense of Medicare: Are Canadian Doctors Threatening the Health Care System?" *Canadian Forum* 62 (Apr.): 12–16.

Nelson, Melvin D. 1992. "Socio-economic Status and Childhood Mortality in North Carolina." *American Journal of Public Health* 82, 8: 1131–3.

Neidhardt, J., M.S. Weinstein, and Robert R. Coury. 1985. *No-Gimmick Guide to Managing Stress.* Vancouver: Self-Counsel Press.

Nestel, Sheryl. 2012. "Colour Coded Health Care: The Impact of Race and Racism on Canadians' Health." Toronto: Wellesley Institute. http://www.wellesleyinstitute.com/wp-content/uploads/2012/02/Colour-Coded-Health-Care-Sheryl-Nestel.pdf.

Nettleton S. 2004. "The Emergence of E-Scaped Medicine." *Sociology* 38, 4: 661–80.

Newbold, K.B., and J. Danforth. 2003. "Health Status and Canada's Immigrant Population." *Social Science and Medicine* 57: 1981–95.

Ng, E., R. Wilkins, F. Gendron, and J. Berthelot. 2005. *The Changing Health of Immigrants.* Ottawa: Statistics Canada Catalogue no. 11-008.

Nicholson, G.W.L. 1967. *The White Cross in Canada.* Montreal: Harvest House.

——. 1975. *Canada's Nursing Sisters.* Toronto: Hakkert.

Nikiforuk, Andrew. 1991. "The Great Fire." *Equinox* 59 (Sept.–Oct.).

Noar, S.M., J.F. Willoughby, J.G. Myrick, and J. Brown. 2014. "Public Figure Announcements about Cancer and Opportunities for Cancer Communication: A Review and Research Agenda." *Health Communication* 29: 445–61.

Nohrestedt, S.A. 1991. "The Information Crisis in Sweden after Chernobyl." *Media, Culture and Society* 13: 477–97.

Nomaguchi, K., and A.N. House. 2013. "Racial-Ethnic Disparities in Maternal Parenting Stress: The Roles of Structural Disadvantages and Parenting Values." *Journal of Health and Social Behavior* 54, 3: 386–404.

Nordquist, G. 2006. "Patient Insurance Status and Do-Not-Resuscitate Orders: Survival of the Richest?" *Journal of Sociology and Social Welfare* 33, 1: 75.

Novotny, T.E. 2013. "Irreconcilable Conflict: The Tobacco Industry and the Public Health Challenge of Tobacco Use." *PLOS Medicine* 10, 5.

Oakley, A. 1984. *The Captured Womb: A History of the Medical Care of Pregnant Women.* Oxford: Basil Blackwell.

Oberg, Gary R. 1990. *An Overview of the Philosophy of the American Academy of Environmental Medicine.* Denver: American Academy of Environmental Medicine.

O'Connor, J. 1973. *The Fiscal Crisis of the State.* New York: St Martin's Press.

Office of the Correctional Investigator. 2014. *Annual Report of the Office of the Correctional Investigator 2013–2014.* http://www.oci-bec.gc.ca/cnt/rpt/annrpt20132014-eng.aspx#sIV.

O'Grady, K. 2003. "New Evidence about Hormone Replacement Therapy Turning the Tide in the Menopause Wars." *Women's Studies Quarterly* 1 and 2: 137–44.

O'Hagan, J., N.J. MacKinnon, D. Persaud, and H. Etchegary. 2009. "Self-reported Medical Error in Seven Countries: Implications for Canada." *Health Quarterly* 12: 55–61.

Olivieri, N. 2010. "Foreword." In Rochon Ford and Saibil (2010: ix–xii).

Ollila, Eeva. 2005. "Global Health Priorities—Priorities of the Wealthy." *Globalization and Health* 1, 6: 1–5.

——— and Elina Hemminki. 1997. "Does Licensing of Drugs in Industrialized Countries Guarantee Drug Quality and Safety for Third World Countries? The Case of Norplant Licensing in Finland." *International Journal of Health Services* 27, 2: 309–25.

Omran, Abdel R. 1979. "Changing Patterns of Health and Disease during the Process of National Development." In G. Albrecht and P.C. Higgins, eds, *Health, Illness and Medicine*, 81–93. Chicago: Rand McNally.

O'Neill, J., D. Wilson, R. Purushothaman, and A. Stupnytska. 2005. "How Strong Are the BRICs?" Global Economics Paper No. 134. https://portal.gs.com.

Ontario Naturopathic Association (ONA). 1983. *Naturopathic Medicine and Health Care in Ontario*. A Brief Prepared by the ONA and the Board of Directors of Drugless Therapy for the Honorable Keith Norton, Minister of Health. Toronto (July).

Oppenheimer, J. 1983. "Childbirth in Ontario: The Transition from Home to Hospital in the Early Twentieth Century." *Ontario History* 75 (Mar.): 36–60.

Orbach, Susie. 1986. *Hunger Strike: An Anorexic's Struggle as a Metaphor for Our Age*. New York: Norton.

Organization for Economic Co-operation and Development (OECD). 2008. *Growing Unequal? Income Distribution and Poverty in OECD Countries*. Paris: OECD. www.oecd.org/document/4/0,3343,en_2649_33933_41460917_1_1_1_1,00.html.

Ornstein, M. 2006. "Extremely Disadvantaged Ethno-Racial Groups in Toronto." *Institute for Social Research* 21, 2: 1–3.

Ostry, A.S., and J. Frank. 2010. "Was Thomas McKeon Right for the Wrong Reasons?" *Critical Public Health* 20, 2: 233–43.

Paget, Marianne A. 1988. *The Unity of Mistakes: A Phenomenological Interpretation of Medical Work*. Philadelphia: Temple University Press.

———. 1993. *A Complex Sorrow: Reflections on Cancer and an Abbreviated Life*. Ed. Marjorie L. Devault. Philadelphia: Temple University Press.

Paim, J., C. Travassos, C. Almeida, L. Bahia, and J. Macinko. 2011. "The Brazilian Health System: History, Advances, and Challenges." *Lancet* 377: 1778–97. www.thelancet.com/journals/lancet/article/PIIS0140-6736%2811%2960054-8/fulltext#.

Pampel, Fred. 2002. "Inequality, Diffusion, and the Status Gradient in Smoking." *Social Problems* 49, 1: 35–57.

Paris, V., and E. Docteur. 2006. *Pharmaceutical Pricing and Reimbursement Policies in Canada*. Paris: OECD.

Park, W.W., and S.Y. Shin. 2009. "Moderating Effects of Group Cohesiveness in Competency-Performance Relationships: A Multi-level Study." *Journal of Behavioral Studies in Business* 6.

Parnell, L., R.E. Davidhizar, J.N. Giger, O.L. Strickland, S. Fishman, and D.M. Allison. 2011. "A Guide to Developing a Culturally Competent Organization." *Journal of Transcultural Nursing* 22, 1: 7–14.

Parsons, Talcott. 1951. *The Social System*. Glencoe, Ill.: Free Press.

Patel, V., and A. Kleinman. 2003. "Poverty and Common Mental Disorders in Developing Countries." *Bulletin of the World Health Organization* 81, 8: 609–15.

Pawluch, Dorothy, R. Cain, and J. Gilbert. 1995. "Ideology and Alternative Therapy Use among People Living with HIV/AIDS." *Health and Canadian Society* (Summer): 63–84.

Pavalko, E.K., K.N. Mossakowski, and V.J. Hamilton. 2003. "Does Perceived Discrimination Affect Health? Longitudinal Relationships between Work Discrimination and Women's Physical and Emotional Health." *Journal of Health and Social Behavior* 43: 18–33.

Payer, Lynn. 1988. *Medicine and Culture: Varieties of Treatment in the United States, England, West Germany and France*. New York: Holt.

Payette, H., and B. Shatenstein. 2005. "Determinants of Healthy Eating in Community-dwelling Elderly People." *Canadian Journal of Public Health* 96 (suppl. 3): S27–S31.

Payne-Jackson, Arvilla. 1999. "Biomedical and Folk Medical Concepts of Adult Onset Diabetes in Jamaica: Implications for Treatment." *Health* 3, 1: 5–46.

Pearce, T. 2009. "Heartache Harder on Women." *Globe and Mail*, 5 Mar., L1, L4.

Pearlin, L.I., S. Schieman, W.M. Fazio, and S. Meersman. 2005. "Stress, Health, and the Life Course: Some Conceptual Perspectives." *Journal of Health and Social Behavior* 46: 205–19.

Peate, I. 2014. "Compassion Fatigue: The Toll of Emotional Labour." *British Journal of Nursing* 23, 5: 251.

Pedersen, A., I. Walker, and M. Wise. 2005. "'Talk Does Not Cook Rice': Beyond Anti-Racism Rhetoric and Social Action." *Australian Psychologist* 40, 1: 20–30.

Peña Fajuri, S. 2013. "Health in All Policies: The Emperor's Old Clothes." Healthy Policies for a Healthier World. www.healthypolicies.com/2011/08/health-in-all-policies-the-emperor's-old-clothes.

Peritz, I. 2010. "Cursed by Miracle Drug, They Wait for an Apology." *Globe and Mail*, 6 Feb., 1, 13.

Perou, R., R.H. Bitsko, S.J. Blumberg, P. Pastor, R.M. Ghandour, J.C. Gfroerer, S.L. Hedden, A.E. Crosby, and S.N. Visser. 2013. "Mental Health Surveillance among Children, United States 2005–2011." *Morbidity and Mortality Weekly Report* 62, 2: 1–35.

Perrow, C. 1999. "Organizing to Reduce the Vulnerabilities of Complexity." *Journal of Contingencies and Crisis Management* 7, 3: 150–5.

Peters-Golden, Holly. 1982. "Breast Cancer: Varied Perceptions of Social Support in the Illness Experience." *Social Science and Medicine* 16: 483–91.

Petryna, Adriana. 2009. *When Experiments Travel: Clinical Trials and the Global Search for Human Subjects*. Princeton, NJ: Princeton University Press.

Pettigrew, Eileen. 1983. *The Silent Enemy: Canada and the Deadly Flu of 1918*. Saskatoon: Western Producer Prairie Books.

Phillips, C. 2009. "Images, Femininity and Cancer: An Analysis of an International Patient Education Program." *Health: An Interdisciplinary Journal for the Social Study of Health, Illness and Medicine* 13, 1: 67–85.

Phillips, D.P., and R.A. Feldman. 1973. "A Dip in Deaths before Ceremonial Occasions: Some New Relationships between Social Integration and Mortality." *American Sociological Review* 38: 678–96.

Phipps, S. 2003. *The Impact of Poverty on Health: A Scan of Research Literature*. Ottawa: Canadian Population Health Initiative. secure.cihi.ca/cihiweb/dispPage.jsp?cw_page=cphi_e.

Phlanz, Manfred. 1975a. "A Critique of Anglo-American Medical Sociology." *International Journal of Health Services* 4, 3: 565–74.

———. 1975b. "Relations between Social Scientists, Physicians and Medical Organizations in Health Research." *Social Science and Medicine* 9: 7–13.

Picard, André. 2002. "Wine Lifestyle Touted as Promoting Health." *Globe and Mail*, 25 July, A3.

———. 2010. "We're Not Short of MDs, We Need NPs." *Globe and Mail*, 1 Apr., L1, L4.

Piketty, Thomas. 2014. *Capital in the Twenty-First Century*. Trans. Arthur Goldhammer. Cambridge, Mass.: Belknap Press of Harvard University Press.

Pilgrim, David, and Anne E. Rogers. 2005. "Psychiatrists as Social Engineers: A Study of an Anti-stigma Campaign." *Social Science and Medicine* 61: 2546–56.

Pilnick, Alison. 1998. "Why Didn't You Say Just That? Dealing with Issues of Asymmetry, Knowledge and Competence in the Pharmacist/Client Encounter." *Sociology of Health and Illness* 20, 1: 29–51.

Pinquart, Martin. 2001. "Creating and Maintaining Purpose in Life in Old Age: A Meta-analysis." *Aging International* 27, 2: 90–114.

Pirie, Marion. 1988. "Women and the Illness Role: Rethinking Feminist Theory." *Canadian Review of Sociology and Anthropology* 25, 4: 628–48.

Pitts, V. 2004. "Illness and Internet Empowerment: Writing and Reading Breast Cancer in Cyberspace." *Health: An Interdisciplinary Journal for the Social Study of Health, Illness, and Medicine* 8, 1: 33–59.

Polanyi, M. 2004. "Understanding and Improving the Health of Work." In Raphael (2004: 95–106).

Poortinga, W. 2006. "Social Relations or Social Capital? Individual and Community Health Effects of Bonding Social Capital." *Social Science and Medicine* 63: 255–70.

Porter, Jody. 2015. "Mercury Levels Still Rising Near Grassy Narrows First Nation, Report Says." CBC News, 15 June.

Potter, P., N. Barr, M. McSweeney, and J. Sledge. 2003. "Collecting Baseline Patient Outcome Data Should Precede Nurse Staffing Changes." *Nursing Economics* 21, 4: 158–66.

Power, E.M. 2005. "Determinants of Healthy Eating among Low-Income Canadians." *Canadian Journal of Public Health* 96: S37–S42.

———. 2006. "Economic Abuse and Intra-household Inequities in Food Security." *Canadian Journal of Public Health* 97, 3: 258–60.

Pridemore, W.A. 2014. "The Mortality Penalty of Incarceration: Evidence from a Population-based Case Control Study of Working Age Males." *Journal of Health and Social Behavior* 55, 2: 215–33.

Priest, Lisa. 1993. "Thalidomide Survivors Have Tackled Life with Gusto." *Calgary Herald*, 21 Feb., B8.

———. 1996. "Mothers-to-be Are Turned Away as Demand Swamps Midwives." *Toronto Star*, 10 Mar., A6.

———. 1997a. "Wake-up Call on Medicare." *Toronto Star*, 20 Sept., A33.

———. 1997b. "The Health Police." *Toronto Star*, 26 Sept., A26.

———. 2008. "Nursing and Hospital Violence." *Globe and Mail*, 8 Jan.

Pruss, A., D. Kay, L. Fewtrell, and J. Bartram. 2002. "Estimating the Burden of Disease from Water, Sanitation, and Hygiene at a Global Level." *Environmental Health Perspectives* 110, 5: 537–42.

Public Health Agency of Canada. 2004. "Income Inequality as a Determinant of Health." www.phac-aspc.gc.ca/ph-sp/phdd/overview_implications/02_income.html.

———. 2006. *HIV and AIDS in Canada: Surveillance Report to June 30, 2006*. www.phac-aspc.gc.ca.

Pulliam, C., J. Hanlon, and S. Moore. 1988. "Medication and Geriatics." In F. Abellah and S. Moore, eds, *Surgeon General's Workshop: Health Promotion and Aging. Background Papers*. Menlo Park, Calif.: Henry J. Kaiser Foundation.

Punnett, Laura. 1976. "Women-Controlled Medicine—Theory and Practice in 19th Century Boston." *Women and Health* 1, 4 (July–Aug.): 3–10.

Purnell, L. 2000. "A Description of the Purnell Model for Cultural Competence." *Journal of Transcultural Nursing* 11, 1: 40–6.

Quan, H., et al. 2006. "Variation in Health Services Utilization among Ethnic Populations." *CMAJ* (14 Mar.) 174, 6: 787–91.

Qureshi, N.A., and A. Mohammed Al-Bedah. 2013. "Mood Disorders and Complementary and Alternative Medicine: A Literature Review." *Neuropsychiatric Disease and Treatment* 3, 9: 639–58.

Rabe, Barry G. 1992. "When Citing Works, Canada Style." *Journal of Health Politics, Policy and Law* 17, 1 (Spring).

Rabin, Roni. 2006. "Breast-Feed or Else." *New York Times*, 13 June. www.nytimes.com/2006/06/13/health/13brea.html?ex=1307851200anden=34fe96e9a.

Rachlis, Michael, and Carol Kushner. 1989. *Second Opinion: What's Wrong with Canada's Health Care System*. Toronto: HarperCollins.

——— and ———. 1994. *Strong Medicine: How to Save Canada's Health Care System*. Toronto: HarperCollins.

Radley, Alan. 1999. "Abhorrence, Compassion and the Social Response to Suffering." *Health* 3, 2 (Apr.): 167–88.

Radway, Scott. 2002. "Soldiers Easing Back to Normal Life." *Globe and Mail*, 27 July, A7.

Raffel, Stanley. 1979. *Matters of Fact: A Sociological Inquiry*. London: Routledge & Kegan Paul.

Rahe, R.H., Jack L. Mahan, and Ransom J. Arthur. 1970. "Prediction of Near-Future Health Change from Subjects Preceding Life Changes." *Journal of Psychosomatic Research* 14, 4: 401–6.

——— and J. Paasikivi. 1971. "Psychosocial Factors and Myocardial Infarction. II. An Outpatient Study in Sweden." *Journal of Psychosomatic Research* 15, 1: 33–9.

Ramage-Morin, P.L. 2009. "Medication Use among Senior Canadians." *Health Reports* 20, 1: 1–8.

Rankin, J.M., and M.L. Campbell. 2006. *Managing to Nurse: Inside Canada's Health Care Reform*. Toronto: University of Toronto Press.

Ranzijn, Rob. 2001. "The Potential of Older Adults to Enhance Community Quality of Life: Links between Positive Psychology and Productive Aging." *Aging International* 27, 2: 30–55.

Raphael, Dennis. 1999. "Health Effects of Economic Inequality: Overview and Purpose." *Canadian Review of Social Policy* 44: 25–40.

———. 2001. *Inequality Is Bad for Our Hearts: Why Low Income and Social Exclusion Are Major Causes of Heart Disease in Canada*. New York: New York Health Network.

———. 2002a. *Social Justice Is Good for Our Hearts: Why Societal Factors—Not Lifestyles—Are Major Causes of Heart Disease in Canada and Elsewhere*. Toronto: CSJ Foundation for Research and Education.

———. 2002b. *Poverty, Income Inequality, and Health in Canada*. Toronto: CSJ Foundation for Research and Education. www.socialjustice.org/uploads/pubs/PovertyIncomeInequalityandHealthinCanada.pdf.

———. 2003a. *A Society in Decline*. Toronto: John Wiley and Sons.

———. 2003b. "A Society in Decline: Political, Economic, and Social Determinants of Health Inequalities in the United States." In Hofrichter (2003: 59–88).

———, ed. 2004. *Social Determinants of Health: Canadian Perspectives*. Toronto: Canadian Scholars' Press.

———, ed. 2009. *Social Determinants of Health*, 2nd edn. Toronto: Canadian Scholars' Press.

———, R. Labonte, R. Colman, K. Hayward, R. Torgerson, and J. Macdonald. 2006. "Income and Health in Canada: Research Gaps and Future Opportunities." *Canadian Journal of Public Health* 97: S16–S23.

Raven, Peter H., Linda R. Berg, and George B. Johnson. 1993. *Environment*. Toronto: Saunders.

Rawson, Nigel S.B., and Carl D'Arcy. 1991. "Sedative-Hypnotic Drug Use in Canada." *Health Reports* 3, 1: 33–57.

Rebollo-Gil, G., and A. Moras. 2006. "Defining an 'Anti' Stance: Key Pedagogical Questions about Engaging Anti-Racism in College Classrooms." *Race, Ethnicity and Education* 9, 4: 381–94.

Redelmeier, D.A., and B.A. McLellan. 2013. "Modern Medicine Is Neglecting Road Traffic Crashes." *PLOS Medicine*, 11 June. http://www.plosmedicine.org/article/info%3Adoi%2F10.1371%2Fjournal.pmed.1001463.

Registered Nurses Association of Ontario. 1987. *The RNAO Responds: A Nursing Perspective on the Events at the Hospital for Sick Children and the Grange Inquiry*. Toronto: RNAO, Apr.

Regush, Nicholas. 1987. *Canada's Health Care System: Condition Critical*. Toronto: Macmillan.

———. 1993. *Safety Last: The Failure of the Consumer Health Protection System in Canada*. Toronto: Key Porter Books.

Reilly, D.T, M. A. Taylor, C. McSharry, and T. Aitchison. 1986. "Is Homoeopathy a Placebo Response? Controlled Trial of Homoeopathic Potency, with Pollen in Hayfever as Model." *Lancet* 2, 8512: 881–6.

Reinharz, Shulamit. 1992. *Feminist Methods in Social Research*. Oxford: Oxford University Press.

Reissman, Catherine Kohler. 1987. "Women and Medicalization: A New Perspective." In Howard D. Schwartz, ed., *Dominant Issues in Medical Sociology*, 2nd edn, 101–21. New York: Random House.

Reitzel, L.R., S.D. Regan, N. Nguyen, E.K. Cromley, L.L. Strong, and D.W. Wetter. 2014. "Density and Proximity of Fast Food Restaurants and Body Mass Index among African Americans." *American Journal of Public Health* 104, 1: 110–16.

Relman, Arnold S. 1987. "The New Medical-Industrial Complex." In Howard D. Schwartz, ed., *Dominant Issues in Medical Sociology*, 2nd edn, 597–607. New York: Random House.

Report to the OMA Board of Directors from the Ad Hoc Committee on Women's Health Issues. 1987. Toronto: Ontario Medical Association.

Revah, Giselle, and Chaim Bell. 2007. "Shopping for High-Technology Treatment in Another Province." *Healthcare Policy* 2, 4: 49–55.

Reverby, Susan M. 1987. *Ordered to Care: The Dilemma of American Nursing*. Cambridge: Cambridge University Press.

Richardson, Astrid H., and Ronald J. Burke. 1991. "Occupational Stress and Job Satisfaction among Physicians: Sex Differences." *Social Science and Medicine* 33, 10: 1179–87.

Richardson, C.R., and P. Ratner. 2005. "Sense of Coherence as a Moderator of Stressful Life Events." *Epidemiology of Community Health* 59: 979–84.

Richardson, Diane, and Victoria Robinson. 1993. *Thinking Feminist: Key Concepts in Women's Studies*. New York: Guilford Press.

Riggio, Ronald E. 2012. "Don't Let Life's Hassles Become Stressors." *Psychology Today*, 23 Oct. http://www.psychologytoday.com/blog/cutting-edge-leadership/201210/don-t-let-life-s-hassles-become-stressors.

Robards, J., M. Evandrou, J. Falkingham, and A. Vlachantoni. 2012. "Marital Status, Health Mortality." *Maturitas* 73, 4: 295–9.

Robles, T.F., and J.K. Kiecolt-Glaser. 2003. "The Physiology of Marriage: Pathways to Health." *Physiology & Behavior* 79, 3: 409–16.

Rochon Ford, A., and D. Saibil. 2010. *The Push to Prescribe Women and Canadian Drug Policy*. Toronto: Women's Press.

Rocourt, J., G. Moy, K. Vierk, and J. Schlundt. 2003. *The Present State of Foodborne Disease in OECD Countries*. Geneva: Food Safety Department, WHO.

Rogers, A.E., W. Hwang, L.D. Scott, L.H. Aiken, and D.F. Dinges. 2004. "Long Working Hours of Hospital RNs Associated with Increased Errors." *Health Affairs* 23, 4: 202–12.

Roland, Charles. 1988. "Medicine, History of." In *The Canadian Encyclopedia*, vol. 2, 1330. Edmonton: Hurtig.

Romelis, Shelly. 1985. "Struggle between Providers and Recipients: The Case of Birth Practices." In Ellen Lewin and Virginia Olesen, eds, *Women, Health and Healing*, 174–208. London: Tavistock.

Ronson, B., and I. Rootman. 2004. "Literacy: One of the Most Important Determinants of Health Today." In Raphael (2004: 155–69).

—— and ——. 2009. "Literacy and Health: Implications for health and Education Professionals." In edited Leona M. English, ed, *Adult Education and Health*, 107–122

Rose, N. 1999. *Powers of Freedom Reframing Political Thought*. Cambridge: Cambridge University Press.

——. 2003. "Neurochemical Selves." *Society* 41, 1: 46–9.

——. 2006. "Disorders without Borders? The Expanding Scope of Psychiatric Practice." *Biosocieties* 1: 465–84.

Rosen, George. 1963. "The Evolution of Social Medicine." In Howard E. Freeman, Sol Levine, and Leo G. Reader, eds, *Handbook of Medical Sociology*, 23–50. Englewood Cliffs, NJ: Prentice-Hall.

Rosenberg, Charles E., and Janet Golden, eds. 1992. *Framing Disease: Studies in Cultural History*. New Brunswick, NJ: Rutgers University Press.

Rosenfeld, D., and C.A. Faircloth, eds. 2006. *Medicalized Masculinities*. Philadelphia: Temple University Press.

Rotermann, M. 2008. "Trends in Teen Sexual Behaviour and Condom Use." *Health Reports* 19, 3: 1–5.

——. 2012. "Sexual Behaviour and Condom Use of 15- to 24-year-olds in 2003 and 2009/2010." *Health Reports* 23, 1: 1–5.

Roth, Julius. 1963. *Timetables: Structuring the Passage of Time in Hospital Treatment and Other Careers*. Indianapolis: Bobbs-Merrill.

Rothouse, Herbert. 1997. "History of Homeopathy Reveals Discipline's Excellence." *Alternative and Complementary Therapies* (June): 223–7.

Roughead, Elizabeth E., Andrew L. Gilbert, and Ken J. Harvey. 1998. "Self-Regulatory Codes of Conduct: Are They Effective in Controlling Pharmaceutical Representatives' Presentation to General Practitioners?" *International Journal of Health Services* 282: 269–79.

Ruedy, J., D.M. Kaufman, and H. MacLeod. 1999. "Alternative and Complementary Medicine in Canadian Medical Schools: A Survey." *CMAJ* 160, 6: 816–17.

Rundell, K.W., R. Caviston, and A.M. Hollenbach. 2006. "Vehicular Air Pollution, Playgrounds, and Youth Athletic Fields." *Inhalation Toxicology* 18: 541–7.

Rush, Joan. 2014. "Dentistry Has a Far Larger 'Boys' Club' Problem." *Globe and Mail*, 24 Dec. http://www.theglobeandmail.com/globe-debate/dentistry-has-a-far-larger-boys-club-problem/article22201391/.

Rutherford, R.D. 1975. *The Changing Sex Differential in Mortality*. International Population and Urban Research, University of California, Berkeley, Studies in Population of Urban Demography No. 1. Westport, Conn.: Greenwood Press.

Rutledge, R., and L. Robinson. 2004. "Taking Care of Us." *Journal for Canadian Cancer Professionals: Oncology Exchange* 3, 5: 24–7.

Salmon, J. Warren. 1984. *Alternative Medicines: Popular and Policy Perspectives*. New York: Tavistock.

Samson, Colin. 2003. *A Way of Life That Does Not Exist: Canada and the Extinguishment of the Innu*. St John's/London: ISER Books/Verso.

——, James Wilson, and Jonathan Mazower. 1999. *Canada's Tibet: The Killing of the Innu*. London: Survival.

Sanders, David, and Mickey Chopra. 2006. "Key Challenges to Achieving Health for All in an Inequitable Society: The Case of South Africa." *American Journal of Public Health* 96, 1: 73–8.

Sarick, Lila. 1994. "Childbirth's Ancients Are Reborn as a Profession." *Globe and Mail*, 14 May, A1, A6.

Scambler, G. 2002. *Health and Social Change: A Critical Theory*. Philadelphia: Open University Press.

Scheff, Thomas J. 1963. "The Role of the Mentally Ill and the Dynamics of Mental Disorder." *Sociometry* 26 (June): 463–83.

Schneider, Joseph, and Peter Conrad. 1980. "In the Closet with Illness: Epilepsy, Stigma Potential and Information Control." *Social Problems* 28, 1 (Oct.): 32–44.

—— and ——. 1983. *Having Epilepsy: The Experience and Control of Illness*. Philadelphia: Temple University Press.

Schofield, P., M. Carey, B. Bonevski, and R. Sanson-Fisher. 2006. "Barriers to the Provision of Evidence-based Psycho-social Care in Oncology." *Psycho-Oncology* 15: 863–72.

Schwabe, Arlette M. 1995. "International Dependency and Health: A Comparative Case Study of Cuba and the Dominican Republic." In Eugene Gallagher and Janardan Subedi, eds, *Global Perspectives on Health Care*, 292–310. Englewood Cliffs, NJ: Prentice-Hall.

Schwappach, D.L.B. 2010. "Review: Engaging Patients as Vigilant Partners in Safety: A Systematic Review." *Medical Care Research and Review* 67, 2: 119–48.

Schwartz, Daniel. 2014. "Workplace Safety by the Numbers." CBC News, 28 Apr. http://www.cbc.ca/news/canada/workplace-safety-by-the-numbers-1.2622466.

Schwarzenbach, R.P., T. Egli, T.B. Hofstetter, U. Von Gunten, and B. Wehrli. 2010. "Global Water Pollution and Human Health." *Annual Review of Environment and Resources* 35: 109–36.

Scully, Diana. 1980. *Men Who Control Women's Health: The Miseducation of Obstetrician-Gynecologists*. Boston: Houghton Mifflin.

Seale, Clive. 2001. "Sporting Cancer: Struggle Language in News Reports of People with Cancer." *Sociology of Health and Illness* 23, 3: 308–29.

———. 2006. "Gender Accommodation in Online Cancer Support Groups." *Health: An Interdisciplinary Journal for the Social Study of Health, Illness, and Medicine* 10, 3: 345–60.

Seear, M. 2007. *An Introduction to Global Health*. Toronto: Canadian Scholars' Press.

Sefa Dei, George J. 1999. "Knowledge and Politics of Social Change: The Implication of Anti-Racism." *British Journal of Social Education* 20, 3: 395–409.

Segall, Alexander, Michael J. Mahon, Judith G. Chipperfield, and Daniel S. Bailis. 1997. *Understanding the Relationship between Perceived Control, Personal Health Practices, and Health Status*. Final Report. Winnipeg: University of Manitoba, Max Bell Centre.

Selye, H. 1956. *The Stress of Life*. New York: McGraw-Hill.

Semanthal, M.J., D.R. Williams, M.A. Musick, and A.C. Buck. 2010. "Depression, Anxiety and Religious Life: A Search for Mediators." *Journal of Health and Social Behavior* 51, 3: 343–59.

Semenza, J.C., et al. 1996. "Heat-related Deaths during the July 1995 Heat Wave in Chicago." *New England Journal of Medicine* 335, 2: 84–90.

Senate of Canada. 2002. *The Health of Canadians: The Federal Role* (Kirby Report). www.parl.gc.ca/37/2/parlbus/commbus/senate/Com-e/soci-e/rep-e/repoct02vol6-e.htm.

Seow, H., et al. 2011. "Trajectory of Performance Status and Symptom Scores for Patients with Cancer in the Last Six Months of Life." *Journal of Clinical Oncology* 29, 9: 1151–8.

Serido, J., D.M. Almeida, and E. Wethington. 2004. "Chronic Stressors and Daily Hassles: Unique and Interactive Relationships with Psychological Distress." *Journal of Health and Social Behavior* 45: 17–33.

Shackleton, Doris French. 1975. *Tommy Douglas*. Toronto: McClelland & Stewart.

Shaffir, William B., Robert A. Stebbins, and Allan Tarowetz. 1980. *Fieldwork Experience: Qualitative Approaches to Social Research*. New York: St Martin's Press.

Shah, C.P. 2004. "The Health of Aboriginal People." In Raphael (2004: 267–80).

Shapiro, Martin. 1978. *Getting Doctored: Critical Reflections on Becoming a Physician*. Toronto: Between the Lines.

Sheitle, C.P., and A. Adamzcyk. 2010. "High-cost Religion, Religious Switching, and Health." *Journal of Health and Social Behavior* 51, 3: 325–42.

Shephard, D.A., ed. 1982. *Norman Bethune—His Times and Legacy*. Ottawa: Canadian Public Health Association.

Shield, K.D., A. Ialomiteanu, B. Fischer, and R.E. Mann. 2011. "Non-medical Use of Prescription Opioids among Ontario Adults: Data from the 2008/2009 CAMH Monitor." *Canadian Review of Public Health* 102, 5: 330–5.

Shields, M. 2003. *The Health of Canada's Shift Workers*. Ottawa: Statistics Canada.

———. 2006. "An Update on Smoking from the 2005 Canadian Community Health Survey." www.statcan.ca.

——— and S. Tremblay. 2002. *The Health of Canada's Communities*. Ottawa: Statistics Canada.

Shieman, S., Y.K. Whitestone, and K. van Gundy. 2006. "The Nature of Work and the Stress of Higher Status." *Journal of Health and Social Behavior* 47, 3: 242–57.

Shingler, Benjamin. 2013. "Sarnia's Aamjiwnaang First Nation near Ontario's 'Chemical Valley' Exposed to Pollutants." *Huffington Post*, 24 Nov. http://www.huffingtonpost.ca/2013/11/24/aamjiwnaang-first-nation-chemical-valley_n_4333685.html.

Shkilnyk, Anastasia. 1985. *A Poison Stronger Than Love*. New Haven: Yale University Press.

Shorr, R.I., S.F. Bauwens, and C.S. Landefeld. 1990. "Failure to Limit Quantities of Benzodiazepine Hypnotic Drugs for Outpatients: Placing the Elderly at Risk." *American Journal of Medicine* 89: 725–32.

Shoshana, A., and E. Teman. 2006. "Coming Out of the Coffin: Life-Self and Death-Self in Six Feet Under." *Symbolic Interaction* 29, 4: 557–76.

Shuchman, M. 2013. "Bioethicists Call for Investigation into Nutritional Experiments on Aboriginal People." *CMAJ* 185, 14: 1201–2.

Sibbald, Barbara. 1998. "In Your Face: A New Wave of Militant Doctors Lashes Out." *CMAJ* 158: 1505–9.

———. 2005. "News at a Glance." *CMAJ* 172, 9: 1170.

Siegel, K.R., A.B. Feigl, S.P. Kishore, and D. Stuckler. 2011. "Misalignment between Perceptions and Actual Burden of Disease: Evidence from the US Population." *Global Health Action* 4 (9 May). www.ncbi.nlm.nih.gov/pmc/articles/PMC3092698/.

Siegrist, T. 1996. "Adverse Health Conditions of High-effort/Low-reward Conditions." *Journal of Occupational Health Psychology* 1, 1: 27–41.

Siirla, Aarne. 1981. *The Voice of Illness: A Study in Therapy and Prophecy*, 2nd edn. New York: Edwin Mellen Press.

Silversides, A. 2010. "Lifting the Curtain on the Drug Approval Process." In Rochon Ford and Saibil (2010: 115–38).

Simkin, J. 1998. "Not All Your Patients Are Strongest." *CMAJ* 159: 370–5.

Simonton, Carl O., Stephanie Matthews Simonton, and James L. Creighton. 1978. *Getting Well Again*. Toronto: Bantam Books.

Sinclair, Murray. 2000. *The Report of the Manitoba Pediatric Cardiac Surgery Inquest: An Inquiry into Twelve Deaths at the Winnipeg Health Sciences Centre in 1994*. Winnipeg: Provincial Court of Manitoba.

Singh, G.K., and B.A. Miller. 2004. "Health, Life Expectancy, and Morality Patterns among Immigrant Populations in the United States." *Canadian Journal of Public Health* 95, 3: 114–21.

—— and M. Siahpush. 2001. "All-Cause and Cause-Specific Mortality of Immigrants and Native-Born in the United States." *American Journal of Public Health* 91: 392–9.

Singh, I. 2001. "A Framework for Understanding Trends in ADHD Diagnoses and Stimulant Drug Treatment: Schools and Schooling as a Case Study." *BioSocieties* 1: 439–52.

Single, Eric, Lynda Robson, Xiaodi Xie, Jurgen Rehm, et al. 1996. *The Cost of Substance Abuse in Canada*. Ottawa: Canadian Centre for Substance Abuse.

Smith, B.L. 2012. "Inappropriate Prescribing." *Monitor on Psychology* 43, 6.

Smith, Dorothy E. 1987. *The Everyday World as Problematic: A Feminist Sociology*. Toronto: University of Toronto Press.

——. 1993. *Texts, Facts, and Femininity: Exploring the Relations of Ruling*. London: Routledge.

Smith, L., and L. Haddad. 2002. "How Potent Is Economic Growth in Reducing Undernutrition? What Are the Pathways of Impact? New Cross-country Evidence." *Economic Development and Cultural Change* 51, 1: 55–76.

Smith, Marianne, and Kathleen Burkwalter. 1992. "Medication Management, Anti-Depressant Drugs, and the Elderly: An Overview." *Journal of Psychosocial Nursing* 30, 10: 30–6.

Smylie, Janet. 2009. "The Health of Aboriginal People." In Raphael (2009: 280–304).

Sontag, Susan. 1978. *Illness as Metaphor*. New York: Random House.

——. 1988. *AIDS and Its Metaphors*. Markham, Ont.: Penguin Books.

Speedling, E.J. 1982. *Heart Attack: The Family Response and the Hospital*. New York: Tavistock.

Spencer, B. 2014. "Moderate Drinking Is Bad for Health: Just Two Glasses a Day Can Cause Problems." *Daily Mail*, 10 July. http://www.dailymail.co.uk/health/article-2688161/Moderate-drinking-IS-bad-health-Just-two-glasses-wine-day-cause-problems.html.

Spiegal, P.B., and R. Salama. 2000. "War and Mortality in Kosovo, 1998–99: An Epidemiological Testimony." *Lancet* 355, 9222: 2204–9.

Spiegel, D., J. Bloom, H. Kraemer, and E. Gotheil. 1989. "Effects of Psychosocial Treatment on Survival of Patients with Metastatic Breast Cancer." *Lancet* (Oct.): 15.

Spitzer, D.L. 2005. "Engendering Health Disparities." *Canadian Journal of Public Health* 96, 2: S78–S96.

Stanley, E.M.G., and M.P. Ramage. 1984. "Sexual Problems and Urological Symptoms." In S.L. Stanton, ed., *Clinical Gynecological Urology*, 398–405. St Louis: Mosby.

Stanley, Liz, and Sue Wise. 1993. *Breaking Out Again: Feminist Ontology and Epistemology*. London: Routledge.

Statistics Canada. n.d. "Body Mass Index (BMI), Canadian Standard, by Age Group and Sex, Household Population Aged 20 to 64 Excluding Pregnant Women, Canada, 2000/01." www.statcan.ca/english/freepub/82-221-XIE/00502/tables/html.

——. n.d. "Frequency of Drinking." www.statcan.ca/english/freepub/82-221-XIE/00502/tables/html.

——. n.d. "Leisure-time Physical Activity, by Age Group and Sex, Household Population Aged 12 and Over, Canada 2000/01." www.statcan.ca/english/preepub/82-221-X1E/00502/tables/html.

——. Various years. *Census of Canada*. Ottawa.

——. 1981. *Health of Canadians*. Report of the Canada Health Survey. Ottawa.

——. 1991. *Accidents in Canada*. Ottawa.

——. 1995a. *Births and Deaths*. Ottawa.

——. 1995b. *Selected Infant Mortality, 1921–90*. Ottawa: Statistics Canada.

——. 1997. *National Population Health Survey. Overview 1996–1997*. Ottawa: Statistics Canada, Catalogue no. 82-567-XPB.

——. 1998. Catalogue no. 82-221-XDE. Ottawa: Statistics Canada.

——. 2000. *Women in Canada 2000: A Gender-based Statistical Report*. Ottawa: Minister of Industry.

——. 2002. "Canadian Community Health Survey: A First Look." *The Daily*, 8 May. www.statcan.ca/Daily/English/020508/d020508a.htm.

——. 2003. *Religions in Canada*. 2001 Census Analysis Series, Catalogue no. 96F0030XIE2001015.Ottawa: Minister of Industry. www12.statcan.ca/english/census01/products/analytic/companion/rel/pdf/96F0030XIE2001015.pdf.

——. 2004. "Youth Smoking Survey." *The Daily*, 14 June. www.statcan.ca/Daily/English/040614/d040614b.htm.

——. 2005. "Health Reports: Use of Alternative Health Care." www.statcan.ca/Daily/English/050315/d050315b.htm.

——. 2006a. *Women in Canada: A Gender-based Statistical Report*, 5th edn. www.statcan.ca/bsolc/english/bsolc?catno=89-503-XIE.pdf.

——. 2006b. *Healthy Canadians: A Federal Report*. www.hc-sc.gc.ca/hcs-sss/pubs/care-soins/2006-fed.

——. 2006c. "Canadian Internet Use Survey." www.statcan.ca/Daily/English/060815/d060815b.htm.

——. 2007. "People Who Quit Smoking, by Province." www40.statcan.ca/101/cst01/health591.htm.

——. 2010. "Study: Projections of the Diversity of the Canadian Population." *The Daily*, 9 Mar. www.statcan.gc.ca/daily-quotidien/100309/dq100309a-eng.htm.

Stein, Howard F. 1990. *American Medicine as Culture*. Boulder, Colo.: Westview Press.

Stein, L. 1987. "The Doctor–Nurse Game." in H.D. Schwartz, ed., *Dominant Issues in Medical Sociology*, 2nd edn. New York: Random House.

Steinem, Gloria. 1983. *Outrageous Acts and Everyday Rebellions*. New York: Holt, Rinehart and Winston.

Stelfox, Henry Thomas, Grace Chua, Keith O'Rourke, and Allan S. Detsky. 1998. "Conflict of Interest in the Debate over Calcium-Channel Antagonists." *New England Journal of Medicine* 338, 2: 101–6.

Stelling, Joan. 1994. "Staff Nurses' Perceptions of Nursing: Issues in a Women's Occupation." In Bolaria and Dickinson (1994: 609–26).

Stevenson, Lloyd. 1946. *Sir Frederick Banting*. Toronto: Ryerson Press.

Stewart, David C., and Thomas J. Sullivan. 1982. "Illness Behaviour and the Sick Role in Chronic Disease: The Case of Multiple Sclerosis." *Social Science and Medicine* 16: 1307–1404.

Stewart, Roderick. 1977. *The Mind of Norman Bethune*. Westport, Conn.: Lawrence Hill.

Stoddart, Greg L., and Roberta J. Labelle. 1985. *Privatization in the Canadian Health Care System: Assertions, Evidence, Ideology and Options*. Ottawa: Health and Welfare Canada.

Stoppard, Janet M. 1992. "A Suitable Case for Treatment: Premenstrual Syndrome and the Medicalization of Women's Bodies." In Currie and Raoul (1992: 119–29).

Strand, B.H., and A. Kunst. 2006. "Childhood Socio-economic Status and Suicide Mortality in Early Adulthood among Norwegian Men and Women: A Prospective Study of Norwegians Born between 1955 and 1965 Followed for Suicide from 1990 to 2001." *Social Science and Medicine* 63: 2825–34.

Strauss, Anselm L., and Barney G. Glaser. 1975. *Chronic Illness and the Quality of Life*. St Louis: Mosby.

Strauss, Arlene. 1987. "Alzheimer's Disease and the Family Care Provider." Supervised research project, Sociology and Anthropology Department, Wilfrid Laurier University.

Strauss, Stephen. 2002. "Global Warming May Not Be So Bad." *Globe and Mail*, 18 May, F7.

Strayhorn, J.M., and J.C. Strayhorn. 2009. "Religiosity and Teen Birth Rate in the United States." *Reproductive Health* 6, 14.

Strike, Carol. 1995. "Women Assaulted by Strangers." *Canadian Social Trends* (Spring): 2–6.

Stuckler, D., S. Basu, and M. McKee. 2011. "Health Care Capacity and Allocation among South Africa's Provinces: Infrastructure-Inequality Traps after the End of Apartheid." *American Journal of Public Health* 101, 1: 165–72.

Studdert, D.M., D.M. Eisenberg, F.H. Miller, D.A. Curto, T.J. Kaptchuk, and T.A. Brennan. 1998. "Medical Malpractice Implications of Alternative Medicine." *JAMA* 280, 18: 1610–15.

Sudnow, D. 1967. *Passing On: The Social Organization of Dying*. Englewood Cliffs, NJ: Prentice-Hall.

Sue, D. W. 2012 *Microaggressions in Everyday Life: Race, Gender and Sexual Orientation*. Hoboken, New Jersey: Wiley.

Suh Jagic, E., O. Sinanovic, E. Tupkovic, and L. Moro. 2000. "Stressful Life Events and Psoriasis during the War in Bosnia." *Dermatology and Psychosomatics* 1: 56–60.

Surtees, P.G., N.W.J. Wainwright, and K.T. Khaw. 2006. "Resilience, Misfortune, and Mortality: Evidence That Sense of Coherence Is a Marker of Social Stress Adaptive Capacity." *Journal of Psychosomatic Research* 61, 2: 221–7.

Sutherland, Lloyd P., and M.J. Verhoef. 1994. "Why Do Patients Seek a Second Opinion or Alternative Medicine?" *Journal of Clinical Gastroenterology* 19, 3: 194–7.

Sylvain, H., and L.R. Talbot. 2002. "Synergy towards Health: A Nursing Intervention Model for Women Living with Fibromyalgia, and Their Spouses." *Journal of Advanced Nursing* 38, 3: 264–73.

Syre, Thomas R. 1997. "Alcohol and Other Drug Use at a University in the Southeastern United States: Survey Findings and Implications." *College Student Journal* 31, 3: 272–381.

Szasz, T.S. 1974 [1961]. *The Myth of Mental Illness*. New York: Harper and Row.

———. 1997 [1970]. *The Manufacture of Madness*. Syracuse, NY: Syracuse University Press.

——— and M.H. Hollender. 1956. "A Contribution to the Philosophy of Medicine: The Basic Models of Doctor–Patient Relationship." *Archives of International Medicine* 97: 585–92.

Szreter, S., and M. Woolcock. 2004. "Health by Association? Social Capital, Social Theory, and the Political Economy of Public Health." *International Journal of Epidemiology* 33, 4: 650–67.

Tallman, Laurna. 2011. *Hemispheric Integration and the Ears: A Scientific and Inclusive Paradigm of Human Behaviour including the Mild and Severe Forms of Mental Illness*. Marmora, Ont.: Northern Light Books.

Tamblyn, R.M., Peter J. MacLeod, et al. 1994. "Questionable Prescribing for Elderly Patients in Quebec." *CMAJ* 151: 1808–9.

Tamburri, R. 2012. "Heavy Drinking a Problem at Most Canadian Universities: Report." *University Affairs*, 29 Aug. http://www.universityaffairs.ca/heavy-drinking-a-problem-at-most-canadian-campuses-report.aspx.

Tan, Lisa, Jennifer Wing, Larry DeGusseme, and Raymond Roch. 1996. "Worksafe Focus Report on the Health Care Industry." Research and Evaluation Section, Prevention Division of the Government of British Columbia.

Tannenbaum, C., and R.T. Tsuyiki. 2013. "The Expanding Scope of Pharmacists' Practice: Implications for Physicians." *CMAJ* 185, 4: 1228–32.

Tarabusi, Claudio Casadio, and Graham Vickery. 1998. "Globalization in the Pharmaceutical Industry Part 1." *International Journal of Health Services* 28, 1: 67–105.

Targ, Elisabeth. 1997. "Evaluating Distant Healing: A Research Review." *Alternative Therapies* 3, 6: 74–8.

Tataryn, Lloyd. 1979. *Dying for a Living*. Ottawa: Deneau and Greenberg.

Taunton, R.L., S.V.M. Klienbeck, R. Stafford, C. Woods, and M. Bott. 1994. "Patient Outcomes: Are They Linked to Registered Nurse Absenteeism, Separation or Workload?" *Journal of Nursing Administration* 24, 45: 48–55.

Taylor, William. 1991. *Macho Medicine: A History of the Anabolic Steroid Epidemic.* Jefferson, NC: McFarland & Company.

"Thalidomide's After-Effects Today." 1989. *Globe and Mail,* 14 Feb.

"Thalidomide Tragedy, Labelling Snag Linked." 1972. *Kitchener-Waterloo Record,* 27 Sept.

Theorell, Tores, and Richard H. Rahe. 1971. "Psychosocial Factors and Myocardial Infarction: I. An Inpatient Study in Sweden." *Journal of Psychosomatic Research* 15, 1: 25–31.

Thoits, P.A. 2006. "Personal Agency in the Stress Process." *Journal of Health and Social Behavior* 47: 309–23.

——. 2010. "Stress and Health: Major Findings and Policy Implications." *Journal of Health and Social Behavior* 51 (suppl. 1): 41–53.

——. 2011. "Mechanisms Linking Social Ties and Support to Mental and Physical Health." *Journal of Health and Social Behavior* 52, 2: 145–61.

Thomas, D.J. 1982. *The Experience of Handicap.* London: Methuen.

Thomas, Lewis. 1985. *The Youngest Science: Notes of a Medicine-Watcher.* London: Oxford University Press.

Thomas, Lewis H., ed. 1982. *The Making of a Socialist: The Recollections of T.C. Douglas.* Edmonton: University of Alberta Press.

Thomson, George, and Nick Wilson. 2005. "Policy Lessons from Comparing Mortality from Two Global Forces: International Terrorism and Tobacco." *Globalization & Health* 1:18 (open access).

Thune-Boyle, I.C., J.A. Stygall, M.R. Keshtgar, and S.P. Newman. 2006. "Do Religious/Spiritual Coping Strategies Affect Illness Adjustment in Patients with Cancer? A Systematic Review of Literature." *Social Science and Medicine* 63: 151–64.

Tierney, D., P. Romita, and K. Messing. 1990. "She Ate Not the Bread of Idleness: Exhaustion Is Related to Domestic and Salaried Working Conditions among 539 Quebec Hospital Workers." *Women and Health* 16, 1: 21–42.

Timmermans, Stefan. 1998. "Social Death No Self-fulfilling Prophecy: David Sudnow's Passing On Revisited." *Sociological Quarterly* 39, 3: 453–72.

—— and Mara Buchbinder. 2010. "Patients–in-Waiting: Living between Sickness and Health in a Genomics Era." *Journal of Health and Social Behavior* 51, 4: 408–23.

—— and ——. 2012. *Saving Babies: The Consequences of Newborn Screening.* Chicago: University of Chicago Press.

Toronto Star. 2002. "Week-old Infant Raped in S. Africa." 31 July, A2.

——. 2003. "Ill-Planned Cuts Hurt SARS Fight." 9 May, A30.

——. 2011. "Braun Test 'Insanely High.'" 13 Dec., S2.

Tone, Andrea. 2009. *The Age of Anxiety A History of America's Turbulent Affair with Tranquilizers.* New York: Basic Books.

Torrance, G. 1987. "Socio-Historical Overview: The Development of the Canadian Health System." In Coburn et al. (1987: 6–32).

Tuck, I., M.W. Moon, P.N. Allocca. 2010. "An Integrative Approach to Cultural Competence Education for Advanced Practice Nurses." *Journal of Transcultural Nursing* 21, 4: 402–9.

Tuckett, David, ed. 1976. *An Introduction to Medical Sociology.* London: Tavistock.

Tully, Patricia, and Etienne Pierre. 1997. "Downsizing Canada's Hospitals, 1986/7 to 1994/5." *Health Reports* 8, 4 (Spring).

Turner, B.S. 1987. *Medical Power and Social Knowledge.* London: Sage.

Turner, R. Jay, and William R. Avison. 1992. "Innovation in the Measurement of Life Stress: Crisis Theory and the Significance of Event Resolution." *Journal of Health and Social Behavior* 33, 1: 36–50.

—— and ——. 2003. "Status Variation in Stress Exposure: Implications for the Interpretations of Research on Race, Socioeconomic Status and Gender." *Journal of Health and Social Behavior* 44: 488–505.

——, B.G. Frankel, and D. Levin. 1983. "Social Support, Conceptualization, Measurement and Implication for Mental Health." In J.R. Greenly, ed., *Research in Community Mental Health,* vol. 3, 27–67. Greenwich, Conn.: JAI.

Turner, L. 2007. "First World Health Care at Third World Prices: Globalization, Bioethics and Medical Tourism." *BioSocieties* 2: 303–25.

Twells, L.K., D.M. Gregory, J. Reddigan, and W.K. Midodzi. 2014. "Current and Predicted Prevalence of Obesity in Canada." *Canadian Medical Association Open Access Journal* 2, 1 (3 Mar.): 18–26.

Tyre, Robert. 1962. *Douglas in Saskatchewan: The Story of a Socialist Experiment.* Vancouver: Mitchell Press.

Ubelacker, S. 2013. "MDs' Gross Income $307,000." *Globe and Mail,* 22 Jan.

Underhill, C., and L. McKeown. 2008. "Getting a Second Opinion: Health Information and the Internet." Statistics Canada. http://www.statcan.gc.ca/pub/82-003-x/2008001/article/10515-eng.pdf.

UNFPA. 2011. "United Nations Population Fund." Last modified Nov. 2011. www.unfpa.org/public/home/factsheets/pid/3856.

UNICEF. n.d. *Child Poverty in Perspective: An Overview of Child Well-Being in Rich Countries.* www.unicef-icdc.org/presscentre/presskit/reportcard7/rc7_pr_final_eng.pdf.

United Nations Development Program (UNDP). 1999. *Human Development Report 1999.* New York: United Nations.

——. 2004. *World Development Indicators 2004.* http://hdr.undp.org/statistics/default.cfm.

——. 2009. *Human Development Report 2009.* New York: UNDP.

——. 2010. *Human Development Report 2010.* "The mutual effects of inequalities in gender, education, income, ethnicity can exacerbate negative effects on health." New York:UNDP. 73.

United Nations Millennium Project. 2005. *Who's Got the Power? Transforming Health Systems for Women and Children.* Summary version of the Report of the Task Force on Child Health and Maternal Health. New York: UN. www.unmillenniumproject.org/reports/reports2.htm.

———. 2006. "Task Force on Child Health and Maternal Health." www.unmillenniumproject.org/reports/reports2.htm.

———. 2006. "Task Force on HIV/AIDS, Malaria, TB, and Access to Essential Medicines, Working Group on HIV/AIDS." www.unmillenniumproject.org/reports/ts_hivaids.ht.

United Nations Online 2000, 2005. *UN Millennium Development Goals.* www.unol.org/millennium goals/.

UN Women. Facts and Figures: Leadership and Political Participation. http://www.unwomen.org/en/what-we-do/leadership-and-political-participation/facts-and-figures.

Urban, Anne-Marie. 2012. "Nurses and Their Work in Hospitals: Ruled by Embedded Ideologies and Moving Discourses." Ph.D. diss., University of Regina. http://ourspace.uregina.ca/bitstream/handle/10294/3553/Urban_Ann-Marie_188003945_PhD_EDUC_Spring2012.pdf?sequence=1.

Usher, W., and J. Skinner. 2012. "EMPIRE and Health Website Recommendations: Technologies of Control." *Social Theory & Health* 10, 1: 20–41.

Valji, R., D. Adams, S. Dagenais, T. Clifford, L. Baydala, W.J. King, and S. Vohra. 2013. "Complementary and Alternative Medicine: A Survey of Its Use in Pediatric Oncology." *Evidence-Based Complementary and Alternative Medicine.* Article ID 527163.

Vavasour, M., and Y. Mennie. 1984. *For Health or Profit.* Ottawa: World Inter-Action Ottawa and Inter-Paris.

Verbrugge, Lois M. 1985. "Gender and Health: An Update on Hypothesis and Evidence." *Journal of Health and Social Behavior* 26: 156–82.

———. 1989. "The Twain Meet: Empirical Explanations of Sex Differences in Health and Mortality." *Journal of Health and Social Behavior* 31, 3: 282–304.

——— and Deborah Wingard. 1987. "Sex Differentials in Health and Mortality." *Women and Health* 12, 2: 103–45.

Verbrugge, L.M. and F.J. Ascione. 1987. "Exploring the Iceberg: Common Symptoms and How People Care for Them." *Medical Care* 25(6): 539–569.

Verhoef, M.J., H.S. Boon, and D.R. Mutasingwa. 2006. "The Scope of Naturopathic Medicine in Canada: An Emerging Profession." *Social Science and Medicine* 63: 409–17.

——— and L.R. Sutherland. 1995. "Alternative Medicine and General Practitioners." *Canadian Family Physician* 41: 1005.

Verrengia, Joseph B. 2002. "Pollution Blamed for African Drought." *Toronto Star*, 22 July, A3.

Verrilli, D.K., Robert Berenson, and Steven J. Katz. 1998. "Comparison of Cardiovascular Procedure Use between the United States and Canada." *Health Reports* 3 (Aug.): 467–87.

Vickers, A., P. Wilson, and J. Kleijnen. 2002. "Acupuncture." *Quality and Safety in Health Care* 11: 92–7.

Vincent, C.A., and A. Coulter. 2002. "Patient Safety: What about the Patient?" *Quality and Safety in Health Care* 11: 76–80.

von Schirnding, Y. 2005. "The World Summit on Sustainable Development: Reaffirming the Centrality of Health." *Globalization and Health* 1, 8: 1–6.

Votova, K., R. Blais, M.J. Penning, and M.K. MacLure. 2013. "Polypharmacy Meets Polyherbacy: Pharmaceutical, Over-the-Counter, and Natural Health Product Use among Canadian Adults." *Canadian Journal of Public Health* 104, 3: 222–8.

Vyncke, V., et al. 2013. "Does Neighbourhood Social Capital Aid in Levelling the Social Gradient in the Health and Well-being of Children and Adolescents? A Literature Review." *BMC Public Health* 13–65.

Wahn, Michael. 1987. "The Decline of Medical Dominance in Hospitals." In Coburn et al. (1987: 422–41).

Waitzkin, Howard. 1989. "A Critical Theory on Medical Discourse: Ideology, Social Control, and the Processing of Social Context in Medical Encounters." *Journal of Health and Social Behavior* 30 (June): 220–39.

Wakabayashi, C., and K.M. Donato. 2006. "Does Caregiving Increase Poverty among Women in Later Life? Evidence from the Health Retirement Survey." *Journal of Health and Social Behavior* 47, 3: 258–74.

Waldron, Ingrid. 1981. "Why Do Women Live Longer than Men?" *Journal of Human Stress* 2: 19–30.

——— and Susan Johnston. 1981. "Why Do Women Live Longer than Men? Part II." *Journal of Human Stress* 2.

Walsh, Kiri, Michael King, Louise Jones, Adrian Tookman, and Robert Blizard. 2002. "Spiritual Beliefs May Affect Outcome of Bereavement: Prospective Study." *British Medical Journal* 324, 7353: 1551.

Walters, Vivienne. 1982. "State, Capital and Labour: The Introduction of Federal–Provincial Insurance for Physician Care in Canada." *Canadian Review of Sociology and Anthropology* 19: 157–72.

———. 1991. "Beyond Medical and Academic Agendas: Lay Perspectives and Priorities." *Atlantis* 17, 1: 28–35.

———. 1992. "Women's Views of Their Main Health Problem." *Canadian Journal of Public Health* 83, 5: 371–4.

———. 1994a. "Women's Perceptions Regarding Health and Illness." In Bolaria and Dickinson (1994: 317–25).

———. 1994b. "The Social Construction of Risk in Nursing: Nurses' Responses to Hazards in Their Work." In Bolaria and Dickinson (1994: 627–43).

——— and J. Haines. 1989. "Workload and Occupational Stress in Nursing." *Canadian Journal of Nursing Research* 21, 3: 49–58.

Warburton, Rennie, and W. Carroll. 1988. "Class and Gender in Nursing Work." In Bolaria and Dickinson (1988: 364–75).

Wardell, Walter. 1988. "Chiropractors: Evolution to Acceptance." In Norman Gentz, ed., *Other Healers: Unorthodox Medicine in America*, 174–84. Baltimore: Johns Hopkins University Press.

Watson, Rory. 2002. "More Women in the Workforce Reduces Mortality." *British Medical Journal* 324 (8 June): 1352. bmj.com/cgi/content/full/324/7350/1352/b.

Weber, Max. 1947. *The Theory of Social and Economic Organization*. Trans. A.M. Henderson and Talcott Parsons. New York: Free Press

———. 1968. *Economy and Society: An Outline of Interpretive Sociology*. Trans. Ephraim Fischoff; eds G. Roth and C. Witlich. New York: Bedminster Press.

Webster, D. 2002. "Somatoform and Pain Disorders." In M. Ballou and L.S. Brown, eds, *Rethinking Mental Health and Disorder: Feminist Perspectives*, 145–73. New York: Guilford Press.

Weeks, C. 2010. "Perfumes Contain Hidden Harmful Chemicals, an Environmental Group Says." *Globe and Mail*, 12 May, L4.

———. 2014. "The Double Standards of Canada's Tobacco Control." Globe and Mail, 17 June. http://www.theglobeandmail.com/life/health-and-fitness/health/the-double-standards-of-canadas-tobacco-control/article19202446/.

Weigts, Wies, Hannecke Hontkoop, and Patricia Mullen. 1993. "Talking Delicately: Speaking about Sexuality during Gynecological Consultation." *Sociology of Health and Illness* 15, 4.

Weil, Andrew. 1983. *Health and Healing: Understanding Conventional and Alternative Medicine*. Boston: Houghton Mifflin.

———. 2011. *Spontaneous Happiness*. New York: Little, Brown.

Weir, Erica. 2002. "Hospitals and the Environment." *CMAJ* 166, 3: 354.

Weiss, G.L., and L.E. Lonnquist. 2012. *The Sociology of Health, Illness and Healing*, 7th edn. Boston: Prentice-Hall.

Weitz, Rose. 1999. "Watching Brian Die: The Rhetoric and Reality of Informed Consent." *Health* 3, 2: 209–27.

Welch, W.P., D.K. Verrilli, S.J. Katz, and E. Latmer. 1996. "A Detailed Comparison of Physician Services in the United States and Canada." *JAMA* 225, 18: 1410–16.

Wennberg, John E. 1984. "Dealing with Medical Practice Variations: A Proposal for Action." *Health Affairs* 4 (Summer): 6–32.

———, John P. Buncker, and Benjamin Barnes. 1980. "The Need for Assessing the Outcomes of Common Medical Practice." *Annual Review of Public Health* 1: 277–95.

Wennemo, Irene. 1993. "Infant Mortality, Public Policy and Inequality—A Comparison of 18 Industrialized Countries, 1950–1985." *Sociology of Health and Illness* 15, 4: 429–46.

Wermuth, L. 2003. *Global Inequality and Human Needs*. Boston: Allyn & Bacon.

Wertz, Richard W., and Dorothy C. Wertz. 1977. *Lying-In: A History of Childbirth in America*. New York: Free Press.

——— and ———. 1986. "Notes on the Decline of Midwives and the Rise of Medical Obstetricians." In Peter Conrad and Rochelle Kern, eds, *The Sociology of Health and Illness: Critical Perspectives*. New York: St Martin's Press.

Whitaker, Robert. 2010. *Anatomy of an Epidemic: Magic Bullets, Psychiatric Drugs, and the Astonishing Rise of Mental Illness in America*. New York: Crown.

Whitbeck, Les B., Dan R. Hoyt, Barbara J. McMorris, Xiaojin Chen, and Jerry D. Stubben. 2001. "Perceived Discrimination and Early Substance Abuse among American Indian Children." *Journal of Health and Social Behavior* 42: 405–24.

White, K.P., M. Speechly, M. Harth, and T. Ostbye. 1999. "Comparing Self-Reported Function and Work Disability in 100 Community Cases of Fibromyalgia Syndrome versus Controls in London, Ontario: The London Fibromyalgia Epidemiology Study." *Arthritis and Rheumatism* 42, 1: 76–83.

White, R. 2002. "Social and Political Aspects of Men's Health." *Health: An Interdisciplinary Journal for the Social Study of Health, Illness and Medicine* 6, 3: 267–85.

Widman, L., and D.A. Tong. 1997. "Requests for Medical Advice from Patients and Families to Health Care Providers Who Publish on the World Wide Web." *Archives of Internal Medicine* 157: 209–12.

Wilensky, Harold L. 1964. "The Professionalization of Everyone." *American Journal of Sociology* 70: 137–58.

Wilkinson, R., and K. Pickett. 2010. *The Spirit Level: Why Equality Is Better for Everyone*. London: Penguin UK.

Williams, A.P., Karin Dominick, and Eugene Vayda. 1993. "Women in Medicine: Toward a Conceptual Understanding of the Potential for Change." *Journal of the American Medical Women's Association* 48, 4: 115–23.

Williams, C. 2003. *Stress at Work*. Ottawa: Statistics Canada. dsp-psd.tpsgc.gc.ca/Collection-R/Statcan/11-008-XIE/0020311-008-XIE.pdf.

Williams, C.C., N. Massaquoi, M. Redmond, S. Chatterjee, and L. James. 2011. *Every Woman Matters: A Report on Accessing Primary Health Care for Black Women and Women of Colour in Ontario*. Toronto, Apr. www.whiwh.com www.socialwork.utoronto.ca.

Williams, Paul A., Rhonda Cockerill, and Frederick H. Lowy. 1995. "The Physician as Prescriber: Relations between Knowledge about Prescription Drugs, Encounters with Patients and the Pharmaceutical Industry, and Prescription Volume." *Health and Canadian Society* 3, 1–2: 135–66.

Williams, P.A., R. Cockerill, and F.H. Lowy. 1995. "The Physician as Prescriber: Relations between Knowledge about Prescription Drugs, Encounters with Patients and the Pharmaceutical Industry, and Prescription Volume." *Health and Canadian Society* 3, 1 and 2: 135–66.

Williams, P.L., et al. 2006. "Can Households Earning Minimum Wage in Nova Scotia Afford a Nutritious Diet?" *Canadian Journal of Public Health* 97, 6: 430–5.

Williams, Simon J., and Michael Calnan. 1996. "The Limits of Medicalization? Modern Medicine and the Lay Population in 'Late' Modernity." *Social Science and Medicine* 42, 12: 1609–20.

———, Jonathan Gabe, and Michael Calnan, eds. 2000. *Health, Medicine, and Society: Key Theories, Future Agendas.* London and New York: Routledge.

Williamson, Deana L., and Janet E. Fast. 1998. "Poverty and Medical Treatment: When Public Policy Compromises Accessibility." *Canadian Journal of Public Health* 89, 2: 120–4.

Willis, Evan. 1983. *Medical Dominance: The Division of Labour in Australian Health Care.* Sydney: George Allen and Unwin.

Willison, Donald J., and Stuart M. MacLeod. 2002. "Patenting of Genetic Material: Are the Benefits to Society Being Realized?" *CMAJ* 167, 3: 259–63.

Willson, A.E., K.M. Shuey, and G.H. Elder Jr. 2007. "Cumulative Advantage Processes as Mechanisms of Inequality in Life Course Health." *American Journal of Sociology* 112, 6: 1886–1924.

Wilson, Edward O. 1991. "Biodiversity, Prosperity and Value." In Herbert F. Brohman and Stephan R. Kellert, eds, "Ecology, Economics and Ethics: The Broken Circle." Special issue of *Society* 30, 1 (Nov.–Dec.): 90–3.

Wilson, Jane. 1987. "Why Nurses Leave Nursing." *The Canadian Nurse* 83 (Mar.): 20–3.

Wilson, K., and M.W. Rosenberg. 2002. "Exploring the Determinants of Health for First Nations People in Canada: Can Existing Frameworks Accommodate Traditional Activities?" *Social Science and Medicine* 55: 2017–31.

Winsor, Hugh. 1973. "Thalidomide." *Globe and Mail*, 10 Mar.

Wnuk-Lipinski, Edmund, and Raymond Illsley. 1990. "International Comparative Analysis: Main Findings and Conclusions." *Social Science and Medicine* 31, 8: 879–89.

Wohl, Stanley. 1984. *The Medical Industrial Complex.* New York: Harmony Books.

Wolf, Naomi. 1991. *The Beauty Myth.* Toronto: Vintage Books.

Wolfe, F., K. Ross, J. Anderson, I.J. Russell, and L. Hebert. 1995. "The Prevalence and Characteristics of Fibromyalgia in the General Population." *Arthritis and Rheumatism* 38, 1: 19–28.

Women's Health Office Newsletter. 1994. Hamilton, Ont.: McMaster University, Apr.

Wood, C. 2014. "Choosing the 'Right' People for Nursing: Can We Recruit to Care?" *British Journal of Nursing* 23, 10: 5.

Woodward, Christel A. 1999. "Medical Students' Attitudes toward Women: Are Medical Schools Microcosms of Society?" *CMAJ* 160: 347–8.

Woolhandler, Steffie, David U. Himmelstein, Ralph Silba, Michael Bader, M. Narnley, and Alice A. Jones. 1985. "Medical Care and Mortality: Racial Differences in Preventable Deaths." *International Journal of Health Services* 15, 1: 1–11.

Workplace Safety and Insurance Board. 2006. "Current Health and Safety Statistics for Ontario." www.wsib.on.ca/wsib/wsibsite.nsf/public/CurrentStatistics.

World Development Report. 1992. *Development and the Environment.* Oxford: Oxford University Press.

———. 1993. *Investing in Health.* Washington: World Bank.

World Health Organization (WHO). n.d. "Why Is Tobacco a Public Health Priority?" www.who.int/tobacco/health_priority/en/index.html.

———. 1981. *International Code* (May 1981, Article 1). Geneva: WHO.

———. 1994. *Declaration of Occupational Health for All.* www.who.int/occupational_health/publications/declaration/en/print.html.

———. 1997. *The World Health Report.* Geneva: WHO.

———. 1998. *The World Health Report. Life in the 21st Century: A Vision for All.* Report of the Director-General. Geneva: WHO.

———. 1999. *The World Health Report: Making a Difference.* Geneva: WHO.

———. 2000. "Bottled Drinking Water." www.who.int/mediacentre/factsheets/fs256/en/print.html.

———. 2002. *WHO Traditional Medicine Strategy 2002–2005.* Geneva: WHO. whqlibdoc.who.int/hq/2002/who_edm_trm_2002.1.pdf.

———. 2003. *The World Health Report 2003: Shaping the Future.* Geneva: WHO.

———. 2004. "One in Three Child Deaths in Europe due to Environment: New WHO Study Details Devastating Effects." www.euro.who.int/mediacentre/PR/2004/20040617_1.

———. 2005. *The World Health Report 2005.* Geneva: WHO. www.who.int/whr/2005/en/index.html.

———. 2005. "Epidemic and Pandemic Alert and Response (EPR)." www.who.int/csr/disease/influenza/pandemic.

———. 2005. "Indoor Air Pollution and Health." www.who.int/mediacentre/factsheets/fs292/en/index.html.

———. 2005. "Ten Things You Need To Know about Pandemic Influenza." www.who.int/csr/disease/influenza/pandemic10things.

———. 2005. "Water, Sanitation and Hygiene Links to Health." www.who.int/water_sanitation_health/publications/facts2004/en/print.html.

———. 2006. "Children's Health and Environment." www.euro.who.int/childhealthenv.

———. 2006. *Elimination of Asbestos-related Diseases.* www.who.int/occupational_health/publications/asbestosrelateddiseases.pdf.

———. 2006. "Healthy Environments for Healthy People." www.euro.who.int/envhealth.

———. 2006. "Number of Work-related Accidents and Illnesses Continues to Increase, WHO and ILO Join in Call for Prevention Strategies." www.who.int/mediacentre/news/release/2005/pr18/en/print.html.

———. 2006. "Occupational Health." www.who.int/occupation_health/en/.

———. 2007. "Global Environmental Change." www.who.int/globalchange/en/.

———. 2008. "Traditional Medicine: Fact Sheet No. 134." www. who.int/mediacentre/factsheets/fs134/en/index.html.

———. 2011. *World Health Statistics 2011*. Geneva: WHO. www. who.int/whosis/whostat/EN_WHS2011_Full.pdf.

———. 2011. *Unsafe Abortion: Global and Regional Estimates of the Incidence of Unsafe Abortion and Associated Mortality in 2008*, 6th edn. whqlibdoc.who.int/ publications/2011/9789241501118_eng.pdf.

———, United Nations Office of Human Rights. n.d. "Fact Sheet 31."

Wotherspoon, T. 1994. "Colonization, Self-Determination and the Health of Canada's First Nations Peoples." In Bolaria and Bolaria (1994a: 247–68).

Yach, D. 2005. "Globalization and Health: Exploring the Opportunities and Constraints for Health Arising from Globalization." *Globalization and Health* 1, 2: 1–2.

Yamada, Seiji. 2004. "Militarism and the Social Production of Disease." In Meredith P. Fort, Mary Anne Mercer, and Oscar Gish, eds, *Sickness and Wealth: The Corporate Assault on Global Health*, ch. 9. Cambridge, Mass.: South End Press.

Yang, C., M.K. McClintock, M. Kozloski, and T. Li. 2013. "Social Isolation and Adult Mortality: The Role of Chronic Inflammation and Sex Differences." *Journal of Health and Social Behavior* 54, 2: 183–203.

Yates, Patsy M., G. Beadle, A. Clavarino, J.M. Najman, D. Thomson, G. Williams, L. Kenny, S. Roberts, B. Mason, and D. Schlect. 1993. "Patients with Terminal Cancer Who Use Alternative Therapies: Their Beliefs and Practices." *Sociology of Health and Illness* 15: 199–216.

Yeaton, W.H., D. Smith, and K. Rogers. 1990. "Evaluating Understanding of Popular Press Reports of Health Research." *Health Education Quarterly* 17: 223–34.

Yerman, Marcia G. 2011. "An Interview with Dr. Diane M. Harper, *HPV* Expert." *Huffington Post*, 17 Nov. http://www. huffingtonpost.com/marcia-g-yerman/an-interview-with-dr-dian_b_405472.html.

Yiu, V. 2005. "Supporting the Well-Being of Medical Students." *CMAJ* 172, 7: 889–90.

Zabolai-Csekme, Eva. 1983. *Women, Health and Development*. Geneva: WHO.

Zborowski, Mark. 1952. "Cultural Components in Response to Pain." In E. Jaco, ed., *Patients, Physicians and Illness*, 256–68. Glencoe, Ill.: Free Press.

———. 1969. *People in Pain*. San Francisco: Jossey-Bass.

Zed, P.J., and P.S. Loewen. 2002. "Pharmacist Scope of Practice: A Response to the 2002 ACP-ASIM Position Paper." *Journal of Informed Pharmacotherapy* 8: 1–8.

Zelek, B., and S.P. Phillips. 2003. "Gender and Power: Nurses and Doctors in Canada." *International Journal for Equity in Health* 2: 1–7.

———, ———, and Y. Lefebre. 1997. "Gender Sensitivity in Medical Curricula." *CMAJ* 156, 9: 1297–300.

Zheng, H., and P.A. Thomas. 2013. "Marital Status, Self-rated Health, and Mortality: Overestimation of Health or Diminishing Protection of Marriage?" *Journal of Health and Social Behaviour* 54, 1: 128–44.

Zitner, D. 2002. "Drug Use in Canada: Opportunity Lost." www.aims.ca/pharmaceuticals.asp?type ID=2&id=448a.

Zlotozynska, M., E. Wood, J.S. Montaner, and T. Kerr. 2013. "Supervised Injection Sites: Prejudice Should Not Trump Evidence of Benefit." *CMAJ* 185, 15: 1303–4.

Zola, Irving. 1972. "Medicine as an Institution of Social Control." *Sociological Review* 20: 487–504.

———. 1973. "Pathways to the Doctor: From Person to Patient." *Social Science and Medicine* 7, 9: 677–89.

———. 1975. "In the Name of Health and Illness: On Some Socio-Political Consequences of Medical Influence." *Social Science and Medicine* 9: 83–7.

Zwiers, A. 2009. "LGBT People and Mental Health: Healing the Wounds." *Visions: BC's Mental Health and Addictions Journal* 6, 2: 10–11.

Index